DIFFERENTIAL

AND

INTEGRAL CALCULUS

DIFFERENTIAL

AND

INTEGRAL CALCULUS

BY

ROSS R. MIDDLEMISS

Professor of Applied Mathematics
Washington University

SECOND EDITION

McGRAW-HILL BOOK COMPANY, INC.

NEW YORK AND LONDON

1946

PREFACE TO THE SECOND EDITION

Although the general plan of the book has not been altered in this new edition, the entire text has been carefully reconsidered. Many sections and several entire chapters have been rewritten for the purpose of making improvements that have been suggested by several years of experience with the original edition. Wherever experience has indicated that additional explanation or a new illustrative example would be desirable, the section has been revised. There has also been a serious attempt to improve the rigor without making the text more difficult for the average student.

A major change has been the addition of a chapter on solid analytic geometry. This topic is treated very briefly or not at all in many short courses in analytic geometry, and it seemed desirable to include a chapter covering those parts of the subject that are essential to the study of partial derivatives and multiple integrals.

The chapter on partial derivatives has been rewritten in order to place more emphasis on the physical and less on the geometrical aspects of partial derivatives and directional derivatives. The chapter on multiple integrals has been reorganized and now includes spherical as well as cylindrical coordinates.

All the sections on applications of the definite integral—those on areas, volumes, fluid pressure, work, etc.—have been revised in order to eliminate the use of Duhamel's principle. The new treatment is simpler, and it appears to be sounder because it avoids unsatisfactory assumptions as to the existence of quantities that have not been defined.

The work on infinite series has been reorganized. Tests for convergence of series of *positive* terms are given first, and more general series are treated afterward.   The new chapter includes a simple and very useful theorem for estimating the remainder.

Finally, most of the sets of problems throughout the book have been replaced, and the total number of problems has been greatly increased.   Answers to odd-numbered problems are given at the end of the book.

The author wishes to take this opportunity to thank the many teachers who have used the original edition and to express his special gratitude to those who have taken the trouble to send in their criticisms and suggestions.   He is especially indebted to Profs. J. R. Britton of the University of Colorado, S. E. Warschawski of the University of Minnesota, and G. C. Helme of Washington University for very valuable assistance.

Ross R. Middlemiss.

St. Louis, Mo.,
  June, 1946.

CONTENTS

CHAPTER I

FUNCTIONS AND THEIR GRAPHS

1. Definition of a function. Notation.—*A variable y is said to be a* **function** *of a second variable x if a relation exists between them such that to each of a certain set of values of x there corresponds one or more values of y.* If there is just *one* value of y corresponding to each admissible value of x, y is said to be a *single-valued* function of x.

The student is familiar with an almost unlimited number of examples of such functional dependence of one quantity upon another. Thus, the area of a circle is a function of its radius, the relation being $A = \pi r^2$. To every (positive) value of r there corresponds a definite value of A. The equation $3x + 4y = 12$ is a relation between x and y such that to every value of x there corresponds a single value of y. We say that the equation *defines y* as a function of x. It also, of course, defines x as a function of y; *i.e.*, we may assign values to y, and the equation determines corresponding values of x. The variable to which we assign values is called the *independent variable;* the other is called the *dependent variable* or *function.*

The statement "y is a function of x" is abbreviated by writing $y = f(x)$. Symbols such as $f(x)$, $g(x)$, and $\varphi(x)$ are also used to denote specific functions of x. Thus, if we are concerned in a particular discussion with the two functions $x^2 - 4x + 2$ and $4x^3 + 6x$, we may find it convenient to designate the first by the symbol $f(x)$ and the second by $g(x)$.

If $f(x)$ denotes a certain function of x, than $f(a)$ denotes the value of $f(x)$ when x has the value a; it is found by substituting a for x. Thus, if

$$f(x) = x^2 - 4x + 2,$$

1

then
$$f(0) = 0^2 - 4(0) + 2 = 2;$$
$$f(1) = 1^2 - 4(1) + 2 = -1;$$
$$f(-3) = (-3)^2 - 4(-3) + 2 = 23.$$

2. Restrictions on the variables.—A relation that defines y as a function of x need not yield a value of y for every possible value of x. Frequently there are restrictions, either implied or explicitly stated, on the values that may be assigned to x. For example, in the equation $A = \pi r^2$ we naturally restrict r to positive values.

Throughout the work in this text we shall be concerned only with *real* values for both variables. The equation

$$y = \sqrt{x - 4}$$

yields real values of y only for $x \geqq 4$. We shall accordingly say that it defines y as a function of x (in the field of real numbers) only over this restricted range. This admissible set of values of x is called the **range of definition** of the function.

Consider now the equation

$$x^2 + y^2 = 25.$$

If we choose x as the independent variable, we may assign to it any value from -5 to $+5$, inclusive. For each value of x inside this interval the equation yields **two** values of y. We say then that this equation defines y as a **double-valued** function of x over this range. In the calculus we shall deal primarily with single-valued functions, and when we speak of the function $y = f(x)$ we shall mean a single-valued function unless the contrary is specifically indicated. Multiple-valued functions are not entirely excluded because such a function can in general be broken up into single-valued parts called *branches*. Each branch can, if necessary, be considered separately. In the above case the branches are

$$y = \sqrt{25 - x^2} \quad \text{and} \quad y = -\sqrt{25 - x^2}.$$

Each of these equations defines y as a single-valued function of x, it being understood that the symbol $\sqrt{}$ stands for the *positive square root* only.

3. Functional relations and analytical formulas.—The definition of a function does not imply that the relation between the variables can be expressed by an analytical formula or equation. It is only necessary that there be some means established for making a value (or values) of y correspond to each admissible value of x. Thus, the relation

$T(n)$ = the minimum official temperature in St. Louis on the nth day of the year 1945

satisfies all the requirements. If n is given we can find T—not by substituting in a formula but by referring to the records of the Weather Bureau. Of course n is restricted to the set of integers from 1 to 365 inclusive. The function $T(n)$ is not defined by the above relation for n outside this set.

If the relation *can* be expressed analytically, it may happen that two or more equations are required—each equation expressing the relation for some definite set of values of the independent variable. Suppose, for example, that a cab driver charges 50 cents for 1 mile or less and at a rate of 20 cents per mile for additional distance. The fare F (in cents) may be expressed analytically in terms of the distance d (in miles) by writing the two equations:

$$\begin{cases} F = 50 & 0 < d \leqq 1 \\ F = 30 + 20d & d > 1. \end{cases}$$

4. Graphical representation.—It is convenient to represent pictorially the relation between two variables by means of a graph. We assume that the student is familiar with the process of making a graph by constructing a table of corresponding values of the variables and plotting the points.

In his study of analytic geometry, the student learned

to interpret the graph as the locus of all points whose coordinates satisfy the given relation. For our present purpose we must emphasize the following additional interpretation: The graph of $y = f(x)$ is a picture indicating the manner in which the value of y increases and decreases with increasing x. Specifically, the following points should be immediately clear:

1. *The value of the function is increasing* (as x increases) *in those intervals in which the curve is rising—and decreasing where the curve is falling.*

2. *The steepness of the curve is a general indication of the* *rapidity with which the value of the function is increasing or decreasing,* relative to x.

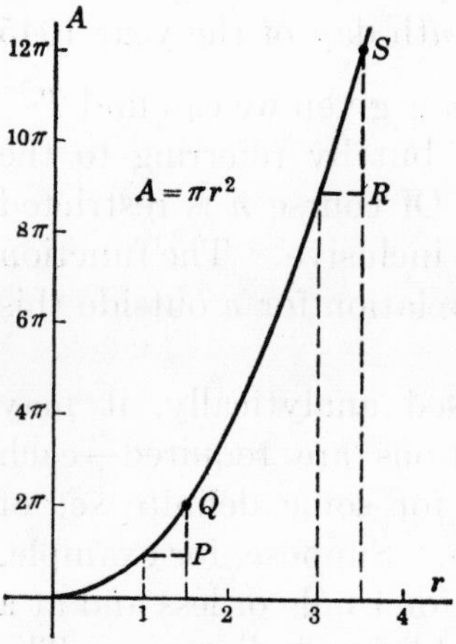

FIG. 1.

In order to fix these ideas let us examine carefully the graph of the function $A = \pi r^2$. It shows pictorially that the area of a circle increases continuously with r, starting at 0 when $r = 0$. The curve becomes continually steeper with increasing r. This means that the area increases more and more rapidly with r as r grows larger. This is evident from the following analysis, *which the student must understand clearly* before proceeding:

The area of a circle of 1 in. radius is represented by the ordinate to the curve at $r = 1$. If the radius is $1\frac{1}{2}$ in., the area is given by the ordinate at $r = 1\frac{1}{2}$. Consequently, the length PQ represents the amount by which the area increases when the radius increases from 1 to $1\frac{1}{2}$ in. Similarly, the length RS represents the increase in area when the radius increases from 3 to $3\frac{1}{2}$ in. Thus the *same* increase in r, starting at $r = 3$, produces a larger increase in A; *i.e.*, on the average, the area is increasing more rapidly with respect to r in this interval where the curve is steeper.

Figure 2 is the graph of the function

$$\begin{cases} F = 50 & 0 < d \leq 1 \\ F = 30 + 20d & d > 1, \end{cases}$$

which was discussed in the preceding section. It shows pictorially that the fare is *constant* for d from 0 to 1 and then increases *linearly* with d.

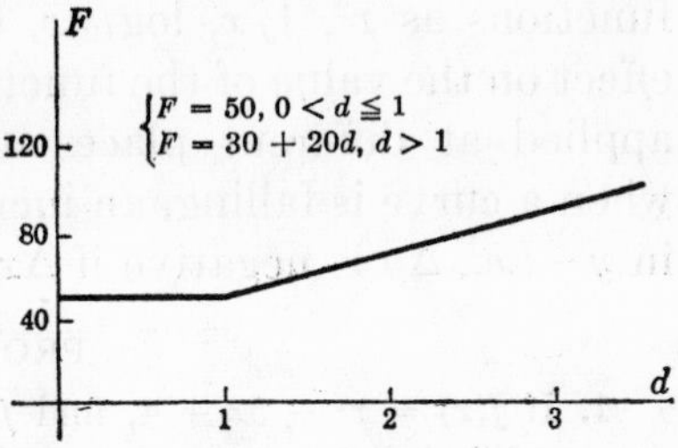

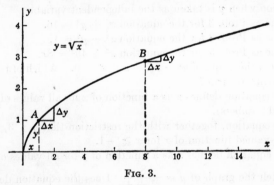

$$\begin{cases} F = 50, \, 0 < d \leq 1 \\ F = 30 + 20d, \, d > 1 \end{cases}$$

FIG. 2.

5. Increments.—Figure 3 is the graph of the function

$$y = \sqrt{x}.$$

At any point such as A, x and y have definite values, that of y being represented of course by the dotted ordinate. Suppose now that, starting at A, we let x increase by an arbitrary amount that we may represent by the symbol Δx. This symbol is read **"increment of x,"** or "delta of x," or simply "delta x."

$y = \sqrt{x}$

FIG. 3.

The change in the value of y, caused by this increment Δx in the value of x, is obviously represented by the length labeled Δy in the figure.

It is immediately clear that, since the curve continually rises, an increase in x starting at *any* point results in an *increase* in the value of y—i.e., Δy is positive. It is furthermore obvious that the same increment in x produces *smaller and smaller* increments in y as we go farther out along this curve. Thus, as illustrated in the figure, $\sqrt{x}$ does not increase nearly so much when x changes from 8 to 9 as when it changes from 1 to 2.

The student should draw corresponding figures for such functions as x^2, $1/x$, $\log_{10} x$, etc., and study carefully the effect on the value of the function of a fixed increase Δx in x, applied at different places along the curve. Note that when a curve is falling, an increase in x results in a *decrease* in y—*i.e.*, Δy is negative if Δx is positive.

PROBLEMS

1. If $f(x) = x^2 - 5x + 4$, find $f(0)$, $f(1)$, $\cdots$, $f(5)$. Sketch the curve. What distances on the graph represent $f(0), f(1), f(3)$?

2. Sketch the graph of $3x + 4y = 12$. Is it true that the equation defines y as a function of x for all values of x? What is the situation if y is taken as the independent variable?

3. Sketch the graph of $y^2 = x^3$. If we take x as the independent variable and say that the equation defines y as a double-valued function of x, into what two simple single-valued functions can it be decomposed? What is the range of definition in the field of real numbers?. Discuss the situation when y is taken as the independent variable.

4. Same as Prob. 3 for the equation $x^2 + y^2 = 16$.

5. Same as Prob. 3 for the equation $x^2 - y^2 = 1$.

6. Same as Prob. 3 for the equation $x^2 + 4y^2 = 8x$.

7. Sketch the graph of $y^2 - 6y - x + 8 = 0$. Which of the following statements are true?

(*a*) The equation defines y as a function of x for all values of x (in the field of real numbers).

(*b*) The equation, together with the restriction that $y \leqq 3$, defines y as a single-valued function of x for $x \geqq -1$.

(*c*) The equation defines x as a function of y for all values of y.

8. Sketch the graph of $y = \dfrac{8}{x^2 + 4}$. Does the equation define y as a function of x for all values of x? Discuss the situation if y is the independent variable.

9. Same as Prob. 8 for the equation $y = e^{-x^2}$.

10. Express the surface area S of a cube as a function of its edge x. Sketch the function carefully. What length represents the surface area of a 1-in. cube; a $1\frac{1}{2}$-in. cube? What length represents the amount by which the surface area increases when the edge increases from 1 to $1\frac{1}{2}$ in.; from 3 to $3\frac{1}{2}$ in.?

11. Solve Prob. 10, using the volume instead of the surface area.

12. Illustrate graphically the fact that the *same* increment Δx applied to x, starting at different points on the line $y = ax + b$, produces the same change in y.

13. Sketch the curve $y = \sin x$ for x from 0 to 180°. What is the significance of the fact that the curve is steeper near $x = 10°$ than near $x = 80°$? How much does $\sin x$ increase when x increases from 10 to 11°; from 80 to 81°? Why does one not obtain $\sin 10\frac{1}{2}°$ exactly by the usual method of interpolation? Is the result too large or too small?

14. Sketch carefully on the same axes the curves $y = \sqrt{x}$, $y = x$, and $y = x^2$ for $x > 0$. Compare the manner in which these functions vary with x.

15. Sketch on the same axes the curves $y = x^2$, $y = x^4$, $y = x^{100}$. Compare the manner in which these functions vary with x as x increases from 0 to 2.

16. Sketch each of the following functions, and discuss the manner in which it varies with x:

(a) $\log_{10} x$ (b) $\cos x$ (c) $\dfrac{1}{x}$

(d) 2^x (e) 4^{-x} (f) $\tan x$

17. Sketch the graph of the function defined by the equations:

$$\begin{aligned} f(x) &= 0 && \text{when} && x < -1 \text{ or } > 1 \\ f(x) &= 1 + x && \text{when} && -1 \leqq x \leqq 0 \\ f(x) &= 1 - x && \text{when} && 0 < x \leqq 1. \end{aligned}$$

18. A taxi company charges at the rate of 30 cents per mile but has a minimum charge of 45 cents. Express the fare analytically as a function of the distance, and sketch the function.

19. At a certain theater the admission charge for adults is 60 cents Children from one to twelve inclusive pay 20 cents, and those under one year of age are admitted free. Express the charge analytically as a function of the age, and sketch the function. Why is this called a *stepwise constant function?*

20. The rate for residence electric service in St. Louis County is as follows:

First 32 kw.-hr. per month at 5 cents per kw.-hr.

Next 168 kw.-hr. per month at $2\frac{1}{2}$ cents per kw.-hr.

All over 200 kw.-hr. per month at $1\frac{1}{2}$ cents per kw.-hr.

Minimum bill 50 cents

Write equations expressing the bill as a function of the amount used. Sketch the function.

21. For n an integer > 1 let

$$f(n) = \text{the largest prime factor of } n.*$$

Does this relation satisfy the requirements of the definition of a function? Can you express it analytically? Construct the graph for $n = 2$ to $n = 12$.

22. For n a positive integer let

$\varphi(n) = $ the number of positive integers not greater than n and prime to n.†

Does this relation satisfy the requirements of the definition of a function? Construct the graph for $n = 1$ to $n = 15$.

23. For any value of x let

$$f(x) = \text{the largest integer not greater than } x.$$

Does this relation satisfy the requirements of the definition of a function? Sketch the graph from $x = 0$ to $x = 6$.

6. Setting up the equation.—Most of the functions which we shall study are defined for all values of x in some interval, and the relation can be expressed by a single equation. In many of the applications of the calculus, the relation between the variables involved is stated in words—or is expressed by a combination of statements and drawings. Our first problem is to translate the information so given into an equation that expresses analytically the relation between the independent variable and the dependent variable or function. Having obtained the relation we may study the manner in which the value of the function varies with that of the independent variable. The graph usually plays an important role. We shall illustrate the procedure by two examples, which the student should study very carefully.

Example 1

From a 12- by 18-in. sheet of tin we wish to make a box by cutting a square from each corner and turning up the sides. How does the volume

---

* A prime number is any integer that is different from 1 and has no divisor except itself and 1.

† Two integers are prime to each other if they have no common factor except 1. This function, which plays an important role in the theory of numbers, is called the *indicator* of n.

of the box obtained vary with the size of the square cut out?   For about
what size square would the largest box be obtained?   See Fig. 4.

Solution

DEPENDENT VARIABLE—volume v of box.

INDEPENDENT VARIABLE—edge x of
square.

RELATION: Since for any value of x
the dimensions of the box are $18 - 2x$,
$12 - 2x$, and x, we have

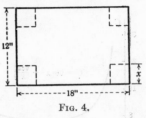

FIG. 4.

$$v = 4x(9 - x)(6 - x); \quad 0 < x < 6. \quad \text{Why?}$$

DISCUSSION: The graphical picture of this relation between x and v is
shown in Fig. 5.   It shows that v increases from 0 to about 230 cu. in.

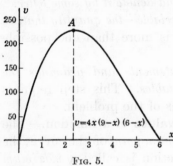

FIG. 5.

as x increases from 0 to a little more
than 2.   Then v decreases as x
increases and finally becomes 0 at
$x = 6$.   We shall learn later how to
find exactly the value of x that
gives the largest value of v.

Example 2

A rectangular box to contain 108
cu. ft. is to be made with a square
base.   The cost per square foot of
material for bottom, top, and sides
is 1, 5, and 6 cents, respectively.   Discuss the manner in which the cost
varies with the dimensions.

Solution

DEPENDENT VARIABLE—cost C of material (dollars).

INDEPENDENT VARIABLE—we could choose either the edge of the base
or the height.   Take the former and denote it in feet by x.

RELATION: The height must be $108/x^2$.   The area of the four sides is
then $4 \cdot x \cdot 108/x^2 = 432/x$.   The areas of top and bottom are each x^2.
The cost is then

$$C = 0.01x^2 + 0.05x^2 + 0.06\frac{432}{x}$$

$$= 0.06\left(x^2 + \frac{432}{x}\right).$$

DISCUSSION: The graph (Fig. 6) shows that the cost would be very
high if x were very small.   Why?   The cost decreases as x increases

(rapidly at first and then more slowly) until x reaches the value 6, where it appears *perhaps* to be least. From this point on, the cost increases. The increase is slow at first, the cost being only slightly more for $x = 7$ or 8 than for $x = 6$.

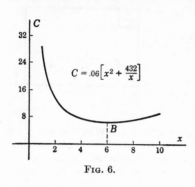

$$C = .06\left[x^2 + \frac{432}{x}\right]$$

Fig. 6.

The examples just given make it clear that in setting up the equation we should proceed somewhat as follows:

1. *Pick out the dependent variable—the function whose properties are to be studied— and denote it by some letter.*

2. *Pick out the independent variable—the quantity that we may vary at will.* Often there is more than one possible choice for this variable.

3. *Obtain from the given statements and drawings the equation connecting the two variables.* This step requires a clear analysis of the conditions of the problem.

7. Maximum and minimum values of a function.—The point A in Fig. 5 is called a *maximum point* on the curve; the corresponding value of the function is called a *maximum value.* The value of the independent variable x for which the maximum value is attained is sometimes called a *critical value* of x. Here the critical value of x is a little more than 2; the maximum value of the function appears to be about 230.

In general we say that a function $f(x)$ has a maximum value at $x = a$ if the value of $f(x)$ is larger when x *equals a* than when x is *slightly more* or *slightly less* than a. A *minimum value* is similarly defined. The point B (Fig. 6) is a minimum point on the curve.

The following exercises are designed to give the student some practice in picking out the variables and expressing the relation between them in analytical form when the conditions of the problem are stated in words. They will serve also to impress upon him the following important fact:

Whatever the physical meaning of the variables may be, the relation between them, at least if it can be expressed analytically, can always be represented by a graph; the manner in which the value of the function varies with that of the independent variable may therefore be studied from the graph.

PROBLEMS

1. A radiator holds 16 qt. and is filled with a solution that is 20 per cent alcohol. Suppose we drain out x qt. and replace this by pure alcohol. Express the concentration of the resulting solution as a function of x. From the graph discuss the way in which the concentration varies with x.

2. A farmer has 90 yd. of fence and wishes to enclose a rectangular plot and divide it into two equal parts by a cross fence joining the midpoints of two sides. Express the area enclosed as a function of the width x. Sketch the function. What dimensions would appear to give the largest area?

3. From a log 8 in. in diameter and 12 ft. long a rectangular beam is to be sawed. Express the cross-sectional area of the beam as a function of its width. Make a graph, and discuss the relation between the weight of the beam and its width.

4. With 60 yd. of woven wire it is desired to fence a rectangular plot of ground along the straight bank of a stream. No fence is necessary along the stream. Set up a function from which you can study the way in which the area enclosed varies with the dimensions of the field. Estimate the shape that would give the largest area.

5. A man in a rowboat at B, 6 miles from shore, wishes to reach a point A on the shore 10 miles away (Fig. 7). He can row 2 m.p.h. and walk 4 m.p.h. If he rows straight to A he will, of course, arrive in 5 hr. If he rows to the nearest point on shore and then walks 8 miles he will also arrive in 5 hr. Possibly the time would be less if he landed at some intermediate point. Discuss this problem by selecting a proper independent variable, expressing the time in terms of it, and drawing a graph.

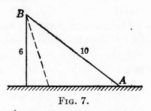

FIG. 7.

6. In a basement 8 ft. high it is desired to construct a coalbin against one wall. The capacity is to be 256 cu. ft. Express the amount of sheathing required as a function of the dimensions; make a graph and determine for what dimensions the amount of lumber appears to be least.

7. Solve Prob. 6 for the case in which the bin is built in one corner of the basement.

8. A ladder 16 ft. long stands vert.cally against a wall. The lower end is then pulled away from the wall at a uniform rate. Express the distance y of the upper end above the floor as a function of the distance x of the lower end from the wall. Sketch the function. What length on the graph represents the amount by which the top slides down when the bottom is pulled out the first foot; the fourth foot; the last foot? Does the top slide down the wall at a uniform speed, or in what general way does its speed vary?

9. A boy 5 ft. tall walks directly away from a lamppost 15 ft. high on which there is a light. Express the length S of his shadow as a function of his distance x from the post. Sketch this function. If he walks at a constant speed does his shadow lengthen also at a constant rate?

10. A ship B is 40 miles due east of a ship A. B starts north at 25 m.p.h., and at the same time A starts in the direction north $\theta°$ east, where $\theta = \arctan \frac{4}{3}$, at 15 m.p.h. Express the distance D between them at the end of T hours as a function of T. From a graph try to determine approximately when they will be closest together. HINT: It will be easier to plot D^2, instead of D, against T.

11. A gutter is to be made from a long piece of sheet metal that is

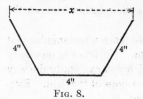

FIG. 8.

12 in. wide by folding up one-third of the width on each side as indicated in Fig. 8. Express the area of the cross section as a function of the width x across the top. Sketch the function for $x = 4$ in. to $x = 12$ in. What width appears to give the greatest capacity?

12. Water is being poured into a right circular cone that is 12 in. across the top and 16 in. deep. Express the volume of water in the cone at any instant as a function of its depth y.

13. A man operates a rooming house containing 24 rooms. He estimates that he could keep all the rooms rented at $16 per month each but would have one vacancy for each dollar per month added to this price; he estimates also that he saves $2 per month in maintenance expense on each vacant room. Set up a function from which you can study the way in which his net income varies with the rental. Try to determine from a graph the rental that would yield the greatest net income.

14. One corner of a sheet 8 in. wide is folded back so as to touch the opposite edge of the sheet. Express the length L of the crease as a function of x (Fig. 9), and study the way in which it varies with x.

15. The radius and height of a right circular cone (Fig. 10a) are $r = 6$ in. and $h = 8$ in. A right circular cylinder of radius $x(0 < x < 6)$

is inscribed in the cone. Express the volume of the cylinder as a function of x, and make a graph. What value of x appears to give the largest cylinder?

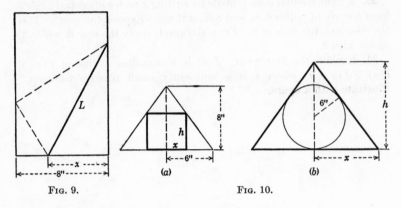

FIG. 9.   FIG. 10.

16. Solve the above problem, considering the lateral area of the cylinder instead of its volume.

17. A right circular cylinder is inscribed in a sphere of radius 8 in. Express its volume as a function of its height h. Sketch the function.

18. A right circular cone is circumscribed about a sphere of radius 6 in. Express its volume as a function of its height h. Sketch the function carefully. Does it appear to have a minimum value? HINT: Note that

$$V = \frac{1}{3}\pi x^2 h \text{ and that } \frac{x}{h} = \frac{6}{\sqrt{(h-6)^2 - 6^2}} \text{ (Fig. 10}b\text{)}.$$

19. A cylindrical can is to contain 600 cu. in. The material used for the top costs 3 cents per square inch and that for the rest of the can costs 1 cent per square inch. Express the cost C of material as a function of the radius x of the can. Sketch the function. What radius appears to give the least cost?

20. A rectangular box is to be made from 200 sq. ft. of lumber. There is no top and the length is to be twice the width. Express the volume V of the box as a function of its width x, and make the graph. For what width does the volume appear to be largest?

21. The radius and height of a right circular cone are, respectively, 6 in. and 12 in. Another right circular cone is to be inscribed in this one with its vertex at the center of the base. Express the volume V of the inscribed cone as a function of its height y. From the graph estimate the value of y for which V is largest.

22. A rectangular box to hold 162 cu. in. is to be made. The length is to be twice the width; the cost of material for the top and sides is

6 cents per square foot and for the bottom it is 2 cents per square foot. Express the cost C of material as a function of the width x, and make the graph.   For what value of x does C appear to be least?

23. A right circular cone is made by cutting a sector of central angle θ from a circle of radius 6 in. and rolling it up.   Express the volume V of the cone as a function of θ.   From the graph study the way in which V varies with θ.

24. Explain the statement "$F(a)$ is a maximum value of $F(x)$ if $F(a) > F(a \pm \epsilon)$ where ϵ is a sufficiently small positive constant." Illustrate with a figure.

CHAPTER II

THE LIMIT OF A FUNCTION

8. Introduction.—The fundamental problem of the differential calculus is that of determining the rate at which the value of a function $f(x)$ changes, relative to x.

Suppose, for example, that one is inflating a toy spherical balloon. At a given instant the radius has a certain value r and the volume V is $\frac{4}{3}\pi r^3$; since the radius is increasing at this instant, the volume is also increasing. We may ask, "At what rate is the volume increasing, *relative to the radius*—i.e., the volume is increasing at a rate of how many cubic inches per inch of increase in the radius?" We may, of course, ask a similar question concerning the rate at which the surface area is increasing.

Before attempting to answer such questions we must digress in the present chapter in order to study the important idea of the limit of a function—for it is upon this idea that the answer is based. The student has already employed the conception of a limit in several instances. The perimeter of a circle is defined, for example, as the *limit* of the perimeter of the inscribed or circumscribed regular polygon of n sides as n increases indefinitely and the length of each side approaches zero.

9. The limit of $f(x)$ as x approaches a constant.—We state that the limit of a certain function $f(x)$ as x approaches some constant a is the number L, by writing

$$\lim_{x \to a} f(x) = L.$$

The statement means, speaking roughly at first, that the value of $f(x)$ can be made to come as near to L as we please, if we take x sufficiently near to a, but not equal to a. It

15

has nothing whatever to do with the value of $f(x)$ when x *equals a.*

As an example, we may write

$$\lim_{x \to 3} (x^2 - 1) = 8;$$

for obviously the value of $x^2 - 1$ is *arbitrarily near* 8 if x is *sufficiently near* 3.   It happens also that the value of this function *is* 8 when x *equals* 3, but that fact has nothing to do with the present idea.

The above example will perhaps appear trivial.   To cite an example that is not so obvious, we may state, as will be proved later, that

$$\lim_{x \to 0} \frac{3 \sin 4x}{2x} = 6.$$

This function has no value at all if x equals 0; for substituting 0 for x leads to the meaningless symbol 0/0.*   For all values of x *near* 0, however, the value is *near* 6.   In fact, if we choose any small positive number ϵ (such as 0.00001), the difference between the value of this function and 6 is less than this ϵ (in absolute value) for *all* values of x sufficiently close to 0, but $\neq$ 0; *i.e.*, for all values of $x \neq 0$ that differ from 0 by less than some corresponding small amount δ.

This last statement expresses more **precisely what is** meant by saying that

$$\lim_{x \to a} f(x) = L.$$

It means that, after choosing *any* positive number ϵ, however small, another positive number δ can be found such that

$$|L - f(x)| < \epsilon$$

for every value of x satisfying the inequality

$$0 < |a - x| < \delta.$$

---

* A function is said to be *undefined* for any value of x for which the given relation does not yield a value of the function.   The symbol 0/0 is discussed in the next article.

A value of δ corresponding to a given ϵ may sometimes be found easily as is indicated in the first problem of the next set.

10. The symbols 0/0 and a/0.—In explanation of the statement which was made in the last section about the symbol 0/0, it is well to examine carefully the definition of the symbol N/D in general.

It will be recalled that if N is any number, and D is any number *except* 0, there exists a *uniquely determined number Q such that*

$$Q \cdot D = N.$$

The symbol N/D is *defined* to stand for this number Q. Thus,

$$\tfrac{16}{2} = 8 \qquad \text{and} \qquad \tfrac{0}{6} = 0.$$

It is clear that this definition assigns no meaning whatever to the symbol 6/0; there is, in fact, no number Q such that $Q \cdot 0 = 6$. The symbol 6/0 has then, as yet, no more meaning than $\square/\triangle$; it does not represent any number. If a meaning is to be assigned to it, such meaning must be obtained by some extension of the original definition.

Likewise the symbol 0/0 is left meaningless by the above definition of N/D. We do not choose here to assign any value or meaning to these symbols.

11. Continuity.—Figure 11 is the graph of the function

$$f(x) = \sqrt{x}.$$

Let us examine carefully the part of the curve in the neighborhood of some particular point—say near $x = 4$. It is evident that

1. When x *equals* 4, the value of $f(x)$, represented by the solid ordinate, is 2.

2. When x has any value very *near* 4, the value of $f(x)$, represented by dotted ordinates, is very *near* 2. In fact if x is *sufficiently* near 4, the value of $f(x)$ is *arbitrarily* near 2; i.e.,

$$\lim_{x \to 4} f(x) = 2.$$

Under these conditions $f(x)$ is said to be *continuous* at the point where $x = 4$.   In general, a function $f(x)$ is said to be

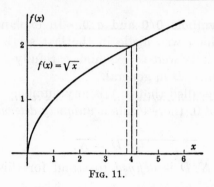

$f(x)$

2

$f(x) = \sqrt{x}$

1

1   2   3   4   5   6

x

Fig. 11.

continuous at a point where $x = a$ if it has a value $f(a)$ at this point and if, in addition,

$$\lim_{\Delta x \to 0} f(a + \Delta x) = f(a).$$

If this condition is satisfied at every point of a certain interval, the function is said to be *continuous over the interval;* in this case its graph in this interval is a continuous curve in the ordinary sense of the word.

As an example in which the condition is *not* satisfied, consider Fig. 12, which is the graph of the postage P

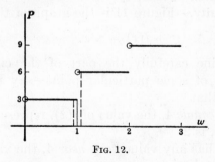

P

9

6

3

1   2   3

w

Fig. 12.

required on a letter as a function of its weight w (in ounces). The postage is 3 cents for each ounce or *fraction thereof.* Considering the part in the neighborhood of $w = 1$ we see that

1. When *w equals* 1, the value of the function P is 3, *i.e.,* the postage is 3 cents if the weight is exactly 1 oz.

2. It is not necessarily true that if w is *near* 1, P is *near* 3; in fact if w exceeds 1 by any amount δ, however small, $P = 6$. Hence,

$$\lim_{w \to 1} P \text{ does not exist.}$$

The function is then discontinuous at this point. The small circle drawn around the end point of a segment indicates that this point is *not* a part of the graph.

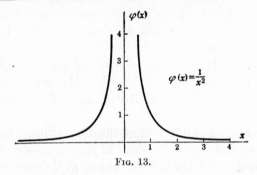

FIG. 13.

Another type of discontinuity is illustrated by Fig. 13, which is the graph of

$$\varphi(x) = \frac{1}{x^2}.$$

Examining the function in the neighborhood of $x = 0$ we find that

1. When x *equals* 0 the function has no value at all; it is *undefined.*

2. When x is *near* 0 the value of $\varphi(x)$ is very large; in fact it is *arbitrarily large* for x sufficiently near 0. Certainly there is no constant L to which the value of $\varphi(x)$ is *near* if x is near 0; *i.e.,*

$$\lim_{x \to 0} \frac{1}{x^2} \text{ does not exist;}$$

hence the function is discontinuous at $x = 0$.

The behavior of this function in the neighborhood of $x = 0$ is described by saying that as x approaches 0, the value of the function "increases without limit," or "increases beyond bound," or "approaches infinity," or "becomes infinite." Symbolically, this is abbreviated by writing

$$\lim_{x \to 0} \frac{1}{x^2} = \infty \quad \text{or} \quad \frac{1}{x^2} \to \infty \text{ as } x \to 0.$$

The student should see clearly that we do not here assign any meaning to the word "infinity" when standing alone. We define only the phrase "approaches infinity." It is important to notice also that we do *not* say that $1/0$ *equals* infinity; in fact we have said nothing whatever about the value of $1/x^2$ when $x = 0$. We have merely coined the phrase "approaches infinity" to describe the obvious fact that the value of $1/x^2$ is *arbitrarily large* if x is sufficiently near 0.

12. Right-hand and left-hand limits.—It must be emphasized that, *by definition*, the limit of $f(x)$ as $x \to a$ exists and is the number L if and only if the values of $f(x)$ are arbitrarily near L for *all* values of x that are sufficiently near to, but not equal to, a. This means, of course, for values of x on *both* sides of a.

It may happen that for all values of x sufficiently near a but *greater* than a the values of $f(x)$ are arbitrarily near some number M. In this case $f(x)$ is said to have a *right-hand* limit M as $x \to a$, and we write

$$\lim_{x \to a^+} f(x) = M.$$

A left-hand limit is similarly defined. In order for $\lim_{x \to a} f(x)$ to exist it is necessary that the right-hand and left-hand limits exist separately, and they must be equal. In Fig. 12 the right-hand limit of the function as $w \to 1$ is 6 while the left-hand limit is 3. In Fig. 13 neither of the limits exists as $x \to 0$.

As a further example, consider the function $2^{\frac{1}{x}}$, whose graph is shown in Fig. 14.   The function is continuous for

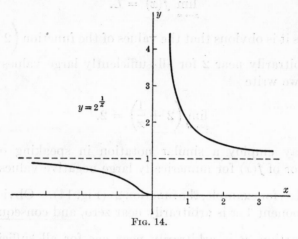

$$y = 2^{\frac{1}{x}}$$

FIG. 14.

all values of x except $x = 0$, where it is undefined.   Considering its behavior near $x = 0$ we see that

$$\lim_{x \to 0^+} 2^{\frac{1}{x}} = \infty \qquad \text{while} \qquad \lim_{x \to 0^-} 2^{\frac{1}{x}} = 0.$$

This situation results from the fact that for $x > 0$ the exponent $1/x$ is positive while for $x < 0$ it is negative; thus,

$$\text{If } x = 0.1, \qquad 2^{\frac{1}{x}} = 2^{10} = 1{,}024.$$

$$\text{If } x = -0.1, \qquad 2^{\frac{1}{x}} = 2^{-10} = 0.00098.$$

13. The limit of $f(x)$ as x increases indefinitely.—The concept of the limit of $f(x)$ as x approaches a is one that concerns the behavior of $f(x)$ when x is near a.   An equally important conception is that which concerns the behavior of $f(x)$ when x increases indefinitely.

It may happen that, as x becomes larger and larger, the value of a function $f(x)$ approaches closer and closer to a fixed constant L; more precisely, it may happen that the value of $f(x)$ is *arbitrarily near* L for all sufficiently large values of x. We say then that L is the limit of $f(x)$ as x increases indefinitely, and write

$$\lim_{x \to \infty} f(x) = L.$$

Thus it is obvious that the values of the function $\left(2 + \dfrac{1}{x}\right)$ are arbitrarily near 2 for all sufficiently large values of x; hence we write

$$\lim_{x \to \infty} \left(2 + \frac{1}{x}\right) = 2.$$

We may employ a similar notation in speaking of the behavior of $f(x)$ for numerically large negative values of x. Consider, for example, the function $2^{\frac{1}{x}}$ (Fig. 14). Obviously, the exponent $1/x$ is arbitrarily near zero, and consequently the function $2^{\frac{1}{x}}$ is arbitrarily near *one* for all sufficiently large positive values of x and also for all negative values of x that are sufficiently large numerically. We therefore write

$$\lim_{x \to \infty} 2^{\frac{1}{x}} = 1 \qquad \text{and also} \qquad \lim_{x \to -\infty} 2^{\frac{1}{x}} = 1.$$

This means, of course, that the curve approaches the line $y = 1$ asymptotically both on the right and on the left.

Finally, we may use the same notation to indicate that the value of $f(x)$ becomes indefinitely large if that of x does. Thus we may write

$$\lim_{x \to \infty} (x^2 - 1) = \infty.$$

PROBLEMS

  1. Is it obvious that the value of $x^2 + 1$ is arbitrarily near 5 if x is sufficiently near 2? How close must x remain to 2 in order that the difference between $x^2 + 1$ and 5 shall be less than 0.1? Illustrate graphically.

HINT: If $x^2 + 1 < 5.1$, $x^2 < 4.1$ and $x < \sqrt{4.1}$. If $x^2 + 1 > 4.9$, $x^2 > 3.9$ and $x > \sqrt{3.9}$.

2. Is it obvious that the value of the function $3 + \dfrac{5}{x^2}$ is arbitrarily near 3 for all sufficiently large values of x? How large must x be in order that the difference may be less than 0.01? Illustrate graphically.

3. Sketch the function $y = 3 + \dfrac{2}{x}$, and show the graphical meaning of the fact that its limit as $x \to \infty$ is 3.

4. Find the value of the function $y = \dfrac{4x + 10}{x - 10}$ when $x = 10$, 100, 1,000; what is the limit of the function as $x \to \infty$? Illustrate graphically.

5. Discuss the behavior of each of the following functions for x near zero; in each case write down an appropriate statement about the limit of the function as $x \to 0$, and illustrate each with a sketch: $x^2 + 1$, $\log x$, $\cos x$, $1/x$.

6. Same as Prob. 5 for the following functions: $\sqrt{x + 4}$, 2^x, $\tan x$, $\dfrac{1}{x^2 + 2}$.

7. Discuss the behavior of each of the following functions for large positive values of x; in each case write down an appropriate statement about the limit of the function as $x \to \infty$, and illustrate with a sketch: $\sqrt{x}$, $1/x^2$, 2^{-x}, $\log x$.

8. Same as Prob. 7 for numerical y large negative values of x for the following functions: x^2, 2^{-x}, $\sqrt[3]{x}$, 2^x.

9. Which of the following functions are continuous in the interval $0 \le x \le \pi$? Illustrate with sketches: $\sin x$, $\tan x$, $1/x$.

10. Is the area of a circle a continuous function of its radius? Is the parcel-post charge on a 5-lb. package a continuous function of the distance to its destination? Illustrate graphically.

11. If x is a variable that takes successively the values 1, $1\frac{1}{2}$, $1\frac{2}{3}$, $1\frac{3}{4}$, $\cdots$, we say that it is approaching 2 as a limit. In what sense are we here speaking of the limit of a *function?* Can one ever speak properly of the limit of an "isolated" variable?

12. Express the perimeter of the regular polygon of n sides inscribed in a circle of radius r as a function of n. What does the limit of this function represent as n increases indefinitely?

13. Solve Prob. 12 for the area of the circumscribed polygon.

14. Sketch the graph of $y = 4^{-\frac{1}{x}}$. What is the limit of this function as $x \to \infty$; as $x \to -\infty$? Discuss its behavior near $x = 0$.

15. Sketch the graph of $y = 2^{\frac{1}{x-1}}$. What is the limit of this function as $x \to \infty$; as $x \to -\infty$? Discuss its behavior near $x = 1$.

16. Sketch the graph of $y = \dfrac{1}{1 + 2^{\frac{1}{x}}}$. What is the limit of this function as $x \to \infty$; as $x \to -\infty$? Discuss its behavior near $x = 0$.

17. Same as Prob. 16 for the equation $y = \dfrac{2^{\frac{1}{x}}}{1 + 2^{\frac{1}{x}}}$.

18. Examine and discuss the following statement: An assertion about $\lim\limits_{x \to a} f(x)$ is an assertion about the values of $f(x)$ for all values of x in a sufficiently small *deleted* neighborhood of a; *i.e.*, for all values of x sufficiently near to but not equal to a. The value of $f(x)$ when x *equals* a is immaterial and the notion of x "approaching a" in the usual sense of the word, while perhaps convenient, is unnecessary.

19. Explain the following statement, illustrating with a graph: $f(x)$ is continuous at $x = a$ if, after choosing a positive number ϵ, however small, a positive number δ can be found such that

$$|f(x) - f(a)| < \epsilon \text{ if } |x - a| < \delta.$$

20. Draw sketches to show that in general the δ of Prob. 19 depends on both ϵ and x; *i.e.*, with a fixed ϵ the value of δ changes as you move along the curve, and at a fixed point on the curve δ changes if you change ϵ.

14. Determination of the limit. Theorems on limits.— We consider now in more detail the problem of determining the limit of a function $f(x)$ as $x \to a$, or as $x \to \infty$.

In many cases the problem is trivial, the limit being immediately apparent. Thus, we find that

$$\lim_{x \to 3} (x^3 - 3x + 2) = 20$$

by observing that if x is near 3, x^3 is near 27, $3x$ is near 9, and hence $(x^3 - 3x + 2)$ must be near 20. It may also be observed that this function is everywhere *continuous*—and that its limit as x approaches any constant a is merely the value that it has when x *equals* a; it may therefore be found by direct substitution.

In some cases in which the limit is not apparent, it can be made apparent by writing the function in a different form.

Thus,

$$\lim_{x \to 4} \frac{x^2 - 16}{x - 4}$$

is not immediately evident. If x is near 4, both numerator and denominator are near 0; the behavior of the value of the function when $x \to 4$ is not at first apparent. However, if we write the function in the form

$$\left(\frac{x - 4}{x - 4}\right)(x + 4),$$

we see immediately that the first factor is *exactly* 1 for all values of x near 4 (but $\neq$ 4), while the second is arbitrarily near 8 for x sufficiently near 4. Hence

$$\lim_{x \to 4} \frac{x^2 - 16}{x - 4} = 8.$$

The same result is obtained by noting that

$$\frac{x^2 - 16}{x - 4} \equiv x + 4 \text{ if } x \neq 4.$$

Since the value when x *equals* 4 is not involved in finding the limit in question, we may say that

$$\lim_{x \to 4} \frac{x^2 - 16}{x - 4} = \lim_{x \to 4} (x + 4),$$

and this latter limit is obviously 8.

In these examples we have used two of the following theorems: If

$$\lim_{x \to a} f(x) = L \qquad \text{and} \qquad \lim_{x \to a} g(x) = M,$$

then

(1) $$\lim_{x \to a} [f(x) + g(x)] = L + M.$$

(2) $$\lim_{x \to a} [f(x) \cdot g(x)] = L \cdot M.$$

(3) $$\lim_{x \to a} \frac{f(x)}{g(x)} = \frac{L}{M} \text{ if } M \neq 0.$$

Stated informally, the proof of the first theorem is as follows: By hypothesis, for x sufficiently near a,

$f(x)$ is arbitrarily near L; .
$g(x)$ is arbitrarily near M.

Hence,

$f(x) + g(x)$ is arbitrarily near $L + M$.

But this last statement means that

$$\lim_{x \to a} [f(x) + g(x)] = L + M.$$

When the student has grasped the simple idea involved in this informal proof, he can easily write out a more formal proof using the ϵ and δ notation employed in the formal definition of the limit of a function. The proofs of the second and third theorems are similar to that for the first.

One sometimes expresses the fact that the limit of a certain function $f(x)$ as x approaches a is L by saying, somewhat carelessly, "$f(x)$ approaches L as x approaches a" and by writing

$$f(x) \to L \quad \text{as} \quad x \to a.$$

This notation is open to criticism on the ground that it does not adequately convey the notion of the *limit* of a function; it is sometimes convenient, however, and when used it should be understood to mean exactly the same thing as the previous notation.

15. The limit of $\dfrac{\sin x}{x}$ as x approaches 0.—This limit, which is of great importance in our later work, cannot be obtained by inspection. If x is near 0, both numerator and denominator are near 0 as in the last example—but in this case we cannot easily transform the function so as to make the limit evident. In order to find it we shall borrow some simple facts from geometry.

Let x, where $0 < x < \frac{1}{2}\pi$, be the *radian* measure of a central angle in a circle of radius $OC = 1$ (Fig. 15). Then:

Area of $\triangle OBC = \frac{1}{2}OC \cdot BC = \frac{1}{2}\tan x.$ Why?
Area of sector $OAC = \frac{1}{2}\overline{OC}^2 \cdot x = \frac{1}{2}x.$ Why?
Area of $\triangle OAC = \frac{1}{2}OC \cdot AD = \frac{1}{2}\sin x.$ Why?

Of these three areas the first is largest and the last is smallest; *i.e.*,

$$\tfrac{1}{2}\tan x > \tfrac{1}{2}x > \tfrac{1}{2}\sin x.$$

Dividing by $\frac{1}{2}\sin x$ (a positive quantity) this becomes

$$\frac{1}{\cos x} > \frac{x}{\sin x} > 1.$$

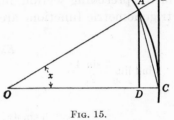

FIG. 15.

Inverting (and reversing the inequality sign) we have

$$\cos x < \frac{\sin x}{x} < 1.$$

This inequality states that the value of $(\sin x)/x$ lies between that of $\cos x$ and 1. But the limit of $\cos x$ as $x \to 0$ is 1. Hence $(\sin x)/x$, since it lies between 1 and a quantity which is approaching 1 as a limit, must also approach 1 when $x \to 0$. That is

$$\lim_{x \to 0} \frac{\sin x}{x} = 1. \qquad x \text{ in radians.}$$

We have considered here only the case where $x > 0$ and have proved that the "right-hand" limit of $(\sin x)/x$ is 1. That the "left-hand" limit is the same follows immediately from the fact that the fraction $(\sin x)/x$ is unaltered when x is replaced by $-x$.

It must be emphasized that this limit is *one* only if x is the *radian measure* of the angle—and it will be seen later that this is the primary reason for using radians rather than degrees in studying the calculus of the trigonometric functions. If $\alpha°$ is the number of degrees in the angle whose radian measure is x, then $\sin \alpha° = \sin x$ while $\alpha° = (180/\pi)x$;

hence,

$$\frac{\sin \alpha^\circ}{\alpha^\circ} = \frac{\pi}{180} \cdot \frac{\sin x}{x} \quad \text{and} \quad \lim_{x \to 0} \frac{\sin \alpha^\circ}{\alpha^\circ} = \frac{\pi}{180}.$$

The following examples illustrate the use of the fundamental limit of this section, and of the theorems on limits of the preceding section, in solving limit problems in which trigonometric functions are involved.

Example 1

Find $\lim\limits_{x \to 0} \dfrac{3 \sin 4x}{2x}$.

Solution

$$\lim_{x \to 0} \frac{3 \sin 4x}{2x} = \lim_{x \to 0} \left(6 \cdot \frac{\sin 4x}{4x} \right)$$
$$= \lim_{x \to 0} 6 \cdot \lim_{x \to 0} \frac{\sin 4x}{4x}$$
$$= 6 \cdot 1 = 6.$$

Example 2

Find $\lim\limits_{x \to 0} \dfrac{1 - \cos x}{x^2}$.

Solution

$$\lim_{x \to 0} \frac{1 - \cos x}{x^2} = \lim_{x \to 0} \frac{2 \sin^2 \frac{1}{2}x}{x^2}$$
$$= \lim_{x \to 0} \left(\frac{1}{2} \cdot \frac{\sin \frac{1}{2}x}{\frac{1}{2}x} \cdot \frac{\sin \frac{1}{2}x}{\frac{1}{2}x} \right)$$
$$= \frac{1}{2} \cdot 1 \cdot 1 = \frac{1}{2}.$$

PROBLEMS

Compute the following limits if they exist:

1. $\lim\limits_{x \to 2} (x^2 - x + 4)$.

2. $\lim\limits_{x \to 4} \dfrac{3x + 4}{x - 2}$.

3. $\lim\limits_{x \to 2} \dfrac{x^3 - 8}{x - 2}$.

4. $\lim\limits_{x \to 3} \dfrac{x^4 - 81}{x^2 - 9}$.

5. $\lim\limits_{x \to 4} \dfrac{x^2 - 2x - 8}{x^2 + 2x - 24}$.

6. $\lim\limits_{x \to 2} \dfrac{x^2 + 6x}{x - 2}$.

7. $\lim\limits_{x \to 4} \dfrac{x^3 - 2x^2 - 7x - 4}{x^2 - 4x}$.

8. $\lim\limits_{x \to -1} \dfrac{x^3 + 3x^2 + 2x}{x^2 - 2x - 3}$.

9. $\lim\limits_{x \to 2} \dfrac{x^2 - 7x + 10}{x^2 + 1}$.

10. $\lim\limits_{x \to -3} \dfrac{x^2 + 6x + 9}{x^2 + 3x}$.

11. Find the value of the fraction $\dfrac{x^2 + 8x - 20}{x^2 - 4}$ when $x = 1.9$ and 2.1. Find the limit of the fraction as $x \to 2$.

12. Find the value of the fraction $\dfrac{x^2 + x - 6}{x^2 - x - 2}$ when $x = 1.95$ and 2.05. Find the limit of the fraction as $x \to 2$.

13. Show that the value of $\dfrac{x^2 - x - 6}{x^2 - 7x + 12}$ is near -5 if x is near 3.

14. Show that $\lim\limits_{x \to 0} \dfrac{\tan x}{x} = 1$. HINT: $\tan x = \dfrac{\sin x}{\cos x}$.

Evaluate the following limits, if they exist:

15. $\lim\limits_{x \to \pi} \dfrac{\sin 2x}{\sin x}$.

16. $\lim\limits_{x \to \pi} \dfrac{\cos 2x}{\cos x}$.

17. $\lim\limits_{x \to \frac{1}{2}\pi} \dfrac{\cos^2 x}{1 - \sin x}$.

18. $\lim\limits_{x \to 0} \dfrac{2 - 2\sec^2 x}{\sin^2 x}$.

19. $\lim\limits_{x \to 0} \dfrac{1 - \cos x}{x \sin x}$.

20. $\lim\limits_{x \to 0} \dfrac{4 - 4\cos x}{x^2}$.

21. Find the value of the fraction $\dfrac{2x^2 + 10}{x + 5}$ when $x = 10$, 100, and 1,000. What is the limit of the fraction as $x \to \infty$?

22. Find the value of the fraction $\dfrac{2x + 5}{x^2 + 10x}$ when $x = 10$, 100, and 1,000. What is the limit of the fraction as $x \to \infty$?

23. Find the value of the fraction $\dfrac{6x^2 - 2x + 10}{2x^2 + 5x + 5}$ when $x = 10$, 100, and 1,000. What is the limit of the fraction as $x \to \infty$?

24. Find $\lim\limits_{x \to \infty} \dfrac{3x^2 + 5x - 7}{x^2 + 2x + 4}$. HINT: Divide each term in the numerator and denominator by the highest power of x occurring in either. Note also that for large values of x the function has the behavior of $3x^2/x^2$.

Find each of the following limits, if it exists, making use of the hint in Prob. 24:

25. $\lim\limits_{x \to \infty} \dfrac{4x^2 + x + 6}{3x^2 + 1}$.

26. $\lim\limits_{x \to -\infty} \dfrac{x^3 + 6x}{8x^2 + 5}$.

27. $\lim\limits_{x \to \infty} \dfrac{2x + 1}{x^2 + 6}$.

28. $\lim\limits_{x \to -\infty} \dfrac{3x^2 + x + 1}{8x^2 + 2x + 4}$.

29. $\lim\limits_{x \to \infty} \dfrac{4x^2 + x}{x^3 + 10x + 2}$.

30. $\lim\limits_{x \to \infty} \dfrac{2x^2 + 4x + 5}{x^3 + 1}$.

31. Let $f(x) = p_m(x)/q_n(x)$ where $p_m(x)$ and $q_n(x)$ are polynomials in x of degree m and n, respectively. What can you say about $\lim\limits_{x \to \infty} f(x)$ if $m > n$, $m = n$, and $m < n$?

32. Express the perimeter of the regular polygon of n sides inscribed in a circle of radius r as a function of n.   Compute the limit of this function as $n \rightarrow \infty$.   Is this an acceptable proof of the formula $C = 2\pi r$, or has the formula been assumed?

33. Solve Prob. 32 for the area of the inscribed polygon.

34. The function $f(x) = \dfrac{3x + 4 \tan x}{x}$ is undefined at $x = 0$.   What value must be assigned to $f(0)$ if $f(x)$ is to be continuous at this point?

35. The function $f(x) = \dfrac{x^2 - 9}{x - 3}$ is undefined at $x = 3$.   What value must be assigned to $f(3)$ if $f(x)$ is to be continuous at this point?

The sum of a geometric progression is $S = a \dfrac{1 - r^n}{1 - r}$ where a is the first term, r the common ratio, and n the number of terms.   In each of the following, express the sum S_n of n terms as a function of n; then compute $\lim\limits_{n \rightarrow \infty} S_n$.   This limit is, by definition, the "sum" of the "infinite progression."

36. $1 + \frac{1}{2} + \frac{1}{4} + \frac{1}{8} + \cdots$.

37. $9 + 3 + 1 + \frac{1}{3} + \cdots$.

38. $0.636363 \cdots$.

39. For what range of values of r does $\lim\limits_{n \rightarrow \infty} S_n$ exist, and what is its value?

40. Sketch the graph of $y = x \sin \dfrac{\pi}{x}$.   HINT: Sketch the separate factors and multiply ordinates.   Use the limit of the function as $x \rightarrow \infty$.

CHAPTER III

THE DERIVATIVE

16. Definition.—The manner in which the value of a function $f(x)$ varies with x was studied in a general way in Chap. I. We saw there that if the graph of the relation

$$y = f(x)$$

has the form shown in Fig. 16, the value of y is increasing, as x increases, throughout an interval such as AB, where the curve is rising.

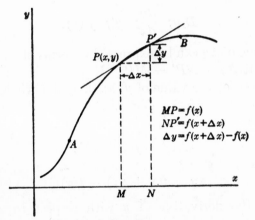

$MP = f(x)$
$NP' = f(x + \Delta x)$
$\Delta y = f(x + \Delta x) - f(x)$

Fig. 16.

Let us now select any point $P(x, y)$ of this interval and ask, "At what rate is y increasing with respect to x at this point—*i.e.*, y is increasing how many times as fast as x, or at a rate of how many units per unit of increase in x?"

A little reflection will convince the student that in order to answer this question we should proceed as follows: Starting at P,

1. Let x increase by an amount Δx, and determine the amount by which y increases.* Call this Δy.

2. Divide the increase in y by that in x. This quotient $\Delta y/\Delta x$ is called the *average rate* of increase of y with respect to x over this interval. (Thus, if an increase of 0.1 in x produced an increase of 0.3 in y, we should say that, on the average, y was increasing three times as fast as x.)

3. Now think of taking for Δx smaller and smaller values. The corresponding set of values of $\Delta y/\Delta x$ represents the average rate of change of y with respect to x over *smaller and smaller intervals beginning at P*. It at once appears reasonable that we should *define* the instantaneous rate *at P* as the *limit* of the quotient $\Delta y/\Delta x$ as $\Delta x \to 0$.

This limit, if it exists, is called the *derivative of y, or the derivative of f(x), with respect to x* at P. It is usually denoted by one of the symbols,

$$D_x y; \quad \frac{dy}{dx}; \quad y'; \quad f'(x).$$

The value of Δy can be expressed in terms of x and Δx by noting that $\Delta y = NP' - MP$. Now MP is the value of the function (or the value of y) at the point whose abscissa is x; hence $MP = f(x)$. NP' is the value of the function at the point whose abscissa is $x + \Delta x$; hence

$$NP' = f(x + \Delta x).$$

Finally then,

$$\Delta y = f(x + \Delta x) - f(x).$$

Denoting the derivative of y with respect to x by the symbol $D_x y$, we may write our definition in the form:

$$D_x y = \lim_{\Delta x \to 0} \frac{\Delta y}{\Delta x} = \lim_{\Delta x \to 0} \frac{f(x + \Delta x) - f(x)}{\Delta x}.$$

In Fig. 16 we have pictured Δx as positive and we have also spoken of the change in y as an increase. More

* The student should draw the corresponding figure for the case in which the value of the function is decreasing—noting in this case that an increase in x produces a *decrease* in y so that Δy and Δx have opposite signs.

generally, Δx may be either positive or negative and, of course, the value of the function may be increasing, decreasing, or remaining constant. When we speak of the limit of $\Delta y/\Delta x$ we mean it in the sense of our definition of the limit of a function as discussed in Chap. II. In this case the fraction $\Delta y/\Delta x$ is regarded as a function of Δx (for any particular value of x).

The function $f(x)$ is said to be *differentiable* at any point P at which the above limit exists—and, if the limit exists at every point of a certain interval, the function is said to be differentiable over the interval. All functions that we shall study here are differentiable except possibly at certain points.

17. Graphical meaning of the derivative.—Referring to Fig. 16, we see that the fraction $\Delta y/\Delta x$ is the slope of the secant line PP'. As $\Delta x \to 0$, and P' approaches P along the curve, this secant line turns about point P approaching a position of tangency to the curve at P. Hence, *the value of the derivative of y with respect to x at P is equal to the slope of the tangent line drawn to the graph of $y = f(x)$ at this point.*

18. Differentiation.—We consider now the problem of calculating the derivative with respect to x of a given function $f(x)$. From the above definition and discussion it is evident that the process, which is called *differentiation*, requires the following three steps:

Step 1. Starting at any point $P(x, y)$ (Fig. 16), let x increase by an amount Δx. Find Δy in terms of x and Δx by subtracting $MP = f(x)$ from $NP' = f(x + \Delta x)$; *i.e.*,

$$\Delta y = f(x + \Delta x) - f(x).$$

This expression for Δy should be simplified as much as possible before proceeding to step 2.

Step 2. Divide Δy by Δx;

$$\frac{\Delta y}{\Delta x} = \frac{f(x + \Delta x) - f(x)}{\Delta x}.$$

Step 3. Determine the limit of this quotient as $\Delta x \to 0$. This limit, which will in general be a function of x, is the required derivative.

$$D_x y = \lim_{\Delta x \to 0} \frac{f(x + \Delta x) - f(x)}{\Delta x}.$$

Example 1

For the function $y = x^2$ find the value of $D_x y$ at any point.

Solution (Fig. 17)

Step 1. The value of this function at any point P having abscissa x is $MP = x^2$; its value at P', where the abscissa is $x + \Delta x$, is

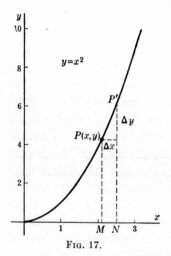

$$NP' = (x + \Delta x)^2.$$

Consequently,

$$\Delta y = (x + \Delta x)^2 - x^2$$
$$= 2x\,\Delta x + (\Delta x)^2.$$

Step 2. Having thus found Δy in terms of x and Δx, we divide by Δx:

$$\frac{\Delta y}{\Delta x} = 2x + \Delta x.$$

Step 3. We now obtain $D_x y$ by taking the limit of the above result as $\Delta x \to 0$:

$$D_x y = \lim_{\Delta x \to 0} (2x + \Delta x)$$

or

$$D_x y = 2x.$$

FIG. 17.

At any point on the curve the value of $D_x y$ is $2x$. At the point where $x = 3$, for example, it is 6; we write

$$D_x y]_{x=3} = 6.$$

This means that the slope of the tangent line to the curve at this point is 6. It also means that at this point the value of y is increasing 6 times as fast as x.

In the next example the algebraic details are not quite so simple. In order to avoid confusing the main issue we have put down only the essential results, leaving the details to the student. Observe that $f(x + \Delta x)$ is always obtained by simply replacing x by $x + \Delta x$ in the function $f(x)$.

Example 2

Given $y = 3x + \dfrac{1}{x}$, find $D_x y$.

Solution

Step 1. $\Delta y = \left[3(x + \Delta x) + \dfrac{1}{x + \Delta x} \right] - \left(3x + \dfrac{1}{x} \right)$

$= \dfrac{3x^2 \Delta x + 3x(\Delta x)^2 - \Delta x}{x(x + \Delta x)}.$

Step 2. $\dfrac{\Delta y}{\Delta x} = \dfrac{3x^2 + 3x \Delta x - 1}{x(x + \Delta x)}.$

Step 3. $D_x y = \lim\limits_{\Delta x \to 0} \dfrac{3x^2 + 3x \Delta x - 1}{x(x + \Delta x)}$

$= \dfrac{3x^2 - 1}{x^2}.$

It should be observed that the algebraic simplification of step 1, in the above examples, has put it in a form containing Δx as a factor so that step 2 merely cancels this factor. Cases in which this cannot be done will be encountered later, but for the present the student should always reduce step 1 to this condition before taking step 2. It is permissible to cancel the factor Δx from numerator and denominator because in taking the limit as $\Delta x \to 0$ we are not letting Δx *equal* zero.

Finally, we give an example that emphasizes the physical interpretation of the derivative.

Example 3

Suppose that the edge x of a cube is increasing; find the rate at which the volume is increasing with respect to x when $x = 2$ in.

Solution (Fig. 18)

When the edge has any length x (inches) the volume is

$$v = x^3 \qquad \text{(cu. in.).}$$

If now the edge increases by a small amount Δx, the increase in volume is

(1) $\Delta v = (x + \Delta x)^3 - x^3$
$= 3x^2 \Delta x + 3x(\Delta x)^2 + (\Delta x)^3.$

(2) $\dfrac{\Delta v}{\Delta x} = 3x^2 + 3x \Delta x + (\Delta x)^2.$

(3) $$\frac{dv}{dx} = \lim_{\Delta x \to 0} [3x^2 + 3x\,\Delta x + (\Delta x)^2] = 3x^2.$$

$$\frac{dv}{dx}\bigg]_{x=2} = 12.$$

This means that at this instant the volume is increasing 12 times as rapidly as x—or at a rate of 12 *cu. in. per inch of increase in x.* If the

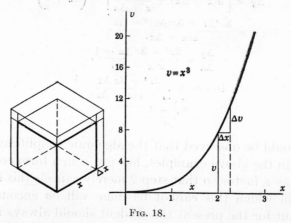

Fig. 18.

edge were increasing at, say, 3 in. per minute, the volume would of course be increasing at $12 \cdot 3 = 36$ *cu. in. per minute.*

19. Notation.—As indicated above, several symbols for denoting the derivative and for indicating the operation of taking the derivative are in common use. In example 1 above we found that the derivative with respect to x of the function x^2 is $2x$. We may indicate this by writing

$$\frac{d}{dx}(x^2) = 2x \qquad \text{or} \qquad D_x(x^2) = 2x.$$

Here the symbol d/dx or D_x denotes the operation of taking the derivative with respect to x of the function of x to which it is applied—just as the symbol $\sqrt{}$ indicates the operation of taking the square root. If we denote the function by y and write $y = x^2$, then we may write

$$D_x y = 2x \qquad \text{or} \qquad \frac{d}{dx}(y) = 2x \qquad \text{or} \qquad \frac{dy}{dx} = 2x.$$

It should be noted that the symbol dy/dx is not introduced here as a fraction with dy as numerator and dx as denomi- *ALTHOUGH IT IS.* nator. It is simply a brief way of writing $\frac{d}{dx}$ (y) where $\frac{d}{dx}$ denotes the operation of taking the derivative with respect to x and y stands for the function of x whose derivative is to be taken. There is perhaps some advantage at this point in using D_x instead of d/dx. Later on we shall assign meanings to the separate symbols dy and dx, and these definitions will be such that the fraction, dy divided by dx, will equal the derivative of y with respect to x.

Other notations often used are as follows: If we write $y = x^2$, we may write $y' = 2x$. If we do not use y at all but *or $\dot{y}$ or* write $f(x) = x^2$, we may write $f'(x) = 2x$. In this last *time derivative* notation $f'(x)$ denotes the function obtained by taking the derivative of $f(x)$ with respect to x.

20. Increasing and decreasing functions. The sign of $D_x y$.—We have frequently spoken of a function as increasing where its graph is rising and decreasing where the curve is falling. We may now make this idea more precise and connect it with the sign of $D_x y$.

A function $f(x)$ is said to be increasing over an interval $a \leq x \leq b$ provided that, if x_1 and x_2 are any two values of x in the interval such that $x_2 > x_1$, then $f(x_2) > f(x_1)$. The corresponding definition for a decreasing function is obvious.

It can be shown that if the value of $D_x y$ is positive at $P(x_1, y_1)$ then y is an increasing function of x over at least a small interval about the point $x = x_1$. The proof is obtained by observing that if $\lim_{\Delta x \to 0} \frac{\Delta y}{\Delta x}$ is positive at P, then Δy and Δx must have the *same sign* for Δx sufficiently near zero.

If the value of $D_x y$ is positive throughout an interval, then y is increasing over the interval. Similarly, if $D_x y$ is negative then y is decreasing.

Conversely, if y is increasing over an interval and if $D_x y$ exists at every point of the interval, then it must be everywhere positive (or zero).   This situation is illustrated by Fig. 19.   The function shown is increasing over the interval $a \leq x \leq b$.   Its derivative is positive (and the tangent line has a positive slope) at every point except at

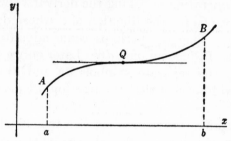

FIG. 19.

Q where $D_x y = 0$ and the tangent line is parallel to the x-axis.

The intervals in which a function is increasing and decreasing can be determined by studying its derivative as indicated in the following:

Example

If y varies with x in accordance with the relation $y = x^3 - 3x^2 + 3$, find the interval in which y is decreasing.

Solution (Fig. 20)

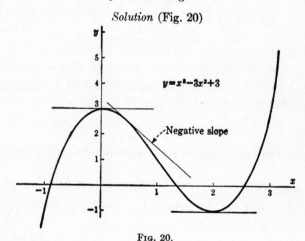

FIG. 20.

The three steps for determining $D_x y$ are, briefly,

(1) $\Delta y = [(x + \Delta x)^3 - 3(x + \Delta x)^2 + 3] - (x^3 - 3x^2 + 3)$
       $\quad = 3x^2\Delta x + 3x(\Delta x)^2 + (\Delta x)^3 - 6x\,\Delta x - 3(\Delta x)^2;$

(2) $\dfrac{\Delta y}{\Delta x} = 3x^2 + 3x\,\Delta x + (\Delta x)^2 - 6x - 3\Delta x;$

(3) $D_x y = 3x^2 - 6x$
       $\quad\;\; = 3x(x - 2).$

It is easy to see that the value of $D_x y$ is negative for all values of x between 0 and 2. In this interval y is decreasing and the tangent line has a negative slope. For $x > 2$, and also for $x < 0$, the derivative is positive and y is increasing. At $x = 0$ and at $x = 2$ the value of $D_x y$ is zero. At these points the tangent line is parallel to the x-axis.

PROBLEMS

1. Find the average rate at which the area A of a square increases with respect to a side x when x increases from 4 to 6 in.; from x to $(x + \Delta x)$ in. Find $D_x A$ and its value when $x = 4$ in. In what units is this rate expressed?

2. Find the average rate at which the surface area S of a cube increases relative to an edge x when x increases from 4 to $4\frac{1}{2}$ in.; from x to $(x + \Delta x)$ in. Find $D_x S$ and its value when $x = 4$ in. In what units is this rate expressed?

3. The length of a rectangular box is twice the width x (ft.) and its height is equal to x. Find the value of $D_x V$, where V is the volume of the box, when $x = 6$ ft.

4. A right pyramid has a rectangular base that is x ft. wide and $4x$ ft. long. Its height is $6x$ ft. Find the derivative of its volume V with respect to x and find the value of $D_x V$ when $x = 2$ ft. If at this instant x is increasing at 0.05 ft. per hour, at what time rate is the volume increasing?

5. The number of grams N of a substance in a solution varies with the time t in minutes according to the law $N = \dfrac{12}{t + 1}$. Find $D_t N]_{t=3}$, in what units is this rate expressed?

6. If an object is dropped from the top of a cliff and falls under the action of gravity alone, its distance S (ft.) below the top of the cliff at the end of t seconds is given approximately by the formula $S = 16t^2$. Compute $\dfrac{dS}{dt}\bigg]_{t=2}$, and explain the meaning of the result. In what units is this rate expressed?

7. A cylinder contains 400 cu. in. of air at a pressure of 15 lb. per square inch. If the air is now compressed by a piston, under conditions of constant temperature, the pressure increases as the volume decreases, the relation between them being $pv = 6,000$. Find the value of dp/dv

when $v = 100$ cu. in.   Interpret the result, and state the units in which
it is expressed.

8. A quantity Q varies with the time t in accordance with the law
$Q = 8t^2 - t^3$.   Find the time interval in which Q is increasing.

In each of the following problems, first sketch the graph and select
any point $P(x, y)$ on it.   Then calculate $D_x y$ at P.   Show the meanings
of $\Delta y/\Delta x$ and $D_x y$ on the graph:

9. $y = x^2 + 3$.

10. $y = 3x^2 + 2x$.

11. $y = x^2 - 4x - 5$.

12. $y = 2x^2 - 5x + 12$.

13. $y = 2x - 8x^2$.

14. $y = \frac{1}{2}x^3$.

15. $y = 4x^2 - x^3$.

16. $y = x^3 - 16x$.

17. $y = x^4 - 16$.

18. $y = 4x^2 - x^4$.

19. $y = 2x^5$.

20. $y = x^6$.

21. $y = \sqrt{x}$.   HINT: After finding $\Delta y = \sqrt{x + \Delta x} - \sqrt{x}$, multiply
and divide by $\sqrt{x + \Delta x} + \sqrt{x}$.

22. $y = \sqrt{4x + 3}$.   See hint in Prob. 21

23. $y = \dfrac{1}{\sqrt{x}}$.   See hint in Prob. 21.

24. $y = \dfrac{1}{3x + 5}$.

25. $y = \dfrac{5x}{x - 1}$.

26. $y = \dfrac{7x + 4}{x}$.

27. $y = \dfrac{x + 2}{x - 4}$.

28. $y = \dfrac{2x + 1}{x + 3}$.

29. $y = \dfrac{1}{x^2}$.

30. $y = \dfrac{3}{x^2 - 4}$.

31. $y = \dfrac{4}{x^2 + 1}$.

32. $y = \dfrac{3x}{x^2 + 2}$.

33. $y = \dfrac{2x^2}{x^2 + 4}$.

34. $y = \dfrac{x^2}{x^2 - 9}$.

35. $y = \dfrac{x^2 - 1}{x^2 + 1}$.

36. $y = \dfrac{x^2 + 4}{x^2 - 4}$.   **37.** $y = 2x^3 + \dfrac{1}{x}$.   **38.** $y = \frac{1}{2}x + \dfrac{4}{x^2}$.

Find the slope of the tangent line to each of the following curves at
the point indicated.   Draw the curve and tangent line:

39. $y = x^2 + 2x - 6$; $(2, 2)$.   **40.** $y = 8 + 2x - x^2$; $(2, 8)$.

41. $xy = 9$; $(4.5, 2)$.   **42.** $y = x^3 - 4x$; $(1, -3)$.

43. $y = x + \dfrac{1}{x}$; $(1, 2)$.   **44.** $y = x^3 - 6x^2 + 3x + 10$; $(1, 8)$.

45. $y = \dfrac{8}{x^2 + 4}$; $(-2, 1)$.   **46.** $y = \dfrac{x}{x^2 + 1}$; $(0, 0)$.

In each of the following problems determine the x-intervals in which y is (a) increasing, (b) decreasing. Draw the graph:

47. $y = x^2 + 5x + 1$.

48. $y = 6x - x^2$.

49. $y = 2x^3 - 5x^2$.

50. $y = \dfrac{x}{x - 1}$.

51. Sketch the curve $y = x^2 - 4$. Suppose that a point moves along this curve from left to right so that its abscissa increases uniformly at 3 units per minute. At what rate is its ordinate increasing when it goes through $(1, -3)$? HINT: You will find that $\dfrac{dy}{dx}\Big]_{1,-3} = 2$; that is, y is increasing twice as fast as x.

52. In the preceding problem compute the time rate of change of the ordinate when the moving point passes through $(3, 5)$. Through $(-1, -3)$. Why is the last result negative?

53. Sketch the parabola $y = 5 + 4x - x^2$. Obtain an expression for the slope of the tangent at any point. Find the slope at the points where the curve crosses the axes. Find the point where the slope is zero.

54. Sketch the curve $V = \frac{4}{3}\pi r^3$. Find the rate of change of the volume with respect to the radius (in cubic inches per inch) when $r = 2$ in. If you were inflating a toy spherical balloon and the radius were increasing at $\frac{1}{2}$ in. per minute, at what rate would the volume be increasing at the instant when $r = 2$ in.?

55. In the above problem we have spoken of the rate of increase of the volume of a sphere *with respect to its radius*. Is it obvious to you that this is equal to the rate at which the volume is increasing with respect to the time (in, say, cubic inches per minute) divided by the rate at which the radius is increasing (in inches per minute)?

56. Find the rate of change of the surface area of a cube with respect to its edge x. In what units is this expressed if x is in inches? If x is 4 in. and is increasing at 2 in. per minute, at what time rate is the surface area increasing?

57. Find the rate of change of the volume of a cube with respect to its edge (in cubic inches per inch). Find also the rate of change of the surface area with respect to the edge (in square inches per inch). If the first of these is divided by the second, what does the quotient represent and in what units is it expressed? How can each of these rates be interpreted as the slope of the tangent to a curve?

CHAPTER IV

DIFFERENTIATION OF ALGEBRAIC FUNCTIONS

21. Introduction.—The method of the last chapter may of course be applied to any function for the purpose of finding its derivative. It is the fundamental method since it is a direct application of the *definition* of the derivative. The procedure is, however, rather tedious and it is natural that we should try to develop some general rules that will enable us to arrive at the result more easily. Thus, after finding that the derivatives of x^2, x^3, and x^4 are, respectively, $2x$, $3x^2$, and $4x^3$, we might suspect that the derivative of x^n is nx^{n-1}—at least if n is a positive integer. It can be shown, *by applying the fundamental method of differentiation* to the function

$$y = x^n,$$

that this is true. We may then remember it as a formula and dispense with the labor of going through the formal process for each case. We might suspect also that the derivative of a function of the form kx^n is merely k times the derivative of x^n. Thus,

$$\frac{d}{dx}(5x^3) = 5 \cdot \frac{d}{dx} x^3 = 5 \cdot (3x^2) = 15x^2.$$

Another rule which is easily proved is that, if a function consists of the sum of several terms, its derivative is merely the sum of the derivatives of the separate terms. Thus, if

$$y = x^3 + 8x^2,$$

$$D_x y \text{ or } \frac{dy}{dx} = \frac{d}{dx}(x^3) + \frac{d}{dx}(8x^2)$$

$$= 3x^2 + 16x.$$

42

This last rule is stated formally by saying that if u and v are any two differentiable functions of x, then

$$\frac{d}{dx}(u + v) = \frac{du}{dx} + \frac{dv}{dx}.$$

In the above example $u = x^3$ and $v = 8x^2$.

22. Formulas for differentiation.—We proceed now to write down and prove a list of 11 formulas that will enable us to dispense with the fundamental differentiation process in calculating the derivatives of simple algebraic functions such as those considered in the last chapter. Later on we shall add to this list the additional formulas necessary for finding the derivatives of trigonometric, exponential, and other transcendental functions.

It must be kept in mind that in these formulas *u and v stand for functions of x* while *c and n are constants.*

FORMULAS

(I)
$$\frac{dc}{dx} = 0$$

The derivative of a constant is zero.

(II)
$$\frac{dx}{dx} = 1$$

The derivative of a variable with respect to itself is one.

(III)
$$\frac{d}{dx}(u + v) = \frac{du}{dx} + \frac{dv}{dx}$$

*The derivative of the sum of two functions is equal to the sum of their separate derivatives. This is easily extended to the case of any finite number of functions.**

(IV)
$$\frac{d}{dx}(u \cdot v) = u\frac{dv}{dx} + v\frac{du}{dx}$$

The derivative of the product of two functions is the first function times the derivative of the second plus the second function times the

---

* The formula is not necessarily true in the case of an *infinite series.* The situation is discussed briefly in Chap. XXVIII.

derivative of the first.

(IVs)*
$$\frac{d}{dx}\,(c \cdot v) = c\,\frac{dv}{dx}$$

The derivative of the product of a constant and a function is the constant times the derivative of the function.

(V)
$$\frac{d}{dx}\,v^n = nv^{n-1}\,\frac{dv}{dx}$$

The derivative of the nth power of a function is n times the (n − 1)th power of the function times the derivative of the function.

(Vs)
$$\frac{d}{dx}\,x^n = nx^{n-1}$$

The derivative of the nth power of x is n times the (n−1)th power of x.

(VI)
$$\frac{d}{dx}\left(\frac{u}{v}\right) = \frac{v\,\dfrac{du}{dx} - u\,\dfrac{dv}{dx}}{v^2}$$

The derivative of the quotient of two functions is the denominator times the derivative of the numerator, minus the numerator times the derivative of the denominator, all divided by the square of the denominator.

(VIs)
$$\frac{d}{dx}\left(\frac{u}{c}\right) = \frac{1}{c}\,\frac{du}{dx}$$

The derivative of the quotient of a function by a constant is the derivative of the function divided by the constant.

(VII)
$$\frac{dy}{dx} = \frac{dy}{dv} \cdot \frac{dv}{dx}$$

If y is a function of v, and v is in turn a function of x, then the derivative of y with respect to x equals the product of the derivative of y with respect to v and the derivative of v with respect to x.

(VIII)
$$\frac{dy}{dx} = \frac{1}{\dfrac{dx}{dy}}$$

* This formula is a special case of (IV).　Why?

The derivative of y with respect to x is the reciprocal of the derivative of x with respect to y.

23. Formulas (I) to (VI).—To prove any of these formulas we may take the corresponding function and apply the fundamental process of differentiation.

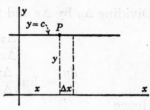

FIG. 21.

(I) Consider the function

$$y = c \qquad \text{(Fig. 21)}.$$

Starting at any point P and letting x increase by any amount Δx, we see immediately that Δy is identically 0. Hence

$$\frac{\Delta y}{\Delta x} \equiv 0, \qquad (\Delta x \neq 0)$$

and consequently

$$\frac{dy}{dx} = \lim_{\Delta x \to 0} \frac{\Delta y}{\Delta x} = 0.$$

(II) It is left for the student to sketch the function

$$y = x$$

and show that in this case

$$\Delta y \equiv \Delta x$$
$$\frac{\Delta y}{\Delta x} = 1$$

and hence

$$\frac{dy}{dx} = 1.$$

(III) Consider the function

$$y = u + v$$

where u and v are differentiable functions of x. If, starting with any fixed value, x increases by an amount Δx, u and v will change by corresponding amounts Δu and Δv, respectively.　The change produced in the value of y is

$$\Delta y = [(u + \Delta u) + (v + \Delta v)] - (u + v)$$
$$= \Delta u + \Delta v.$$

Dividing Δy by Δx and then letting $\Delta x \to 0$, we have

$$\frac{\Delta y}{\Delta x} = \frac{\Delta u}{\Delta x} + \frac{\Delta v}{\Delta x};$$

$$\frac{dy}{dx} = \lim_{\Delta x \to 0} \frac{\Delta y}{\Delta x} = \lim_{\Delta x \to 0} \frac{\Delta u}{\Delta x} + \lim_{\Delta x \to 0} \frac{\Delta v}{\Delta x}.$$

Hence

$$\frac{dy}{dx} = \frac{du}{dx} + \frac{dv}{dx}. \quad \text{Why?}$$

(IV)　Consider the function

$$y = u \cdot v$$

and apply to it the procedure just used on the function $u \perp v$.　We obtain

$$\Delta y = [(u + \Delta u)(v + \Delta v)] - (uv)$$
$$= u\,\Delta v + v\,\Delta u + \Delta u\,\Delta v.$$

$$\frac{\Delta y}{\Delta x} = u\,\frac{\Delta v}{\Delta x} + v\,\frac{\Delta u}{\Delta x} + \frac{\Delta u}{\Delta x}\,\Delta v.$$

$$\frac{dy}{dx} = u\,\frac{dv}{dx} + v\,\frac{du}{dx} + 0. \quad \text{Explain.}$$

(IVs)　This is a special case of (IV).　Why?　Show that (IV) reduces to this if one of the factors in the product is a constant.

(V)　Consider the function

$$y = v^n$$

where v is a differentiable function of x.　An increment Δx in x produces a change Δv in the value of v, and the corresponding change in y is

$$\Delta y = (v + \Delta v)^n - v^n.$$

Assuming that n is a positive integer we have, using the

binomial theorem,

$$\Delta y = \left[v^n + nv^{n-1}\Delta v + \frac{n(n-1)}{2!} v^{n-2}(\Delta v)^2 + \cdots \right.$$
$$\left. + (\Delta v)^n \right] - v^n$$

$$= nv^{n-1}\Delta v + \frac{n(n-1)}{2!} v^{n-2}(\Delta v)^2 + \cdots + (\Delta v)^n.$$

$$\frac{\Delta y}{\Delta x} = nv^{n-1}\frac{\Delta v}{\Delta x} + \frac{n(n-1)}{2!} v^{n-2}\frac{\Delta v}{\Delta x} \cdot \Delta v + \cdots$$
$$+ \frac{\Delta v}{\Delta x} \cdot (\Delta v)^{n-1}.$$

All the terms after the first have the limit *zero* as $\Delta x \to 0$. Why?   We have then

$$\frac{dy}{dx} = nv^{n-1}\frac{dv}{dx}.$$

This proof applies only if n is a positive integer.   However, *the formula is valid for all values of n.*   We shall therefore use it in this sense although the proof will be left until later.*

(Vs) This is a special case of (V).   Explain.

(VI) Applying to the function

$$y = \frac{u}{v}$$

the procedure used above on the function $(u + v)$ we obtain

$$\Delta y = \frac{u + \Delta u}{v + \Delta v} - \frac{u}{v}$$

$$= \frac{v\,\Delta u - u\,\Delta v}{v(v + \Delta v)}.$$

$$\frac{\Delta y}{\Delta x} = \frac{v\dfrac{\Delta u}{\Delta x} - u\dfrac{\Delta v}{\Delta x}}{v(v + \Delta v)}.$$

$$\frac{dy}{dx} = \frac{v\dfrac{du}{dx} - u\dfrac{dv}{dx}}{v^2}. \quad \text{Explain.}$$

* See p. 121.

(VIs) This is a special case of (VI). Is this also equivalent to (IVs)?

Usually, in finding the derivative of a given function, one must use not one but *several* of the formulas. The details will be illustrated by four examples.

Example 1

$$y = 8x^4 + 5x^2 - 9x.$$

Solution

$$\frac{dy}{dx} = \frac{d}{dx}(8x^4) + \frac{d}{dx}(5x^2) - \frac{d}{dx}(9x) \qquad \text{[by (III.)]}$$

$$= 8\frac{d}{dx}x^4 + 5\frac{d}{dx}x^2 - 9\frac{d}{dx}x \qquad \text{[by (IVs)]}$$

$$= 8(4x^3) + 5(2x) - 9(1) \qquad \text{[by (Vs)]}$$

$$= 32x^3 + 10x - 9.$$

Example 2

$$y = (4x^2 + 5)^3.$$

Solution

$$\frac{dy}{dx} = 3(4x^2 + 5)^2 \frac{d}{dx}(4x^2 + 5) \qquad \text{[by (V)]}$$

$$= 3(4x^2 + 5)^2(8x + 0)$$

$$= 24x(4x^2 + 5)^2.$$

Example 3

$$f(x) = (2x + 1)\sqrt{x^2 + 4}.$$

Solution

$$f'(x) = (2x + 1)\frac{d}{dx}\sqrt{x^2 + 4} + \sqrt{x^2 + 4}\frac{d}{dx}(2x + 1) \qquad \text{[by (IV)]}$$

$$= (2x + 1)\tfrac{1}{2}(x^2 + 4)^{-\frac{1}{2}}\frac{d}{dx}(x^2 + 4) + \sqrt{x^2 + 4} \cdot 2$$

$$= \frac{(2x + 1)x}{\sqrt{x^2 + 4}} + 2\sqrt{x^2 + 4}$$

$$= \frac{4x^2 + x + 8}{\sqrt{x^2 + 4}}.$$

Example 4

$$s = \frac{a - t}{a + t}.$$

Solution

$$\frac{ds}{dt} = \frac{(a+t)\dfrac{d}{dt}(a-t) - (a-t)\dfrac{d}{dt}(a+t)}{(a+t)^2} \quad \text{[by (VI)]}$$

$$= \frac{(a+t)(0-1) - (a-t)(0+1)}{(a+t)^2}$$

$$= \frac{-2a}{(a+t)^2}.$$

PROBLEMS

1. How may the function $f(x) = x^2 + 3x - 4$ be regarded as the sum of two functions u and v? Can its graph be obtained by sketching $y = x^2$ and $y = 3x - 4$ and adding ordinates? How may it be regarded as the sum of three functions?

2. Find the derivative of $y = x(x^2 + 4)$ both with and without the use of formula (IV). Explain why formula (IV) would be used in finding the derivative of the function $x \sin x$. What else would we have to know?

3. Which formulas out of the given list would be required in finding the derivative of $\varphi(x) = (\log x)/x^2$? What additional information would be necessary? How do you think this information might be obtained?

4. Differentiate the function $y = (x^2 + 1)^3$ with and without the use of formula (V). Why is the derivative *not* equal to $3(x^2 + 1)^2$?

5. Show how formula (III) may be extended to the sum of any number of functions. HINT: $u + v + w$ may be written $(u + v) + w$.

Differentiate the following functions, using formulas (I) to (III) and (Vs):

6. $y = 4x^2 - 7x + 4.$ **7.** $y = x^3 + 4x.$

8. $s = 2t^3 + 6t + 2.$ **9.** $w = 3t^2 - t + 7.$

10. $y = 4x^6 + 2x^4 - 3x + 3.$ **11.** $y = \frac{2}{3}x^3 - 4x^2 + 5x.$

12. $y = 6x^{-2} + 3x^{-1} + 2.$ **13.** $y = x^3 + \dfrac{32}{x}.$

14. $y = 4x^2 + \dfrac{1}{x^2}.$ **15.** $y = x^6 - \dfrac{2}{x^3}.$

16. $y = 2x^4 + 5x^3 - 4 - \dfrac{2}{x} + \dfrac{1}{x^2}.$ **17.** $y = 2x^{\frac{3}{2}} + 4x^{\frac{1}{2}} + 2.$

18. $y = x^{\frac{1}{2}} + 6x^{\frac{1}{3}}.$ **19.** $y = 4x^{-\frac{1}{2}} + 6x^{-\frac{1}{3}} + 1.$

20. $y = 2\sqrt{t} + 9\sqrt[3]{t}.$ **21.** $y = \dfrac{3}{5x^2} + \dfrac{1}{x^4} + 2.$

22. $y = \dfrac{1}{\sqrt{4x}} + 9x^{\frac{2}{3}}.$

Differentiate the following functions, using formulas (I) to (Vs):

23. $y = (3x + 1)^4$.

24. $y = 3(2x + 1)^5$.

25. $y = 2(4 - x^2)^{\frac{1}{2}}$.

26. $y = 9\sqrt{t^2 + 4}$.

27. $y = (x^3 - 8)^{\frac{2}{3}}$.

28. $y = (x^2 + 4)^{-\frac{1}{2}}$.

29. $y = x^2(x + 1)^3$.

30. $y = 4x(3x - 1)^2$.

31. $y = (x^2 + 1)(x^2 - 1)$.

32. $y = 3x - 7)(x^2 + 1)^3$.

33. $y = (x^2 + 4)^3(x^2 + 1)^2$.

34. $y = x\sqrt{x^2 + 4}$.

35. $y = 4x^2\sqrt{x^2 - 1}$.

36. $y = x^{-2}\sqrt{4x - 2}$.

Differentiate the following functions, using formulas (I) to (VIs):

37. $y = \dfrac{4}{3x - 1}$.

38. $y = \dfrac{6}{2x + 5}$.

39. $y = \dfrac{x - 2}{x + 5}$.

40. $y = \dfrac{3x + 7}{2x - 3}$.

41. $y = \dfrac{3}{x^2 + 1}$.

42. $y = \dfrac{1}{x^3 + x}$.

43. $y = \dfrac{6x}{x^2 + 4}$.

44. $y = \dfrac{3x^2}{6x - 1}$.

45. $y = \dfrac{t^2}{t^2 + 1}$.

46. $w = \dfrac{4t}{t^2 + 4}$.

47. $w = \dfrac{y}{\sqrt{1 - 4y^2}}$.

48. $y = \dfrac{8a^3}{x^2 + 4a^2}$.

49. $y = \left(\dfrac{x^2 - 4}{x^2 + 4}\right)^2$.

50. $y = \sqrt{\dfrac{1 + x^2}{1 - x^2}}$.

51. $y = \dfrac{x^2 - 4}{x^3 + 27}$.

52. $y = \dfrac{4(x^4 + 16)}{(x + 2)^2}$.

53. $y = \dfrac{x\sqrt{x^2 + 4}}{x^2 - 4}$.

54. $y = \dfrac{x^2(4x - 1)^{\frac{3}{2}}}{x^2 + 4}$.

In each of the following, find $D_x y$ after first solving for y in terms of x. In cases where the given equation defines y as a double-valued function of x, separate it into single-valued branches and differentiate these functions individually; sketch the curve:

55. $4x = 2y + 7$.

56. $x + 3y + 6 = 0$.

57. $y^2 = 4 + x$.

58. $4x^2 + y^2 = 20$.

59. $x^2 - y^2 = 6$.

60. $x^2 + y^2 = 10x$.

61. $y^2 - 6y - x = 0$.

62. $y^2 + 3y - x = 4$.

63. $9x^2 + 16y^2 = 144$.

64. $x^2 + 4y^2 = 12x$.

Find the slope of the tangent line to each of the following curves at the point indicated. Sketch the curve and tangent line:

65. $y = \dfrac{8}{x^2}$; $(2, 2)$.

66. $xy = 2$; $(-1, -2)$.

67. $xy - 4y - 2 = 0$; $(8, \frac{1}{2})$.

68. $xy - y - x = 0$; $(2, 2)$.

69. $y^2 = 2x$; $(8, -4)$.

70. $y = \dfrac{20}{x^2 + 4}$; $(2, 2.5)$.

71. $y = \dfrac{10x}{x^2 + 1}$; $(2, 4)$.

72. $x^2 + y^2 = 25$; $(-3, 4)$.

73. $9x^2 + 16y^2 = 144;\ \left(2, \dfrac{3\sqrt{3}}{2}\right).$

74. $x^2 + y^2 = 10x;\ (8, 4).$

75. Show that if u, v, and w are differentiable functions of x,

$$\frac{d}{dx}(uvw) = uv\frac{dw}{dx} + vw\frac{du}{dx} + uw\frac{dv}{dx}.$$

HINT: Apply the product formula to $(uv)(w)$.

Differentiate each of the following functions using the formula of Prob. 75. Check by multiplying out the right-hand side and then differentiating.

76. $y = x(x - 1)(x - 2).$

77. $y = x(x^2 + 3)(2x - 3).$

78. $y = (4x + 1)(x^2 - 3)(x - 2).$

79. Suppose we sketch the curves $y = f(x)$ and $y = \varphi(x)$, and then obtain the product curve $y = f(x) \cdot \varphi(x)$ by multiplying ordinates. Is the slope of the product curve at $x = a$ equal to the product of the slopes of the component curves, or what is the relation?

80. Show that if the tangent to each of the component curves of Prob. 79 is horizontal at $x = a$, then the same is true of the tangent to the product curve.

81. Find the rates of change of both the volume v and the surface area s of a sphere with respect to the radius. If the radius is in inches, in what units are these rates expressed?

82. Find the rate of change of the volume of a sphere with respect to its surface area using the results of Prob. 81 and also by expressing v as a function of s and differentiating.

83. The gravitational attraction between two particles is a force whose magnitude F varies inversely as the square of the distance x between them; i.e., $F = k/x^2$ where k is a constant. Find the rate of change of F with respect to x. Does F increase or decrease as x increases?

84. Find the rate of change of the area of an equilateral triangle with respect to a side. If the side is expressed in feet, what are the units of this rate?

85. Each edge of a regular tetrahedron is x. Express its volume v as a function of x and find $D_x v$.

86. Assuming that the edge x of a cube is increasing, find the rates of change of the volume v and the surface area s with respect to the edge. Find the numerical values of these rates when $x = 6$ in., and state the units in which they are expressed. If the edge is increasing at 2 in. per minute, find the *time* rates at which v and s are increasing.

87. Water is being poured into an inverted right circular cone that is 24 in. in diameter at the top and 24 in. deep. Express the volume v of water in the cone as a function of its depth y. Find $D_y v$, and find its value when $y = 12$ in. In what units is this rate expressed? If water is being poured in at 6 cu. in. per minute, at what time rate (in inches per minute) is the water level rising at this instant?

24. Differentiation of a function of a function. Formula (VII).—Suppose that y is expressed, not directly in terms of x, but as a function of another variable v which is in turn a function of x. Thus, we may have

$$y = v^2 - 3v + 2, \qquad v = 4x^2 + 1.$$

If we regard x as the independent variable it is clear that y is a function of x through v, and we could express y directly in terms of x by eliminating v. A method of obtaining dy/dx without doing this is contained in the formula

(VII) $$\frac{dy}{dx} = \frac{dy}{dv} \cdot \frac{dv}{dx}.$$

Thus, in the above example,

$$\frac{dy}{dv} = 2v - 3 \qquad \text{and} \qquad \frac{dv}{dx} = 8x.$$

Using (VII) we have

$$\frac{dy}{dx} = (2v - 3) \cdot (8x)$$
$$= 8x(8x^2 - 1).$$

In order to prove the formula we need merely to note that for any value of x for which v is a differentiable function of x and y is in turn a differentiable function of v, the quantities

$$\frac{\Delta y}{\Delta x} \qquad \text{and} \qquad \frac{\Delta y}{\Delta v} \cdot \frac{\Delta v}{\Delta x}.$$

are two functions of Δx that are *identically equal* for all values of $\Delta x (\neq 0)$; their limits, as Δx approaches zero, must therefore be equal.* These limits are, respectively, dy/dx

---

* It should be specified also that Δv should not be zero. The student should consider the case in which $\Delta v = 0$.

and $dy/dv \cdot dv/dx$; hence,

$$\frac{dy}{dx} = \frac{dy}{dv} \cdot \frac{dv}{dx}.$$

An important special case is that in which x and y are connected by a relation $y = f(x)$, and x is known to vary with the time according to some law $x = \varphi(t)$. The rate at which x is changing at any instant (with respect to time) is given by dx/dt; if we wish to find the time rate of change of y, we have

$$\frac{dy}{dt} = \frac{dy}{dx} \cdot \frac{dx}{dt}.$$

The student should notice that, written in the form

$$\frac{dy}{dx} = \frac{\dfrac{dy}{dt}}{\dfrac{dx}{dt}}, \qquad \left(\frac{dx}{dt} \neq 0\right),$$

the formula merely states that the rate of change of y, *measured with respect to x*, is equal to the quotient of the rates at which y and x are changing with respect to the time.

25. Differentiation of inverse functions.   Formula (VIII). We may have y defined as a function of the independent variable x by an equation of the form

$$x = \varphi(y).$$

If we solve this equation for y in terms of x, we obtain the "inverse" function $y = f(x)$. It may, however, be difficult or even impossible to solve for y, and a method of calculating dy/dx without this preliminary step is contained in the formula

(VIII) $$\frac{dy}{dx} = \frac{1}{\dfrac{dx}{dy}}.$$

Example

Compute dy/dx for the curve $x = y^3 - 4y$.

Solution

Considering y as the independent variable, we have

$$\frac{dx}{dy} = 3y^2 - 4.$$

If we wish now to consider x the independent variable we have, using (VIII),

$$\frac{dy}{dx} = \frac{1}{3y^2 - 4}.$$

The student should sketch the curve for the above example, noting carefully that while the given relation defines x as a single-valued function of y when y is taken as the independent variable it defines y as a *triple-valued* function of x (for some values of x) when x is taken as the independent variable. Proper care must therefore be taken to restrict the discussion to one branch of the function at a time.

The proof of the formula follows immediately from the fact that the quantities

$$\frac{\Delta y}{\Delta x} \quad \text{and} \quad \frac{1}{\dfrac{\Delta x}{\Delta y}}$$

are identically equal for all values of Δx and $\Delta y (\neq 0)$ and hence must have the same limit as Δx and Δy approach zero simultaneously, no matter which variable is considered independent, if the limits exist and are $\neq 0$.

PROBLEMS

In each of the following, find $D_x y$ in terms of x:

1. $y = v^2 + 3v, \quad v = 4x - 7$. 2. $y = 4v^3 + 6, \quad v = \sqrt{x + 1}$.

3. $y = \dfrac{3u}{u + 4}, \quad u = \dfrac{2}{x^2}$. 4. $y = 2\sqrt{\dfrac{5}{v^3}}, \quad v = x^{\frac{2}{3}}$.

5. $y = \dfrac{u^2}{u^2 - 4}, \quad u = \dfrac{1}{x}$. 6. $y = \dfrac{v^2 + 1}{v^2 - 1}, \quad v = x^3$.

In each of the following, y is assumed to vary with x according to the law expressed by the first equation, while x varies with the time t as indicated by the second; in each case find dy/dt in terms of t:

7. $y = \dfrac{x+1}{x-1}$, $x = 2t + 1$. **8.** $y = \dfrac{8}{x^2 + 4}$, $x = 2\sqrt{t}$.

9. $y = \dfrac{4x}{x^2 + 1}$, $x = t^2$. **10.** $y = x^3 - 9x$, $x = \frac{1}{2}(t + 2)$.

11. A point moves along the line $y = 3x - 5$ so that $x = 2t$. At what rate is y changing when the moving point goes through $P(6, 13)$?

12. A point moves along the parabola $y = x^2 - 2x - 15$ so that $x = 2t$ where t is the time. Compute the time rate of change of y when $t = 0$, $\frac{1}{2}$, and 2. Sketch the curve and describe the motion.

13. A point moves along the hyperbola $y = 6/x$ so that $x = 2/t$. Is y increasing or decreasing and at what time rate when $t = 2$? Sketch the curve and describe the motion.

14. If y is changing three times as rapidly as x, then, of course, x is changing $\frac{1}{3}$ as rapidly as y. What connection does this statement have with the formula $\dfrac{dy}{dx} = \dfrac{1}{dx/dy}$?

15. Sketch a curve to represent $y = f(x)$. Show the geometrical significance of the value of dx/dy at a point P on this curve. HINT: Starting at P give an increment Δy to y; show the change Δx produced in x; study the meaning of $\Delta x/\Delta y$.

In each of the following, first sketch the curve and evaluate $D_x y$ at the given point using formula (VIII). Then check the result by solving the given equation for y in terms of x, taking the branch on which the given point lies and differentiating directly:

16. $x = \dfrac{4}{y+4}$; $(2, -2)$. **17.** $x = \dfrac{y+1}{y-1}$; $(-1, 0)$.

18. $x = -4y - y^2$; $(0, 0)$. **19.** $x = \dfrac{8}{y^2 + 4}$; $(1, 2)$.

20. $x = y^2 - 6y + 8$; $(3, 5)$. **21.** $x = y^4 - 4y^2$; $(-3, 1)$.

22. Sketch the curve $x = y^3 - 9y$ and compute the value of dy/dx at the points where it crosses the y-axis.

23. Sketch the curve $x = \dfrac{2y + 8}{y + 1}$. Compute the value of dy/dx at the points where it crosses the axes, both with and without solving for y.

24. Compute the rate of change of the volume of a sphere with respect to its surface area. If the radius of a sphere is increasing, for what size sphere is the volume (in cubic inches) increasing at the same time rate as the surface area (in square inches)?

25. Write out a formal proof of the formula

$$\frac{dy}{dx} = \frac{dy}{dv}\frac{dv}{dx}.$$

Discuss the case in which $\Delta v \equiv 0$.

26. Write out a formal proof of the formula

$$\frac{dy}{dx} = \frac{1}{\dfrac{dx}{dy}}.$$

Discuss its limitations.

26. Implicit functions.—An equation which defines y as a function of x, but which is not solved for y in terms of x, is said to define y as an *implicit* function of x. Thus the equation

(1) $$x^3 + 5x^2 + xy^2 - 5y^2 = 0,$$

whose graph is shown in Fig. 22, defines y as an implicit

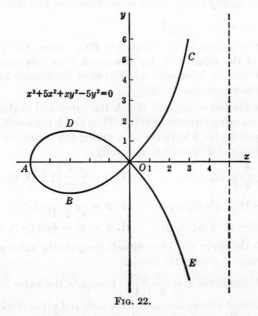

$x^3+5x^2+xy^2-5y^2=0$

FIG. 22.

(double-valued) function of x over the interval $-5 \leqq x < 5$. If we solve (1) for y in terms of x we get the two solutions

(2) $$y = x\sqrt{\frac{5+x}{5-x}} \quad \text{and} \quad y = -x\sqrt{\frac{5+x}{5-x}}.$$

The graph of the first of these is the arc $ABOC$ of the curve while that of the second is the arc $ADOE$. If we wished to compute dy/dx at a given point on $ABOC$ we should take the first of equations (2), find dy/dx, and substitute the given value of x.   If the point were on $ADOE$ we should use the second of the two equations.

The right-hand member of either of the equations (2) is a single-valued function of x, which, if substituted for y in (1), would reduce (1) to an *identity*.   Each is called a *branch* of the double-valued function defined by (1).*

In many cases it may be inconvenient or even impossible to solve a given equation of the form $\varphi(x, y) = 0$ for y in terms of x.   Nevertheless, the equation *may* define y as a differentiable function of x, and we, therefore, should have a method of computing dy/dx without having to solve for y.

The method consists in differentiating each term in the equation with respect to x, regarding y as an unknown function of x having a derivative dy/dx, and then solving the resulting equation for dy/dx.

Example

Find dy/dx from the equation $x^3 + 5x^2 + xy^2 - 5y^2 = 0$.

Solution

First, differentiate each term with respect to x:

$$\frac{d}{dx}(x^3) + \frac{d}{dx}(5x^2) + \frac{d}{dx}(xy^2) + \frac{d}{dx}(-5y^2) = \frac{d}{dx}(0).$$

$$3x^2 + 10x + (x \cdot 2y\frac{dy}{dx} + y^2 \cdot 1) - 10y\frac{dy}{dx} = 0.$$

Now regard dy/dx as the unknown in this equation and solve for it by the usual methods of algebra.   Thus,

$$2xy\frac{dy}{dx} - 10y\frac{dy}{dx} = -3x^2 - 10x - y^2.$$

$$(10y - 2xy)\frac{dy}{dx} = 3x^2 + 10x + y^2.$$

(3) $$\frac{dy}{dx} = \frac{3x^2 + 10x + y^2}{10y - 2xy}.$$

---

* A strict definition of *branch* will not be given here.   The student may observe that the *positive* values of y satisfying (1) for $-5 \leqq x < 5$ constitute also a single-valued function, whose graph is the arc $ADOC$.   This does not constitute a branch as the term is ordinarily used.

Any pair of coordinates (x, y) satisfying (1) may be substituted in (3). If the right-hand member of (3) has a value then this is the slope of the tangent line drawn to the graph of (1) at this point. Thus the point $(-4, \frac{1}{3})$ is on the curve and we find by substitution that $\dfrac{dy}{dx}\bigg]_{-4,\,\frac{1}{3}} = \frac{11}{27}$. The point $(0, 0)$ is also on the graph of (1) but the right-hand member of (3) does not have a value at this point. The slope of either branch at $(0, 0)$ could be found by differentiating the corresponding one of equations (2) and substituting $x = 0$.

In using this procedure the student must be careful to differentiate each term *with respect to x*. Since y is regarded as an unknown function of x, the term xy^2 is a product of two functions of x, and the product formula (IV) must be used. In order to obtain the derivative of y^2 with respect to x we must use formula (V); thus,

$$\frac{d}{dx}(y^2) = 2y \cdot \frac{d}{dx}(y) = 2y \frac{dy}{dx}.$$

Here, since y is a function of x, y^2 is of the form v^n.

Finally, it should be mentioned that an equation of the form $\varphi(x, y) = 0$ *may not define y as a function of x*. No adequate discussion of the situation can be given here* but the following examples will show the student that a certain amount of caution is necessary.

Example 1

The above procedure, applied to the equation $x^2 + y^2 = 0$, yields

$$\frac{dy}{dx} = -\frac{x}{y}.$$

The given equation is satisfied only by $(0, 0)$, and for this pair of values the expression obtained for $\dfrac{dy}{dx}$ is meaningless.

Example 2

The equation $x^2 + 2xy + (y - x)^2 = y^2 + 8$ does not define y as a function of x for *any* value of x. In fact, it can be reduced to $x^2 = 4$.

PROBLEMS

In each of the following, find $D_x y$ both with and without solving for y in terms of x; show that the results are equivalent:

* See p. 369.

1. $2x + 5y = 10.$

2. $ax + by + c = 0.$

3. $x^2 + y^2 = a^2.$

4. $x^2 - y^2 = 4.$

5. $b^2x^2 + a^2y^2 = a^2b^2.$

6. $\dfrac{x^2}{4} + \dfrac{y^2}{2} = 1.$

7. $y^2 = 2px.$

8. $y^2 = 12x.$

9. $x^2 + y^2 = 4x.$

10. $x^{\frac{1}{3}} + y^{\frac{1}{3}} = a^{\frac{1}{3}}.$

11. $y^2 = \dfrac{4 + x}{4 - x}.$

12. $xy - y - 2x - 5 = 0.$

Sketch each of the following curves; find the slopes of tangent lines drawn at the given points, both with and without solving for y in terms of x:

13. $xy - 2y = 8;\ (4, 4).$

14. $xy - x^2 = 3;\ (1, 4).$

15. $x^2y + y - 4 = 0;\ (-1, 2).$

16. $x^2y - 4y = 8;\ (4, \frac{2}{3}).$

17. $x^2y - 4y - 2x^2 - 10 = 0;\ (1, -4)$ and $(-4, \frac{1}{2}).$

18. $x^2y + 4y - 4x = 0;\ (0, 0)$ and $(2, 1).$

19. $x^2 - y^2 = 9;\ (5, -4).$

20. $9x^2 + 36y^2 = 324;\ (-2, \sqrt{8}).$

21. $x^2 + y^2 = 10x;\ (8, -4).$

22. $x^2 + y^2 + 26y = 0;\ (-12, -8).$

23. $x^4 + 2y^4 = 48;\ (-2, 2).$

24. $y^2 = x(x - 4)(x - 6);\ (2, 4).$

In each of the following, find the value of $D_x y$ at the given point:

25. $y^2 - 8x + 6y + 17 = 0;\ (3, -7).$

26. $x^2 + y^2 - 4x - 6y - 12 = 0;\ (6, 0).$

27. $x^2 + 4y^2 - 20x - 40y + 100 = 0;\ (4, 1).$

28. $x^2 - 2xy + 4y^2 - 4x = 0;\ (4, 0).$

29. $x^2 + 2xy + y^2 - 8x - 6y = 0;\ (0, 0).$

30. $x^2y^2 - 3y^2 = 2x^2 + 6;\ (3, 2).$

31. $x^4 - 3xy^2 + 2y^3 = 0;\ (-4, -8).$

32. $x^2 - 2y^3 - 8y^2 = 0;\ (-4, -2).$

In each of the following, find dy/dx:

33. $x^2 + xy - 4y^2 = 1.$

34. $x^2 + y^2 - 8x - 24y = 10.$

35. $2xy + 5y = 3x - 3.$

36. $x^2 + 4y^2 + 4y = 32.$

37. $y^2 - 2x^2 = 4 + 3xy.$

38. $x^3 + y^3 = 3axy.$

39. $x^3 + 4y^3 = 6 - 4xy^2.$

40. $x^3 = 4y^3 + 6xy.$

41. $4x^2y + 2y^3 = 1 + xy^2.$

42. $x^4 - 2y^4 = x^2y^2 - 6.$

43. $3x^2 + 8xy - 3y^2 - 4x - y = 6.$

44. $x^4 + xy^3 + y - 2x + 4 = 0.$

45. $x^4 - 5x^2y^2 + xy - 4 = 0.$

46. $x^4 + 2xy^3 + y + 4x + 4 = 0.$

47. $x^3 + y^3 + x^2 - 4xy - 3x + y = 4.$

48. $y^2 = \dfrac{x^3}{x^2 + 4}.$

49. $y^2 = \dfrac{16}{x^4 - 4x^2}.$

50. $y^3 = \dfrac{x + 2}{x - 2}.$

CHAPTER V

APPLICATIONS OF THE DERIVATIVE

27. Angle of intersection of curves.—If the two curves $y = f(x)$ and $y = F(x)$ intersect at a point P, their angle of intersection is defined to be the angle ϕ between the tangents drawn to the curves at P (Fig. 23).

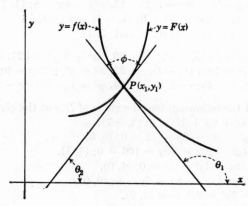

FIG. 23.

This angle is found easily as follows:

1. Determine the coordinates (x_1, y_1) of a point P of intersection by solving the equations simultaneously.

2. Find the slope of the tangent to each curve at P. Call these slopes m_1 and m_2.

3. From the figure it is evident that

$$\phi = \theta_1 - \theta_2;$$

hence,

$$\tan \phi = \tan (\theta_1 - \theta_2) = \frac{\tan \theta_1 - \tan \theta_2}{1 + \tan \theta_1 \tan \theta_2}$$

or

$$\tan \phi = \frac{m_1 - m_2}{1 + m_1 m_2}.$$

If there are several points of intersection, each one must of course be considered separately.

Example

At what angle do the parabolas $y = x^2/8$ and $y^2 = x$ intersect?

Solution (Fig. 24)

1. Solving the equations we find that the curves intersect at $P(4, 2)$. [We disregard the obvious 90° intersection at (0, 0).]

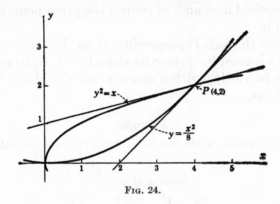

FIG. 24.

2. We next find the slope of each curve at P as follows:

$$y = \frac{x^2}{8} \qquad\qquad y^2 = x$$

$$\frac{dy}{dx} = \frac{x}{4} \qquad\qquad 2y\,\frac{dy}{dx} = 1$$

$$m_1 = \frac{dy}{dx}\bigg]_{4,\,2} = 1. \qquad\qquad \frac{dy}{dx} = \frac{1}{2y}$$

$$m_2 = \frac{dy}{dx}\bigg]_{4,\,2} = \frac{1}{4}.$$

3. The tangent of the required angle is then,

$$\tan \phi = \frac{m_1 - m_2}{1 + m_1 m_2} = \frac{1 - \frac{1}{4}}{1 + 1 \cdot \frac{1}{4}} = \frac{3}{5}.^*$$

$$\phi = \arctan \frac{3}{5} = 30° \, 58'.$$

---

* If we interchange m_1 and m_2, taking $m_1 = \frac{1}{4}$ and $m_2 = 1$, we get tan $\phi = -\frac{3}{5}$. The positive result corresponds to the acute angle and the negative one to its supplement.

28. Equations of tangent and normal.—The student will recall from his study of analytic geometry that the equation of the line that passes through a given point (x_1, y_1) and has slope m is

$$y - y_1 = m(x - x_1).$$

Using this, one can easily write down the *equation* of the line that is tangent to the curve $y = f(x)$ at a given point $P(x_1, y_1)$ on the curve. The value of dy/dx at P is the slope of the required line, and, of course, the given point P is one point on it.

The line through P perpendicular to the tangent line is called the *normal line;* since its slope is $-1/m$, its equation can also be easily written down using the above "point-slope" form.

Example

Write the equation of the line that is tangent to the parabola $y^2 = x$ at $P(4, 2)$.

Solution (Fig. 24)

$$\frac{dy}{dx} = \frac{1}{2y}; \qquad \frac{dy}{dx}\bigg]_{4,2} = \tfrac{1}{4}.$$

The equation of the line through $P(4, 2)$ with slope $\tfrac{1}{4}$ is

$$y - 2 = \tfrac{1}{4}(x - 4)$$

or

$$4y - x = 4.$$

PROBLEMS

In each of the following, sketch the given pair of curves and find their points of intersection. At each such point find the tangent of the acute angle of intersection:

1. $x^2 + y^2 = 25$; $2y = x + 5$.　　2. $y = x^2 - 6x + 5$; $y = x - 1$.
3. $x^2 + y^2 = 8$; $x^2 + y^2 = 4x$.　　4. $y^2 = 4x$; $y = 2x^2$.
5. $x^2 + y^2 = 100$; $2y^2 = 9x$.　　6. $x^2 + y^2 = 10y$; $y = x + 4$.
7. $x^2 + y^2 = 34$; $xy = 15$.　　8. $xy = 3$; $9y = x^2$.
9. $4y^2 + x^2 = 25$; $x = 2y - 1$.　　10. $4x^2 + y^2 = 32$; $y^2 = 8x$.

11. $8x^2 + 3y^2 = 120$; $2x^2 = 3y + 6$.
12. $x^2 + 8y^2 = 6x$; $4y = x^2$.

13. $x^2 + y^2 = 169; x^2 + 2y^2 = 194.$

14. $2xy + 36 = x; xy + 3y + 5 = 0.$

15. $x^2y = 1; y = 2x + 3.$ **16.** $x^2y + 4y = 8; 2y^2 = x.$

17. $x^2y + 2y = 11; x^2 + y^2 = 10y.$

Sketch each of the following curves and draw the tangent and normal lines at the given point.   Find the equations of these lines:

18. $xy = 6; (3, 2).$ **19.** $y^2 - y - 2 = x; (0, 2).$

20. $y = \tfrac{1}{2}x^3 - 4; (2, 0).$ **21.** $x^2 + 4y^2 = 25; (3, 2).$

22. $x^2 + 9y^2 = 40; (-2, 2).$ **23.** $x^2 + y^2 = 10x; (8, 4).$

24. $xy - y = x^2; (2, 4).$ **25.** $x^2y - 4y - 4x = 0; (1, -\tfrac{4}{3}).$

26. $4x^2 + y^2 + 8x + 2y = 20; (-3, 2).$

27. $9x^2 + 4y^2 + 36x + 24y = 0; (0, 0).$

28. $y = x^3 - 3x^2 + 5x - 15; (3, 0).$

29. $4y^2 - xy^2 = x^3; (2, -2).$

30. What is the equation of the line with slope 6 which is tangent to the curve $y = x^2 - 4x - 5$?

31. A line is parallel to the line $3x + y = 2$ and is also tangent to the curve $y = x^2 + x - 6$.   What is its equation?

32. Find the equation of the line with slope $\tfrac{1}{2}$ which is normal to the parabola $y = x^2 - 4x - 5$.

33. Show that the equation of the line tangent to the circle $x^2 + y^2 = r^2$ at (x_1, y_1) is $x_1x + y_1y = r^2$.

34. Show that the equation of the line tangent to the ellipse

$$\frac{x^2}{a^2} + \frac{y^2}{b^2} = 1 \text{ at } (x_1, y_1) \text{ is } \frac{x_1x}{a^2} + \frac{y_1y}{b^2} = 1.$$

35. Sketch the curve $y = x^3 - 6x^2 + 3x + 10$.   A line is drawn tangent to this curve at $(3, -8)$.   Find the angle at which this line intersects the curve at the other point of intersection.

29. Time rates.

—We have emphasized the fact that the derivative of a function $f(x)$ with respect to x is the **rate of change of $f(x)$,** *measured with respect to x.*   Suppose now that we have a variable quantity Q which is **known to vary with the time according to some definite law**

$$Q = f(t).$$

The value of dQ/dt at any instant is evidently the rate at which Q is changing at that instant, *measured with respect to the time.*   If Q were expressed, for example, in pounds and

t in minutes, the value of dQ/dt would be the rate of change of Q in pounds per minute.

A purely artificial example that will make the idea clear is as follows: Suppose that water is being run into a tank in such a way that the number of gallons in the tank at the end of t min. is given by the equation

$$G = 4 + \sqrt{t + 1}.$$

The rate at which water must be entering the tank at any time t is

$$\frac{dG}{dt} = \frac{1}{2\sqrt{t + 1}} \text{ gal. per minute.}$$

At the end of say 15 min., the tank would contain 8 gal., and water would be entering at a rate of

$$\left. \frac{dG}{dt} \right]_{t=15} = \tfrac{1}{8} \text{ gal. per minute.}$$

30. Velocity in rectilinear motion.—Let a particle P move along the straight line AB in such a way that its distance

FIG. 25.

from A at the end of time t is (Fig. 25)

$$s = f(t).$$

In a small additional time Δt it moves a corresponding small distance Δs, and its average velocity over this distance is expressed by the fraction

$$\frac{\Delta s}{\Delta t}. \quad \text{Why?}$$

The instantaneous velocity of the particle is defined as the limit of this quotient as Δs and Δt approach zero simultaneously; *i.e.*,

$$v = \lim_{\Delta t \to 0} \frac{\Delta s}{\Delta t} = \frac{ds}{dt}.$$

As an interesting special case we may consider the motion of a projectile that is thrown vertically upward from a point A with initial velocity v_0; its distance from A at the end of t sec. is known to be (neglecting air resistance)

$$s = v_0 t - \tfrac{1}{2}gt^2, \qquad (g = 32.2).$$

Its velocity at any time t, in feet per second, is given by

$$\frac{ds}{dt} = v_0 - gt.$$

31. Related rates.—A frequently encountered type of rate problem is that in which two variable quantities x and y are connected by a relation, say $y = f(x)$. The time rate of change of x is known, and the corresponding time rate of change of y is to be found. The fundamental formula that applies is, of course,

$$\frac{dy}{dt} = \frac{dy}{dx} \cdot \frac{dx}{dt}.$$

In solving problems of this type the student should adopt the following procedure:

1. From the statement of the problem pick out the two variables—that whose rate of change is given, and that whose rate is to be found.

2. Express the relation between these variables in the form of an equation—say $y = f(x)$ or $\varphi(x, y) = 0$.

3. From the equation of step 2 find dy/dx and then obtain dy/dt from the formula

$$\frac{dy}{dt} = \frac{dy}{dx} \cdot \frac{dx}{dt}.$$

4. Finally, substitute the numerical values which x, y, and dx/dt have at the particular instant at which the value of dy/dt is required.

The student is warned against the rather common error of substituting the given values of x and y *before* computing the necessary derivatives. The following examples should make the procedure clear.

Example 1

A ladder 25 ft. long rests against a wall and the lower end is being pulled out from the wall at 6 ft. per minute. At what rate is the top descending at the instant when the lower end is 7 ft. from the wall?

Solution (Fig. 26)

The variables x and y are connected by the relation

$$x^2 + y^2 = 25^2.$$

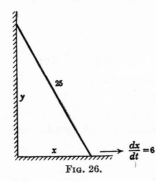

We are given $dx/dt = 6$, and must find the value of dy/dt at the instant when $x = 7$. Differentiating the relation between x and y we find first that

$$\frac{dy}{dx} = -\frac{x}{y}.$$

Hence,

$$\frac{dy}{dt} = -\frac{x}{y}\frac{dx}{dt}.$$

Fig. 26.

At this instant $x = 7$, $y = 24$, and $dx/dt = 6$; hence,

$$\frac{dy}{dt} = -\frac{7}{24}\cdot 6 = -\frac{7}{4} \text{ ft. per minute.}$$

The negative sign indicates that y is *decreasing*.

Example 2

A cone is 10 in. in diameter and 10 in. deep. Water is poured into it at 4 cu. in. per minute. At what rate is the water level rising at the instant when the depth is 6 in.?

Solution (Fig. 27)

We must first express the volume V of water in the cone in terms of its depth y. We are given that $dV/dt = 4$ cu. in. per minute and must compute the value of dy/dt at the instant when $y = 6$ in.

$$V = \frac{1}{3}\pi x^2 y;$$

but

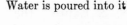
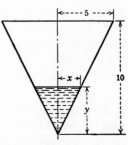

Fig. 27.

$$\frac{x}{y} = \frac{5}{10}, \quad \text{or} \quad x = \frac{1}{2}y;$$

therefore,

$$V = \frac{\pi y^3}{12}.$$

$$\frac{dV}{dy} = \frac{\pi y^2}{4};$$

$$\frac{dV}{dt} = \frac{\pi y^2}{4}\frac{dy}{dt}.$$

At this instant $y = 6$ and $dV/dt = 4$; hence,

$$\frac{dy}{dt} = \frac{4}{9\pi} \text{ in. per minute.}$$

PROBLEMS

1. A small lead ball is thrown vertically upward from a point A on the ground with initial velocity 120 ft. per second. Find:

(*a*) Its velocity at the end of 2 sec.; 4 sec.

(*b*) Its greatest distance from the ground.

(*c*) The total time in the air.

2. A small heavy object is dropped from the top of a cliff 300 ft. high. With what velocity will it strike the ground below?

3. Solve Prob. 2 for the case in which the object is thrown *downward* with initial velocity 60 ft. per second; for the case in which it is thrown *upward* with this velocity.

4. A particle moves along the x-axis so that its distance from the origin at the end of t min. is $x = 2 + \sqrt{t + 1}$. Describe the motion. Find the position and velocity of the particle at the end of 8 min.

5. A man walking across a bridge at 6 ft. per second observes at a certain instant that a boat is passing directly under him. The bridge is 30 ft. above the water; the boat is traveling at 12 ft. per second. At what rate is the distance s between the man and boat changing 2 sec. later?

6. A boat B is 12 miles west of another boat A. B starts east at 8 m.p.h. and at the same time A starts north at 12 m.p.h. At what rate is the distance between them changing at the end of $\frac{1}{2}$ hr.?

7. The legs a and b of a right triangle are 4 in. and 6 in., respectively. At the same instant, a starts increasing at 2 in. per minute and b starts decreasing at 1 in. per minute. Express the area of the triangle after t min. as a function of t. Is the area increasing or decreasing at the end of 1 min. and at what rate? What is the situation at the end of 4 min.?

8. Sketch the function $y = \sqrt{625 - x^2}$. Explain how Example 1 (page 66) may be considered as a problem on the motion of a point along this curve.

9. The side of a square is increasing at 2 in. per minute. At what rate is the area increasing when each side is 8 in. long?

10. If the radius of a sphere is 10 in. and is decreasing at the rate of 1 in. per minute, at what rate is the volume decreasing?

11. At what rate is the area of an equilateral triangle increasing if each side is 6 ft. long and is increasing at $\sqrt{3}$ ft. per minute?

12. A baseball diamond is a square 90 ft. on each side. A player is running from first base to second at a rate of 24 ft. per second. At what rate is his distance from third base changing when he reaches a point 30 ft. from second base?

13. A street light hangs 18 ft. above the street. A man 6 ft. tall walks away from it at 5 m.p.h. At what rate does the farther end of his shadow move? At what rate does his shadow lengthen?

14. A point moves along the parabola $y^2 = 16x$. At what rate is its distance from the focus changing when it passes through (1, 4) if x is increasing at 8 units per minute? Could you have anticipated this result from the definition of a parabola?

15. A point moves along the parabola $y = x^2$, its abscissa increasing uniformly at 2 units per minute. At what rate is its distance from $(-1, 1)$ changing when it passes through (2, 4)?

16. A funnel is 12 in. in diameter and 8 in. deep. Water is poured in at 20 cu. in. per minute. At what rate will the surface be rising at the instant when it begins to overflow if water is flowing out at the bottom of the funnel at 4 cu. in. per minute?

17. Sand is being poured from a hopper onto a conical pile. The angle of repose of the sand is such that the height of the pile is always equal to one-fourth of its radius. When the pile is 6 ft. high, what rate of discharge of sand from the hopper would cause the height of the pile to increase at $\frac{1}{16}$ in. per minute?

18. A liquid is being pumped out of a hemispherical vat 12 ft. in diameter at a rate of 2 cu. ft. per minute. At what rate is the liquid surface falling when the depth is 3 ft? HINT: The volume of a spherical segment of altitude h is $\frac{1}{3}\pi h^2(3r - h)$.

19. Water is being poured into a hemispherical bowl. Show that the time rates at which the volume v and depth y of water are increasing at any instant are connected by the relation $\dfrac{dv}{dt} = A\,\dfrac{dy}{dt}$ where A is the area of the liquid surface at that instant. See hint in Prob. 18.

20. Solve Prob. 19 for the case of a conical vessel.

21. A swimming pool is 120 ft. long and 50 ft. wide. It is 12 ft. deep at one end and 2 ft. deep at the other, the bottom being an inclined plane. The pool is being filled by a pipe that discharges 60 cu. ft. per minute. How fast will the water level be rising when the depth is 4 ft. at the deep end; 11 ft.?

22. A water trough is 8 ft. long and 4 ft. deep. Its cross section is a trapezoid 2 ft. wide at the bottom and 4 ft. wide at the top. At what rate must water be poured in to cause the surface to rise at 3 in. per minute when the depth is 1 ft.?

23. A man standing on a dock 40 ft. above the water pulls a boat toward the dock by taking in rope at 4 ft. per second. At what rate is the boat approaching the dock when 80 ft. of rope are out?

24. A weight is attached to a rope 42 ft. long. The rope passes over a pulley 22 ft. above the ground. A man takes hold of the end of the rope and walks back at 10 ft. per second holding the end at a level of 6 ft. above the ground. At what rate is the weight ascending when it is 6 ft. above the ground? See Fig. 28.

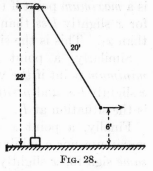

Fig. 28.

25. A cistern has the form of a frustum of a cone. It is 12 ft. deep and the diameter is 8 ft. at the top and 4 ft. at the bottom. Water is being run in at 10 cu. ft. per minute. When the water is 6 ft. deep the surface is observed to be rising at 3 in. per minute. At what rate is water seeping into the banks?

32. Maxima and minima.—The definitions of maximum and minimum values of a function were given in Chap. I. We now consider the problem of determining such values.

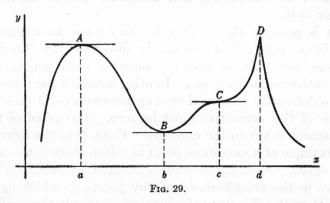

Fig. 29.

Let the curve shown in Fig. 29 be the graph of the equation $y = f(x)$. The value of dy/dx at any point is the slope of the tangent line drawn to the curve at that point. By setting $dy/dx = 0$ and solving for x, we can locate the points at which the tangent line is parallel to the x-axis; thus in the figure

$$\frac{dy}{dx} = 0 \quad \text{at} \quad x = a, \quad x = b, \quad \text{and} \quad x = c.$$

It is intuitively clear that a point $x = x_1$ where $dy/dx = 0$ is a *maximum* point if the value of this derivative is *positive* for x slightly *less* than x_1 and *negative* for x slightly *more* than x_1. This is the situation at A in the figure.

Similarly, a point $x = x_1$ at which $dy/dx = 0$ is a *minimum* point if the value of the derivative is *negative* for x slightly *less* and *positive* for x slightly *more* than x_1. This is the situation at B.

Finally, a point $x = x_1$ where $dy/dx = 0$ is *neither* a maximum nor a minimum point if this derivative has the *same* sign for x slightly less than x_1 as it has for x slightly more than x_1. We have this condition at C in the figure.

Thus by setting $dy/dx = 0$, solving for x, and testing each point so obtained in the above manner, we can discover all maximum and minimum points at which $dy/dx = 0$.

It is possible that a function may have maximum or minimum points that will not be discovered by this procedure, but only in case the function does not have a derivative at such a point. In other words, if the function *has* a derivative at a maximum or minimum point then the value of this derivative must be zero. The proof of this statement is left to the exercises. Point D in the figure is an example of a maximum point at which there is no value for dy/dx. Such points can be located by studying the curve in the neighborhood of any points at which dy/dx fails to exist. They are of minor importance in the applications and will not be treated in detail here (see Probs. 36 and 37, page 74).

The procedure for determining the maximum and minimum points at which $dy/dx = 0$ will be illustrated by two examples.

Example 1

Find the maximum and minimum points on the curve

$$y = x^3 - x^2 - 8x + 6.$$

Solution

$$\frac{dy}{dx} = 3x^2 - 2x - 8.$$

Setting $dy/dx = 0$ and solving for x we have

$$3x^2 - 2x - 8 = 0$$
$$(3x + 4)(x - 2) = 0$$
$$x = 2, \text{ or } -\tfrac{4}{3}.$$

The tangent line is then horizontal at the points where $x = 2$ and $x = -\tfrac{4}{3}$. To determine whether $x = 2$ gives a maximum or minimum point on the curve we write dy/dx in the factored form:

$$\frac{dy}{dx} = (3x + 4)(x - 2).$$

The first factor is obviously $+$ for all values of x near 2. However,

If x is slightly *less* than 2, $(x - 2)$ is $-$ and $\dfrac{dy}{dx}$ is $-$;

If x is slightly *more* than 2, $(x - 2)$ is $+$ and $\dfrac{dy}{dx}$ is $+$.

Since the value of dy/dx is zero *at* $(2, -6)$ and changes from minus to plus when we go through this point from left to right, the point is a

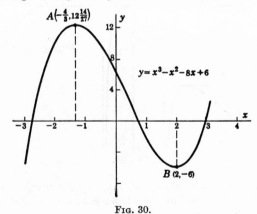

FIG. 30.

minimum point. Similarly, it may be shown that $(-\tfrac{4}{3}, 12\tfrac{14}{27})$ is a maximum point. The curve is shown in Fig. 30.

Example 2

Locate the maximum and minimum points on the curve $y = \dfrac{x^3}{x^2 - 3}$. Sketch the curve.

Solution

$$\frac{dy}{dx} = \frac{(x^2 - 3)3x^2 - x^3(2x)}{(x^2 - 3)^2} = \frac{x^2(x^2 - 9)}{(x^2 - 3)^2}.$$

Setting $dy/dx = 0$ and solving for x, we find that the curve has hori- zontal tangent lines at $x = 0, 3,$ and -3. Thus the critical points are $(0, 0), (3, 4\frac{1}{2})$ and $(-3, -4\frac{1}{2})$.

In order to test the point where $x = 3$, we note that for x slightly less than 3 the factor $x^2 - 9$ is negative while for x slightly more than 3 it is

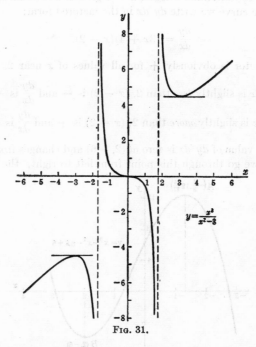

FIG. 31.

positive. The quantities x^2 and $(x^2 - 3)^2$ remain positive so the sign of dy/dx changes from minus to plus when x goes through the value 3 from left to right. This is therefore a *minimum* point.

It can be similarly shown that $(-3, -4\frac{1}{2})$ is a *maximum* point.

The point $(0, 0)$ is *neither* a maximum nor a minimum point because the sign of dy/dx is negative for x slightly less than zero and also for x slightly more than zero.

In sketching the graph (Fig. 31) we must use the fundamental principles of analytic geometry in addition to the above information regarding maximum and minimum points. Thus we note from the given equation that the graph is symmetrical with respect to the origin, that its only intercept on either axis is at the origin, and that it has vertical asymptotes at $x = \pm \sqrt{3}$. Also, from the fact that $\dfrac{x^3}{x^2 - 3} \equiv x + \dfrac{3x}{x^2 - 3}$ we may infer that the curve is asymptotic to the line $y = x$.

PROBLEMS

Locate the maximum and minimum points on each of the following curves. Sketch the curve:

1. $y = 6x - x^2$.   **2.** $2y = x^2 + 4x - 5$.

3. $y = ax^2 + bx + c$.   **4.** $-2y = 8x^2 - x^4$.

5. $y = \frac{1}{4}x^3 - \frac{3}{2}x^2$.   **6.** $4y = (x^2 - 4x)^2$.

7. $y = x^3 - 6x^2 + 9x - 2$.   **8.** $y = x^3 + 3x^2 - 1$.

9. $y = x^3 - 3x^2 + 4$.   **10.** $y = 2x^3 - 9x^2 + 12x + 3$.

11. $3y = x^3 - 3x^2 - 9x$.   **12.** $y = \frac{1}{2}x^4 - 2x^3 + 2$.

13. $4y = x^4 - 4x^3 + 16x - 13$.   **14.** $4y = 3x^4 + 4x^3 - 12x^2 - 4$.

15. $y = 3x^5 - 15x^4 + 25x^3 - 15x^2 + 3$.

16. $y = \frac{1}{2}x^2 + \dfrac{8}{x}$.   **17.** $y = \frac{1}{4}x^3 + \dfrac{12}{x}$.

18. $y = \dfrac{1}{x} + \dfrac{1}{x^2}$.   **19.** $y = \dfrac{x - 2}{x^2}$.

20. $D = \dfrac{4}{x} + \dfrac{1}{1 - x}$.   **21.** $y = \dfrac{x^2}{x + 2}$.

22. $y = \dfrac{6}{x^2 + 1}$.   **23.** $y = \dfrac{18}{x^2 + 6}$.

24. $y = \dfrac{4t}{t^2 + 4}$.   **25.** $y = \dfrac{8x}{x^2 + 1}$.

26. $y = \dfrac{9 - x^2}{x^2 - 4}$.   **27.** $y = \dfrac{8x + 4}{(x - 2)^2}$.

28. $y = \dfrac{3x^2}{x^2 + 1}$.   **29.** $y = \dfrac{2x^2 + 5}{x^2 - 3}$.

30. $y = \dfrac{x^3}{3x + 6}$.   **31.** $y = \dfrac{x^2 + 2x + 10}{x - 3}$.

32. $y = \dfrac{x^2 - 7x + 16}{x - 4}$.   **33.** $y = \dfrac{x^3}{x^2 - 12}$.

34. $y = x \sqrt{16 - x^2}$.   **35.** $y = x^2 \sqrt{24 - x^2}$.

36. Show that the graph of $y = x^{\frac{2}{3}}$ does not have a horizontal tangent line. Draw the curve and locate its minimum point.

37. Draw the graph of $y = 4 - \sqrt[3]{2x + 4}$. Investigate for maximum and minimum values.

38. Show that if $f(x)$ has a derivative at a maximum or minimum point the value of this derivative must be zero. HINT: If $f'(x_1) \neq 0$, then it must be either positive or negative. If it is positive, then $f(x)$ is increasing throughout at least a small interval about the point $x = x_1$ so that this could not be a maximum or minimum point, etc.

33. Applications of maxima and minima.

—The problems of the next set illustrate some of the many applications of the ideas of the preceding section. In order to solve a particular problem the student should first read the problem very carefully, making certain that he understands which of the various quantities mentioned are fixed and which are variable. If appropriate he should draw a figure to illustrate the situation. After thus obtaining a clear understanding of just what the problem is, he may proceed as follows:

1. Pick out the variable quantity Q for which a maximum or minimum value is required.

2. Pick out a *single* independent variable x on which Q depends. There may be several possible choices for this variable.

3. Express Q in terms of x—say $Q = f(x)$.

4. Find the value of x for which Q may be a maximum or a minimum by setting $dQ/dx = 0$ and solving for x. Find the corresponding value of Q, if required, by substituting this value of x in the equation $Q = f(x)$.

5. If necessary make the usual test to show that the result is actually a maximum value or a minimum value, whichever was required in the problem. Often the nature of the problem enables one to omit this test.

Example

A man is in a rowboat 6 miles from shore. He wishes to reach a point A on the shore 10 miles away (Fig. 32). He can row 2 m.p.h. and walk 4 m.p.h. Where should he land in order to reach A in the least time?

Solution

1. Quantity to be made a minimum: time required to go from C to A. Call this T.

2. Independent variable: We assume that he may land at any point B between D and A and let $DB = x$ be the independent variable.

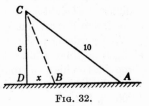

Fig. 32.

3. He rows a distance $CB = \sqrt{x^2 + 36}$ at 2 m.p.h. and then walks a distance $BA = 8 - x$ at 4 m.p.h.   The total time is then

$$T = \frac{\sqrt{x^2 + 36}}{2} + \frac{8 - x}{4}.$$

4. $\dfrac{dT}{dx} = \dfrac{x}{2\sqrt{x^2 + 36}} - \dfrac{1}{4} = 0$

$$x = 2\sqrt{3}$$
$$T = 4.60 \text{ hr. (approximately).}$$

5. Without a formal test the student can easily see that this is a *minimum* value of T.

The way in which T varies with x is shown graphically in Fig. 33. The point $B(2\sqrt{3}, 4.60)$ is the minimum point on the curve.   It is obvious that one could always represent the relation between the variables by a graph and interpret his problem as one of finding maximum or minimum points on this curve.

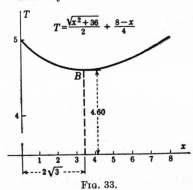

Fig. 33.

PROBLEMS

1. The sum of two positive numbers is 20.   Find the numbers if the product obtained by multiplying one of them by the cube of the other is a maximum.

2. What is the smallest number that can be obtained by adding a positive number x to its reciprocal?

3. Divide the number 24 into two parts so that the sum of the squares of the parts will be as small as possible.

4. Find the volume of the largest box that can be made from a sheet of tin 20 in. long and 12.5 in. wide by cutting a square from each corner and turning up the sides as indicated in Fig. 4.

5. The base of a triangle is 20 in. and its altitude is 12 in. Find the area of the largest rectangle that can be inscribed in the triangle, the base of the rectangle falling on that of the triangle.

6. A right circular cylinder is inscribed in a right circular cone of radius r and height h. Show that the lateral area of the cylinder will be a maximum if its radius is $\frac{1}{2}r$.

7. A gardener wishes to enclose a rectangular plot that has one side along a neighbor's lot. The gardener is to pay for the fence for the three sides on his own ground and for half of that along the dividing line. What dimensions would give him the least cost if the plot is to contain 1,200 sq. ft.?

8. A farmer has 1,200 ft. of fence and wishes to enclose a rectangular plot and divide it into three equal parts by cross fences parallel to the ends. What dimensions would give the largest enclosed area?

9. A lot has the form of a right triangle with the two legs equal to 60 ft. and 100 ft., respectively. A rectangular building is to be erected on the lot. Determine its dimensions for maximum floor area.

10. Show that the largest rectangle that can be inscribed in a circle is a square.

11. Find the dimensions of the cylinder of largest volume that can be inscribed in a right circular cone of radius 12 in. and height 15 in.

12. Find the volume of the largest right circular cylinder that can be inscribed in a sphere whose radius is a.

13. A right circular cone is inscribed in a sphere whose radius is 6 in. Express the volume V of the cone as a function of its height y, and find the value of y for which V is a maximum.

14. An isosceles trapezoid is inscribed in a semicircle whose radius is 10 in., the longer base coinciding with the diameter. Find the length of the shorter base if the trapezoid has maximum area.

15. An isosceles triangle is drawn in a semicircle of radius 4 in. with its vertex at the center of the circle. Show that for maximum area its base should be $4\sqrt{2}$ in.

16. Find the dimensions of the largest rectangle that can be inscribed in the ellipse $18x^2 + 8y^2 = 144$.

17. Locate the point on the parabola $y = 4x - x^2$ that is nearest to the point $(-1, 4)$.

18. Determine the length of the shortest line segment that has its ends on the coordinate axes and is tangent to the hyperbola $xy = 16$.

19. A rectangular box without a lid is to be made to hold 144 cu. ft. The length is to be twice the width and the material for the bottom costs four times as much per unit area as that for the sides. Find the dimensions for minimum cost.

20. A cylindrical can without a lid is to have a fixed volume V.

Show that the amount of material required will be a minimum if its radius and height are equal.

21. Show that a cylindrical can (with lid) will require a minimum amount of material for a specified volume V if its diameter and height are equal.

22. A cylindrical tank with given volume V is to be made without a lid. The material for the bottom costs four times as much per unit area as that for the sides. What should be the ratio of height to radius for minimum cost?

23. A right circular cone of height y is circumscribed about a sphere whose radius is 4 in. Express the volume V of the cone as a function of y, and determine the value of y for which V is a minimum. Show that the volume of this smallest cone is twice that of the sphere.

24. A Norman window has the form of a rectangle surmounted by a semicircle. What shape will have the greatest area for a given perimeter?

25. A figure consists of a rectangle surmounted by an equilateral triangle, one side of the triangle coinciding with the upper base of the rectangle. If the perimeter of the figure is a fixed number P, how long should the side of the triangle be for maximum area of the figure?

26. From a circle whose radius is less than 12 in. a sector with perimeter 24 in. is to be cut. What should be the radius of the circle if the area of this sector is to be a maximum?

27. A gutter with trapezoidal cross section is to be made from a long sheet of tin that is 15 in. wide by turning up one-third of the width on each side. What width across the top will give the greatest capacity?

28. A tank consists of a hemisphere surmounted by a right circular cylinder. Determine the proportions for minimum cost of material if that for the hemisphere costs twice as much per unit area as that for the cylinder.

29. A bus company will transport 100 passengers or less on an excursion trip for $12 each. If there are more than 100 passengers the company agrees to reduce the price of every ticket 5 cents for each passenger in excess of 100 (*e.g.*, if there are 102 passengers each fare is $11.90). What number of passengers will produce the greatest gross revenue?

30. A telephone company has 10,000 telephones in a certain city where the charge is $4 per month. The officials believe that if the charge is reduced, the number of telephones in use will increase at an estimated rate of 200 additional telephones for each 5 cent reduction. What monthly charge would yield the greatest gross revenue on this basis?

31. What is the most favorable charge in Prob. 30 if it must be assumed that each additional telephone increases operating expenses by 20 cents per month?

32. The straight shore of a large lake runs east and west. A and B are two points on this shore 12 miles apart. There is a town C, 9 miles north of A, and another town D, 15 miles north of B. A single pumping station on the lake shore is to supply water to both towns. Where should it be located in order that the sum of its distances from C and D may be a minimum?

33. A ray of light from C (Fig. 34) strikes a plane mirror and is reflected through D. Show that if $CE + ED$ is a minimum, angles α and β are equal. Compare this with Prob. 32. Hint: Find a and b and show that $l_1/a = l_2/b$.

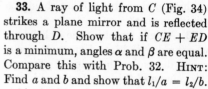

Fig. 34.

34. A ship B is 40 miles due east of a ship A. B starts due north at 25 m.p.h. and at the same time A starts in the direction north $\theta°$ east where $\theta = \arctan \frac{4}{3}$ at 15 m.p.h. When will they be closest together?

35. At any distance x from a source of light the intensity of illumination varies directly as the intensity of the source and inversely as the square of x. Suppose that there is a light at A and another at B, the one at B having an intensity 8 times that at A. The distance AB is 12 ft. At what point on the line AB will the intensity of illumination be least?

36. One corner of a sheet of width a is turned back so as to touch the opposite edge. Find the minimum length of the crease. See Fig. 9, Chap. I.

37. Find the equation of the ellipse of smallest area which can be circumscribed about a rectangle whose sides are 6 in. and 8 in. The area of an ellipse with semiaxes a and b is πab.

CHAPTER VI

THE SECOND DERIVATIVE

34. Successive differentiation.—The derivative with respect to x of a function $f(x)$ may itself be a differentiable function of x. Its derivative is then called the *second derivative* of the original function. If we denote $f(x)$ by y, and write $y = f(x)$, then we may denote this second derivative by any of the symbols

$$\frac{d^2y}{dx^2}; \quad D_x{}^2y; \quad f''(x); \quad y''.$$

Just as the symbol d/dx or D_x denotes the operation of taking the derivative with respect to x of the function to which it is applied, the symbol d^2/dx^2 or $D_x{}^2$ denotes the operation of taking the second derivative. Thus $d^2/dx^2(x^3)$ or $D_x{}^2(x^3) = 6x$.

The second derivative may in turn be a differentiable function of x, and its derivative is called the third derivative of the original function, etc. The nth derivative may be denoted by any of the symbols

$$\frac{d^ny}{dx^n}; \quad D_x{}^ny; \quad f^{(n)}(x); \quad y^{(n)}.$$

Example 1
$$y = x^3 - 4x^2 + \sqrt{x};$$
$$D_xy \text{ or } \frac{dy}{dx} = 3x^2 - 8x + \tfrac{1}{2}x^{-\frac{1}{2}};$$
$$D_x{}^2y \text{ or } \frac{d^2y}{dx^2} = 6x - 8 - \tfrac{1}{4}x^{-\frac{3}{2}};$$
$$D_x{}^3y \text{ or } \frac{d^3y}{dx^3} = 6 + \tfrac{3}{8}x^{-\frac{5}{2}}.$$

In some cases it may be possible, after writing down the first few derivatives, to devise a general formula for the nth derivative.

Example 2

$$f(x) = \frac{1}{x};$$

$$f'(x) = -\frac{1}{x^2};$$

$$f''(x) = +\frac{2 \cdot 1}{x^3};$$

$$f'''(x) = -\frac{3 \cdot 2 \cdot 1}{x^4};$$

$$\cdots\cdots\cdots\cdots$$

$$f^{(n)}(x) = (-1)^n \frac{n!}{x^{n+1}}.$$

Here, the factor $(-1)^n$ plays the role of a "sign changer." It has the value $+1$ when n is even and -1 when n is odd, and thus gives each of the above derivatives the proper sign.

35. Successive differentiation of implicit functions.—If y is defined as a function of x by an equation not solved for y in terms of x, the successive derivatives can be found as indicated in the following example:

$$x^2 - y^2 = a^2;$$

$$2x - 2y \frac{dy}{dx} = 0;$$

$$\frac{dy}{dx} = \frac{x}{y}.$$

Now, the second derivative of y with respect to x is the derivative, with respect to x, of the first derivative; *i.e.*,

$$\frac{d^2y}{dx^2} = \frac{d}{dx}\left(\frac{dy}{dx}\right) = \frac{d}{dx}\left(\frac{x}{y}\right)$$

$$= \frac{y \cdot \dfrac{dx}{dx} - x \cdot \dfrac{dy}{dx}}{y^2}.$$

Of course, $dx/dx = 1$, and we had found above that

$dy/dx = x/y$; we therefore have

$$\frac{d^2y}{dx^2} = \frac{y - x \cdot \dfrac{x}{y}}{y^2}$$

$$= \frac{y^2 - x^2}{y^3}.$$

All admissible values of x and y must satisfy the original equation $x^2 - y^2 = a^2$; hence we may replace $y^2 - x^2$ by $-a^2$, and write the result in the simpler form

$$\frac{d^2y}{dx^2} = -\frac{a^2}{y^3}.$$

The third derivative can be obtained by taking the derivative of this result with respect to x:

$$\frac{d^3y}{dx^3} = \frac{d}{dx}\left(-\frac{a^2}{y^3}\right) = -a^2 \frac{d}{dx}\left(\frac{1}{y^3}\right)$$

$$= -a^2\left(\frac{y^3 \cdot 0 - 1 \cdot 3y^2 \dfrac{dy}{dx}}{y^6}\right)$$

$$= \frac{+3a^2 \dfrac{dy}{dx}}{y^4}.$$

Again using the fact that $dy/dx = x/y$, we may put this last result in the form

$$\frac{d^3y}{dx^3} = \frac{3a^2 x}{y^5}.$$

PROBLEMS

In each of the following, find $D_x y$ and $D_x^2 y$:

1. $y = 3x^2 + 5x - 7.$ 2. $y = x^4 + 4\sqrt{x}.$

3. $y = \frac{1}{6}x^3 + 4x^{\frac{3}{2}} + 2x.$ 4. $y = \sqrt{6 - x^2}.$

5. $y = \dfrac{4}{2 - x}.$ 6. $y = \dfrac{x}{1 - x}.$

7. $y = \dfrac{x + 3}{2x - 3}.$ 8. $y = \dfrac{4x}{x^2 + 1}.$

9. $y = \dfrac{x^2 + 4}{x^2 - 4}.$

10. $y = \dfrac{2}{x^3 + 2}.$

11. $y = \dfrac{(x - 1)^2}{2x}.$

12. $y = \dfrac{x^3}{(x - 1)^2}.$

Find d^2y/dx^2 from each of the following equations:

13. $y^2 = 8x.$

14. $x^2 + y^2 = 25.$

15. $x^{\frac{1}{2}} + y^{\frac{1}{2}} = a^{\frac{1}{2}}.$

16. $4x^2 + 9y^2 = 36.$

17. $\dfrac{x^2}{a^2} - \dfrac{y^2}{b^2} = 1.$

18. $\dfrac{x^2}{a^2} + \dfrac{y^2}{b^2} = 1.$

19. $xy - x^2 - 8y = 0.$

20. $xy + y = x - 4.$

21. $x^2 + (y + 4)^2 = 16.$

22. $x^2 + 2y^2 - 2x - 12y + 15 = 0.$

23. $x^2y - 4y = x^2.$

24. $x^4 + y^4 = 16.$

In each of the following, draw the curve and find the values of dy/dx and d^2y/dx^2 at the given point or points:

25. $x^2 + y^2 = 10x;$ $(8, 4),$ $(5, -5).$

26. $x^2 + 4y^2 = 25;$ $(3, -2).$

27. $x = 3y - \frac{1}{2}y^2;$ $(4, 2),$ $(4, 4).$

28. $xy + 2y = 2x - 1;$ $(0, -\frac{1}{2}).$

29. Find the values of dy/dx and d^2y/dx^2 at the point $(4, 2)$ on the ellipse whose equation is $x^2 + 4y^2 = 2xy + 4x.$

In each of the following, find the derivatives indicated:

30. $xy = 4;$ $\dfrac{d^n y}{dx^n}.$

31. $y = \dfrac{1}{x^2};$ $\dfrac{d^n y}{dx^n}.$

32. $x^2 + y^2 = a^2;$ $\dfrac{d^3 y}{dx^3}.$

33. $b^2x^2 + a^2y^2 = a^2b^2;$ $\dfrac{d^3 y}{dx^3}.$

34. $x^2 - 2y^2 = 9;$ $\dfrac{d^3 y}{dx^3}.$

35. $x^2 + y^2 = 4y;$ $\dfrac{d^3 y}{dx^3}.$

36. We have proved that $\dfrac{dy}{dx} = \dfrac{1}{\dfrac{dx}{dy}}.$ Show, by differentiating this

result with respect to x, that $\dfrac{d^2y}{dx^2} = -\dfrac{\dfrac{d^2x}{dy^2}}{(dx/dy)^3}.$

37. Derive a formula for $d^2/dx^2 \, (uv)$ where u and v are functions of x having first and second derivatives with respect to x.

38. Derive a formula for $D_x{}^3(uv)$ under assumptions corresponding to those of Prob. 37.

36. The sign of d^2y/dx^2. Concavity.—Since d^2y/dx^2 is the derivative with respect to x of dy/dx, its value at any point on the curve $y = f(x)$ is the rate at which the value of

dy/dx (or the slope of the tangent line) is changing relative to x.

If over a certain interval d^2y/dx^2 is *positive* then the slope is *increasing* as x increases. The tangent line in this case turns in the counterclockwise sense as it traverses the curve from left to right and the curve lies above the tangent line. Such an arc is said to be *concave upward*. In Fig. 35 the arc PNB is concave upward.

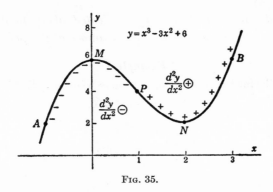

FIG. 35.

Similarly, if d^2y/dx^2 is *negative* over a certain interval, the slope is *decreasing*. In this case the tangent line turns in the clockwise sense and the curve lies below the tangent line. Such an arc is said to be *concave downward*. The arc AMP in Fig. 35 is concave downward.

37. Inflection points.—An inflection point on a curve is a point at which the sense of concavity changes. More precisely, a point $P(x_1, y_1)$ on the curve $y = f(x)$ is an inflection point if the curve is concave upward for x slightly less than x_1 and downward for x slightly more than x_1, or vice versa.

It can be shown that *if d^2y/dx^2 exists at an inflection point its value must be* **zero.** The proof follows from the fact that if this derivative were positive (or negative) at P then the curve must be concave upward (or downward) throughout at least a small interval about this point. Thus P could not be an inflection point.

A point $P(x_1, y_1)$ at which $d^2y/dx^2 = 0$ *is* an inflection point if the sign of this second derivative is positive for x slightly less than x_1 and negative for x slightly greater than x_1, or vice versa. It *is not* an inflection point if d^2y/dx^2 has the *same* sign for x slightly more than x_1 as it has for x slightly less than x_1. A procedure for locating inflection points is then as follows:

1. *Set $d^2y/dx^2 = 0$ and solve for x, thus obtaining the critical points.*

2. *Test each such point as indicated above to determine whether or not the sign of d^2y/dx^2 changes at the point.*

Example 1

Locate the inflection points on the curve whose equation is

$$y = x^3 - 3x^2 + 6.$$

Solution

$$\frac{dy}{dx} = 3x^2 - 6x;$$

$$\frac{d^2y}{dx^2} = 6x - 6.$$

Setting $d^2y/dx^2 = 0$ and solving for x, we have

$$6x - 6 = 0;$$
$$x = 1.$$

The value of d^2y/dx^2 is obviously negative for $x < 1$ and positive for $x > 1$. Hence the point $P(1, 4)$ *is* an inflection point. The graph is shown in Fig. 35.

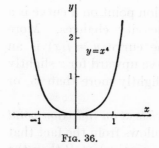

FIG. 36.

Example 2

Locate the inflection points on the curve whose equation is $y = x^4$.

Solution (Fig. 36)

$$D_x y = 4x^3;$$
$$D_x^2 y = 12x^2;$$

Setting $D_x^2 y = 0$ and solving for x, we, of course, find $x = 0$. This is *not* an inflection point because $D_x^2 y$ *does not change sign* when x goes through the value 0. For all values of x except $x = 0$ $D_x^2 y$ is positive, and the curve is everywhere concave upward.

It should be observed that a curve *may* have an inflection point at which d^2y/dx^2 is *not* equal to zero. This can happen, however, only if the second derivative fails to exist at such a point. Such points may be discovered by studying the behavior of the curve in the neighborhood of any points at which d^2y/dx^2 becomes infinite or otherwise fails to exist.

Example

For the curve whose equation is $y = \sqrt[3]{x}$ we have

$$\frac{dy}{dx} = \tfrac{1}{3}x^{-\frac{2}{3}};$$

$$\frac{d^2y}{dx^2} = -\tfrac{2}{9}x^{-\frac{5}{3}} = -\frac{2}{9x^{\frac{5}{3}}}.$$

There is no value of x for which $d^2y/dx^2 = 0$, but this derivative fails to exist at $x = 0$. To the right of this point d^2y/dx^2 is *negative* and the arc is *concave downward;* to the left, this second derivative is *positive*

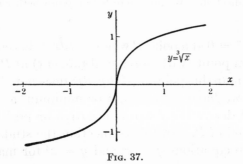

$$y = \sqrt[3]{x}$$

FIG. 37.

and the curve is *concave upward.* The point $(0, 0)$ *is* then an inflection point. The curve is shown in Fig. 37.

38. Use of $D_x{}^2y$ in problems of maxima and minima.—

Our first step in locating maximum and minimum points on a curve $y = f(x)$ has been to set $dy/dx = 0$ and solve for x, thus finding the critical points. If the value of d^2y/dx^2 is *negative* at such a point, then the arc is *concave downward* and the critical point is a *maximum point.* Similarly, if d^2y/dx^2 is *positive,* the arc is *concave upward* and the critical point is a *minimum point.*

Example

Find the maximum and minimum points on the curve whose equation
is $y = x^3 - 3x^2 + 6$.

Solution (Fig. 35)

$$\frac{dy}{dx} = 3x^2 - 6x;$$

$$3x^2 - 6x = 0 \qquad \text{at} \qquad x = 0 \qquad \text{and} \qquad x = 2.$$

In order to test these critical points we employ the second derivative:

$$\frac{d^2y}{dx^2} = 6x - 6.$$

$\dfrac{d^2y}{dx^2}\bigg]_{x=0}$ is *negative;* hence this is a *maximum* point.

$\dfrac{d^2y}{dx^2}\bigg]_{x=2}$ is *positive;* hence this is a *minimum* point.

The numerical value of the second derivative is of no importance in this
particular connection.   We are interested only in whether it is positive
or negative.

If $d^2y/dx^2 = 0$ at a point P where $dy/dx = 0$, then we have
an inflection point (with horizontal tangent) at P if d^2y/dx^2
changes sign at this point.   If d^2y/dx^2 does not change sign
at P, then we have a maximum or minimum according as
this second derivative remains negative or positive in the
neighborhood of P.   In this connection the student should
examine the equations $y = x^3$ and $y = x^4$ for maxima and
minima.

39. Acceleration in rectilinear motion.—We have already
found that if a point moves along *a straight line path* so that
its distance from a fixed point A on the path varies with the
time according to the law

$$s = f(t),$$

the value of ds/dt at any instant is the velocity v of the
moving point at that instant.

The rate at which the velocity is changing (with respect
to time) is called the *acceleration* of the moving point.   This

rate is obviously given by the value of

$$\frac{dv}{dt} = \frac{d}{dt}\left(\frac{ds}{dt}\right) = \frac{d^2s}{dt^2}.$$

If s is expressed in feet and t in seconds, the velocity is, of course, in feet per second. The acceleration, being the rate of change of velocity with respect to time, is expressed in feet per second per second; this is often abbreviated by writing ft./sec.^{2} Acceleration may of course also be expressed in such units as miles per hour per hour, miles per hour per second, feet per second per minute, etc.

PROBLEMS

In each of the following, locate the maximum, minimum, and inflection points; sketch the curve:

1. $y = x^3 - 3x - 2.$ **2.** $y = 3x^2 - x^3.$

3. $y = 2x^3 - 9x^2 + 12x - 2.$ **4.** $4y = x^3 - 3x^2 - 9x + 3.$

5. $y = x^3 - 9x^2 + 24x - 20.$ **6.** $y = x^3 - 3x^2 + 3x + 2.$

7. $y = x^4 - 16.$ **8.** $y = 32x^2 - x^4.$

9. $4y = x^4 - 4x^3 + 16x - 9.$ **10.** $4y = 3x^4 + 4x^3 - 12x^2 + 4.$

11. $y = \dfrac{1}{x} + \dfrac{1}{x^2}.$ **12.** $y = \dfrac{x}{2} + \dfrac{2}{x}.$

13. $6y = \dfrac{x^3}{3} + \dfrac{81}{x}.$ **14.** $y = \dfrac{2x - 1}{x^2}.$

15. $y = \dfrac{6}{x^2 + 1}.$ **16.** $y = \dfrac{8a^3}{x^2 + 4a^2}.$

17. $y = \dfrac{16}{x^3 + 8}.$ **18.** $y = \dfrac{(x - 1)^2}{x}.$

19. $y = \dfrac{4x^2}{x^2 + 4}.$ **20.** $y = \dfrac{10x + 5}{(x - 2)^2}.$

21. $y = \dfrac{x^2 + 9}{x^2 - 4}.$ **22.** $y = \dfrac{x^2 - 4}{x^2 - 9}.$

23. $y = \dfrac{x^2}{x^2 - 3}.$ **24.** $y = \dfrac{12x}{x^2 + 12}.$

25. Show that the cubic curve $y = ax^3 + bx^2 + cx + d$ always has an inflection point and that the abscissa of this point is $-b/3a$.

26. Show that the equation of Prob. 25 takes the form $y = ax^3 + Cx$ when the axes are translated so that the new origin is at the inflection point. Hence infer that the cubic curve is always symmetrical with respect to its inflection point.

27. Under what condition does the curve $y = ax^3 + bx^2 + cx + d$ have its inflection point on the y-axis?

28. A particle moves along a straight line in such a way that its distance S(ft.) from a fixed point A on the line at the end of t min. is given by the equation:

$$S = t^2 - 8t + 18.$$

Find the position, velocity, and acceleration of the particle at the end of 2 min. On the same axes plot S, dS/dt, and d^2S/dt^2 against t and interpret these graphs. They are called *displacement-time*, *velocity-time*, and *acceleration-time* curves, respectively.

29. Same as Prob. 28 for the equation $S = 9t^2 - t^3$.

30. A particle moves along a straight line in such a way that its distance S(ft.) from a fixed point A on the line at the end of t min. is $S = t(t - 12)^2$. Find the position, velocity, and acceleration of the particle at the end of 3 min. During what time interval is it moving toward A?

31. Same as Prob. 30 for the equation $S = t^2(t - 4)^2$.

32. A particle moves along the y-axis in such a way that its distance (in.) from the origin at the end of t min. is given by $y = \sqrt{4t + 8}$. Find its velocity and acceleration at the end of 7 min.

33. Explain the following statement: The condition that $f'(x_1) = 0$ and $f''(x_1) = k < 0$ is sufficient, but not necessary, for a maximum value of $f(x)$ at $x = x_1$.

34. Explain the following statement: The condition that $f''(x_1) = 0$ is neither necessary nor sufficient for an inflection point on the graph of $f(x)$ at $x = x_1$.

CHAPTER VII

THE TRIGONOMETRIC FUNCTIONS

40. Review of definitions and fundamental relations.—
Before entering into a study of the derivatives of the
trigonometric functions it is necessary to review briefly the
definitions of these functions and their fundamental
properties.

The review given in this section constitutes a bare minimum of essential facts that every student of the calculus
must have at his finger tips. No student can afford to
proceed without making certain that he has a thorough
understanding of these elementary ideas.

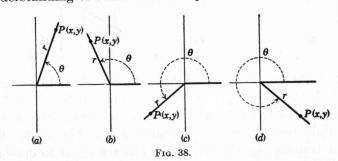

Fig. 38.

1. *The definitions.*—If θ is any *number*, the trigonometric
functions of θ are defined as follows: Construct an angle of
θ radians with vertex at the origin and initial side along
positive x-axis, measuring the angle counterclockwise if θ
is positive. Choose any point $P(x, y)$ on the terminal side;
denote its distance from the origin by r. Then (Fig. 38)

$$\sin \theta = \frac{y}{r}, \qquad \csc \theta = \frac{r}{y},$$

$$\cos \theta = \frac{x}{r}, \qquad \sec \theta = \frac{r}{x},$$

$$\tan \theta = \frac{y}{x}, \qquad \cot \theta = \frac{x}{y}.$$

2. *The signs of the functions.*—We may agree to consider that: x is positive when measured to the right and negative to the left of the origin; y is positive when measured upward and negative downward from the origin. We may further agree to regard r as always positive.

With these conventions as to the signs of x, y, and r in mind, one can easily determine whether a given function of a given angle is positive or negative. Thus if α is an angle whose terminal side lies in the second quadrant, $\cos \alpha$ is negative; for $\cos \alpha = x/r$ and x is $-$ while r is $+$.

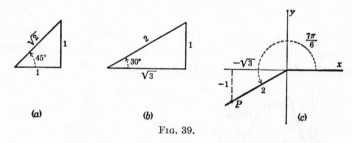

Fig. 39.

3. *Values of the functions for certain angles.*—In order to find the value of any function of any angle which is a multiple of 30 or 45°, one has only to remember that in the 45° right triangle the two legs are equal and in the 30—60° right triangle the shortest leg is exactly equal to one-half of the hypotenuse. The values of x, y, and r may then be taken as shown in Fig. 39, a or b. Thus, to find sin 210° or, as we prefer, sin $7\pi/6$, one draws Fig. 39c and writes down from it

$$\sin \frac{7\pi}{6} = -\tfrac{1}{2}.$$

The values of the functions for the quadrantal angles 0, $\pi/2$, π, and $3\pi/2$ can also be easily found. For this, one needs only to note that for such angles either x or y is zero and the other equals $\pm r$. Thus for the angle $3\pi/2$, $x = 0$

and $y = -r$; hence (Fig. 40),

$$\sin \frac{3\pi}{2} = \frac{-r}{r} = -1.$$

$$\cos \frac{3\pi}{2} = \frac{0}{r} = 0.$$

4. *The values of the functions when that of one is known.*— If, for a certain angle, the value of one of the six trigono- metric functions and the quad- rant in which the terminal side lies are known, the values of the other five functions can be found easily. Several problems involving this are given in the next set.

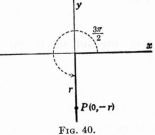

FIG. 40.

5. *The fundamental identities.* —From the way in which the trigonometric functions of θ are defined it is evident that they are not independent of each other. The student should memorize and be able to prove the following funda- mental relations that exist between them:

(a) $\sin^2 \theta + \cos^2 \theta = 1.$

(b) $\quad 1 + \tan^2 \theta = \sec^2 \theta.$

(c) $\quad 1 + \cot^2 \theta = \csc^2 \theta.$

(d) $\quad \tan \theta = \dfrac{\sin \theta}{\cos \theta}.$

(e) $\begin{cases} \csc \theta = \dfrac{1}{\sin \theta}. \\[2mm] \sec \theta = \dfrac{1}{\cos \theta}. \\[2mm] \cot \theta = \dfrac{1}{\tan \theta}. \end{cases}$

The proofs follow immediately from the definitions of the functions.

6. *The functions of* $-\theta$.—By comparing the values of x, y, and r for any angle θ with those for $-\theta$ (an angle equal to θ but measured *clockwise* from the positive x-axis), it is easy to show that

$$\sin (-\theta) = -\sin \theta;$$
$$\cos (-\theta) = \cos \theta;$$
$$\tan (-\theta) = -\tan \theta.$$

7. *Reduction to acute angles.*—Tables ordinarily give the values of the functions for angles only up to 90°. For a larger angle the value of any function can be found as follows:

Subtract from the angle whatever multiple of 90° is necessary in order to have a remainder less than 90°. Then take the same function or the cofunction of the remainder according as an even or odd multiple of 90° was subtracted. That is

Any function of $(n \cdot 90° + \theta) = \pm \begin{cases} \text{same function of } \theta \text{ if } n \\ \quad \text{is even.} \\ \text{cofunction of } \theta \text{ if } n \text{ is} \\ \quad \text{odd.} \end{cases}$

The sign is determined by the particular function required and the quadrant in which the terminal side lies, as discussed in Part 2 of this section.

Example

Find sin 285° from the tables.

Solution

$$\sin 285° = \sin (3 \cdot 90° + 15°) = \pm \cos 15°.$$

Since the terminal side of 285° lies in the fourth quadrant, sin 285° must be *negative;* hence,

$$\sin 285° = - \cos 15° = -0.9659.$$

8. *The functions of the sum and difference of two angles. Double- and half-angle formulas.*—From the definitions of the functions, it can be shown that if one adds together two angles x and y, the sine, cosine, and tangent of the sum are

(*a*) $\sin (x + y) = \sin x \cos y + \cos x \sin y.$

(*b*) $\cos (x + y) = \cos x \cos y - \sin x \sin y.$

(*c*) $\tan (x + y) = \dfrac{\tan x + \tan y}{1 - \tan x \tan y}.$

Replacing y by $-y$ in (*a*), (*b*), and (*c*), we have for the difference between two angles, (*d*) $\sin (x - y) = \sin x \cos y - \cos x \sin y.$

(*e*) $\cos (x - y) = \cos x \cos y + \sin x \sin y.$

(*f*) $\tan (x - y) = \dfrac{\tan x - \tan y}{1 + \tan x \tan y}.$

If $y = x$ formulas (*a*), (*b*), and (*c*) reduce to

(*g*) $\sin 2x = 2 \sin x \cos x.$

(*h*) $\cos 2x = \cos^2 x - \sin^2 x.$

(*i*) $\tan 2x = \dfrac{2 \tan x}{1 - \tan^2 x}.$

From formula (*h*) one can easily show that

(*j*) $\sin \tfrac{1}{2}x = \pm \sqrt{\dfrac{1 - \cos x}{2}}.$

(*k*) $\cos \tfrac{1}{2}x = \pm \sqrt{\dfrac{1 + \cos x}{2}}.$

(*l*) $\tan \tfrac{1}{2}x = \pm \sqrt{\dfrac{1 - \cos x}{1 + \cos x}} = \dfrac{1 - \cos x}{\sin x} = \dfrac{\sin x}{1 + \cos x}.$

It should be noticed that the $\pm$ sign is omitted in the last two forms of the formula for $\tan \tfrac{1}{2}x$. This is because $(1 \pm \cos x)$ is never negative and $\tan \tfrac{1}{2}x$ always has the same sign as $\sin x$.

9. *Sine and cosine laws.*—**Sine law:** In any triangle the sides are proportional to the sines of the opposite angles. That is (Fig. 41),

$$\frac{a}{\sin \alpha} = \frac{b}{\sin \beta} = \frac{c}{\sin \gamma}.$$

Cosine law: The square of any side of a triangle is equal to the sum of the squares of the two other sides minus twice the product of these sides and the cosine of the included angle. Thus, in Fig. 41,

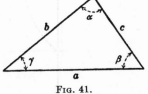

Fig. 41.

$$c^2 = a^2 + b^2 - 2ab \cos \gamma.$$

10. *General behavior and graphs of the functions.*—The functions $\sin x$ and $\cos x$ are single-valued and continuous

for all values of x. The same statement applies to tan x except at the points where x is an odd multiple of $\pi/2$; at these points it is undefined.

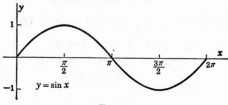

Fig. 42.

The manner in which each of these functions varies with x can be discussed in a general way from the corresponding graph. Thus, Fig. 42 indicates that sin x increases from 0 at $x = 0$ to 1 at $x = \frac{1}{2}\pi$, the *rate* of increase becoming

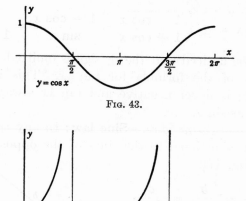

Fig. 43.

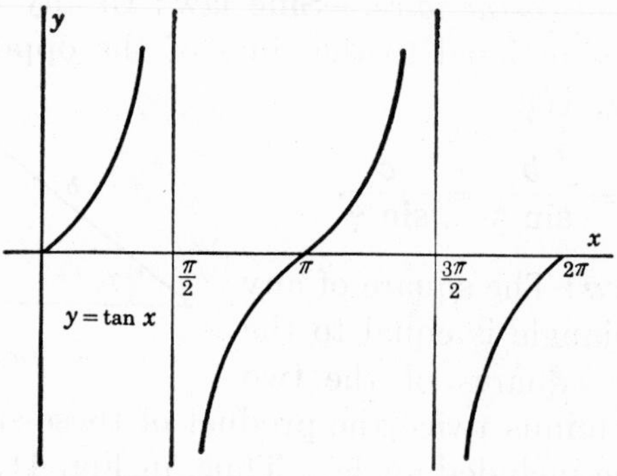

Fig. 44.

continuously smaller as we move from left to right. In the interval from $x = \frac{1}{2}\pi$ to $x = \frac{3}{2}\pi$, sin x decreases from $+1$ to -1; it then increases to 0 at $x = 2\pi$. The function is periodic with period 2π; *i.e.*, for any value of x,

$$\sin (x + 2\pi) = \sin x.$$

A similar discussion could be given for the functions $\cos x$ and $\tan x$ whose graphs are shown in Figs. 43 and 44. Since $\cot x$, $\sec x$, and $\csc x$ are the reciprocals of these functions, their graphs may easily be sketched and their general behavior discussed from the graphs.

PROBLEMS

Evaluate the following expressions without using tables:

1. $2 \cos 135° - \sin 210° + 3 \cot 225° + \sec 315°$.

2. $4 \cos \pi + \sec \frac{1}{3}\pi - 4 \cos \frac{1}{3}\pi + 2 \sin \frac{3}{2}\pi$.

3. $4 \tan \frac{11}{4}\pi - 2 \sec 480° - 6 \csc (-\frac{5}{4}\pi)$.

4. $8 \cos \frac{3}{2}\pi + 4 \sec \pi - 5 \cot 0 + 3 \sin \frac{1}{2}\pi$.

5. Using tables, find $\cos 264°$, $\tan (-514°)$, and $\sin 324°$.

6. Show that $\sin (-x) = - \sin x$ and $\cos (-x) = \cos x$ if the terminal side of x is in the first quadrant; the third quadrant.

7. Prove the fundamental identities listed in Part 5 of this section.

8. Prove the formulas for $\sin (x + y)$ and $\cos (x + y)$, assuming that x and y are positive acute angles such that $x + y < \frac{1}{2}\pi$. Discuss possible methods of extending the proof to the general case.

9. Show how formulas (c) to (l) in Part 8 of this section may be deduced from formulas (a) and (b).

10. If $\tan \theta = \frac{3}{4}$, θ being a positive acute angle, find $\sin 2\theta$, $\cos 2\theta$, and $\tan \frac{1}{2}\theta$.

11. Given that $\sin \theta = - \frac{2}{3}$ and that θ is an angle between 270 and 360°, find the value of $15 \cos \theta + 6 \cot \theta$.

12. If $\tan \theta = 3$ and θ is an angle between 180 and 270°, what is the value of $\frac{1}{2} \sec^2 \theta - 5 \cos 2\theta$?

13. If $\tan \alpha = \frac{1}{2}$, α being a positive acute angle, and $\tan \beta = -3$, β being an angle between 90 and 180°, what is the value of $\sin (\alpha + \beta)$; of $\tan (\beta - \alpha)$?

14. Prove the sine law and the cosine law.

15. Draw the graph of $y = \sin x$, and on the same axes sketch that of $y = \csc x$ making use of the relation $\csc x = 1/\sin x$.

16. As in Prob. 15 for the curves $y = \cos x$ and $y = \sec x$.

17. Sketch on the same axes the curves $y = \sin x$, $y = \sin 2x$, and $y = 2 \sin x$. Compare their amplitudes and periods.

18. Show that the curves $y = a \sin nx$ and $y = a \cos nx$ are periodic with period $2\pi/n$.

19. Sketch the curve $y = 2 \sin x + \cos 2x$ by drawing the separate graphs of $y = 2 \sin x$ and $y = \cos 2x$ and adding ordinates.

20. Show that the function $A \cos nx + B \sin nx$ can be written in the form $C \sin (nx + \alpha)$ where $C = \sqrt{A^2 + B^2}$ and $\tan \alpha = A/B$.

Solve the following equations for positive values of $x < 2\pi$:

21. $6 \cos^2 x = 5 \cos x - 1$.   **22.** $2 \sin^2 x = 1 + \cos x$.

23. $\tan 2x = 2 \sin x$.   **24.** $4 \tan^2 x = 3 \sec x + 6$.

25. $3 \sin x + 4 \cos x = 5$.   **26.** $\sin 3x = \sin 2x + \sin x$.

27. $2(1 - \cos 2x) = \sin x + \cos 2x$.

Prove the following identities:

28. $(\sin \tfrac{1}{2}x - \cos \tfrac{1}{2}x)^2 = 1 - \sin x$.

29. $\dfrac{2 \sin \theta - \sin 2\theta}{2 \sin \theta + \sin 2\theta} = \tan^2 \tfrac{1}{2}\theta$.

30. $\sin 2\theta \tan \tfrac{1}{2}\theta + \cos 2\theta = 2 \cos \theta - 1$.

31. Simplify:

$$\frac{\left[1 + \left(\dfrac{\sin \theta}{1 - \cos \theta}\right)^2\right]^{\frac{3}{2}}}{\dfrac{1}{(1 - \cos \theta)^2}}.$$

32. The following formulas express the sum or difference of sines or cosines of two angles as a product. Show how they are derived from the formulas for the sine and cosine of $(x + y)$ and $(x - y)$.

(a) $\sin A + \sin B = 2 \sin \tfrac{1}{2}(A + B) \cos \tfrac{1}{2}(A - B)$.

(b) $\sin A - \sin B = 2 \cos \tfrac{1}{2}(A + B) \sin \tfrac{1}{2}(A - B)$.

(c) $\cos A + \cos B = 2 \cos \tfrac{1}{2}(A + B) \cos \tfrac{1}{2}(A - B)$.

(d) $\cos A - \cos B = -2 \sin \tfrac{1}{2}(A + B) \sin \tfrac{1}{2}(A - B)$.

41. The derivative of sin v.—To find the derivative of the function $y = \sin x$ we must apply the fundamental process of differentiation. Starting at any point $P(x, \sin x)$ on the curve, and letting x increase by an amount Δx we have (Fig. 45)

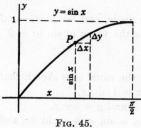

$$\Delta y = \sin (x + \Delta x) - \sin x;$$
$$\frac{\Delta y}{\Delta x} = \frac{\sin (x + \Delta x) - \sin x}{\Delta x}.$$

Fig. 45.

The required derivative is of course the limit of this quotient as $\Delta x \to 0$. This limit is not apparent from the present form of the fraction; however, if we apply the formula

$$\sin A - \sin B = 2 \cos \tfrac{1}{2}(A + B) \sin \tfrac{1}{2}(A - B)$$

to the numerator, the fraction becomes

$$\frac{\Delta y}{\Delta x} = \frac{2 \cos (x + \tfrac{1}{2}\Delta x) \sin \tfrac{1}{2}\Delta x}{\Delta x}$$

$$= \cos (x + \tfrac{1}{2}\Delta x) \frac{\sin \tfrac{1}{2}\Delta x}{\tfrac{1}{2}\Delta x}.$$

We have then immediately,

$$\frac{dy}{dx} = \lim_{\Delta x \to 0} \cos (x + \tfrac{1}{2}\Delta x) \lim_{\Delta x \to 0} \frac{\sin \tfrac{1}{2}\Delta x}{\tfrac{1}{2}\Delta x}$$

$$= \cos x \; \textit{if } x \textit{ is in radians.}$$

If we consider the more general function $y = \sin v$ where v is a differentiable function of x, the derivative *with respect to* v is $\cos v$ by virtue of the above result. To obtain the derivative with respect to x we must multiply this by dv/dx. That is

(**IX**) $$\frac{d}{dx} \sin v = \cos v \frac{dv}{dx}.$$

Thus, for the function

$$y = \sin 4x,$$

$$\frac{dy}{dx} = \cos 4x \frac{d}{dx}(4x)$$

$$= 4 \cos 4x.$$

It should be observed that if x is the number of *degrees* in the angle, instead of the number of *radians*, then

$$\lim_{\Delta x \to 0} \frac{\sin \tfrac{1}{2}\Delta x}{\tfrac{1}{2}\Delta x} = \frac{\pi}{180}$$

rather than 1, and the above formula is

$$\frac{d}{dx}(\sin x) = \frac{\pi}{180} \cos x.$$

In order to avoid the factor $\pi/180$ we always use radian measure in studying the calculus of the trigonometric functions.

42. Derivatives of the other trigonometric functions.—
The derivatives of the other trigonometric functions could
of course be obtained by the procedure used above. They
can be found more easily, however, by other means. Thus,
since

$$\cos v = \sin \left(\frac{\pi}{2} - v\right),$$

we have

$$\frac{d}{dx} \cos v = \frac{d}{dx} \sin \left(\frac{\pi}{2} - v\right)$$

$$= \cos \left(\frac{\pi}{2} - v\right) \frac{d}{dx} \left(\frac{\pi}{2} - v\right) \quad \text{[by (IX)]}$$

$$= - \sin v \frac{dv}{dx}.$$

The formula for the derivative of $\tan v$ can now be
obtained by writing

$$\tan v = \frac{\sin v}{\cos v}$$

and differentiating the quotient. The formulas are all
listed below; the proofs are left to the exercises.

(IX) $$\frac{d}{dx} \sin v = \cos v \frac{dv}{dx}.$$

(X) $$\frac{d}{dx} \cos v = - \sin v \frac{dv}{dx}.$$

(XI) $$\frac{d}{dx} \tan v = \sec^2 v \frac{dv}{dx}.$$

(XII) $$\frac{d}{dx} \cot v = - \csc^2 v \frac{dv}{dx}.$$

(XIII) $$\frac{d}{dx} \sec v = \sec v \tan v \frac{dv}{dx}.$$

(XIV) $$\frac{d}{dx} \csc v = - \csc v \cot v \frac{dv}{dx}.$$

In finding the derivative of a function that involves the
trigonometric functions one must use formulas (IX) to

(XIV) in addition to formulas (I) to (VIII). The details are illustrated by the following examples:

Example 1

$$y = \sqrt{\tan x}.$$

$$\frac{dy}{dx} = \tfrac{1}{2}(\tan x)^{-\frac{1}{2}} \frac{d}{dx} \tan x \qquad \text{[by (V)]}$$

$$= \frac{\sec^2 x}{2\sqrt{\tan x}} \qquad \text{[by (XI)]}$$

Example 2

$$y = \sec^2 2\theta.$$

$$\frac{dy}{d\theta} = 2 \sec 2\theta \frac{d}{d\theta} \sec 2\theta \qquad \text{[by (V)]}$$

$$= 2 \sec 2\theta \sec 2\theta \tan 2\theta \frac{d}{d\theta} 2\theta \qquad \text{[by (XIII)]}$$

$$= 4 \sec^2 2\theta \tan 2\theta.$$

Example 3

$$y = \frac{\sin x}{x}.$$

$$\frac{dy}{dx} = \frac{x \dfrac{d}{dx} \sin x - \sin x \dfrac{dx}{dx}}{x^2} \qquad \text{[by (VI)]}$$

$$= \frac{x \cos x - \sin x}{x^2}.$$

PROBLEMS

1. Derive the formula for the derivative of cos x using the fundamental differentiation process.

2. Derive the formula for the derivative of tan x using the fundamental differentiation process.

3. Derive formulas (XI) to (XIV) inclusive without using the fundamental process.

Differentiate the following functions:

4. $y = 3 \cos 4x.$

5. $y = 4\sqrt{\tan 2x}.$

6. $y = 6 \sec \tfrac{1}{2}x.$

7. $y = \tfrac{1}{2} \cot^2 2x.$

8. $y = 2 \sin^3 \pi\theta.$

9. $s = 4t + \cos^2 t.$

10. $y = \sqrt{1 - 2\sin x}.$

11. $x = 2a \csc \tfrac{1}{2}t.$

12. $y = x^2 \cot^2 2x.$

13. $y = 4x \cos^2 \pi x.$

14. $S = (\sin t + \cos t)^2.$

15. $y = \csc x \cot^2 x.$

16. $y = 4x \tan \sqrt{x}.$

17. $y = x^2 \cot (x^2 + 5).$

18. $y = \dfrac{1 + \cos 2\theta}{\sin 2\theta}$.

19. $y = \dfrac{1 - \sin x}{1 + \sin x}$.

20. $y = \sqrt{\dfrac{1 - \cos x}{1 + \cos x}}$.

21. $y = \dfrac{\tan x}{1 - \tan^2 x}$.

22. $y = \dfrac{\sec x + \tan x}{\sec x - \tan x}$.

23. $s = \dfrac{2 \tan t - 1}{4 \tan t + 1}$.

In each of the following, find d^2y/dx^2:

24. $y = 5 \sin^2 kx$.

25. $y = 2 \tan \frac{1}{2}x$.

26. $y = a \sin^3 x \cos x$.

27. $y = 2 \sin x + \cos 2x$.

28. $y = x \sin x$.

29. $4 \tan^2 \frac{1}{2}x$.

30. $y = \dfrac{\cos x}{x}$.

31. $y = \dfrac{\sin x}{1 - \cos x}$.

In each of the following, find the values of $D_x y$ and $D_x^2 y$ for the given value of x:

32. $y = \cos^3 x; \ x = \frac{1}{4}\pi$.

33. $y = x \sin \pi x; \ x = \frac{1}{2}$.

34. $y = x \cos^2 x; \ x = 0$.

35. $y = \sec x \tan x; \ x = 0$.

36. Show that if $y = A \cos mx + B \sin mx$ then $\dfrac{d^2y}{dx^2} + m^2 y = 0$.

37. Find dy/dx from the equation $x \cos y + y \cos x = 0$.

38. Find dy/dx from the equation $y^2 \sin x - x^2 \sin y = 8$.

In each of the following, sketch the two curves for x from 0 to 2π, and find their angle or angles of intersection:

39. $y = \sin x; \ y = \cos x$.

40. $y = \sin x; \ y = \cos 2x$.

41. $y = 2 \sin^2 x; \ y = \cos 2x$.

42. $y = \sin x; \ y = \frac{1}{2} \tan x$.

43. $y = 4 \cos^2 x; \ y = \sin 2x$.

44. $y = \tan 2x; \ y = \cot x$.

45. Show that the derivative of $\tan x$ with respect to $\sin x$ is equal to $\sec^3 x$; hence, show that when $x = \frac{1}{3}\pi$, $\tan x$ is increasing eight times as fast as $\sin x$.

In each of the following, locate the maximum, minimum, and inflection points, and sketch the curve; take the interval from $x = 0$ to 2π except where otherwise specified:

46. $y = 2 \sin^2 x$.

47. $y = \cos^2 x$.

48. $y = \sin^3 x$.

49. $y = \cos^4 \frac{1}{2}x$.

50. $y = \sin x + \cos x$.

51. $y = 4 \sin x + 3 \cos x$.

52. $y = \cos x + \frac{1}{2} \sin 2x$.

53. $y = 4 \sin^2 x + 3 \cos 2x$.

54. $y = 2 \sin x + \sin 2x$.

55. $y = 2 \sin^2 x + \sin 2x$. $\ 0 \leqq x \leqq \pi$.

56. $y = 3 \tan x - 4x; \ -\frac{1}{2}\pi < x < \frac{1}{2}\pi$.

57. $y = \sin 2x + 2 \cos x$.

58. A quantity Q varies with the time t according to the law $Q = 9 \sin^2 t \cos t$. Between what greatest and least values does Q vary? Make a graph showing how Q varies with t.

59. What is the smallest value of the quantity $\sin^3 x + \cos^2 x$ in the interval $0 \leqq x \leqq \pi$?

60. It can be shown that the magnitude of the force required to drag the block of weight W (Fig. 46) along a rough horizon-

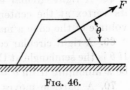

Fig. 46.

tal floor depends upon the angle θ in accordance with the formula

$$F = \frac{kW}{\cos \theta + k \sin \theta}$$

where k is the coefficient of friction (a constant). Show that the value of θ for which F is smallest is given by $\tan \theta = k$.

61. A man starts at a point A and walks 40 ft. north; then turns and walks east at 5 ft. per second. If a searchlight placed at A follows him, at what rate is it turning at the end of 6 sec.?

62. On the top of a wall 27 ft. high is another wall which is inset 1 ft. What are the length and the inclination of the shortest ladder that would reach from the ground to this wall?

63. A corridor $13\frac{1}{2}$ ft. wide meets at right angles another which is 4 ft. wide. Could a pole 24 ft. long be carried horizontally around the corner?

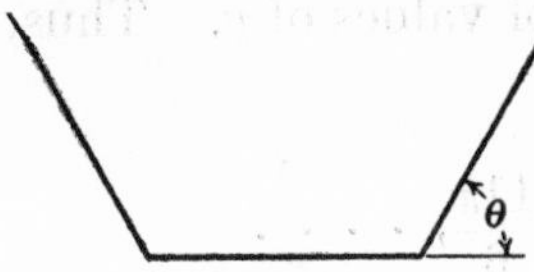

64. An open gutter with sloping sides of equal inclination is to be made from a long piece of sheet metal which is 15 in. wide, by bending up one-third of the sheet on each side as indicated in Fig. 47. For what inclination θ of the sides is the capacity a maximum?

Fig. 47.

65. A right circular cone is inscribed in a sphere of radius a. Find its height if the lateral surface is to be a maximum. Hint: Let the semiangle θ at the vertex be the independent variable. Note from Fig. 48 that the length of an element is $2a \cos \theta$; hence $h = 2a \cos^2 \theta$ and $r = 2a \cos \theta \sin \theta$.

66. Solve Prob. 65 if the volume instead of the lateral surface of the cone is to be a maximum.

67. A right circular cone is circumscribed about a right circular cylinder of radius r and height h. Show that the

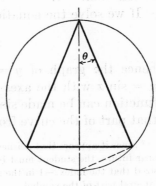

Fig. 48.

volume of the cone is a minimum if $\tan \theta = r/2h$, where θ is the semi-angle at the vertex.

68. A right circular cone is placed inside a sphere of radius a with its vertex at the center. For what semiangle θ at the vertex is the volume of the cone a maximum?

69. A right circular cone is circumscribed about a sphere of radius a. If θ is the semiangle at the vertex, show that the volume of the cone will be a minimum if $\sin \theta = \frac{1}{3}$.

70. A particle moves around the circle $x^2 + y^2 = r^2$ at a constant angular velocity of ω radians per second. Show that the projection of the particle on the x-axis moves back and forth from $(-r, 0)$ to $(+r, 0)$ in such a way that its acceleration is always toward the origin and proportional to its distance from the origin. This type of motion of a point along a straight line is called *simple harmonic motion.*

43. The functions arcsin x and arccos x.—We define the abbreviation

$$y = \arcsin x, \quad \text{or} \quad y = \sin^{-1} x*$$

to mean "y is the radian measure of an angle whose sine is x." For each value of x between -1 and $+1$ this relation of course yields an indefinite number of values of y. Thus, corresponding to $x = \frac{1}{2}$ we have

$$y = \frac{\pi}{6}, \frac{5\pi}{6}, \cdots, -\frac{7\pi}{6}, -\frac{11\pi}{6}, \cdots$$

The function is undefined for values of x greater than $+1$ or less than -1.

If we solve the equation for x in terms of y, we obtain

$$x = \sin y;$$

hence the graph of $y = \arcsin x$ is the same as that of $y = \sin x$ with the axes interchanged. See Fig. 49. The function can be made single-valued by agreeing to use only that part of the curve from A to B. This part is called the

---

* Since it appears that neither notation will be universally adopted in the near future, the student must be familiar with both. It should be emphasized that the index -1 in the symbol $\sin^{-1} x$ is *not* an exponent, but is an integral part of the symbol.

principal branch of the curve, and the corresponding values
of the function are called the *principal values*. Throughout
this work we shall assume this restriction to be made; thus,
for example, we agree that

$$\arcsin \tfrac{1}{2} = \frac{\pi}{6}; \qquad \arcsin \left(- \tfrac{1}{2}\right) = -\frac{\pi}{6}.$$

The function $y = \arcsin x$ thus becomes a *single-valued*
continuous function defined for all values of x in the interval
$-1 \leq x \leq +1$ and having for its graph
the arc AB in Fig. 49. It is obvious
from the graph that the function is
everywhere increasing *and its deriva-*
tive is everywhere positive.

To obtain its derivative we observe
that, if

$$y = \arcsin x,$$

then

$$x = \sin y,$$

and

$$\frac{dx}{dy} = \cos y.$$

Then, using formula (VIII),

$$\frac{dy}{dx} = \frac{1}{\cos y}.$$

But

$$\cos y = \sqrt{1 - \sin^2 y} = \sqrt{1 - x^2};$$

hence,

$$\frac{dy}{dx} = \frac{1}{\sqrt{1 - x^2}}.$$

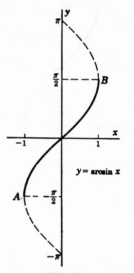

$y = \text{arcsin } x$

Fig. 49.

It should be noticed that the positive sign only is used here
for the radical. This is because we are considering only
the principal branch of the function and the derivative is
everywhere positive on this branch.

In a similar manner we define the function

$$y = \arccos x$$

as a single-valued continuous function in the interval from
$x = -1$ to $x = +1$, having for its graph the arc AB in
Fig. 50.   Considering only this prin-
cipal branch we have, for example,

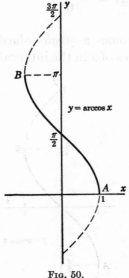

$$\arccos \tfrac{1}{2} = \frac{\pi}{3};$$

$$\arccos \left(-\tfrac{1}{2}\right) = \frac{2\pi}{3}.$$

The derivative of this function is
obviously everywhere negative.   To
obtain its derivative we proceed exactly as in the previous case and find
that for

$$y = \arccos x,$$
$$\frac{dy}{dx} = -\frac{1}{\sqrt{1 - x^2}}.$$

Finally, if v is a differentiable function of x, we have the formulas

Fig. 50.

$y = \arccos x$

(XV) $$\frac{d}{dx}(\arcsin v) = \frac{\dfrac{dv}{dx}}{\sqrt{1 - v^2}}.$$

(XVI) $$\frac{d}{dx}(\arccos v) = -\frac{\dfrac{dv}{dx}}{\sqrt{1 - v^2}}.$$

Example
$$y = \arcsin 2x.$$

$$\frac{dy}{dx} = \frac{\dfrac{d}{dx}(2x)}{\sqrt{1 - (2x)^2}}$$

$$= \frac{2}{\sqrt{1 - 4x^2}}.$$

44. The functions arctan x and arccot x.—The relation

$$y = \arctan x, \quad \text{or} \quad y = \tan^{-1} x$$

means that y is the radian measure of an angle whose tangent is x. The function is defined for all values of x and is of course multiple-valued. It can be made single-valued by agreeing to use only the part indicated by AB in Fig. 51.

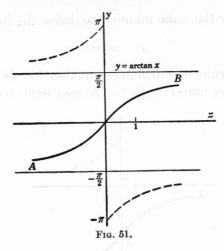

FIG. 51.

Thus, considering only this *principal branch* of the function we have, for example,

$$\arctan 1 = \frac{\pi}{4}; \quad \arctan (-1) = -\frac{\pi}{4}.$$

It is obvious from the graph that the derivative of this function is everywhere positive. To find its value we proceed as before, noting that, if

$$y = \arctan x,$$

then

$$x = \tan y,$$

and

$$\frac{dx}{dy} = \sec^2 y.$$

Then, using formula (VIII),

$$\frac{dy}{dx} = \frac{1}{\sec^2 y}$$
$$= \frac{1}{1 + \tan^2 y}$$
$$= \frac{1}{1 + x^2}.$$

In exactly the same manner we define the function

$$y = \text{arccot } x$$

as a single-valued continuous function for all values of x by restricting ourselves to the branch indicated by AB in

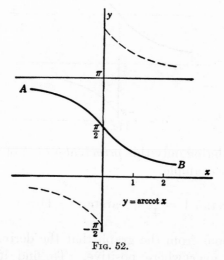

$$y = \text{arccot } x$$

FIG. 52.

Fig. 52. It is evident that the derivative of this function is everywhere negative, and it is easy to show that in this case

$$\frac{dy}{dx} = -\frac{1}{1 + x^2}.$$

Finally, if v is a differentiable function of x we have the formulas,

(XVII) $\quad \dfrac{d}{dx} (\arctan v) = \dfrac{\dfrac{dv}{dx}}{1 + v^2}.$

(XVIII) $\quad \dfrac{d}{dx} (\operatorname{arccot} v) = -\dfrac{\dfrac{dv}{dx}}{1 + v^2}.$

Example 1

$$y = \arctan \frac{2x - 1}{3}.$$

$$\frac{dy}{dx} = \frac{\dfrac{d}{dx}\left(\dfrac{2x - 1}{3}\right)}{1 + \left(\dfrac{2x - 1}{3}\right)^2} \qquad \text{[by (XVII)]}$$

$$= \frac{\frac{2}{3}}{1 + \dfrac{(2x - 1)^2}{9}}$$

$$= \frac{6}{9 + (2x - 1)^2}.$$

Example 2

$$y = x^2 \operatorname{arccot} \tfrac{1}{2}x.$$

$$\frac{dy}{dx} = x^2 \frac{d}{dx} (\operatorname{arccot} \tfrac{1}{2}x) + \operatorname{arccot} \tfrac{1}{2}x \, \frac{d}{dx} (x^2) \qquad \text{[by (IV)]}$$

$$= x^2 \left[-\frac{\dfrac{d}{dx}(\tfrac{1}{2}x)}{1 + (\tfrac{1}{2}x)^2} \right] + 2x \operatorname{arccot} \tfrac{1}{2}x$$

$$= x^2 \left[-\frac{\tfrac{1}{2}}{1 + (\tfrac{1}{2}x)^2} \right] + 2x \operatorname{arccot} \tfrac{1}{2}x$$

$$= -\frac{2x^2}{4 + x^2} + 2x \operatorname{arccot} \tfrac{1}{2}x.$$

PROBLEMS

The first 12 problems in this set are given for the purpose of reviewing some fundamental ideas. Only the principal values of the inverse trigonometric functions are to be considered here.

1. $\sin (\tfrac{1}{2} \arccos \tfrac{7}{9}) = ?$

2. $\cos (2 \arctan \tfrac{1}{3}) = ?$

3. $\tan [2 \arcsin (- \tfrac{2}{3})] = ?$

4. $\cos [\tfrac{1}{2} \arccos (- \tfrac{1}{2})] = ?$

5. $\cos (\arcsin \tfrac{2}{3} + \arccos \tfrac{2}{3}) = ?$

6. $\tan (\arcsin \tfrac{3}{5} + \arctan \tfrac{1}{3}) = ?$

7. Show that $\arctan \tfrac{1}{2} + \arctan \tfrac{1}{3} = \dfrac{\pi}{4}.$

8. Show that $2 \arctan \frac{1}{3} + \arctan \frac{1}{7} = \frac{\pi}{4}$.

9. Show that $\arctan \frac{1}{3} + \arctan \frac{1}{5} = \arctan \frac{4}{7}$.

10. Solve for x: $\arctan 2x + \arctan 3x = \frac{\pi}{4}$.

11. Solve for x: $\arcsin 2x + \arcsin x = \frac{\pi}{3}$.

12. Solve for x: $\tan \left(\frac{1}{4}\pi + \arctan x\right) = 5$.

13. What change must be made in the formulas for the derivatives of arcsin x and arccos x if the restriction to the principal branch is removed? Answer the same question for arctan x and arccot x.

14. Show that the slope of $y = \arctan x$ is never more than 1 while that of $y = \arcsin x$ is never less than 1.

15. Sketch the curve $y = \operatorname{arcsec} x$ and derive an expression for its derivative. Why is it desirable to take the part from 0 to $\pi/2$ and $-\pi/2$ to $-\pi$ as the principal branch instead of the part from 0 to π?

16. Solve Prob. 15 for the function $y = \operatorname{arccsc} x$.

Differentiate the following functions:

17. $y = \arccos \frac{1}{2}x$.   **18.** $y = \arcsin 3x$.

19. $y = \arccos \sqrt{x}$.   **20.** $y = \arcsin \frac{x}{a}$.

21. $y = 2 \arctan \frac{1}{2}x$.   **22.** $y = \operatorname{arccot} 2x$.

23. $y = \operatorname{arcsec} x$.   **24.** $y = \operatorname{arccsc} \frac{1}{x}$.

25. $y = \frac{1}{4} \arctan \frac{x}{4} + 6$.   **26.** $y = x \arccos x$.

27. $y = x^2 \arctan x$.   **28.** $y = 4x^2 \arccos x$.

29. $z = \arcsin \frac{1-x}{x}$.   **30.** $s = \arccos \frac{1}{\sqrt{1+x^2}}$.

31. $y = \arctan \frac{x}{\sqrt{1-x^2}}$.   **32.** $y = \arcsin \frac{1-x}{1+x}$.

33. $y = \arctan \frac{x+4}{1-4x}$.   **34.** $y = x\sqrt{1-x^2} + \arcsin x$.

35. $y = \sqrt{a^2 - x^2} + a \arcsin \frac{x}{a}$.

36. $y = \arcsin \frac{1}{2}x + \frac{\sqrt{4-x^2}}{x}$.

37. $y = \sqrt{x^2 - 4} - 2 \arctan \frac{1}{2}\sqrt{x^2 - 4}$.

In each of the following, find d^2y/dx^2:

38. $y = \arcsin \frac{1}{2}x$.   **39.** $y = 4 \arccos 3x$.

40. $y = \arctan 2x$.   **41.** $y = \operatorname{arccot} \frac{1}{2}x$.

42. $y = \arcsin \dfrac{1}{\sqrt{1 + x^2}}.$ **43.** $y = \text{arccot} \dfrac{x}{\sqrt{1 - x^2}}.$

44. Find the inflection point on the curve $y = \arctan x$.

45. Show that the part of $y = \arccos x$ for which $x < 0$ is concave upward while the part for which $x > 0$ is concave downward.

46. Show that $\arcsin x$ increases at the same rate as x when $x = 0$ and more rapidly than x at every other point.

47. The radius of a right circular cone is 2 ft. If the altitude is 4 ft. and is increasing at 3 in. per minute, at what rate is the vertex angle changing?

48. A kite is 90 ft. above the ground with 150 ft. of string out. It is moving horizontally, directly away from the boy who holds the string, at a speed of 15 ft. per second. At what rate is the inclination of the string to the horizontal changing?

49. Find the equation of the line which is tangent to the curve $y = \arctan x$ at the point where $x = 1$.

50. Sketch on the same axes the curves $y = \arctan x$ and $y = \arctan 2x$. Find their angle of intersection.

51. A sign 10 ft. high is erected with its lower edge 13 ft. above the ground. At what distance would a man whose eyes are 5 ft. above the ground obtain the best view, assuming that this is when the angle subtended by the sign at the eye is a maximum? See Fig. 53.

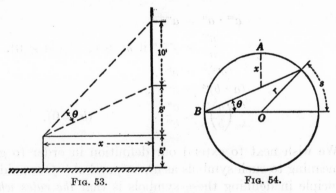

FIG. 53.   FIG. 54.

52. A circular race track is surrounded by a board fence. A man walks from A (Fig. 54) toward the center O at 5 ft. per second. If there is a light at B, at what rate will his shadow be moving along the fence when he is two-thirds of the way from A to O? HINT: Note that

$$s = r \cdot 2\theta \text{ where } \theta = \arctan \frac{r - x}{r}.$$

CHAPTER VIII

THE EXPONENTIAL AND LOGARITHMIC FUNCTIONS

45. Review.—At first we define the symbol a^n for n a *positive integer* only, as follows:

$$a^1 = a$$
$$a^2 = a \cdot a$$
$$a^3 = a \cdot a \cdot a$$
$$a^n = a \cdot a \cdot a \cdots \text{ to } n \text{ factors.}$$

This definition obviously assigns no meaning whatever to a^x if x is not a positive integer.

From the above definition one can easily deduce the following laws that govern the use of exponents:

(1) $$a^m \cdot a^n = a^{m+n}.$$

(2) $$\frac{a^m}{a^n} = a^{m-n} \text{ if } m > n, \qquad (a \neq 0).$$

(3) $$(a^m)^n = a^{mn}.$$

(4) $$(a \cdot b)^m = a^m b^m.$$

(5) $$\left(\frac{a}{b}\right)^m = \frac{a^m}{b^m}, \qquad (b \neq 0).$$

We wish next to extend our definition in order to give a meaning to such symbols as a^0, a^{-2}, and $a^{\frac{1}{2}}$. Our guiding principle in defining these symbols is that *the rules which govern the use of positive integral exponents shall apply in all cases.* Thus, if we wish that

$$a^m \cdot a^0 = a^{m+0} = a^m, \qquad (a \neq 0)$$

we must assign the value *one* to the symbol a^0 if $a \neq 0$. We do not here assign any meaning to the symbol 0^0.

Considering negative exponents next, we wish that

$$a^m \cdot a^{-m} = a^{m-m} = a^0 = 1, \qquad (a \neq 0),$$

Hence, we must agree that $a^{-m} = 1/a^m$.

Similarly, for fractional exponents, if we wish that

$$a^{\frac{1}{2}} \cdot a^{\frac{1}{2}} = a^{\frac{1}{2}+\frac{1}{2}} = a, \qquad (a > 0),$$

we must define the symbol $a^{\frac{1}{2}}$ to stand for a square root of a. To avoid ambiguity we may define it to stand for the *positive* square root. In general, we define the symbol $a^{\frac{1}{q}}$ to stand for the positive qth root of a.* Then of course $a^{\frac{p}{q}}$ stands for the pth power of this root.

We thus assign a definite value to a^x $(a > 0)$ for all *rational* values of x. We shall assume, without attempting to justify the assumption here, that there is also a definite value of a^x if x is irrational. Thus, for example, $5^{\sqrt{2}}$ represents a definite number between $5^{1.41}$ and $5^{1.42}$.

46. The exponential function $y = a^x$, $(a > 1)$.—The definitions just discussed, together with the assumption concerning irrational exponents, give a definite value to a^x for every real value of x; *i.e.*, the function

$$y = a^x$$

is a single-valued function, defined for all values of x. It is a continuous function and its graph (if $a > 1$) has the

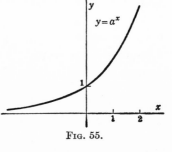

FIG. 55.

general form shown in Fig. 55. It is evident from the graph that its derivative is everywhere positive and increases with increasing values of x. We shall shortly attempt to compute its derivative.

---

* If $a > 0$. For $a < 0$, $a^{\frac{1}{q}}$ is undefined in the domain of real numbers if q is even and is negative if q is odd.

47. The logarithmic function $y = \log_a x$, $(a > 1)$.—The logarithmic function is defined as the inverse of the exponential function; *i.e.*, if

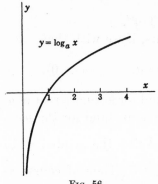

$$a^y = x,$$
then
$$y = \log_a x.$$

It is evident that the graph of this function (Fig. 56) is the same as that of $y = a^x$ with the axes interchanged. The function is defined only for positive values of x,* is single-valued and continuous, and is everywhere

FIG. 56.

increasing. Before trying to compute its derivative, we must next introduce an important limit which will arise in that process.

48. The number *e*.—Consider the function

$$(1 + v)^{\frac{1}{v}}$$

and think of v becoming smaller and smaller (in absolute value) approaching zero. Evidently the exponent becomes numerically larger and larger while simultaneously the quantity $(1 + v)$ approaches 1. What happens to the value of the function? The following table gives a partial answer.

Value of v	0.5	0.1	0.01	0.001
Value of $(1 + v)^{\frac{1}{v}}$	2.25	2.5937	2.7048	2.7169
Value of v	−0.5	−0.1	−0.01	−0.001
Value of $(1 + v)^{\frac{1}{v}}$	4.00	2.8680	2.7320	2.7196

* In the domain of real numbers.

It appears probable from this table that, although the function $(1 + v)^{\frac{1}{v}}$ has no value when v *equals* 0, its limit as v *approaches* 0 may exist; *i.e.*, there probably is some constant in the neighborhood of 2.7 to which the values of $(1 + v)^{\frac{1}{v}}$ are arbitrarily near for all values of v which are sufficiently near to 0 but $\neq 0$.

Assuming this limit to exist, we may try to compute it as follows: Let v approach zero by taking the values indicated by the sequence,

$$1, \tfrac{1}{2}, \tfrac{1}{3}, \tfrac{1}{4}, \tfrac{1}{5}, \cdots .$$

For each of these values of v, the exponent $1/v$ is an integer. Using the binomial theorem, we have, for any such value of v,

$$(1 + v)^{\frac{1}{v}} = 1 + \frac{1}{v} v + \frac{\frac{1}{v}\left(\frac{1}{v} - 1\right)}{2!} v^2$$

$$+ \frac{\frac{1}{v}\left(\frac{1}{v} - 1\right)\left(\frac{1}{v} - 2\right)}{3!} v^3 + \cdots + v^{\frac{1}{v}}.$$

$$= 1 + 1 + \frac{1 - v}{2!} + \frac{(1 - v)(1 - 2v)}{3!}$$

$$+ \cdots + v^{\frac{1}{v}}.$$

If v is allowed to approach zero through the sequence of values indicated above, this expansion is valid for each value of v; the number of terms in it increases indefinitely as $v \rightarrow 0$. This suggests that the required limit *may* be approximated to any desired degree of accuracy by setting $v = 0$ in the expansion and taking a sufficiently large number of terms of the resulting *infinite series*. This conclusion is valid although no rigorous justification of it can be given at this point. Denoting the value of the limit by e, we have

$$\lim_{v \rightarrow 0} (1 + v)^{\frac{1}{v}} = e = 1 + 1 + \frac{1}{2!} + \frac{1}{3!} + \frac{1}{4!} + \frac{1}{5!} + \cdots$$

$$= 2.718 + .$$

The corresponding functions $y = e^x$ and $y = \log_e x$ are, of course, special cases of the functions $y = a^x$ and $y = \log_a x$, respectively. It will be found that these functions play a particularly important role in many applications of the calculus.

Logarithms to the base e are called *natural logarithms*. For a reason that will appear presently they will be used almost exclusively in our work. We accordingly adopt the following notation:

log x (base omitted) *will always mean* **log$_e$ x.**

The *common logarithm* of x, which will rarely be encountered, will always be written $\log_{10} x$.

The general formula for change of base, namely,

$$\log_b N = \log_a N \cdot \log_b a$$

furnishes the following relation between the natural and common logarithms of x:

$$\log_e x = \log_{10} x \cdot \log_e 10.$$

Using the fact that $\log_e 10 = 2.30259$ and denoting $\log_e x$ by $\log x$, we may write this in the form

log x = 2.30259 log$_{10}$ x.

This relation enables one to compute the natural logarithm of a number from its common logarithm. There are, however, tables (such as Table IV in this book) that give the natural logarithms directly.

The fundamental properties of logarithms are expressed by the equations:

$$\log_a (xy) = \log_a x + \log_a y.$$
$$\log_a \frac{x}{y} = \log_a x - \log_a y.$$
$$\log_a x^p = p \log_a x.$$
$$a^{\log_a x} = x.$$

The last of these follows immediately from the fact that $\log_a x$ is the exponent of the power to which a must be raised to obtain x; if a is raised to the power to which it must be raised to obtain x, the result will be x.

PROBLEMS

1. (a) Show that $a^m \cdot a^n = a^{m+n}$ if m and n are positive integers.

(b) Show that $(a^m)^n = a^{mn}$ if m and n are positive integers.

(c) Show that $(a \cdot b)^n = a^n \cdot b^n$ if n is a positive integer.

2. (a) Show that $\log_a (xy) = \log_a x + \log_a y$.

(b) Show that $\log_a \dfrac{x}{y} = \log_a x - \log_a y$.

(c) Show that $\log_a x^p = p \log_a x$.

3. Prove the formula $\log_b N = \log_a N \cdot \log_b a$. HINT: Let $\log_a N = x$; then $N = a^x$. Take logarithms of both sides to the base b.

4. Show that $\log_b a = 1/\log_a b$. HINT: Let $\log_b a = x$; then $a = b^x$. Take logarithms of both sides to the base a.

5. Calculate $\log_{16} 1840$.

6. Find $\log 654$ (*natural logarithm*), using a table of common logarithms. Check by referring to a table of natural logarithms.

7. If $\log N = 6.4825$, find N. If $\log M = 7.3462 - 10$, find M. These are *natural logarithms*.

8. Explain why the following are true: $e^{\frac{1}{2} \log 64} = 8$; $e^{-\frac{1}{2} \log x} = \dfrac{1}{\sqrt{x}}$; $e^{2 \log x} = x^2$.

9. Show that the equation $y = A \cdot b^{rx}$ is equivalent to $y = Ae^{r'x}$ where $r' = r \log b$. Change the equation $y = 4(10)^{1.54x}$ into the form $y = 4e^{kx}$.

10. Draw on the same axes the graphs of the equations $y = 2^x$, $y = (1.5)^x$, and $y = (0.5)^x$.

11. Draw the graph of the equation $y = 2^x + 2^{-x}$.

12. Draw on the same axes the graphs of the equations $y = e^{-x}$ and $y = e^{-x^2}$.

13. Sketch the curve whose equation is $y = 2^{x-1}$. Show that this equation is equivalent to $y = \frac{1}{2}(2^x)$.

Sketch the graphs of the following equations:

14. $y = \dfrac{x}{2} + \dfrac{1}{2^x}$.   **15.** $y = \frac{1}{3}x + (\frac{2}{3})^x$.   **16.** $y = 2^x - x^2$.

17. $y = \log \sqrt{x}$.   **18.** $y = \log (x - 2)$.   **19.** $y = \log_2 (x + 1)$.

20. Show that the graph of $y = \log_a (kx)$ $(k > 0)$ is simply that of $y = \log_a x$ translated in the y-direction by an amount $\log_a k$.

49. The derivative of $\log_a v$.—To find the derivative of the function

$$y = \log_a x$$

we apply the fundamental differentiation process.   Starting at any point P (Fig. 57) and letting x increase by an amount Δx we have

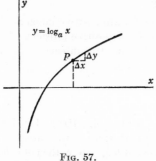

FIG. 57.

$$\Delta y = \log_a (x + \Delta x) - \log_a (x)$$

$$= \log_a \frac{x + \Delta x}{x}$$

$$= \log_a \left(1 + \frac{\Delta x}{x}\right).$$

$$\frac{\Delta y}{\Delta x} = \frac{1}{\Delta x} \log_a \left(1 + \frac{\Delta x}{x}\right).$$

We cannot easily see what happens to the value of this fraction when $\Delta x \to 0$.   However, multiplying numerator and denominator by x, it may be written in the form

$$\frac{\Delta y}{\Delta x} = \frac{1}{x} \frac{x}{\Delta x} \log_a \left(1 + \frac{\Delta x}{x}\right)$$

$$= \frac{1}{x} \log_a \left(1 + \frac{\Delta x}{x}\right)^{\frac{x}{\Delta x}}.$$

If now $\Delta x \to 0$, the quantity $\left(1 + \frac{\Delta x}{x}\right)^{\frac{x}{\Delta x}}$ approaches as a limit the number e because it is of the form $(1 + v)^{\frac{1}{v}}$ with v approaching zero.   We have then

$$\frac{dy}{dx} = \frac{1}{x} \lim_{\Delta x \to 0} \log_a \left(1 + \frac{\Delta x}{x}\right)^{\frac{x}{\Delta x}}$$

$$= \frac{1}{x} \log_a e.$$

Finally, if we consider the function $y = \log_a v$ where v is a differentiable function of x, its derivative *with respect to v* is $\frac{1}{v} \log_a e$ by virtue of the above result.   In order to obtain its derivative with respect to x we must multiply this result by dv/dx.   That is,

(XIX) $$\frac{d}{dx} \log_a v = \frac{1}{v} \log_a e \frac{dv}{dx}.$$

For the special case of *natural* logarithms this becomes

(XIXs) $$\frac{d}{dx} \log v = \frac{1}{v}\frac{dv}{dx}.$$

Example 1

$y = \log (x^3 + 4)$.

$$\frac{dy}{dx} = \frac{1}{x^3 + 4}\frac{d}{dx}(x^3 + 4) \qquad \text{[by (XIXs)]}$$

$$= \frac{3x^2}{x^3 + 4}.$$

Example 2

$y = \log_{10} \sin x$.

$$\frac{dy}{dx} = \frac{1}{\sin x} \log_{10} e \frac{d}{dx}(\sin x) \qquad \text{[by (XIX)]}$$

$$= (\log_{10} e) \cot x.$$

It is in order to avoid the cumbersome factor $\log_{10} e$ ($= 0.43429$) that we use natural instead of common logarithms in the calculus.   Thus, while

$$\frac{d}{dx} \log x = \frac{1}{x},$$

we have

$$\frac{d}{dx} \log_{10} x = \frac{1}{x} \cdot \log_{10} e = (0.43429)\frac{1}{x}.$$

Common logarithms are convenient for computational purposes because of the simple rules concerning characteristic and mantissa.   When operations of calculus are involved, natural logarithms are preferable.   Some writers use the symbol *ln x* to denote the natural logarithm of x. In this notation formula XIXs becomes

$$\frac{d}{dx} \ln v = \frac{1}{v}\frac{dv}{dx}.$$

As indicated above, we shall use log x in this text, but the student may adopt the symbol ln x if he wishes.

50. The derivative of a^v.—The derivative of this function is obtained easily from that of $\log_a v$ as follows: If

$$y = a^v$$

then

$$v = \log_a y,$$

and

$$\frac{dv}{dy} = \frac{1}{y} \log_a e \qquad \text{[by (XIX)]}.$$

Then, using formula (VIII),

$$\frac{dy}{dv} = y \frac{1}{\log_a e}$$
$$= y \log_e a$$
$$= a^v \log_e a.$$

Finally, if v is a differentiable function of x we have the formula,

(**XX**) $$\frac{d}{dx} a^v = a^v \log a \frac{dv}{dx}.$$

If the constant is the particular number e, the formula becomes

(**XXs**) $$\frac{d}{dx} e^v = e^v \frac{dv}{dx}.$$

Example 1

$$y = e^{-x^2}$$
$$\frac{dy}{dx} = e^{-x^2} \frac{d}{dx} (-x^2) \qquad \text{[by (XXs)]}$$
$$= -2xe^{-x^2}.$$

Example 2

$$y = 4^{3x-5}.$$
$$\frac{dy}{dx} = 4^{3x-5} \log 4 \frac{d}{dx} (3x - 5) \qquad \text{[by (XX)]}$$
$$= 4^{3x-5}(3 \log 4).$$

Example 3

$y = e^{-x} \log x$.

$$\frac{dy}{dx} = e^{-x} \frac{d}{dx} \log x + \log x \frac{d}{dx} e^{-x}$$

$$= e^{-x} \frac{1}{x} + (\log x)e^{-x}(-1)$$

$$= e^{-x} \left(\frac{1}{x} - \log x \right).$$

PROBLEMS

1. Write the equation of the line that is normal to the curve $y = \log x$ at the point where the curve crosses the x-axis.

2. Show that when $x = 10$, $\log x$ is increasing at a rate of 0.1 of a unit per unit of increase in x.

3. A quantity Q varies with the time t according to the law $Q = Ae^{kt}$. Show that the rate at which Q is changing at any instant is proportional to the value of Q at that instant.

4. If $Q = 4.84e^{0.2t}$ find the value of dQ/dt when $t = 6$. (Find the value of $e^{1.2}$ from Table V.)

Differentiate the following functions:

5. $y = 4 \log x^2$.   **6.** $y = \log_{10} \sec \theta$.   **7.** $y = \log \sin x$.

8. $y = 2 \sec^2 x + \log \cos x$.   **9.** $y = x^2 \log x$.

10. $y = x \log x - x + 4$.   **11.** $y = \log \csc^2 x$.

12. $y = \log \tan^2 2\theta$.   **13.** $y = \log_2 (x^2 + 6)$.

14. $y = \log_{10} 4x^3$.   **15.** $y = \frac{1}{2} \log (3x^2 - 5)$.

16. $y = \log \sqrt{1 - 4x^2}$.   **17.** $y = 4 \log^2 (3x)$.

18. $y = \log (x \sqrt{3 + 2x})$.   **19.** $y = \log (\log x)$.

20. $y = \log (\sec \theta + \tan \theta)$.   **21.** $y = \log (x + \sqrt{x^2 + a^2})$.

22. $y = x^2 \log \sqrt{x^2 - 5}$.   **23.** $y = \log \dfrac{x^2}{x^2 + 1}$.

24. $y = \log \dfrac{x^2 + a^2}{x^2 - a^2}$.

Differentiate the following functions using the method suggested in the hint in Prob. 25:

25. $y = \log (x \sqrt{x^2 - 4})$.   HINT: First write the equation in the form $y = \log x + \frac{1}{2} \log (x^2 - 4)$.

26. $y = \log \sqrt{\dfrac{4 + x^2}{4 - x^2}}$.   **27.** $y = \log \sqrt{\dfrac{1 + \sin x}{1 - \sin x}}$.

28. $y = \log (x^2 \sqrt{x^2 + 1})$.   **29.** $y = \log [x^3(3x^2 + 4)^{\frac{2}{3}}]$.

30. Show that if $y = \sec x \tan x + \log (\sec x + \tan x)$ then

$$D_x y = 2 \sec^3 x.$$

31. Show that the curve whose equation is $y = x \log x$ is everywhere concave upward. Locate its minimum point, and sketch the curve.

Differentiate the following functions:

32. $y = 7e^{-3x}$.   **33.** $y = 4e^{-\frac{1}{2}x^2}$.   **34.** $y = x^2 \cdot 2^x$.

35. $y = 3^{-x} + x^{-3}$.   **36.** $y = 4xe^{-x}$.   **37.** $y = x^2 e^{-x^2}$.

38. $y = \dfrac{e^x}{x}$.   **39.** $y = \dfrac{1}{x} e^{\frac{1}{x}}$.   **40.** $y = \dfrac{a}{2} [e^{\frac{x}{a}} + e^{-\frac{x}{a}}]$.

41. $y = e^{-x} \log x$.   **42.** $y = \frac{1}{2} e^{-2x} \cos 2x$.

43. $y = 4e^{\frac{1}{2}x} \sin \frac{1}{2}x$.

In each of the following, find $D_x^2 y$:

44. $y = x^2 \log x$.   **45.** $y = x (\log x)^2$.

46. $y = x^2 e^{-x}$.   **47.** $y = 4xe^{-x^2}$.

48. $y = e^{-x} \sin x$.   **49.** $y = \dfrac{\log x}{x}$.

50. Show that if $y = e^x \cos 2x$ then $\dfrac{d^2y}{dx^2} - 2 \dfrac{dy}{dx} + 5y = 0$.

51. Show that if $s = e^{3t} \sin 2t$ then $\dfrac{d^2s}{dt^2} - 6 \dfrac{ds}{dt} + 13s = 0$.

52. Show that if $y = Ae^{2x} + Bxe^{2x}$, where A and B are any constants, then $\dfrac{d^2y}{dx^2} - 4 \dfrac{dy}{dx} + 4y = 0$.

53. For what value or values of m does the relation $x = Ae^{mt}$ satisfy the differential equation $\dfrac{d^2x}{dt^2} + \dfrac{dx}{dt} = 6x$?

54. Find the angle of intersection of the curves $y = \log x$ and

$$y = \log x^2.$$

In each of the following, locate the maximum, minimum, and inflection points on the curve whose equation is given, and sketch the curve:

55. $y = 2xe^x$.   **56.** $y = 3xe^{-\frac{1}{2}x}$.

57. $y = xe^{-x^2}$.   **58.** $y = x^2 e^{-x}$.

59. $y = 2e^{-\frac{1}{2}x^2}$.   **60.** $y = x^2 e^{-\frac{1}{2}x^2}$.

61. $y = x^2 \log x$.   **62.** $y = x (\log x)^2$.

63. $y = e^{-\frac{1}{2}x} + \frac{1}{2}x - 1$.   **64.** $y = \frac{1}{4}x^2(2 \log x - 3)$.

65. $y = e^x - ex$.   **66.** $y = e^{-x} \cos x; 0 \leqq x \leqq 2\pi$.

67. $y = e^{-\frac{\pi x}{2}} \sin \dfrac{\pi x}{2}; 0 \leqq x \leqq 4$.

51. Logarithmic differentiation.

—If a function which is to be differentiated is a product of several factors, the work may be materially simplified by taking the natural logarithm of the function *before* differentiating.

Example

Differentiate $y = \dfrac{x\sqrt{4x + 3}}{(3x + 1)^2}$.

Solution

Taking the natural logarithm of each side of the given equation, we may write

$$\log y = \log x + \tfrac{1}{2}\log (4x + 3) - 2\log (3x + 1).$$

Then using implicit differentiation we have

$$\frac{1}{y}\frac{dy}{dx} = \frac{1}{x} + \frac{2}{4x + 3} - \frac{6}{3x + 1};$$

$$\frac{dy}{dx} = y\left(\frac{1}{x} + \frac{2}{4x + 3} - \frac{6}{3x + 1}\right).$$

52. The derivative of u^v.—The derivative of a function of the form

$$y = u^v,$$

where u and v are both differentiable functions of x, can be found by the method of logarithmic differentiation.

Example

Differentiate $y = (x + 1)^x$.

Solution

Taking the natural logarithm of each side we have

$$\log y = x \log (x + 1).$$

Differentiating this relation implicitly with respect to x, we find

$$\frac{1}{y}\frac{dy}{dx} = x \cdot \frac{1}{x + 1} + \log (x + 1);$$

$$\frac{dy}{dx} = y\left[\frac{x}{x + 1} + \log (x + 1)\right].$$

The student should notice that neither the formula for the derivative of v^n nor that for the derivative of a^v applies to functions of this type.   Why?

53. The derivative of v^n for any value of n.—In Chap. IV the proof of the formula for the derivative of v^n was given only for n a positive integer.   The proof for *any* value of n

may now be given as follows.   Let

$$y = v^n;$$
$$\log y = n \log v$$
$$\frac{1}{y}\frac{dy}{dx} = n\frac{1}{v}\frac{dv}{dx}$$
$$\frac{dy}{dx} = \frac{ny}{v}\frac{dv}{dx}.$$

But, since

$$y = v^n,$$

this reduces to

$$\frac{dy}{dx} = nv^{n-1}\frac{dv}{dx}.$$

PROBLEMS

Find the derivative of each of the following functions using logarithmic differentiation

1. $y = x^2\sqrt{x^2+3}.$

2. $y = x\sqrt{2x+3}\sqrt{x+1}.$

3. $y = x^{\frac{1}{2}}\sqrt[3]{6x+4}.$

4. $y = x^2\sqrt[3]{x^2+4}\sqrt{x^2-4}.$

5. $y = \sqrt{\dfrac{(x+1)(2x+3)}{x}}.$

6. $y = \dfrac{x^2\sqrt{x^2+4}}{\sqrt[3]{3x+1}}.$

7. $y = \sqrt{\dfrac{(x+5)(4x+3)}{(x^2+1)(2x+1)}}.$

8. $y = \dfrac{x^2\sqrt[3]{4x+1}}{\sqrt{2x+5}}.$

9. $y = \dfrac{x\sqrt{x^2-a^2}}{\sqrt{x^2+a^2}}.$

10. $y = \dfrac{4x^2}{\sqrt{x^2+1}\sqrt{x^2+4}}.$

11. $y = x^x.$

12. $y = x^{\sqrt{x}}.$

13. $y = x^{\log x}.$

14. $y = (\log x)^x.$

15. $y = \left(\dfrac{2}{x}\right)^x.$

16. $y = x^{\sin x}.$

17. Using logarithmic differentiation, show that the derivative of u^v is given by the formula

$$\frac{d}{dx}u^v = vu^{v-1}\frac{du}{dx} + u^v\log u\frac{dv}{dx}.$$

Note that this amounts to differentiating the function as if v were constant and then as if u were constant and adding the results.

18. Find the derivative of x^x both with and without using the formula of Prob. 17, and show that the results are the same.

19. Find the derivative of $(\log x)^x$ both with and without using the formula of Prob. 17, and show that the results are the same.

CHAPTER IX

DERIVATIVE OF ARC. CURVATURE

54. Smooth curves.—Suppose that a given curve has, at every point of a certain interval, a tangent line; suppose furthermore that the tangent line turns continuously as it traverses the curve. The curve is then said to be *smooth* in the interval. Throughout this chapter it will be assumed that the curves under discussion have this property of smoothness.

55. Derivative of arc.—Think of a point P moving along the smooth curve whose equation is $y = f(x)$. Denote by s the length of arc measured from an arbitrarily chosen fixed point A, to P. We wish to determine the rate at which this length s is changing with respect to x; *i.e.*, we wish to find the rate, measured with respect to x, at which the arc itself is being traced when the moving point is at any position $P(x, y)$ on the curve.

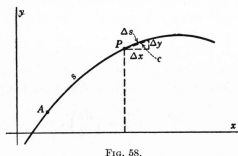

Fig. 58.

We may denote by Δs the distance, measured along the arc, which the point P must traverse in order that its abscissa may increase by a small amount Δx. The required rate is then given by

$$\lim_{\Delta x \to 0} \frac{\Delta s}{\Delta x} = \frac{ds}{dx}.$$

In order to compute this limit we observe that (Fig. 58),

$$\frac{\Delta s}{\Delta x} = \frac{\Delta s}{c} \frac{c}{\Delta x}.$$

From the figure it is evident that $c^2 = (\Delta x)^2 + (\Delta y)^2$; hence,

$$\frac{\Delta s}{\Delta x} = \frac{\Delta s}{c} \frac{\sqrt{(\Delta x)^2 + (\Delta y)^2}}{\Delta x}$$

$$= \frac{\Delta s}{c} \sqrt{1 + \left(\frac{\Delta y}{\Delta x}\right)^2}.$$

It is fairly obvious that as $\Delta x \to 0$, the quotient $\Delta s/c$ approaches 1 as a limit. This can be proved but we shall not give the proof here. We have then

$$\lim_{\Delta x \to 0} \frac{\Delta s}{\Delta x} = \lim_{\Delta x \to 0} \frac{\Delta s}{c} \cdot \lim_{\Delta x \to 0} \sqrt{1 + \left(\frac{\Delta y}{\Delta x}\right)^2},$$

or

(**XXI**) $$\frac{ds}{dx} = \sqrt{1 + \left(\frac{dy}{dx}\right)^2}.^*$$

This expression gives the rate at which the *arc* is lengthening with respect to x in the same way that the value of dy/dx gives the rate at which the *ordinate* is increasing or decreasing relative to x. It is of course measured in units such as inches per inch; *i.e.*, in inches moved along the arc per inch moved in the direction of the x-axis.

The student may easily show that a corresponding expression for the derivative *with respect to y* of the length of arc is

$$\frac{ds}{dy} = \sqrt{1 + \left(\frac{dx}{dy}\right)^2}.$$

Example

Find ds/dx for the circle $x^2 + y^2 = 25$. If a point moves along the arc from $(0, 5)$ to $(5, 0)$ in such a way that its abscissa increases uniformly at 2 units per minute, at what rate is the arc being traced when it passes through $(3, 4)$?

---

* The choice of the positive sign for the radical amounts to designating the positive direction on the arc as that in which x is increasing.

Solution

$$x^2 + y^2 = 25.$$

$$\frac{dy}{dx} = -\frac{x}{y}.$$

$$\frac{ds}{dx} = \sqrt{1 + \frac{x^2}{y^2}} = \frac{\sqrt{y^2 + x^2}}{y} = \frac{5}{y}.$$

The value of ds/dx at the point $(3, 4)$ is

$$\frac{ds}{dx}\bigg]_{3,4} = \frac{5}{4}.$$

This means that the arc is being traced $\frac{5}{4}$ times as fast as the abscissa is changing, or at a rate of $2\frac{1}{2}$ units per minute. This is of course the speed of the moving point at this instant.

PROBLEMS

1. Show that $ds/dy = \sqrt{1 + (dx/dy)^2}$.

2. Show that when a point, in moving along a curve, passes through a maximum or minimum point where $dy/dx = 0$, the arc is increasing at the same rate as x. Does this fact appear obvious from the graph?

3. In deriving the formula for ds/dx, only the positive sign was used before the radical. Under what condition should the negative sign be used? HINT: If A (Fig. 58) is to the right of P then s decreases as x increases.

Evaluate ds/dx at the given point for each of the following curves and explain the meaning of the result:

4. $y = x^2$; $x = 2$.
5. $y = x^{\frac{3}{2}}$; $x = 5$.
6. $y = \sin x$; $x = \frac{1}{3}\pi$.
7. $y = \log x$; $x = 1$.
8. $y = \arcsin x$; $x = 0$.
9. $x^2 - y^2 = 7$; $(4, 3)$.
10. $x^2 + 4y^2 = 4$; $(\sqrt{3}, \frac{1}{2})$.
11. $x^2 + y^2 = 10x$; $(2, 4)$.
12. $y = \dfrac{1}{x^2 + 1}$; $(1, \frac{1}{2})$.
13. $y = \dfrac{4x}{x^2 + 1}$; $(1, 2)$.

14. A point moves along the curve $x^2 - 4y^2 = 5$. What is its speed when it passes through $(3, 1)$ if its abscissa is increasing at 8 units per minute?

15. For what points on a curve is $ds/dx = ds/dy$?

16. Show that if θ is the inclination of the tangent line to a curve at P, then $|\cos \theta| = dx/ds$ while $|\sin \theta| = dy/ds$.

17. Show that for the catenary $y = \dfrac{e^x + e^{-x}}{2}$, the value of ds/dx at any point is equal to y.

56. Curvature of a circle.—In Fig. 59 the tangent line to the circle at P makes an angle θ with the x-axis.   In

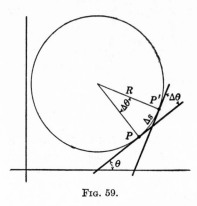

moving to the position P' it turns through an angle $\Delta\theta$.   The amount of turning *per unit distance moved along the arc* is obviously

$$\frac{\Delta\theta}{\Delta s} = \frac{\Delta\theta}{R\,\Delta\theta} = \frac{1}{R}.$$

This is called the *curvature* of the circular arc.   Thus the curvature of a circle whose radius is 4 ft. is

FIG. 59.

$$K = \frac{1}{R} = \frac{1}{4} \text{ radian per foot.}$$

This means of course that the tangent line, in traversing the circle, turns at a rate of $\frac{1}{4}$ radian per foot moved along the arc.

57. Curvature of any curve.—Consider now any smooth curve.   A tangent line traversing it turns at a *variable* rate,

with respect to the distance moved along the arc, instead of at a constant rate as it obviously does in the case of the circle.   The value of this rate at any point P on the curve is called the *curvature* of the arc at P.

In order to compute this rate we first observe from

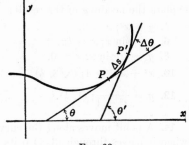

FIG. 60.

Fig. 60 that the average curvature of the arc from P to a neighboring point P' is expressed by the fraction

$$\frac{\Delta\theta}{\Delta s}$$

where $\Delta\theta = \theta' - \theta$ is the angle turned through by the tangent line moving from P to P', and Δs is the corresponding length of arc. It is natural that we should define the curvature at P as the *limit* approached by this fraction as $\Delta s \to 0$; *i.e.*,

$$K = \lim_{\Delta s \to 0} \frac{\Delta \theta}{\Delta s} = \frac{d\theta}{ds}.$$

To obtain an expression for the curvature in terms of dy/dx and d^2y/dx^2 we need only to notice from the figure that the value of dy/dx at P is equal to $\tan \theta$; hence,

$$\theta = \arctan \frac{dy}{dx}.$$

Differentiating carefully *with respect to s* we find

$$\begin{aligned}
\frac{d\theta}{ds} &= \frac{d\theta}{dx} \cdot \frac{dx}{ds} \\
&= \frac{d}{dx}\left(\arctan \frac{dy}{dx}\right) \cdot \frac{dx}{ds} \\
&= \frac{\dfrac{d}{dx}\left(\dfrac{dy}{dx}\right)}{1 + \left(\dfrac{dy}{dx}\right)^2} \cdot \frac{dx}{ds} \\
&= \frac{\dfrac{d^2y}{dx^2}}{1 + \left(\dfrac{dy}{dx}\right)^2} \cdot \frac{dx}{ds}.
\end{aligned}$$

Since

$$\frac{dx}{ds} = \frac{1}{\dfrac{ds}{dx}} = \frac{1}{\sqrt{1 + \left(\dfrac{dy}{dx}\right)^2}},$$

this reduces to

(**XXII**) $$\frac{d\theta}{ds} = K = \frac{\dfrac{d^2y}{dx^2}}{\left[1 + \left(\dfrac{dy}{dx}\right)^2\right]^{\frac{3}{2}}}.$$

Example

Find the curvature of the cubical parabola $y = x^3$ at $(1, 1)$.

Solution

$$\frac{dy}{dx} = 3x^2 \qquad \frac{dy}{dx}\bigg]_{1,1} = 3.$$

$$\frac{d^2y}{dx^2} = 6x \qquad \frac{d^2y}{dx^2}\bigg]_{1,1} = 6.$$

$$K = \frac{6}{(1+3^2)^{\frac{3}{2}}} = \frac{6\sqrt{10}}{100} = 0.1897.$$

It should be observed that the sign of K, as determined by (XXII), is positive if D_x^2y is positive and negative if D_x^2y is negative. It is customary, however, to regard the curvature as being given by the *absolute value* of K so that it is always positive.

58. Transition curves.—The curvature of a curve at a point P, being the rate at which the tangent line is turning with respect to the distance moved along the arc, obviously measures the rate at which a particle traversing the curve is changing its direction. Suppose now that in laying out a railroad curve one joined the straight track directly to a circular arc of radius R (in feet) as indicated in Fig. 61.

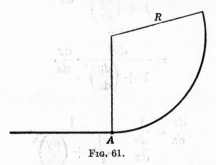

Fig. 61.

The curvature would of course change suddenly from 0 to $1/R$ radians per foot at the junction A. When a train was passing this point there would be brought into play certain suddenly applied radial forces which would result in undesirable stresses as well as disagreeable lurching, etc.

It is much more desirable to have the straight track joined to the circular arc by a section AB (Fig. 62) whose curvature increases gradually from 0 at A to $1/R$ at B. Such a curve is called a *transition* or easement curve. The cubical parabola has often been used as a transition curve although it appears to have no property which makes it

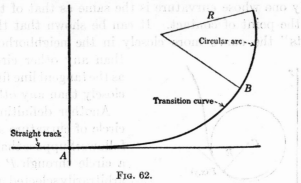

Circular arc

R

B

Transition curve

Straight track

A

FIG. 62.

particularly desirable for this purpose other than the fact that its equation is simple. Probably the best curve for the purpose is one whose curvature increases linearly with the distance s measured along the curve from A to B. Such a curve is called a transition spiral. Its equation cannot be expressed in simple form but methods of laying out the curve, with sufficient accuracy for practical purposes, are given in books on railway surveying.*

59. Radius of curvature.—We have seen that the radius of a circle is equal to the reciprocal of its curvature. By analogy we may define the *radius of curvature* of any curve at a point P as the reciprocal of its curvature at this point. This radius, which is usually regarded as positive, is of course given by

(XXIII) $$R = \frac{\left[1 + \left(\dfrac{dy}{dx}\right)^2\right]^{\frac{3}{2}}}{\left|\dfrac{d^2y}{dx^2}\right|}.$$

---

* See, for example, A. N. Talbot, "The Railway Transition Spiral," McGraw-Hill Book Company, Inc., New York, 1927.

By measuring off along the normal to the curve at P, on the concave side, a distance R as determined by (XXIII), one can locate a point C called the *center of curvature*. The circle with center at C and radius R is called the *circle of curvature*. Of the indefinitely large number of circles that can be drawn tangent to the curve at P, this is the only one whose curvature is the same as that of the curve at the point of contact. It can be shown that this circle "fits" the curve more closely in the neighborhood of P than any other circle—just as the tangent line fits it more closely than any other line.

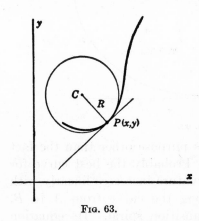

Fig. 63.

Another definition of the circle of curvature at P is as follows: Suppose that we pass a circle through P and two arbitrarily selected neighboring points P' and P'' on the curve. The limiting position of this circle as P' and P'' both approach P along the curve can be shown to be identical with that of the circle of curvature as defined above. This definition of the circle suggests an approximate method of constructing it graphically.

Another formula for R, which is equivalent to (XXIII), and which may be used in case it is more convenient to take derivatives with respect to y, is

(XXIV)
$$R = \frac{\left[1 + \left(\dfrac{dx}{dy}\right)^2\right]^{\frac{3}{2}}}{\left|\dfrac{d^2x}{dy^2}\right|}.$$

This formula should also be used in finding R at a point where the tangent line to the curve is parallel to the y-axis; for at such a point $dx/dy = 0$.

Example

Compute R at $(a, 0)$ on the ellipse $b^2x^2 + a^2y^2 = a^2b^2$.

Solution

Differentiating implicitly *with respect to y*, we have

$$2b^2x \frac{dx}{dy} + 2a^2y = 0$$

$$\frac{dx}{dy} = -\frac{a^2y}{b^2x}; \quad \frac{dx}{dy}\bigg]_{a,0} = 0.$$

$$\frac{d^2x}{dy^2} = \left(-\frac{a^2}{b^2}\right)\left(\frac{x - y\dfrac{dx}{dy}}{x^2}\right); \quad \frac{d^2x}{dy^2}\bigg]_{a,0} = -\frac{a}{b^2}.$$

$$R = \frac{(1 + 0)^{\frac{3}{2}}}{\dfrac{a}{b^2}} = \frac{b^2}{a}.$$

PROBLEMS

1. What is the curvature in radians per foot and in degrees per foot of a circular arc whose radius is 100 ft.?

2. At what rate, in degrees per 100 ft. of arc, is a train changing its direction when it is running on a circular curve of radius 500 ft.? NOTE: This rate is called by surveyors the *degree-of-curve*. Thus at 5° the curve is one whose curvature is 5° per 100 ft.

Compute K and R for each of the following curves at the point indicated:

3. $y = x^2 - 1$; $(1, 0)$.   **4.** $y = x^2 - 4x - 5$; $(2, -9)$.

5. $y = 3x^2 - x^3$; $(1, 2)$.   **6.** $y = x^2(x^2 - 4)$; $(2, 0)$.

7. $y = x^3 - 5x^2 + 12$; $(3, -6)$.   **8.** $b^2x^2 - a^2y^2 = a^2b^2$; $(a, 0)$.

9. $9x^2 + 4y^2 = 36x$; $(2, 3)$.   **10.** $x^2 + y^2 + 4x + 6y = 0$; $(0, 0)$.

11. $4x^2 - y^2 = 20$; $(3, 4)$ **12.** $x^4 + y^4 = 32$; $(2, 2)$.

13. $y = 2 \cos x$; $(0, 2.)$ **14.** $y = \sin^2 x$; $\left(\frac{\pi}{4}, \frac{1}{2}\right)$.

15. $y = \log x$; $(x = \frac{1}{2})$.   **16.** $y = \log \sec x$; $\left(x = \frac{\pi}{3}\right)$.

17. $y = e^{-x^2}$; $(0, 1)$.   **18.** $y = xe^{-x}$ $(0, 0)$.

19. Sketch the curve whose equation is $y = 12x - x^3$. Locate its maximum point and find the curvature at this point.

In each of the following, sketch the curve and locate its minimum point. Compute the curvature of the curve at this point:

20. $3y = x^3 - 6x^2$.   **21.** $y = e^{\frac{1}{2}x} + e^{-\frac{1}{2}x}$.

22. $y = x \log x$.   **23.** $y = x^2e^{-x}$.

24. $y = \sin^3 x; 0 \leqq x \leqq 2\pi$.

25. $y = \cos x + \frac{1}{2} \sin 2x; 0 \leqq x \leqq 2\pi$.

26. Express the curvature of the curve $y = \log x$ as a function of x. For what value of x is $|K|$ a maximum, and what is this maximum value?

27. Show that the absolute value of the curvature of the curve $y = f(x)$ at a point $P(x, y)$ is equal to $\left| \dfrac{d^2 y}{dx^2} \cos^3 \theta \right|$ where θ is the inclination of the tangent line to the curve at P.

28. Derive expressions for the coordinates α and β of the center of curvature of $y = f(x)$ at $P(x, y)$ in terms of x, y, dy/dx and d^2y/dx^2.

29. Find the coordinates of the center of curvature of the curve $y = \log x$ at $(1, 0)$.

30. Derive formula (XXIV) from (XXIII) by substituting for dy/dx and d^2y/dx^2 their values in terms of dx/dy and d^2x/dy^2. HINT: We know that $\dfrac{dy}{dx} = \dfrac{1}{dx/dy}$. Differentiate this very carefully with respect to x to obtain d^2y/dx^2 in terms of dx/dy and d^2x/dy^2. Note that $\dfrac{d^2y}{dx^2}$ is *not* equal to $\dfrac{1}{d^2x/dy^2}$.

CHAPTER X

PARAMETRIC EQUATIONS

60. Introduction.—In many cases it is convenient to define y indirectly as a function of x by means of two equations of the form

$$y = G(\theta) \qquad x = H(\theta)$$

where θ is a third variable called a *parameter*. The direct relation, $y = f(x)$, would result from the operation of eliminating θ between these equations. This relation, if obtained, might be very complicated, and often it is simpler to deal with the relation in the original parametric form.

The problems of determining maximum and minimum points, inflection points, curvature, etc., for a curve defined in this way, present no new principles. One proceeds in the usual way after having found the necessary derivatives. We need then only show how to obtain the successive derivatives *without eliminating the parameter*.

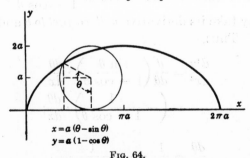

$$x = a(\theta - \sin \theta)$$
$$y = a(1 - \cos \theta)$$

Fig. 64.

61. To find dy/dx and d^2y/dx^2.—In order to illustrate the procedure let us compute dy/dx and d^2y/dx^2 for the cycloid (Fig. 64) whose parametric equations are

$$y = a(1 - \cos \theta), \qquad x = a(\theta - \sin \theta).$$

Regarding θ as the independent variable, we have

$$\frac{dy}{d\theta} = a \sin \theta, \qquad \frac{dx}{d\theta} = a(1 - \cos \theta).$$

Then since

$$\frac{dy}{dx} = \frac{\dfrac{dy}{d\theta}}{\dfrac{dx}{d\theta}}$$

we obtain

$$\frac{dy}{dx} = \frac{\sin \theta}{1 - \cos \theta}.$$

It is evident that this procedure always gives dy/dx in terms of the parameter θ rather than in terms of x.

To obtain d^2y/dx^2 we must proceed very carefully, remembering that d^2y/dx^2 is the derivative *with respect to x* of dy/dx. That is,

$$\frac{d^2y}{dx^2} = \frac{d}{dx}\left(\frac{dy}{dx}\right)$$
$$= \frac{d}{dx}\left(\frac{\sin \theta}{1 - \cos \theta}\right).$$

In order to obtain the derivative of $\dfrac{\sin \theta}{1 - \cos \theta}$ *with respect to x* we may take its derivative *with respect to θ* and multiply by $d\theta/dx$. Thus,

$$\frac{d^2y}{dx^2} = \frac{d}{d\theta}\left(\frac{\sin \theta}{1 - \cos \theta}\right) \cdot \frac{d\theta}{dx}$$
$$= \left(-\frac{1}{1 - \cos \theta}\right) \cdot \frac{d\theta}{dx};$$

since

$$\frac{d\theta}{dx} = \frac{1}{\dfrac{dx}{d\theta}} = \frac{1}{a(1 - \cos \theta)},$$

this reduces to

$$\frac{d^2y}{dx^2} = -\frac{1}{a(1 - \cos \theta)^2}.$$

PROBLEMS

In each of the following, find $D_x y$ and $D_x^2 y$ in terms of the parameter:

1. $y = \dfrac{4}{t}$; $x = \frac{1}{2}t$.   **2.** $y = 2t^3 - 6t$; $x = t^2 - 2t$.

3. $y = t^3 + 3t$; $x = t^2 + 1$.   **4.** $y = 3\sqrt{1 - t^2}$; $x = 4t$.

5. $y = 2 \sin \theta$; $x = 4 \cos \theta$.

6. $y = 5 \sin \theta - 2$; $x = 3 \cos \theta + 4$.

7. $y = 3 \sin^2 t$; $x = 6 \cos t$.   **8.** $y = \cos 2\theta$; $x = 4 \cos \theta$.

9. $y = 4 \sin \theta$; $x = 8 - 8 \sin \theta$.   **10.** $y = 2 \sin^3 t$; $x = 2 \cos^3 t$.

11. $y = 3 \cot \theta$; $x = 3 \sin^2 \theta$.   **12.** $y = 2e^t$; $x = 4e^{-t}$.

13. Find the equations of tangent and normal lines to the curve

$$x = t^2 - 1, \qquad y = t^4 - 4,$$

at the point where $t = 2$. Eliminate the parameter and sketch the curve.

14. Locate the minimum point on the curve of Prob. 13, and compute the radius of curvature at this point.

15. Show that $d^2y/dx^2 = 0$ at every point of the curve $x = 3 \sin^2 \theta$, $y = 6 \cos^2 \theta$. Sketch the graph.

16. Show that at any point on the curve $x = \log t$, $y = t + 4$, the values of dy/dx and d^2y/dx^2 are equal. Eliminate the parameter and sketch the curve.

17. Find the radius of curvature at any point of the curve $y = 2p \tan \theta$, $x = p \tan^2 \theta$. Show by eliminating θ that the curve is a parabola.

18. For the curve $x = a \sec \theta$, $y = b \tan \theta$, compute d^2y/dx^2. Then eliminate the parameter and compute d^2y/dx^2 from the resulting equation. Show that the results are equivalent. Sketch the curve.

19. Locate the maximum, minimum, and inflection points on the curve $x = 4 \cot \theta$, $y = 4 \sin^2 \theta$. Sketch the curve.

20. Locate the maximum, minimum, and inflection points on the curve; $y = 2 \sin 2\theta$; $x = \tan \theta$. Sketch the curve. Check your results by eliminating θ and using the resulting equation.

21. Compute the radius of curvature at a maximum point on the cycloid $x = a(\theta - \sin \theta)$, $y = a(1 - \cos \theta)$.

22. Let y be defined as a function of x by the equations $x = f(t)$, $y = g(t)$. Show that

$$\frac{d^2y}{dx^2} = \frac{\begin{vmatrix} \dfrac{dx}{dt} & \dfrac{dy}{dt} \\[2mm] \dfrac{d^2x}{dt^2} & \dfrac{d^2y}{dt^2} \end{vmatrix}}{\left(\dfrac{dx}{dt}\right)^3}.$$

62. Vectors and their components.—A quantity, such as temperature or volume, that can be completely specified by means of a real number representing its magnitude is called a **scalar quantity.** A quantity, such as force or velocity, that requires the specification of both its magnitude and its *direction* in order to characterize it completely is called a **vector quantity.**

A vector quantity may be represented by an arrow or *vector*. In this representation the length of the vector represents, to some convenient scale, the magnitude of the quantity, and its direction gives the direction of the quantity. Thus, if a particle has a velocity of 10 ft. per minute in a direction 30° north of due east, we may represent its velocity by the vector AB in Fig. 65. If this velocity were maintained for 1 min. the particle would travel 10 ft. in the direction of AB. In so doing it would move

$$10 \cos 30° = 8.66 \text{ ft. east,}$$

and

$$10 \sin 30° = 5 \text{ ft. north.}$$

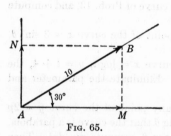

Fig. 65.

It is therefore evident that the projections AM and AN of the vector AB represent the *components* of the velocity in the respective directions.

In general, if we denote the magnitude (length) of a vector representing a velocity by v and its angle with the x-axis by θ, then its components along the axes have the magnitudes

$$v_x = v \cos \theta; \qquad v_y = v \sin \theta.$$

Conversely, the magnitude and direction of the vector having components v_x and v_y along the axes are

$$v = \sqrt{v_x{}^2 + v_y{}^2}; \qquad \theta = \arctan \frac{v_y}{v_x}.$$

The magnitude of the velocity of a particle is called its *speed*.

Example

An airplane is flying due north at 200 m.p.h. relative to the air mass in which it is moving. Find the magnitude and direction of its velocity relative to the earth if the air mass is moving due east at 50 m.p.h.

Solution (Fig. 66)

The components of the required velocity are as shown in the figure. We have then

$$v = \sqrt{(200)^2 + (50)^2} = 206 \text{ m.p.h.}$$
$$\theta = \arctan \tfrac{200}{50} = 76° \text{ (approximately).}$$

Relative to the earth, the airplane is moving at 206 m.p.h. in a direction 14° east of north.

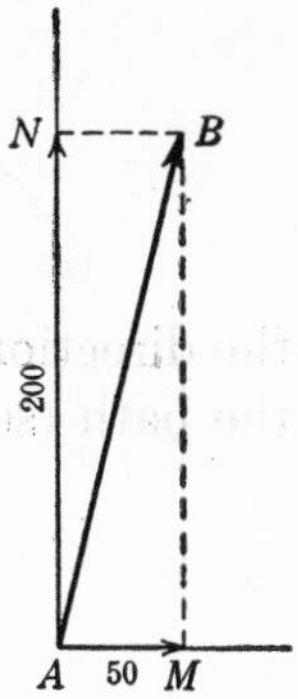

63. Velocity and acceleration in curvilinear motion.—Suppose that a point moves in the xy-plane in such a way that its coordinates at any time t are given by

$$x = G(t), \qquad y = H(t).$$

It will describe a curve whose equation, in the form $y = f(x)$, would be obtained by eliminating t.

The velocity of the moving point at any instant may be determined by finding its components parallel to the coordinate axes. For this purpose we observe that the value of dx/dt at any instant is the time rate at which the x-coordinate is changing; *i.e.*, it is the rate at which the projection of the point on the x-axis is moving along this axis. It is therefore the component of the velocity in this direction. Similarly, the value of dy/dt is the component of the velocity in the y-direction. Denoting these components by v_x and v_y we have

$$v_x = \frac{dx}{dt}, \qquad v_y = \frac{dy}{dt}.$$

Fig. 66.

The magnitude and direction of the velocity are then given by

$$v = \sqrt{v_x{}^2 + v_y{}^2}, \qquad \theta = \arctan \frac{v_y}{v_x}.$$

It should be observed that, since

$$\frac{v_y}{v_x} = \frac{\dfrac{dy}{dt}}{\dfrac{dx}{dt}} = \frac{dy}{dx},$$

the direction of the velocity vector is that of the tangent to the path (see Fig. 67).

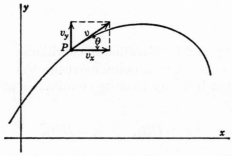

Fig. 67.

In a similar manner the *acceleration* of the moving point at any instant may be determined by finding its components. Thus, the time rate at which v_x is changing is the x-component of the acceleration while the rate at which v_y is changing is the y-component. Denoting these components by a_x and a_y we have

$$a_x = \frac{d^2x}{dt^2}, \qquad a_y = \frac{d^2y}{dt^2}.$$

The magnitude and direction of the acceleration are then expressed by

$$a = \sqrt{a_x{}^2 + a_y{}^2}, \qquad \phi = \arctan \frac{a_y}{a_x}.$$

It should be carefully observed that, since

$$\frac{a_y}{a_x} = \frac{\dfrac{d^2y}{dt^2}}{\dfrac{d^2x}{dt^2}} \neq \frac{dy}{dx},$$

the direction of the acceleration vector (Fig. 68) is *not*, in general, that of the tangent to the path. It can be shown that it is always directed toward the concave side of the

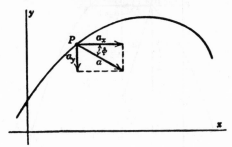

Fig. 68.

path and, in particular, is *normal* to the path if the *speed* of the moving point is *constant*.

Example

A point moves in the xy-plane so that at any time t its coordinates are

$$x = t^2 - 2, \qquad y = 3t^2 - \frac{t^4}{4}.$$

Compute the magnitude and direction of its velocity and acceleration when $t = 2$. Find the Cartesian equation of its path.

Solution

$$v_x = \frac{dx}{dt} = 2t; \qquad v_y = \frac{dy}{dt} = 6t - t^3;$$

$$v_x]_{t=2} = 4. \qquad v_y]_{t=2} = 4.$$

$$v = \sqrt{4^2 + 4^2} = 4\sqrt{2},$$

$$\theta = \arctan 1.$$

$$a_x = \frac{d^2x}{dt^2} = 2; \qquad a_y = \frac{d^2y}{dt^2} = 6 - 3t^2;$$

$$a_x]_{t=2} = 2. \qquad a_y]_{t=2} = -6.$$

$$a = \sqrt{2^2 + (-6)^2} = 2\sqrt{10}.$$

$$\phi = \arctan(-3).$$

Eliminating t we find that the path described by the moving point is the parabola

$$4y = 20 + 8x - x^2.$$

The position of the point on the path when $t = 2$ and the corresponding vectors representing v_x, v_y, v, and a_x, a_y, a, are shown in Fig. 69.

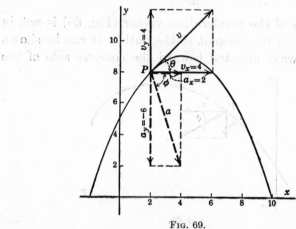

FIG. 69.

PROBLEMS

1. The velocity of a point that is moving along a straight or curved path may be defined as the *vector* whose magnitude is ds/dt and whose direction is that of the tangent to the path.   Show that

$$\frac{ds}{dt} = \sqrt{\left(\frac{dx}{dt}\right)^2 + \left(\frac{dy}{dt}\right)^2}.$$

HINT: $\dfrac{ds}{dt} = \dfrac{ds}{dx} \cdot \dfrac{dx}{dt}$ and $\dfrac{ds}{dx} = \sqrt{1 + \left(\dfrac{dy}{dx}\right)^2}.$

2. In the above illustrative example find v and a when $t = 3$.   Sketch the curve and draw the vectors.

In each of the following, compute the values of v and a at the instant indicated.   Find the Cartesian equation of the path, sketch it, and draw the vectors:

3. $x = 2t^2 - 4$; $y = t^4 - 8t^2$; $t = 2$.

4. $x = \frac{1}{2}t^2 - 2$; $y = \frac{1}{4}t^4 - 4t^2$; $t = 2$.

5. $x = 4 - t$; $y = t(t - 4)^2$; $t = 3$.

6. $x = 2t + 1$; $y = t^3$; $t = 1$.

7. $x = 4 \cos t$; $y = 4 \sin t$; $t = \frac{1}{6}\pi$.

8. $x = 2 + 5 \sin t$; $y = 5 \cos t - 3$; $t = \pi$.

9. $x = 5 + 5 \sin t$; $y = 3 \cos t - 3$; $t = \frac{1}{2}\pi$.

10. $x = 8(1 - \sin t)$; $y = 4 \cos t$; $t = \tfrac{1}{2}\pi$.

11. $x = \log t$; $y = \dfrac{1}{t} \log t$; $t = 1$.

12. $x = 4t - \tfrac{1}{2}t^3$; $y = \tfrac{1}{2}t^2 - 4$; $t = 1$.

13. A point moves so that its coordinates at any time t are $x = 8 \tan t$, $y = 4 \sin^2 t$ $(0 \leqq t < \tfrac{1}{2}\pi)$. Sketch its path.

14. A point moves so that its coordinates at any time t are $x = 2 \sin t$, $y = 2(1 - \cos t)$. Show that its velocity and acceleration are constant in magnitude. Find the Cartesian equation of the path and describe the motion.

15. A point starts at $(r, 0)$ when $t = 0$ and moves around the circle $x^2 + y^2 = r^2$ at a constant angular velocity of ω radians per second. Show that its coordinates at any time t are $x = r \cos \omega t$, $y = r \sin \omega t$. Show that its acceleration is constant in magnitude and is always directed toward the center of the circle.

16. Solve Prob. 15 for the case in which the radius drawn to the initial position of the moving point makes an angle α with the x-axis.

17. A wheel of radius r rolls along a straight line at a constant angular velocity of ω radians per second. Consider the point A, which is in contact with the ground when $t = 0$, and show that its coordinates after t sec. are

$$x = r(\omega t - \sin \omega t), \qquad y = r(1 - \cos \omega t).$$

Show that its acceleration at any instant is $r\omega^2$ and is directed toward the center of the wheel. The coordinate axes are assumed as shown in Fig. 64.

18. A bug starts at the center of a wheel of radius 4 ft. and crawls out along a spoke at 2 ft. per minute while the wheel rolls along a straight line at $\tfrac{1}{4}$ r.p.m. Derive parametric equations of the path followed by the bug in space. Find the components of his velocity at the end of 1 min.

19. If a projectile is fired from A (Fig. 70) with initial velocity v_0 at an angle α, its position at the end of t sec. (neglecting air resistance) is given by

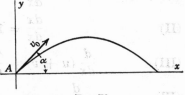

FIG. 70.

$$x = (v_0 \cos \alpha)t$$
$$y = (v_0 \sin \alpha)t - \tfrac{1}{2}gt^2.$$

Find the components of its velocity and acceleration at any time. Show by eliminating t that the path is a parabola.

20. Using the data of Prob. 19, find the maximum height reached by the projectile. Find also the horizontal distance traveled.

21. Using the data of Prob. 19, find the angle α for which the horizontal distance traveled (range) is a maximum.

CHAPTER XI

COLLECTION OF FORMULAS
REVIEW PROBLEMS

64. Review.—The purpose of this chapter is to present an opportunity for a brief review. In this connection the student should again study the definition and the physical and geometrical interpretation of the derivative. He should make certain that he has a clear understanding of the fundamental process of differentiation and of its use in deriving the various formulas for differentiation. He should also make a step by step outline of the procedure to be followed in solving the important types of applied problems. The first 15 problems in the review set are designed to cover some of these points. The others may be used for review practice in formal differentiation and in solving the various types of applied problems. The formulas are listed below for easy reference.

FORMULAS

(I)
$$\frac{dc}{dx} = 0.$$

(II)
$$\frac{dx}{dx} = 1.$$

(III)
$$\frac{d}{dx}(u + v) = \frac{du}{dx} + \frac{dv}{dx}.$$

(IV)
$$\frac{d}{dx}(u \cdot v) = u\frac{dv}{dx} + v\frac{du}{dx}.$$

(V)
$$\frac{d}{dx}(v^n) = nv^{n-1}\frac{dv}{dx}.$$

(VI)
$$\frac{d}{dx}\left(\frac{u}{v}\right) = \frac{v\frac{du}{dx} - u\frac{dv}{dx}}{v^2}.$$

(VII)
$$\frac{dy}{dx} = \frac{dy}{dv} \cdot \frac{dv}{dx}.$$

(VIII)
$$\frac{dy}{dx} = \frac{1}{\frac{dx}{dy}}.$$

(IX)
$$\frac{d}{dx} \sin v = \cos v \frac{dv}{dx}.$$

(X)
$$\frac{d}{dx} \cos v = -\sin v \frac{dv}{dx}.$$

(XI)
$$\frac{d}{dx} \tan v = \sec^2 v \frac{dv}{dx}.$$

(XII)
$$\frac{d}{dx} \cot v = -\csc^2 v \frac{dv}{dx}.$$

(XIII)
$$\frac{d}{dx} \sec v = \sec v \tan v \frac{dv}{dx}.$$

(XIV)
$$\frac{d}{dx} \csc v = -\csc v \cot v \frac{dv}{dx}.$$

(XV)
$$\frac{d}{dx} \arcsin v = \frac{\frac{dv}{dx}}{\sqrt{1 - v^2}}.$$

(XVI)
$$\frac{d}{dx} \arccos v = - \frac{\frac{dv}{dx}}{\sqrt{1 - v^2}}.$$

(XVII)
$$\frac{d}{dx} \arctan v = \frac{\frac{dv}{dx}}{1 + v^2}.$$

(XVIII)
$$\frac{d}{dx} \operatorname{arccot} v = - \frac{\frac{dv}{dx}}{1 + v^2}.$$

(XIX)
$$\frac{d}{dx} \log_a v = \frac{1}{v} \log_a e \frac{dv}{dx}.$$

(XIXs)
$$\frac{d}{dx} \log v = \frac{1}{v} \frac{dv}{dx}.$$

(XX)
$$\frac{d}{dx} a^v = a^v \log a \frac{dv}{dx}.$$

(XXs)
$$\frac{d}{dx} e^v = e^v \frac{dv}{dx}.$$

(**XXI**)
$$\frac{ds}{dx} = \sqrt{1 + \left(\frac{dy}{dx}\right)^2}.$$

(**XXII**)
$$K = \frac{d\theta}{ds} = \frac{\left|\dfrac{d^2y}{dx^2}\right|}{\left[1 + \left(\dfrac{dy}{dx}\right)^2\right]^{\frac{3}{2}}}$$

(**XXIII**)
$$R = \frac{1}{K} = \frac{\left[1 + \left(\dfrac{dy}{dx}\right)^2\right]^{\frac{3}{2}}}{\left|\dfrac{d^2y}{dx^2}\right|}.$$

REVIEW PROBLEMS

1. Write out a definition of the derivative of a function in words and in symbols. Illustrate graphically.

2. Show why the value of dy/dx at a point P on the curve $y = f(x)$ represents the slope of the tangent line.

3. Using the fundamental differentiation process, find the derivative of x^3; of $\cos x$.

4. Show that if a cube is expanding, its volume is increasing at a rate of 12 cu. in. per inch of increase in the edge at the instant when each edge is 2 in. long. If the edge is increasing at $\frac{1}{4}$ in. per minute, at what time rate is the volume increasing?

5. Show that $\tan x$ increases four times as rapidly as x when $x = \pi/3$. If x increases from 60° to 60° 10′ (10′ = 0.003 radian), what should be the *approximate* increase in the value of $\tan x$? Check your answer by referring to a table.

6. Show that the natural logarithm of x increases at a rate of $\frac{1}{100}$ unit per unit increase in x when $x = 100$.

7. How many of the formulas from (IX) to (XVIII) inclusive must be derived by the fundamental differentiation process? How are the others obtained?

8. Show that the derivative of $\sec x$ with respect to $\tan x$ is $\sin x$; hence, show that $\sec x$ increases half as rapidly as $\tan x$ when $x = \pi/6$. What is the situation when x is near $\pi/2$?

9. Derive the formula for the derivative of $\tan x$ both with and without using the fundamental differentiation process.

Outline the procedure to be followed in solving each of the following problems. Number the steps:

10. To find the equation of the line that is tangent to the curve $y = f(x)$ at a given point $P(x_1, y_1)$ on the curve.

11. To determine the angle at which two given curves, $y = f(x)$ and $y = \varphi(x)$, intersect.

12. To determine the maximum and minimum values of a given function.

13. To determine the inflection points on a given curve.

14. To compute the curvature of a given curve at a given point.

15. To determine the point on a given curve at which the radius of curvature is a maximum or minimum.

In each of the following, find dy/dx:

16. $y = x^2 \sqrt{3 - x}.$

17. $y = (2 \sqrt{x} + 5)^2.$

18. $y = x^2 \sqrt{a^2 - x}.$

19. $y = 2 \left(\sqrt{x} + \dfrac{1}{\sqrt{x}} \right).$

20. $y = \dfrac{4 + x}{2 - 3x}.$

21. $y = \dfrac{8x^2}{x^2 + 3}.$

22. $y = \sqrt{\dfrac{4x + 5}{4x - 5}}.$

23. $y^2 = \dfrac{x^2 - 1}{x^2 + 1}.$

24. $y = \log (x^2 \sqrt{x^2 + 4}).$

25. $y = x^2 \log \sqrt{x}.$

26. $y = 4 \log^2 (5x).$

27. $y = 6xe^{x^2}.$

28. $y = 5.6e^{1.5x}.$

29. $y = 4^{3x}.$

30. $y = (x + 1)^x.$

31. $y = \log_{10} (x^3 + 3).$

32. $y = 4 \sin^2 \tfrac{1}{2}x.$

33. $y = \dfrac{4}{\pi} \cos^3 \tfrac{1}{2}\pi x.$

34. $y = 2 \sqrt{\sec 2x}.$

35. $y = 6 \sin^2 x \cos x.$

36. $y = \log (\sec x + \tan x).$

37. $y = \tfrac{1}{2}[\sec x \tan x + \log (\sec x + \tan x)].$

38. $y = x^2 \arctan x.$

39. $y = \arccos \sqrt{x}.$

40. $y = \text{arcot } \dfrac{4 - x}{4}.$

41. $y = 4x \arcsin x.$

42. $y = x \sqrt{4 - x^2} + 4 \arcsin \tfrac{1}{4}x.$

43. $y = (x^2 + 1) \arctan x - x.$

44. $y = x \arcsin ax + \sqrt{1 - a^2x^2}.$

45. $x^2y^2 = 4 - y.$

46. $x^3 + y^3 = 6xy.$

47. $xy - \sin x = 0.$

48. $x^2 + 3xy + 5y^2 = 16.$

49. $y^2(4 - x) = x^2(4 + x).$

50. $x^2y^2 = y^2 + 1.$

51. $y^3 + 3x^2y = x^2 - y^2.$

52. $x^3 - xy^2 = 3xy + 15.$

In each of the following, find d^2y/dx^2:

53. $y = 3 \sin^2 \tfrac{1}{2}x.$

54. $y = x \arccos x.$

55. $y = x^2e^{-x}.$

56. $y = x^2 \log x.$

57. $x^2 + 4y^2 = 6x.$

58. $y = \tfrac{1}{2}x \arctan x.$

59. $y = 5 \sin \theta - 2$; $x = \cos \theta + 3$.

60. $x = \frac{1}{2} \tan \theta$; $y = 4 \sin^2 \theta$.

61. Draw the ellipse whose equation is $3x^2 + y^2 + 12x = 0$, and find the equation of the line tangent to it at $(-3, -3)$.

62. Find the equations of the lines that are normal to the curve $y = \frac{1}{3}x^3 + 2x^2$ and parallel to the line $3y - x + 6 = 0$.

63. A line is drawn through the points $(-2, -8)$ and $(4, 4)$ on the curve $y = 3x - \frac{1}{2}x^2$. Find the angles at which it cuts the curve.

64. Determine the angles of intersection of the parabolas $y = x^2 - 4$ and $y^2 = 24(x + 2)$.

65. Compute the curvature of the parabola $y^2 - 4y - 4x = 8$ at the point where it crosses the x-axis.

66. Sketch the curve $y = xe^x$; compute its curvature at its minimum point.

67. In what interval is the curve whose equation is $y = e^{-\frac{1}{2}x^2}$ concave downward? Sketch the curve.

68. Compute the area of the largest rectangle that can be drawn with its base on the x-axis and two vertices on the curve $y = e^{-\frac{1}{2}x^2}$.

69. A glass jar of given volume is to be made with a metal top. The top costs four times as much per unit area as the glass. Determine the ratio of height to diameter for minimum cost.

70. An open gutter with sloping sides of equal inclination is to be made from a long piece of sheet metal that is 22 in. wide, by turning up 4 in. on each side in the manner shown in Fig. 47. For what inclination θ is the capacity a maximum?

71. The distances of the top and bottom of a picture above the level of the observer's eye are p and q, respectively. Show that the picture subtends a maximum angle at the eye if the observer stands back a distance $\sqrt{pq}$.

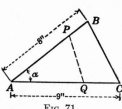

Fig. 71.

72. Locate points P and Q (Fig. 71) if area $APQ = \frac{1}{2}ABC$ and the length PQ is a minimum.

73. The sum of the length and the girth of a parcel-post package cannot exceed 100 in. What dimensions would give the greatest volume if the package is to be rectangular with a square cross section?

74. The crank arm OA (Fig. 72) rotates at a uniform angular velocity of 60 r.p.m. Express the linear velocity of the piston at B as a function of θ.

75. A kite is 120 ft. high and 200 ft. of string is out. If the kite is moving horizontally at 6 m.p.h., how fast is the string being paid out if the person flying the kite is walking in the same direction at 2 m.p.h.?

76. In the cam and follower arrangement shown in Fig. 73 the eccentrically mounted disk rotates on shaft A, thus causing the follower to move up and down.   If the disk rotates clockwise at 30 r.p.m., what is the speed of the follower when $\theta = 30°$?

77. The frictional resistance to flow of a liquid in an open channel is proportional to the area of the wetted surface. Show that for a rectangular channel the width should be twice the depth for minimum wetted area.

78. An open channel is to be constructed

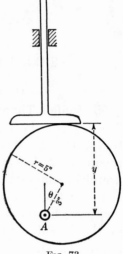

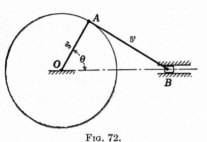

FIG. 72.   FIG. 73.

with trapezoidal cross section of area A.   The inclination of the sides is a given angle α.   Determine the shape that gives a minimum wetted area.

79. A fence h ft. high is parallel to, and b ft. distant from, the wall of a building. Show that the inclination of the shortest ladder that will reach to the wall from the ground outside the fence is given by $\tan^3 \theta = h/b$.

80. Prove that the area of the smallest ellipse that can be circumscribed about a rectangle of area A is independent of the shape of this rectangle and equal to $\pi A/2$.

CHAPTER XII

THE LIMIT OF A FUNCTION

(*Continued from Chapter* II)

65. Rolle's Theorem and the Theorem of Mean Value.— The idea of the limit of $f(x)$ as $x \to a$ was introduced in Chap. II. In the present chapter we shall introduce a theorem, known as *Lhopital's* * *Theorem*, which is often useful in connection with the problem of finding the limit of a function. First, however, we shall present two preliminary theorems that have many important applications in the calculus. One of these will be used in proving Lhopital's Theorem in the next section.

Rolle's Theorem: *Let* $f(x)$ *be a function which is continuous over the interval* $a \leqq x \leqq b$ *and has a derivative at every interior point of the interval. Then if* $f(a) = f(b) = 0$, *there must be at least one point* x_1 *between a and b for which* $f'(x_1) = 0$.

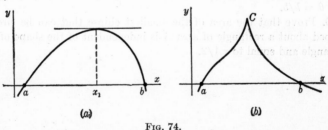

(a)   (b)

Fig. 74.

The geometrical interpretation of this theorem is given by Fig. 74(a). The curve crosses the x-axis at $x = a$ and $x = b$ [$f(a) = f(b) = 0$]. Then there must be some point x_1 between a and b for which $f'(x_1) = 0$.

* G. F. A. de L'Hôpital (1661–1704). The latest edition of Webster's, "New International Dictionary," 2d ed., 1934, gives Lhopital as the preferred spelling and L'Hôpital as second choice.

If $f(x)$ does not have a derivative at every point of the interval, the theorem does not apply and there may not be any point between a and b for which $f'(x) = 0$. This is illustrated by Fig. 74(b). The function shown here is continuous but it does not have a derivative at C.

A proof of Rolle's Theorem, based upon a fundamental property of a continuous function, can be given. We shall, however, assume that the theorem is intuitively evident from geometrical considerations and omit the proof. The second theorem is the following:

Theorem of Mean Value: *Let $f(x)$ be a function which is continuous over the interval $a \leqq x \leqq b$ and has a derivative at every interior point of the interval. Then there must be at least one point x_1 between a and b such that*

$$f'(x_1) = \frac{f(b) - f(a)}{b - a}.$$

This theorem is also geometrically obvious. The slope of chord AB (Fig. 75) is

$$\frac{CB}{AC} = \frac{f(b) - f(a)}{b - a}.$$

The theorem then merely states that under the conditions specified there must be a point x_1 between a and b such that the tangent to the curve at $x = x_1$ is parallel to this chord.

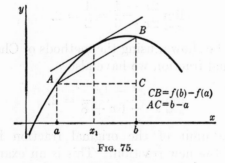

$$CB = f(b) - f(a)$$
$$AC = b - a$$

FIG. 75.

The theorem can be proved analytically, the proof being based upon Rolle's Theorem. We shall, however, omit the proof.

66. Lhopital's Theorem.—We have defined the limit of a function $f(x)$ as $x \to a$ to be the constant L (if it exists) to which the value of $f(x)$ is arbitrarily near for x sufficiently near to, but not equal to, a. We have found that the problem of computing this limit is trivial if $f(x)$ is continuous at $x = a$; for we can find $f(a)$ by direct substitution and this is the desired limit. Thus

$$\lim_{x \to 2} (3x + 2) = 8; \qquad \lim_{x \to 4} \frac{x^2 + 2}{x^2 - 3x} = \frac{18}{4} = 4\tfrac{1}{2}.$$

If, however, the substitution of a for x leads to a meaningless symbol, such as $0/0$, the problem of computing $\lim_{x \to a} f(x)$, if it exists, is more difficult. As an example, consider the problem of finding

$$\lim_{x \to 4} \frac{x^2 - 4x}{x^2 - 6x + 8}.$$

If we substitute 4 for x, the fraction takes the meaningless or *indeterminate* form $0/0$. Let us now

replace $x^2 - 4x$ by its derivative, which is $2x - 4$;
replace $x^2 - 6x + 8$ by its derivative, which is $2x - 6$.

We now have a new fraction $\dfrac{2x - 4}{2x - 6}$; and, obviously,

$$\lim_{x \to 4} \frac{2x - 4}{2x - 6} = \frac{4}{2} = 2.$$

It can easily be shown, using the methods of Chap. II, that for the original fraction we have also

$$\lim_{x \to 4} \frac{x^2 - 4x}{x^2 - 6x + 8} = 2.$$

That is, the limit of the original fraction is identical with that of the new fraction. This is an example of the following:

Lhopital's Theorem: *Let $g(x)$ and $h(x)$ be two functions both having the value zero at $x = a$. Then the limit of their* *quotient as* $x \to a$ *is equal to the limit of the quotient of their derivatives, if the latter limit exists; i.e., if* $g(a) = h(a) = 0$, *then*

$$\lim_{x \to a} \frac{g(x)}{h(x)} = \lim_{x \to a} \frac{g'(x)}{h'(x)} \quad \textit{(if this limit exists)}.$$

A proof of the theorem for the case in which $h'(a) \neq 0$ is as follows: If $g(a) = h(a) = 0$, then

$$g(x) \equiv g(x) - g(a) \qquad \text{and} \qquad h(x) \equiv h(x) - h(a).$$

Now, from the Theorem of Mean Value,

$$g(x) - g(a) = (x - a)g'(x_1) \qquad \text{where } a < x_1 < x;$$
$$h(x) - h(a) = (x - a)h'(x_2) \qquad \text{where } a < x_2 < x.$$

Thus,

$$\frac{g(x)}{h(x)} = \frac{g(x) - g(a)}{h(x) - h(a)} = \frac{g'(x_1)}{h'(x_2)}.$$

When $x \to a$ both x_1 and x_2 also approach a because both lie between a and x. We have then

$$\lim_{x \to a} \frac{g(x)}{h(x)} = \lim_{x \to a} \frac{g'(x_1)}{h'(x_2)} = \frac{g'(a)}{h'(a)} \text{ [if } h'(a) \neq 0].$$

If $h'(a) = 0$ and $g'(a) \neq 0$ then $\lim\limits_{x \to a} \dfrac{g(x)}{h(x)} = \infty$. If $g'(a) = h'(a) = 0$ then it can be shown that

$$\lim_{x \to a} \frac{g(x)}{h(x)} = \lim_{x \to a} \frac{g'(x)}{h'(x)} = \lim_{x \to a} \frac{g''(x)}{h''(x)} = \frac{g''(a)}{h''(a)}$$

provided that $h''(a) \neq 0$. If $g''(a) = h''(a) = 0$, then we consider $g'''(x)/h'''(x)$, etc.

Example

Compute $\lim\limits_{x \to 0} \dfrac{e^x + e^{-x} - 2 \cos x}{x \sin x}$.

Solution

For $x = 0$ the fraction reduces to $0/0$; hence,

$$\lim_{x \to 0} \frac{e^x + e^{-x} - 2 \cos x}{x \sin x} = \lim_{x \to 0} \frac{e^x - e^{-x} + 2 \sin x}{x \cos x + \sin x}.$$

But the new fraction also takes the form 0/0 for $x = 0$; we then apply the theorem again:

$$= \lim_{x \to 0} \frac{e^x + e^{-x} + 2\cos x}{-x \sin x + 2\cos x}$$

$$= \frac{4}{2} = 2.$$

If we are seeking the limit of the fraction as $x \to \infty$ and if it happens that both numerator and denominator approach zero as $x \to \infty$, the same theorem applies. And finally, if the fraction takes symbolically the form ∞/∞ * when $x \to a$ or when $x \to \infty$, the theorem again applies. The proofs for these cases will not be given.

Example

Compute

$$\lim_{x \to 0} \frac{\log x}{\cot x}.$$

Solution

As $x \to 0$ the absolute values of both $\log x$ and $\cot x$ increase beyond bound. (We may restrict x to positive values so that $\log x$ is real and let $x \to 0^+$.) Then

$$\lim_{x \to 0} \frac{\log x}{\cot x} = \lim_{x \to 0} \frac{\frac{1}{x}}{-\csc^2 x}$$

$$= \lim_{x \to 0} \frac{-\sin^2 x}{x}$$

$$= \lim_{x \to 0} \left(\frac{\sin x}{x}\right) \cdot \lim_{x \to 0} (-\sin x)$$

$$= 1 \cdot 0 = 0.$$

PROBLEMS

1. Verify Rolle's Theorem for each of the following functions:

(a) $f(x) = 5x^2 - x^3$.   (b) $f(x) = x^3 + 2x^2 - 8x$.

2. Verify the Theorem of Mean Value for each of the following functions in the given interval:

(a) $f(x) = x^2 - 2x + 2$; $0 \leqq x \leqq 4$.
(b) $f(x) = x^3 - 6x$; $1 \leqq x \leqq 3$.

* The fraction $g(x)/h(x)$ is said to take the meaningless or *indeterminate* form ∞/∞ for $x = a$ if $\lim_{x \to a} g(x) = \infty$ and $\lim_{x \to a} h(x) = \infty$.

3. Compute $\lim\limits_{x\to 5} \dfrac{x^2 - 5}{x + 3}$. Explain why Lhopital's Theorem does not apply.

4. Compute $\lim\limits_{x\to 2} \dfrac{x^2 - 4}{x + 3}$. Explain why Lhopital's Theorem does not apply.

5. Compute $\lim\limits_{x\to 0} \dfrac{3 \sin 2x}{4x}$ both with and without the use of Lhopital's Theorem.

6. Show that, if x is near 3, the value of $\dfrac{2x^2 - 3x - 9}{x^2 - 4x + 3}$ is near $4\frac{1}{2}$.

7. Show that, if x is near 2, the value of $\dfrac{3x^3 - 6x^2 + 2x - 4}{x^2 - 4}$ is near $3\frac{1}{2}$.

8. Show that $\lim\limits_{\theta\to 0} \dfrac{\theta - \sin\theta}{\theta^3} = \frac{1}{6}$. Hence infer that for very small values of θ, the difference between θ(radians) and $\sin\theta$ is nearly equal to $\frac{1}{6}\theta^3$. Verify this numerically for $\theta = 5°$.

9. Show that $\lim\limits_{\theta\to 0} \dfrac{\tan\theta - \theta}{\theta^3} = \frac{1}{3}$. Hence infer that for very small values of θ, the difference between $\tan\theta$ and θ(radians) is nearly equal to $\frac{1}{3}\theta^3$. Verify this numerically for $\theta = 5°$.

10. Show that the value of $(e^x - e^{-x})$ is about twice that of $\sin x$ if x is near zero. HINT: Show that $\lim\limits_{x\to 0} \dfrac{e^x - e^{-x}}{\sin x} = 2$.

Determine each of the following limits, if it exists, both with and without using Lhopital's Theorem:

11. $\lim\limits_{x\to 2} \dfrac{x^3 - 2x^2 + 2x - 4}{x^2 - 5x + 6}$.

12. $\lim\limits_{x\to \frac{3}{2}} \dfrac{2x^2 + 5x - 12}{2x^2 - x - 3}$.

13. $\lim\limits_{x\to \infty} \dfrac{7x^2 + 6x}{2x^2 + 5x + 4}$.

14. $\lim\limits_{x\to \infty} \dfrac{6x^2 + 9x}{2x^3 + 5}$.

15. $\lim\limits_{x\to \infty} \dfrac{4x + 5}{5x^2 + 3x}$.

16. $\lim\limits_{x\to 0} \dfrac{3x^2 + 2x}{4x^2 + 5x}$.

17. $\lim\limits_{x\to 0} \dfrac{x^3}{8x^2 + 4x}$.

18. $\lim\limits_{x\to 0} \dfrac{7x}{4x^2 + 3x}$.

19. $\lim\limits_{x\to 0} \dfrac{x^2 \cos x}{\sin^2 \frac{1}{2}x}$.

20. $\lim\limits_{x\to 0} \dfrac{\sin x - \sin x \cos x}{x^3}$.

21. $\lim\limits_{\theta\to 0} \dfrac{\sin 4\theta}{\tan 2\theta}$.

22. $\lim\limits_{\theta\to 0} \dfrac{1 - \cos^4\theta}{\theta^2}$.

Determine the following limits if they exist:

23. $\lim\limits_{x\to 0} \dfrac{1 - \cos x}{x^2}$.

24. $\lim\limits_{x\to 0} \dfrac{\sec x - 1}{x}$.

25. $\lim\limits_{x\to 0} \dfrac{\sec 2x - 1}{x^2}$.

26. $\lim\limits_{x\to \infty} \dfrac{\log x}{x}$.

27. $\lim\limits_{x \to 0} \dfrac{\log \sec x}{x^2}.$

28. $\lim\limits_{x \to 0} \dfrac{x^2 \cos x}{1 - \cos x}.$

29. $\lim\limits_{x \to \infty} \dfrac{\log (x + 1)^3}{6x}.$

30. $\lim\limits_{x \to 0} \dfrac{\sin x - x}{\tan x - x}.$

31. $\lim\limits_{x \to 0} \dfrac{8^x - 2^x}{x}.$

32. $\lim\limits_{x \to 0} \dfrac{\cot 4x}{\cot x}.$

33. $\lim\limits_{x \to \frac{1}{2}\pi} \dfrac{\log \sec x}{\sec x}.$

34. $\lim\limits_{x \to 2} \dfrac{\log(x - 2)}{\cot \pi x}.$

35. $\lim\limits_{x \to 0} \dfrac{e^x - e^{-x} - 2x}{x - \sin x}.$

36. $\lim\limits_{x \to \infty} \dfrac{e^x}{x^3}.$

37. $\lim\limits_{x \to 0} \dfrac{x^2 - x \sin x}{e^x + e^{-x} - (x^2 + 2)}.$

38. $\lim\limits_{x \to \infty} \dfrac{4^x}{x^4}.$

39. Is the value of the fraction $2^x/x^{100}$ large or small for very large values of x?

40. Is the value of the fraction $x^{10}/3^x$ large or small for very large values of x?

41. What happens to the value of the fraction $(10)^n/n!$ when n(a positive integer) becomes very large? HINT: Lhopital's Theorem does not apply. Study the behavior of the fraction, observing that the effect of increasing n by one is to multiply the numerator by 10 and the denominator by $(n + 1)$. Hence, the fraction has its largest value for $n = 9$ and 10 and then decreases.

Determine each of the following limits by transforming the given expression into a quotient and then applying Lhopital's Theorem:

42. $\lim\limits_{x \to \infty} x \sin \dfrac{\pi}{x}.$ HINT: Transform to $\dfrac{\sin \dfrac{\pi}{x}}{\dfrac{1}{x}}.$

43. $\lim\limits_{x \to 0} \left(\dfrac{1}{x} - \dfrac{1}{x^2}\right).$ HINT: Reduce to $\dfrac{x - 1}{x^2}.$

44. $\lim\limits_{x \to 0} (x^2 e^{-x}).$

45. $\lim\limits_{x \to \frac{1}{2}\pi} (\sec x - \tan x).$

46. $\lim\limits_{x \to 0} \left(\dfrac{1}{\sin^2 x} - \dfrac{1}{x^2}\right).$

47. $\lim\limits_{x \to 1} (x - 1) \tan \dfrac{\pi x}{2}.$

48. $\lim\limits_{x \to 0} (3x \csc 2x).$

49. $\lim\limits_{x \to \frac{1}{2}\pi} (\sec x \cos 3x).$

50. $\lim\limits_{x \to 0} x^2 \log^2 x.$

CHAPTER XIII

THE DIFFERENTIAL

67. Infinitesimals.—In this book we shall use the word *infinitesimal* to denote a variable quantity that is approaching *zero* as a limit.* Thus if $x \to 0$ the functions $\sin^2 x$, $4 \tan 2x$, and $x^2 + 3x$ are infinitesimals because they all have the limit zero. The function $\cos x$ is not an infinitesimal when $x \to 0$ because it approaches 1, but if $x \to \frac{1}{2}\pi$ then $\cos x$ becomes an infinitesimal.

We have already employed infinitesimals in connection with the definition of the derivative and the development of formulas for differentiation. Thus in defining $D_x y$ at a point A on the curve whose equation is $y = f(x)$ (Fig.

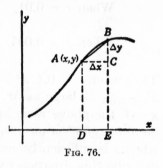

Fig. 76.

76) we formed the quotient $\Delta y/\Delta x$ and then let $\Delta x \to 0$. Δy was a function of Δx having the limit zero as $\Delta x \to 0$ and was therefore an infinitesimal.

Other quantities that approach zero along with Δx are the length of chord AB, the area of triangle ABC, which is equal to $\frac{1}{2} \Delta x \Delta y$, the area of rectangle $ACED (= y \Delta x)$, etc. These quantities are functions of Δx that have the limit zero as $\Delta x \to 0$.

68. Relative order of infinitesimals.—One ordinarily compares two magnitudes by considering not their difference but their *ratio*. Thus one might well say that two automobiles weighing 3,200 and 3,220 lb., respectively, are about equal in weight. He would not make the same remark about two dogs weighing 5 and 25 lb., respectively.

* More precisely, $f(x)$ is an infinitesimal as $x \to a$ if $\lim_{x \to a} f(x) = 0$.

The difference is 20 lb. in each case but one is thinking of the *ratio* rather than of the difference when he compares them.

Now let α and β represent two infinitesimals, *i.e.*, two variable quantities that are simultaneously approaching zero as a limit. If we wished to make a relative comparison of their magnitudes at any instant we would, of course, consider the value of their ratio at that instant. Consider, for example, the quantities x^2 and $5x$, both of which approach zero when $x \to 0$. We have

When $x = 0.1$, $\qquad \dfrac{x^2}{5x} = \dfrac{0.01}{0.5} = \dfrac{1}{50}$;

When $x = 0.01$, $\qquad \dfrac{x^2}{5x} = \dfrac{0.0001}{0.05} = \dfrac{1}{500}$;

When $x = 0.001$, $\qquad \dfrac{x^2}{5x} = \dfrac{0.000001}{0.005} = \dfrac{1}{5000}$.

Thus when $x = 0.1$, x^2 is $\frac{1}{50}$ as large as $5x$; when $x = 0.01$, x^2 is $\frac{1}{500}$ as large as $5x$, etc. It is fairly obvious that as $x \to 0$ the above ratio approaches *zero*. This means that *the value of x^2 is an arbitrarily small fraction of that of $5x$* when x is sufficiently near to, but not equal to, zero. We describe this situation by saying that x^2 is an infinitesimal of *higher order* than $5x$. The definitions concerning the relative order of infinitesimals are as follows:

Let α and β represent two functions of the same independent variable x and let both have the limit zero as $x \to a$. Then α and β are infinitesimals (when $x \to a$), and

If $\displaystyle \lim_{x \to a} \frac{\alpha}{\beta} = 0$, α *is of higher order than* β.

If $\displaystyle \lim_{x \to a} \frac{\alpha}{\beta} = k \neq 0$, α *is of the same order as* β.

If $\displaystyle \lim_{x \to a} \frac{\alpha}{\beta} = \infty$, α *is of lower order than* β.

Example 1

Show that $\sin 2x$ and $\tan x$ are infinitesimals of the same order when $x \to 0$.

Solution

When $x \to 0$, both $\sin 2x$ and $\tan x$ approach zero; and

$$\lim_{x \to 0} \frac{\sin 2x}{\tan x} = \lim_{x \to 0} \frac{2 \cos 2x}{\sec^2 x} = 2.$$

The infinitesimals are then of the *same* order.   The fact that the limit is 2 means that the value of $\sin 2x$ is practically *twice* that of $\tan x$ when x is near to, but not equal to, zero.

Example 2

Show that the difference between $\sec x$ and $\cos x$ is an infinitesimal of higher order than x when $x \to 0$.

Solution

When $x \to 0$, both $\sec x$ and $\cos x$ approach 1 and the difference ($\sec x - \cos x$) approaches 0; furthermore,

$$\lim_{x \to 0} \frac{\sec x - \cos x}{x} = \lim_{x \to 0} \frac{\sec x \tan x + \sin x}{1} = \frac{0}{1} = 0.$$

Hence ($\sec x - \cos x$) is of higher order than x.   The result means, roughly speaking, that as $x \to 0$ the difference between $\sec x$ and $\cos x$ becomes very small *compared with x.*

If we now compare ($\sec x - \cos x$) with x^2 when $x \to 0$ we have

$$\lim_{x \to 0} \frac{\sec x - \cos x}{x^2} = \lim_{x \to 0} \frac{\sec x \tan x + \sin x}{2x}$$

$$= \lim_{x \to 0} \frac{\sec^3 x + \tan^2 x \sec x + \cos x}{2}$$

$$= \frac{1 + 0 + 1}{2} = 1.$$

Thus ($\sec x - \cos x$) is of the *same order as x^2*, and we say that it is of *second order relative to x*.   In general, if there exists a positive number n such that

$$\lim \frac{\alpha}{\beta^n} = k \neq 0,$$

then α is said to be of the *nth order* relative to β.

Example

Show that when $x \to 0$ the difference between sin x and x is an infinitesimal of third order relative to x.

Solution

The student can verify that

$$\lim_{x \to 0} \frac{x - \sin x}{x} = 0 \quad \text{and} \quad \lim_{x \to 0} \frac{x - \sin x}{x^2} = 0;$$

but

$$\lim_{x \to 0} \frac{x - \sin x}{x^3} = \frac{1}{6}$$

Thus $(x - \sin x)$ is of the *same* order as x^3 and is of *third* order relative to x. The result means that if x is small, $(x - \sin x)$ is nearly equal to $\frac{1}{6}x^3$.

69. The case in which lim $\alpha/\beta = 1$.—Two infinitesimals are of the same order, by definition, if the limit of their ratio is *any* number $k \neq 0$. Thus $6x$ and $2x$ are infinitesimals of the same order when $x \to 0$ because

$$\lim_{x \to 0} \frac{6x}{2x} = 3.$$

Observe that in this case their difference, $4x$, is not of higher order but is also of the same order. It can easily be shown that *the difference between two infinitesimals α and β is an infinitesimal of higher order than either α or β if and only if*

$$\lim \frac{\alpha}{\beta} = 1.$$

In order to prove this we compare $(\alpha - \beta)$ with β(or α) as follows:

$$\lim \frac{\alpha - \beta}{\beta} = \lim \frac{\alpha}{\beta} - \lim \frac{\beta}{\beta}$$

$$= \lim \frac{\alpha}{\beta} - 1$$

$$= 0 \text{ if and only if } \lim \frac{\alpha}{\beta} = 1.$$

Example

From the fact that

$$\lim_{x \to 0} \frac{\sin x}{\tan x} = 1$$

it follows that the difference between $\sin x$ and $\tan x$ is an infinitesimal of higher order than either when $x \to 0$.

PROBLEMS

1. State which of the following functions of x are infinitesimals if $x \to 0$: $\tan x$, $\cos x$, $\log (1 - x)$, $(e^x - e^{-x})$, $(x^2 + 2)$.

2. Show that $\log (1 + x)$ is an infinitesimal of the same order as x when $x \to 0$.

3. Show that $\tan 2x$ and $\tan x$ are infinitesimals of the same order when $x \to 0$.

4. Show that $\cos x$ and $\cot x$ are infinitesimals of the same order when $x \to \frac{1}{2}\pi$. What statement can be made about the order of their difference?

5. Show that the difference between $\cos x$ and 1 is an infinitesimal of second order relative to x when $x \to 0$.

6. Show that the difference between the quantities $\cos x$ and $(1 - \frac{1}{2}x^2)$ is an infinitesimal of fourth order relative to x when $x \to 0$. What, approximately, is the difference between $\cos x$ and $(1 - \frac{1}{2}x^2)$ when x is small?

7. Show that the difference between $\tan x$ and x is an infinitesimal of third order relative to x when $x \to 0$. What, approximately, is the error involved in substituting x for $\tan x$ when x is small?

8. Find the order, relative to x, of the difference between $\sin x$ and $\tan x$ when $x \to 0$.

9. Find the order, relative to x, of the difference between $\sin 2x$ and $2 \sin x$ when $x \to 0$.

10. Show that the difference between $\sin x$ and the quantity $(x - \frac{1}{6}x^3)$ is an infinitesimal of fifth order relative to x when $x \to 0$.

11. Show that if $\lim (\alpha/\alpha') = 1$ and $\lim (\beta/\beta') = 1$ then $\lim (\alpha/\beta) = \lim (\alpha'/\beta')$.

HINT: $\dfrac{\alpha'}{\beta'} \equiv \dfrac{\alpha}{\beta} \left[\dfrac{\alpha'}{\alpha} \cdot \dfrac{\beta}{\beta'} \right].$

12. Referring to Fig. 76 show that, in general, Δy is an infinitesimal of the same order as Δx. What is the situation at a maximum point where $D_x y = 0$?

13. When $\Delta x \to 0$ the length of the chord AB in Fig. 76 also approaches zero. Show that these infinitesimals are in general of the same order. What is the geometrical significance of the limit of their quotient?

14. Show that the area of the rectangle $DACE$ in Fig. 76 differs from that of the trapezoid $DABE$ by an infinitesimal of higher order than either when $\Delta x \to 0$. Show in particular that the difference is of second order in general.

15. Let $A = x^2$ be the area of a square of side x. Show that the increment ΔA in the area, due to an increment Δx in x, differs from $2x\,\Delta x$ by an infinitesimal of higher order than Δx. HINT: $\Delta A = (x + \Delta x)^2 - x^2$.

16. Let $V = x^3$ be the volume of a cube of edge x. Show that the increment ΔV in the volume, due to an increment Δx in x, differs from $3x^2\Delta x$ by an infinitesimal of higher order than Δx. HINT:

$$\Delta V = (x + \Delta x)^3 - x^3.$$

70. The differential of a function.—Consider the differentiable function $y = f(x)$ whose graph is shown in Fig. 77. Starting at any point $A(x, y)$, let x increase, or decrease, by

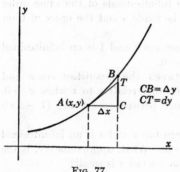

Fig. 77.

a small amount Δx. The corresponding increment in y is represented by $CB = \Delta y$.

In order to obtain an approximation to Δy, let us multiply the slope of the tangent at A by Δx obtaining

$$CT = f'(x) \cdot \Delta x.$$

It is fairly obvious that if Δx is small and $f'(x) \neq 0$, this quantity is a good approximation to Δy. In fact, the difference between them is an infinitesimal of higher order than Δx (or Δy) when $\Delta x \to 0$. For

$$\lim_{\Delta x \to 0} \frac{\Delta y}{f'(x)\Delta x} = \lim_{\Delta x \to 0} \frac{\dfrac{\Delta y}{\Delta x}}{f'(x)} = \frac{f'(x)}{f'(x)} = 1.$$

The increment Δy may therefore be regarded as consisting of two parts:

1. The part represented by $CT = f'(x)\Delta x$; this is the larger part, if Δx is sufficiently small and $f'(x) \neq 0$, and it is called the *principal part** of Δy relative to Δx.

* Let α and β be infinitesimals, α being a function of β, such that

2. The part represented by TB; this part is an arbitrarily small fractional part of Δy under the conditions stated above.

If x is an independent variable we call the quantity $f'(x) \cdot \Delta x$ the *differential* of the function $f(x)$ and denote it by the symbol $d[f(x)]$. Thus

$$d(x^2) = 2x \cdot \Delta x;$$
$$d(\sin x) = \cos x \cdot \Delta x.$$

If we denote the function $f(x)$ by the single letter y, we denote its differential by dy and write

$$dy = f'(x)\Delta x.$$

It is customary to replace Δx by dx and to define the differential of the independent variable x by the equation $dx \equiv \Delta x$. This is consistent with the fact that if we take $f(x) = x$ in the above definition, $f'(x) = 1$ and we have $d(x) = 1 \cdot \Delta x$.

Finally, *whether x is the independent variable or not, we define the differential of the function $y = f(x)$ by the equation*

$$dy = f'(x)dx.$$

If x is independent, $dx \equiv \Delta x$. If we have

$$y = f(x) \quad \text{and} \quad x = g(t) \quad (t \text{ independent}),$$

then,

$$dy = f'(x)dx \quad \text{where} \quad dx = g'(t)dt \quad (dt \equiv \Delta t).$$

Up to now we have not regarded the symbol dy/dx as a fraction. The separate symbols dy and dx had no meanings. With the above definitions it is clear that we may now, if we choose, think of dy/dx as an ordinary fraction.

Example

The volume and surface area of a sphere are, respectively,

$$V = \tfrac{4}{3}\pi r^3; \quad S = 4\pi r^2.$$

$\lim (\alpha/\beta) = k$; then $\alpha = k\beta + \epsilon\beta$ where $\epsilon \to 0$ along with α and β, and $k\beta$ is called the *principal part* of α relative to β.

Their differentials are

$$dV = 4\pi r^2 dr; \qquad dS = 8\pi r\, dr.$$

If we divide dV by dS we have

$$\frac{dV}{dS} = \frac{4\pi r^2 dr}{8\pi r\, dr} = \tfrac{1}{2}r.$$

This is the derivative of the volume with respect to the surface area.

71. Method of obtaining the differential.—From the definition it is evident that in order to obtain the differential dy of a function $y = f(x)$ it is only necessary to multiply the derivative by dx.

Example 1

$$y = 6x^2 + 3;$$
$$\frac{dy}{dx} = 12x$$
$$dy = 12x\, dx.$$

Example 2

$$A = \pi r^2;$$
$$\frac{dA}{dr} = 2\pi r$$
$$dA = 2\pi r\, dr.$$

72. Application to approximate formulas.—An immediate application of the differential of a function comes from the fact that, if Δx is small, dy is a good approximation to Δy.

Example 1

Compute approximately the volume of metal in a hollow spherical shell, the thickness being 0.05 in. and the inside radius 5 in.

Solution

The volume of metal is equal to the amount by which the volume of a sphere increases when its radius changes from 5 to 5.05 in. Using dv as an approximation to this, we have

$$v = \tfrac{4}{3}\pi r^3;$$
$$\frac{dv}{dr} = 4\pi r^2$$
$$dv = 4\pi r^2 dr.$$

Taking $r = 5$ in. and $dr = 0.05$ in., we find

$$dv = 4\pi(25)(0.05) = 15.7 \text{ cu. in.}$$

By the usual methods one finds the actual volume to be 15.87 cu. in.

Example 2

Compute approximately $(1.98)^5$.

Solution

We may find the amount by which x^5 decreases when x decreases from 2 to 1.98 and subtract this from 32.

$$y = x^5$$
$$dy = 5x^4 dx.$$

Taking $x = 2$ and $dx = -0.02$, we find

$$dy = 5(16)(-0.02) = -1.6;$$

i.e., x^5 decreases by 1.6 when x changes from 2 to 1.98.   Hence

$$(1.98)^5 = 32 - 1.6 = 30.4.$$

Using logarithms, one obtains the value 30.43.

PROBLEMS

Find the differential of each of the following functions:

1. $y = \sqrt{x^2 + 5}$.

2. $z = (x^2 - a^2)^3$.

3. $s = \dfrac{x}{\sqrt{x^2 - 1}}$.

4. $s = \dfrac{x^2}{x^2 + 4}$.

5. $y = 7 \sin 3\theta$.

6. $y = \sqrt{\tan x}$.

7. $y = \arccos \frac{1}{2}x$.

8. $y = \log(x + \sqrt{x^2 + a^2})$

9. $y = \dfrac{1}{a} \arctan \dfrac{x}{a}$.

10. $y = \dfrac{1}{2a} \log \dfrac{x - a}{x + a}$.

In each of the following problems, find $D_x y$ by dividing dy by dx:

11. $y = a \sin \theta$
$\quad\ x = a \cos \theta$.

12. $y = t^3 + 4t$
$\quad\ \ x = 2t^2 - 1$.

13. $y = a(1 - \cos \theta)$
$\quad\ \ x = a(\theta - \sin \theta)$.

14. $y = 2 \sin t - \sin 2t$
$\quad\ \ x = 2 \cos t - \cos 2t$.

15. Find the derivative of the volume of a cube with respect to its surface area by dividing dV by dS.

16. Sketch the curve $y = \frac{1}{4}x^2$.   Compute both Δy and dy corresponding to $x = 3$ and $\Delta x = 0.5$.   Show both on the graph.

17. Sketch the curve $y = 8 - \frac{1}{8}x^3$.   Compute both Δy and dy corresponding to $x = 2$ and $\Delta x = 0.5$.   Show both on the graph.

18. The base of a right triangle is 4 ft. and the altitude is 3 ft.   If the altitude changes by a small amount Δh, the base remaining fixed, find approximately the change in the hypotenuse.

19. Compute approximately the area of a walk 3.5 ft. wide around a city square that is 400 ft. on a side. Make a sketch showing the square and walk, and indicate the part of the walk that is neglected in your approximation.

20. The radius of a circle is 24 in. By approximately how much does the area decrease if the radius decreases $\frac{1}{32}$ in.?

21. Derive an approximate formula for the volume of metal in a thin spherical shell.

22. Derive an approximate formula for the volume of metal in a can having the shape of a cube of edge x, the thickness t of the metal being small.

23. Derive an approximate formula for the volume of metal in a cylindrical pipe of diameter D and length L, the thickness t of the metal being small.

24. Sketch the curve $y = 1/x$. Show that a small change Δx in x produces a change of approximately $-\Delta x/x^2$ in y. Use this result to compute the decimal equivalent of $\frac{1}{47}$.

25. What is approximately the change in $\sin \theta$ per minute of change in θ in the neighborhood of 60°? ($1' = 0.00029$ radian.)

26. Compute approximately the value of $\tan 43°$. ($1° = 0.0175$ radian.)

27. Compute approximately the value of $\sec^2 46°$.

28. Compute approximately the value of $\sqrt[3]{25}$, using the differential. Show that the process is equivalent to expanding $(27 - 2)^{\frac{1}{3}}$ by the binomial theorem and using only the first two terms.

Make the following calculations approximately using differentials:

29. $\sqrt{6.33}$.   HINT: $\sqrt{6.25} = 2.5$.

30. $\sqrt{10.35}$.   HINT: $\sqrt{10.24} = 3.2$.

31. $\sqrt{3.15}$.   **32.** $\sqrt[3]{1.704}$.   **33.** $(3.02)^3$.

34. $4^{2.1}$.   **35.** $\dfrac{1}{9.92}$.   **36.** $\sqrt[3]{127}$.

37. The area of a sector of a circle of radius r and central angle α is $A = \frac{1}{2}r^2\alpha$. Show that if r increases by a small amount Δr, α remaining fixed, the increase in area is approximately $dA = (r\alpha) \cdot \Delta r$. Draw the figure and show that this added area is approximately a rectangle with dimensions $r\alpha$ and Δr.

73. Application to small errors.—In scientific work one often determines the value of a quantity x by measurement and uses this measured value in computing the value of

another quantity y.   From a knowledge of the instruments used he may be able to estimate the greatest possible error in the measurement of x.   He is then interested in knowing the corresponding possible error in y.

Example

The diameter of a cylindrical bar is found to be 4.2 in. with a possible error of 0.05 in.   What is the greatest possible error in the computed area?

Solution

The true diameter is between 4.15 and 4.25 in.   The greatest possible error is then the amount by which the area of a circle increases when its diameter changes from 4.2 to 4.25 in.   Using dA as an approximation to this we have

$$A = \frac{\pi D^2}{4}$$

$$dA = \frac{\pi D}{2} dD.$$

Taking

$$D = 4.2 \qquad \text{and} \qquad dD = 0.05,$$

we find

$$dA = \pi(2.1)(0.05) = 0.33 \text{ sq. in.}$$

The *possible relative error* may be defined as the ratio of the maximum possible error to the computed value. In the above case the possible relative error is

$$\frac{dA}{A} = \frac{0.33}{\pi(2.1)^2} = \frac{0.33}{13.85} = 0.024, \text{ or } 2.4 \text{ per cent.}$$

It is possible to find the relative error dA/A directly by taking the natural logarithm of each side before differentiating; thus

$$A = \frac{\pi D^2}{4}$$

$$\log A = \log \frac{\pi}{4} + 2 \log D$$

$$\frac{1}{A} \frac{dA}{dD} = \frac{2}{D}$$

$$\frac{dA}{A} = 2 \frac{dD}{D}.$$

This equation states that the relative error in A is twice the relative error in D; taking $D = 4.2$ and $dD = 0.05$ we have

$$\frac{dA}{A} = 2\,\frac{0.05}{4.2} = 0.024, \text{ or } 2.4 \text{ per cent.}$$

PROBLEMS

1. A square with each side equal to 30 ft. is laid out. If there is a possible error of 0.05 ft. in each side, what is approximately the greatest possible error in the computed area?

2. An equilateral triangle is laid out with sides 12 ft. long. If there is a possible error of 2 in. in each side, what is approximately the greatest possible error in the computed area?

3. The edges of a cube are each 10 in. by measurement. If there is a possible error of 0.05 in. in each edge, what is approximately the greatest possible error in the volume?

4. A cubical box is to be made to hold 1,000 cu. in. What is the allowable error in the edge if the error in the volume is not to exceed 2 cu. in.

5. The diameter of a circle is to be measured and its area computed. The diameter can be measured with an error not exceeding 0.005 in. and the error in the area must not exceed 0.1 sq. in. For what size circles is this process satisfactory?

6. The diameter of a sphere is to be measured and its volume computed. If the possible error in the diameter is 0.002, and the allowable error in the volume is 0.5 cu. in., for what size spheres is the process satisfactory?

7. A certain instrument will measure an angle θ with an error not greater than $1'$. It is necessary that the error in $\sin \theta$ shall not exceed 0.00015. For what range of acute angles is this instrument satisfactory? ($1' = 0.00029$ radian.)

8. If an angle θ can be measured with an error not more than $0.05°$, for what size acute angles will the error in $\tan \theta$ be less than 0.02?

9. What is the error in $\cos \theta$ due to a small error $\Delta\theta$ in measuring θ? Explain the negative sign.

10. An angle θ is measured, with an error not exceeding $10'$, and its cosine is found from tables. For what range of acute angles is this process satisfactory if the error in $\cos \theta$ must not exceed 0.001?

11. For what range of acute angles will an error of $15'$ in measuring θ result in an error of not more than 0.005 in the value of $\log_{10} \tan \theta$?

12. Show that the error in $\tan \theta$, due to a small error $\Delta\theta$ in measuring θ, is approximately three times as large when θ is near $60°$ as when it is near $30°$.

13. The magnitude of an angle is to be found by measuring its tangent. If the tangent can be determined with an error not exceeding 0.001 and the error in the angle must not exceed 1', for what range of acute angles is the method satisfactory?

14. For what range of values of x can $\sqrt[3]{x+1}$ be replaced by $\sqrt[3]{x}$ with an error not more than 0.01?

15. If $\log_{10} N = 1.936$ with a possible error of 0.002 find N and the corresponding possible error.

16. If $\log_{10} N = 2.366$ with a possible error of 0.003, find N and the corresponding possible error.

17. Show that an error of 1 per cent in measuring the radius of a sphere will result in an error of approximately 3 per cent in the computed volume.

18. Find the approximate relative error in the computed volume and surface area of a cube due to an error of 1 per cent in the edge.

19. Show that the relative error in the computed value of a function of the form kx^n, due to a small error dx in x, is approximately n times the relative error in x.

20. The period of a simple pendulum is $T = 2\pi \sqrt{\dfrac{l}{g}}$. By what per cent should the length be changed to correct for a loss of 2 min. per day?

21. Show that if θ is near $\pi/4$ the relative error in $\tan \theta$, due to a small error $d\theta$ in measuring θ, is approximately $\pi/2$ times the relative error in θ.

CHAPTER XIV

INTEGRATION

74. Introduction.—Up to now we have been concerned with the problem: Given a function $f(x)$, to obtain its derivative. In many important applications of the calculus we are confronted by the inverse problem, namely: Given the derivative $f'(x)$ or the differential $f'(x)dx$ of a function, to find the function. We shall see later that the problems of finding the length of a curve, the area bounded by a curve, the work done by a variable force, etc., all lead to this inverse problem.

Suppose, for example, that we wished to find the length of the arc of the parabola $y = x^2$ from $(0, 0)$ to $(2, 4)$. Regarding the length s of the arc from $(0, 0)$ to any other point (x, y) on the curve as a function of x, we know from the formula for the derivative of arc that

$$\frac{ds}{dx} = \sqrt{1 + 4x^2}.$$

The first step in solving our problem would, therefore, be to find a function

$$s = F(x)$$

whose derivative is $\sqrt{1 + 4x^2}$, or whose differential is $\sqrt{1 + 4x^2}\, dx$. Such a function is called an *integral* of $\sqrt{1 + 4x^2}\, dx$ and the process of finding it is called *integration*. It is denoted by the symbol

$$\int (\quad)dx,$$

which thus denotes the inverse of the operation which was denoted by the symbol

$$\frac{d}{dx} (\quad).$$

168

Thus, just as we use the abbreviation $\frac{d}{dx}(x^2) = ?$ to mean, "what is the derivative with respect to x of x^2?", we use the abbreviation

$$\int x^2 dx = ?$$

to mean, "what is the function whose derivative is x^2—or whose differential is $x^2 dx$?" The function that is to be integrated (x^2 in this case) is called the *integrand*.

The present chapter will be devoted to the problem of gaining some facility in the technique of integration.

75. The problem of integration.—The definition of the derivative carried with it a formal process by which one could find the derivative of a given function. There is no process for integration which quite corresponds to this. Given a function to be integrated one tries to determine, from his knowledge of differentiation, what function or what type of function might have this given function for its derivative. Thus, one finds easily that

$$\int \cos x \, dx = \sin x$$

since the derivative of $\sin x$ is known to be $\cos x$. Almost as easily as one finds that

$$\int x^2 dx = \frac{x^3}{3},$$

since the derivative of $x^3/3$ is x^2. In the case of

$$\int \sqrt{1 + 4x^2} \, dx,$$

the result cannot be obtained by inspection; *i.e.*, one cannot think of any simple function whose derivative is $\sqrt{1 + 4x^2}$. The result, which is obtained by methods to be explained later, is

$$\int \sqrt{1 + 4x^2} \, dx = \frac{x \sqrt{1 + 4x^2}}{2} + \frac{\log (\sqrt{1 + 4x^2} + 2x)}{4}.$$

The student may verify this integration by differentiating the right-hand side.

There is of course no assurance that an arbitrarily selected function can be integrated at all. Thus, while the integrand in

$$\int \sqrt{\sin x}\, dx$$

appears to be quite simple, it happens that there is no finite combination of the elementary functions that we have studied whose derivative is $\sqrt{\sin x}$. The integration cannot therefore be performed in the elementary sense.

76. The constant of integration.—Since the derivative of $x^3/3$ is x^2, it follows that $x^3/3$ is *an* integral of $x^2 dx$. It is obvious, however, that

$$\frac{x^3}{3} + 4 \qquad \text{or} \qquad \frac{x^3}{3} - 7 \qquad \text{or} \qquad \frac{x^3}{3} + C$$

where C is *any* constant is also an integral, since the derivative is x^2 in each case. This last integral is the *most general function whose derivative is x^2*, in the sense that there is no function whose derivative is x^2 except those which can be obtained from it by giving particular values to C. It is called the *indefinite integral* and C is called the *constant of integration*. Integrals that may be obtained by giving particular values to C are called *particular integrals*.

That the indefinite integral obtained by adding an arbitrary constant C to any particular integral has the property just mentioned may be shown by proving that if $F(x)$ and $G(x)$ are two functions having the same derivative, they can differ only by a constant. Thus, if

$$\frac{d}{dx} F(x) = \phi(x) \qquad \text{and} \qquad \frac{d}{dx} G(x) = \phi(x)$$

then

$$\frac{d}{dx} [F(x) - G(x)] = 0.$$

Since the only function whose derivative is 0 for all values of x is a constant,* we have

$$F(x) - G(x) = k.$$

* From the theorem of mean value, $f(x) - f(a) = (x - a)f'(x_1)$ **where**

77. Formulas for integration.—From the known formulas for differentiation, we can write down immediately a list of formulas for integration. They can be easily memorized by thinking of the corresponding formulas for differentiation.

(1) $$\int (du + dv + dw) = \int du + \int dv + \int dw.$$

(2) $$\int a \, dv = a \int dv.$$

(3) $$\int v^n dv = \frac{v^{n+1}}{n+1} + C, \quad (n \neq -1).$$

(4) $$\int \frac{dv}{v} = \log v + C.$$

(5) $$\int a^v dv = \frac{a^v}{\log a} + C.$$

(6) $$\int e^v dv = e^v + C.$$

(7) $$\int \sin v \, dv = -\cos v + C.$$

(8) $$\int \cos v \, dv = \sin v + C.$$

(9) $$\int \sec^2 v \, dv = \tan v + C.$$

(10) $$\int \csc^2 v \, dv = -\cot v + C.$$

(11) $$\int \sec v \tan v \, dv = \sec v + C.$$

(12) $$\int \csc v \cot v \, dv = -\csc v + C.$$

(13) $$\int \frac{dv}{v^2 + a^2} = \frac{1}{a} \arctan \frac{v}{a} + C.$$

(14) $$\int \frac{dv}{\sqrt{a^2 - v^2}} = \arcsin \frac{v}{a} + C.$$

There are four additional formulas that the student will find convenient. They are not obtained from differentia-

$a < x_1 < x.$ If $f'(x) = 0$ throughout an interval, then over the interval $f(x) = f(a) = k.$

tion formulas and hence are more difficult to remember. The direct derivation of these will be assigned later as problems.

$$(15) \qquad \int \frac{dv}{v^2 - a^2} = \frac{1}{2a} \log \frac{v - a}{v + a} + C.$$

$$(16) \qquad \int \frac{dv}{\sqrt{v^2 \pm a^2}} = \log (v + \sqrt{v^2 \pm a^2}) + C.$$

$$(17) \qquad \int \sec v \, dv = \log (\sec v + \tan v) + C.$$

$$(18) \qquad \int \csc v \, dv = \log (\csc v - \cot v) + C.$$

78. Formulas (1) to (4).—It is extremely important that the student understand clearly the meaning of the formulas. Formula (1) states that the integral of the sum of several functions is equal to the sum of their separate integrals. Thus,

$$\int (x^3 + 4x^2 - 3)dx = \int x^3 dx + \int 4x^2 dx - \int 3 \, dx.$$

Formula (2) states that the integral of the product of a constant and a function is equal to the constant times the integral of the function. Thus, in the above example,

$$\int 4x^2 dx = 4 \int x^2 dx = 4 \cdot \frac{x^3}{3}.$$

$$\int 3 \, dx = 3 \int dx = 3x.$$

Finally, then,

$$\int (x^3 + 4x^2 - 3)dx = \int x^3 dx + 4 \int x^2 dx - 3 \int dx$$

$$= \frac{x^4}{4} + \frac{4}{3} x^3 - 3x + C.$$

Great care must be exercised in applying formulas (3) and (4). Formula (3) states that the integral of the product of the nth power of a function v and **the differential dv of this function** is equal to the $(n + 1)$th power divided by $(n + 1)$. Thus,

$$\int (x^2 + 4x + 1)^3(2x + 4)dx = \frac{(x^2 + 4x + 1)^4}{4} + C.$$

Here

$$v = x^2 + 4x + 1, \qquad dv = (2x + 4)dx.$$

The formula does not say, for example, that

$$\int (4x^2 + 1)^2 dx = \frac{(4x^2 + 1)^3}{3} + C.$$

This integrand is not in the form $v^n dv$ because, if it were, $v = 4x^2 + 1$, and differentiating $dv = 8x\ dx$. Since we do not have $8x\ dx$, the formula does not apply. The problem can be solved, however, by squaring out the integrand and then integrating. Thus,

$$\int (4x^2 + 1)^2 dx = \int (16x^4 + 8x^2 + 1)dx$$
$$= \frac{16x^5}{5} + \frac{8x^3}{3} + x + C.$$

If only a *constant factor* is lacking, this can be easily supplied. Consider, for example,

$$\int x^2 \sqrt{2x^3 + 9}\ dx.$$

If we let $v = 2x^3 + 9$, then $n = \frac{1}{2}$ and dv is $6x^2 dx$. The above may be written in the form

$$\int (2x^3 + 9)^{\frac{1}{2}}(x^2 dx)$$

where only the *constant* 6 is lacking. We may now *without changing the value of the integrand* multiply by 6/6 and we have

$$\int (2x^3 + 9)^{\frac{1}{2}} \frac{6x^2 dx}{6}.$$

The 6 in the denominator may be taken outside, leaving the integrand exactly in the form $v^n dv$. We have, then, finally

$$\int x^2 \sqrt{2x^3 + 9}\ dx = \int (2x^3 + 9)^{\frac{1}{2}} x^2 dx$$
$$= \tfrac{1}{6}\int (2x^3 + 9)^{\frac{1}{2}} 6x^2 dx$$
$$= \frac{1}{6} \frac{(2x^3 + 9)^{\frac{3}{2}}}{\frac{3}{2}} + C$$
$$= \frac{1}{9} (2x^3 + 9)^{\frac{3}{2}} + C.$$

As an example of the use of formula (4) consider

$$\int \frac{3x\ dx}{5 - 4x^2}.$$

We may let

$$v = 5 - 4x^2,$$

and differentiating

$$dv = -8x\ dx,$$

hence,

$$\int \frac{3x\ dx}{5 - 4x^2} = 3 \int \frac{x\ dx}{5 - 4x^2}$$

$$= -\frac{3}{8} \int \frac{-8x\ dx}{5 - 4x^2}$$

$$= -\frac{3}{8} \log (5 - 4x^2) + C.$$

PROBLEMS

Integrate each of the following by reducing to the form $\int v^n dv$:

1. $\int (3x^4 + 4x^2 + 2)dx.$

2. $\int \sqrt{2x}\ dx.$

3. $\int \sqrt[3]{4x + 1}\ dx.$

4. $\int \frac{dx}{x^3}.$

5. $\int 6t^{-\frac{1}{2}}dt.$

6. $\int \frac{y^4 + 1}{\sqrt{y}}\ dy.$

7. $\int 2s \sqrt{s}\ ds.$

8. $\int \sqrt{a^2 - x^2}\ x\ dx.$

9. $\int (4 + x + x^2)^2 dx.$

10. $\int \sin x \cos x\ dx.$

11. $\int \tan^2 3x \sec^2 3x\ dx.$

12. $\int \frac{\log^2 x\ dx}{x}.$

13. $\int \frac{2\ dx}{x^2 - 6x + 9}.$

14. $\int (a^{\frac{1}{2}} - x^{\frac{1}{2}})^2 dx.$

15. $\int \frac{e^x dx}{\sqrt{e^x + 4}}.$

16. $\int \frac{3 \arctan x\ dx}{x^2 + 1}.$

17. $\int \frac{(x^2 + 2)^3}{x^2}\ dx.$

18. $\int (1 + x)^2 \sqrt{x}\ dx.$

19. $\int (4 + x)(3 - x)\ dx.$

20. $\int \left(\frac{1}{x^2} - \sqrt[3]{8x} + \sqrt{x}\right) dx.$

Integrate the following by reducing to the form $\int \frac{dv}{v}$:

21. $\displaystyle\int \frac{dx}{2x+1}.$

22. $\displaystyle\int \frac{x\,dx}{3x^2-1}.$

23. $\displaystyle\int \frac{\sec^2\theta\,d\theta}{3\tan\theta+6}.$

24. $\displaystyle\int \tan x\,dx.$

HINT: $\tan x = \dfrac{\sin x}{\cos x}.$

25. $\displaystyle\int \cot x\,dx.$

26. $\displaystyle\int \frac{(x-3)dx}{x^2-6x+4}.$

27. $\displaystyle\int \frac{\sin\frac{1}{2}x\,dx}{4\cos\frac{1}{2}x+3}.$

28. $\displaystyle\int \frac{2^x\,dx}{2^x+3}.$

29. $\displaystyle\int \frac{e^x dx}{3e^x+4}.$

30. $\displaystyle\int \frac{ds}{s\log s}.$

Integrate the following using formulas (1) to (4):

31. $\displaystyle\int \frac{3x\,dx}{(4-2x^2)^2}.$

32. $\displaystyle\int (x^2+2)^2 x^2 dx.$

33. $\displaystyle\int \frac{x\,dx}{\sqrt{a^2-x^2}}.$

34. $\displaystyle\int \frac{\sec^2\theta\,d\theta}{(1+\tan\theta)^3}.$

35. $\displaystyle\int \frac{\csc^2 2x\,dx}{3+4\cot 2x}.$

36. $\displaystyle\int \sin 2x \sin x\,dx.$

HINT: $\sin 2x = 2\sin x \cos x.$

37. $\displaystyle\int \cot\theta \log\sin\theta\,d\theta.$

38. $\displaystyle\int \frac{\log\tan\frac{1}{2}\theta}{\sin\theta}\,d\theta.$

39. $\displaystyle\int \sec\theta\,d\theta.$ *Formula* (17)

HINT: Multiply and divide by $(\sec\theta + \tan\theta)$.

40. $\displaystyle\int \csc\theta\,d\theta.$ *Formula* (18)

41. Evaluate $\displaystyle\int (x+1)^2 dx$ both with and without expanding the integrand. Are the results equivalent?

42. Show that $\int \sin x \cos x\,dx = \frac{1}{2}\sin^2 x + C$ and that $\int \cos x \sin x\,dx = -\frac{1}{2}\cos^2 x + C.$ Explain the apparent difference in the two results.

43. Explain why formula (3) cannot be used to evaluate

$$\int (x^2+4)^{\frac{1}{2}}dx.$$

44. Explain why formula (3) but not formula (4) could be used to evaluate $\displaystyle\int \frac{x\,dx}{\sqrt{4-x^2}}.$

45. Explain why formula (3) cannot be used directly to evaluate $\int \cos^3 x\,dx.$ Perform the integration using the fact that

$$\cos^2 x = 1 - \sin^2 x.$$

Could this same procedure be used on $\int \cos^4 x\,dx$?

79. Formulas (5) to (12), (17), (18).—Again the student is warned that he must exercise great care in fitting the given problem to the formula to be used. For example, in using formula (5) he must make certain that the quantity used for *dv is actually the differential of the function v* which is the exponent. Constant factors can of course be supplied as before. Thus,

$$\int 4^{3x+2}dx = \tfrac{1}{3}\int 4^{3x+2}\, 3\, dx = \frac{4^{3x+2}}{3\log 4} + C.$$

Formula (6) could not be used to evaluate

$$\int e^{x^2}dx,$$

since, if this were to be $e^v dv$, then

$$v = x^2 \quad \text{and} \quad dv = 2x\, dx.$$

PROBLEMS

Integrate the following by reducing to the form $\int a^v dv$ or $\int e^v dv$:

1. $\int e^{2x}dx.$

2. $\int 4^{3x+5}dx.$

3. $\int 6^{\tan 2\theta}\sec^2 2\theta\, d\theta.$

4. $\int xe^{x^2}dx.$

5. $\int a^x e^x dx.$

6. $\int 4x^2 e^{-x^3}dx.$

7. $\int (e^{\frac{x}{2}} + e^{-\frac{x}{2}})dx.$

8. $\int (e^x + e^{-x})^2 dx.$

9. $\int \frac{a}{2}\left(e^{\frac{x}{a}} + e^{-\frac{x}{a}}\right)^2 dx.$

10. $\int \frac{e^{\log x^2}dx}{x}.$

11. $\int \frac{10^{\frac{1}{x^2}}dx}{x^3}.$

12. $\int e^{\sin x \cos x}\cos 2x\, dx.$

13. $\int e^{(\sin x + \cos x)^2}\cos 2x\, dx.$

14. $\int \frac{2^{\arctan x}dx}{x^2 + 1}.$

15. $\int (4x^2 e^{-x^3} + e^{-x})dx.$

Integrate the following using formulas (1) to (4), (7) to (12), (17), (18):

16. $\int \sin 4x\, dx = \tfrac{1}{4}\int \sin 4x \cdot 4\, dx = -\tfrac{1}{4}\cos 4x + C.$

17. $\int \cos 2x\, dx.$

18. $\int \sec^2 (4x + 2)dx.$

19. $\int x \csc^2 (x^2 + 1)dx.$

20. $\int \frac{dx}{\sec \frac{1}{2}x}.$

21. $\int \sec 3\theta \tan 3\theta\, d\theta.$

22. $\int \dfrac{dt}{3\cos^2 2t}.$

23. $\int \cot \tfrac12 x \sin \tfrac12 x\, dx.$

24. $\int 3\sin \pi x\, dx.$

25. $\int (\sin x + \cos x)^2 dx.$

26. $\int \sec (3x + 4)dx.$

27. $\int x \csc x^2 dx.$

28. $\int \dfrac{dx}{\sin 3x}.$

29. $\int \dfrac{d\theta}{\cos \pi\theta}.$

30. $\int \dfrac{\tan \theta\, d\theta}{\sin 2\theta}.$

31. $\int \dfrac{\cos 2x\, dx}{\cos x}.$

32. $\int \dfrac{\cos x\, dx}{\sin \tfrac12 x}.$

33. $\int \dfrac{\sin 2\theta\, d\theta}{\cos^2 \theta \sin \theta}.$

34. $\int \dfrac{\tan x}{\cos x}\, dx.$

35. $\int 4\sin 2x \sec x\, dx.$

36. $\int \dfrac{2\cos x\, dx}{\sin^2 x}.$

37. $\int \sin \pi x \cos \pi x\, dx.$

38. Evaluate $\int \sin 2x\, dx$ using formula (7) and also by writing the integrand as $2\sin x \cos x$. Explain the apparent difference in the results.

39. $\int \cos 2\theta \sin \theta\, d\theta.$

40. $\int \sec^2 \theta \tan 2\theta\, d\theta.$

80. Formulas (13) to (16).—In applying these formulas the student must again exercise great care. In using formula (13) for example, he must make certain that the *numerator* of the integrand is *exactly the differential of the function whose square occurs in the denominator.* Constant factors can be supplied as before. Thus, we may fit

$$\int \frac{dx}{(3x + 1)^2 + 6}$$

to formula (13), letting

$$v = 3x + 1 \quad \text{and} \quad a = \sqrt{6}.$$

Of course $dv = 3\, dx$ and we then have

$$\int \frac{dx}{(3x + 1)^2 + 6} = \frac{1}{3} \int \frac{3\, dx}{(3x + 1)^2 + \sqrt{6}^2}$$

$$= \frac{1}{3}\left(\frac{1}{\sqrt{6}} \arctan \frac{3x + 1}{\sqrt{6}}\right) + C.$$

PROBLEMS

1. $\int \dfrac{dx}{9x^2 + 4}$.

2. $\int \dfrac{dx}{\sqrt{9 - x^2}}$.

3. $\int \dfrac{dx}{\sqrt{10 - 4x^2}}$.

4. $\int \dfrac{x\,dx}{x^4 - 16}$.

5. $\int \dfrac{\sin x\,dx}{\sqrt{\cos^2 x + 16}}$.

6. $\int \dfrac{e^x dx}{e^{2x} + 4}$.

7. $\int \dfrac{dx}{\sqrt{a^2 - b^2 x^2}}$.

8. $\int \dfrac{dx}{x(\log^2 x + 9)}$.

9. $\int \dfrac{t\,dt}{(t^2 + 4)^2 - 9}$.

10. $\int \dfrac{dx}{\sqrt{10 - (1 + 2x)^2}}$.

11. $\int \dfrac{dx}{x^2 + 2x + 5}$.

12. $\int \dfrac{dt}{4t^2 - 4t + 7}$.

Hint: $x^2 + 2x + 5 = (x + 1)^2 + 4$.

13. $\int \dfrac{dx}{\sqrt{2x - x^2}}$.

14. $\int \dfrac{ds}{\sqrt{6s - s^2 - 5}}$.

Hint: $2x - x^2 = 1 - (1 - x)^2$.

15. $\int \dfrac{x\,dx}{x^4 + 4x^2 + 14}$.

16. $\int \dfrac{dt}{4t^2 - 4t - 3}$.

17. $\int \dfrac{t\,dt}{\sqrt{23 + 12t^2 - 4t^4}}$.

18. $\int \dfrac{dz}{\sqrt{z^2 + 2z + 7}}$.

19. $\int \dfrac{2^x dx}{\sqrt{9 - 4^x}}$.

20. $\int \dfrac{dx}{\sqrt{16x^2 - 24x - 7}}$.

21. $\int \dfrac{\sec^2 u\,du}{\tan^2 u + 1}$ by two methods.

22. $\int \dfrac{e^{\frac{x}{2}} dx}{e^x - 1}$.

23. $\int \dfrac{(2x + 6)dx}{x^2 + 4x + 8}$.

Hint: Write $2x + 6$ as $(2x + 4) + 2$ and separate into two integrals.

24. $\int \dfrac{(8x - 1)dx}{4x^2 - 4x - 3}$.

25. $\int \dfrac{(18x - 3)dx}{\sqrt{9x^2 - 12x}}$.

26.
$$\int \frac{(2x + 1)dx}{4x^2 + 12x + 13} = \frac{1}{4} \int \frac{(8x + 4)dx}{4x^2 + 12x + 13}$$
$$= \frac{1}{4} \int \frac{(8x + 12 - 8)dx}{4x^2 + 12x + 13}$$
$$= \frac{1}{4} \int \frac{(8x + 12)dx}{4x^2 + 12x + 13}$$
$$- 2 \int \frac{dx}{4x^2 + 12x + 13}.$$

27. $\int \dfrac{(x+3)dx}{x^2+4x-5}.$

28. $\int \dfrac{(3x+5)dx}{x^2+x+1}.$

29. $\int \dfrac{(2x-7)dx}{\sqrt{3-6x-9x^2}}.$

30. $\int \dfrac{(4x+1)dx}{\sqrt{4x^2-12x+5}}.$

31. $\int \dfrac{(4x+7)dx}{\sqrt{x^2-3x+2}}.$

32. $\int \dfrac{(x+6)dx}{\sqrt{x^2-5x+1}}.$

33. $\int \dfrac{(7x+2)dx}{15+6x-9x^2}.$

34. $\int \dfrac{(ax+b)dx}{cx^2+dx+e}.$

81. Miscellaneous problems.—Success in integrating depends largely on one's ability to pick out the formula or procedure that is most apt to yield the desired result. Solving a large number of problems will give the student some facility in doing this.

PROBLEMS

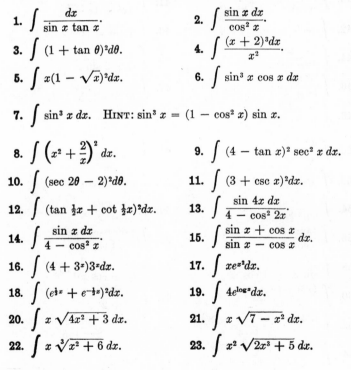

1. $\int \dfrac{dx}{\sin x \tan x}.$

2. $\int \dfrac{\sin x\, dx}{\cos^2 x}.$

3. $\int (1+\tan\theta)^2 d\theta.$

4. $\int \dfrac{(x+2)^3 dx}{x^2}.$

5. $\int x(1-\sqrt{x})^2 dx.$

6. $\int \sin^3 x \cos x\, dx$

7. $\int \sin^3 x\, dx.$ HINT: $\sin^3 x = (1-\cos^2 x)\sin x.$

8. $\int \left(x^2 + \dfrac{2}{x}\right)^2 dx.$

9. $\int (4-\tan x)^2 \sec^2 x\, dx.$

10. $\int (\sec 2\theta - 2)^2 d\theta.$

11. $\int (3+\csc x)^2 dx.$

12. $\int (\tan\tfrac{1}{2}x + \cot\tfrac{1}{2}x)^2 dx.$

13. $\int \dfrac{\sin 4x\, dx}{4-\cos^2 2x}.$

14. $\int \dfrac{\sin x\, dx}{4-\cos^2 x}.$

15. $\int \dfrac{\sin x + \cos x}{\sin x - \cos x}\, dx.$

16. $\int (4+3^x)3^x dx.$

17. $\int xe^{x^2} dx.$

18. $\int (e^{\frac{1}{2}x} + e^{-\frac{1}{2}x})^2 dx.$

19. $\int 4e^{\log x} dx.$

20. $\int x\sqrt{4x^2+3}\, dx.$

21. $\int x\sqrt{7-x^2}\, dx.$

22. $\int x\sqrt[3]{x^2+6}\, dx.$

23. $\int x^2\sqrt{2x^3+5}\, dx.$

In Probs. 24 to 31 first perform the indicated division:

24. $\int \dfrac{(3x^2 + 5x + 4)dx}{x + 3}.$

25. $\int \dfrac{(x^2 - 6x + 11)dx}{2x - 6}.$

26. $\int \dfrac{(2x - 9)dx}{x - 3}.$

27. $\int \dfrac{(4x + 13)dx}{2x + 5}.$

28. $\int \dfrac{(2x^3 + 4)dx}{x - 6}.$

29. $\int \dfrac{x(x + 1)dx}{x + 2}.$

30. $\int \dfrac{(x - 1)(x - 3)dx}{x - 6}.$

31. $\int \dfrac{(2x + 5)(x - 2)dx}{x + 3}.$

32. $\int \dfrac{dx}{4x^2 + 9}.$

33. $\int \dfrac{dx}{5x^2 - 4}.$

34. $\int \dfrac{x \, dx}{x^4 - 16}.$

35. $\int \dfrac{x \, dx}{\sqrt{9 - 4x^4}}.$

36. $\int \dfrac{(3x + 7)dx}{x^2 + 6x + 3}.$

37. $\int \dfrac{(5x + 6)dx}{x^2 + 4x + 8}.$

38. $\int \dfrac{(9x + 2)dx}{\sqrt{1 - 4x + x^2}}.$

39. $\int \dfrac{(4x + 5)dx}{\sqrt{32x - 4x^2}}.$

40. $\int \dfrac{(3x - 1)dx}{\sqrt{x^2 + x + 1}}.$

41. $\int \dfrac{(x - 3)dx}{4x^2 - 4x + 7}.$

42. $\int \sec^2 \tfrac{1}{2}x \tan^3 \tfrac{1}{2}x \, dx.$

43. $\int 7 \sin 2x \cos^2 x \, dx.$

44. $\int \dfrac{dx}{1 - \cos x}.$

45. $\int \dfrac{3 \, dx}{2 + 2 \sin x}.$

46. $\int \dfrac{e^{2x}dx}{e^x + 4}.$

47. $\int \dfrac{dx}{e^x + e^{-x}}.$

48. $\int \dfrac{dx}{9e^x + 4e^{-x}}.$

49. $\int \dfrac{dx}{e^x + 2}.$

50. $\int \dfrac{e^{\sqrt{x}}}{\sqrt{x}} \, dx.$

51. $\int \dfrac{dx}{\cos^2 x(3 \tan x + 5)}.$

52. $\int 4 \sin x \cos 2x \, dx.$

53. $\int \csc^2 3\theta \cot^2 3\theta \, d\theta.$

54. $\int \dfrac{dx}{\sin^2 \tfrac{1}{2}x \tan \tfrac{1}{2}x}.$

55. $\int \dfrac{\sin^2 x \, dx}{\cos^4 x}.$

56. $\int \dfrac{\tan \theta \, d\theta}{\cot \theta}.$

57. $\int \dfrac{\tan^3 \theta \sec \theta \, d\theta}{4 \cos \theta}.$

58. $\int \dfrac{dx}{\sin 2x - 4 \cos^2 x}.$

59. $\int \dfrac{\sin x - 1}{(x + \cos x)^2} \, dx.$

60. $\int \dfrac{(x^4 - 4)dx}{x^2 + 4}.$

61. $\int \dfrac{x^3 dx}{x^2 + 2}.$

62. $\int \dfrac{(3x^4 - 10x^2 - x - 8)dx}{x^2 - 4}.$

63. $\int \dfrac{(4x^5 + 10x^3 + 3x)dx}{2x^2 + 5}.$

64. $\int \dfrac{(16x^3 + 16x^2 - 5)dx}{4x^2 + 4x + 1}.$

CHAPTER XV

APPLICATIONS OF THE
INDEFINITE INTEGRAL

82. Introduction.—By adding the constant of integration we have been writing down the *most general* function whose derivative is a given function. In many applications to geometry, physics, chemistry, etc., some *particular* integral is required. From the available information one determines what value must be assigned to C in order to satisfy the conditions of the particular problem.

83. Applications to geometry.—Suppose that we wish to determine the equation of the curve through (3, 1) for which at any point

$$\frac{dy}{dx} = 2x + 4.$$

Integrating, we find at first that

$$y = x^2 + 4x + C.$$

This is the equation of a family of parabolas, one of which corresponds to each particular value of C, as indicated in Fig. 78. Any one of these parabolas satisfies the condition imposed upon the derivative. For the particular curve required we know that when $x = 3$, $y = 1$. Substituting and solving for C, we have

$$1 = 3^2 + 4(3) + C, \quad \text{or} \quad C = -20.$$

The equation of the required curve is then

$$y = x^2 + 4x - 20.$$

Somewhat more generally we may ask for the family of curves for which, at every point, the slope of the tangent is any given function of the coordinates; *i.e.*, for which

$$\frac{dy}{dx} = \varphi(x, y).$$

The solution of such a problem is in general difficult or impossible. It can be accomplished in certain simple cases by *separating the variables; i.e.*, by putting all the y terms together with dy on one side, and all the x terms together

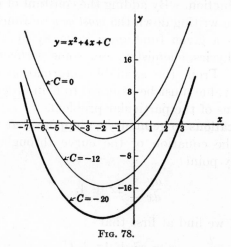

FIG. 78.

with dx on the other. When this can be done, each side may be integrated separately. The constant of integration may be added on either side and in any form; it is sometimes more convenient to add it in some such form as $\log C$ or C^2.

Example

What curve through $(0, 2)$ has at every point the slope of its tangent equal to twice the product of the coordinates of that point?

Solution

We are given that at any point (x, y),

$$\frac{dy}{dx} = 2xy.$$

Separating the variables we have

$$\frac{dy}{y} = 2x \, dx.$$

Integrating both sides "simultaneously" we find

$$\log y = x^2 + C.$$

Since $y = 2$ when $x = 0$, $C = \log 2$. The equation of the required curve is then

$$\log y = x^2 + \log 2$$

or

$$\log \frac{y}{2} = x^2$$

or

$$y = 2e^{x^2}.$$

PROBLEMS

In each of the following problems, find the equation of the curve determined by the given conditions:

1. $\frac{dy}{dx} = \frac{1}{2}x^2 - 3x$; when $x = 3$, $y = -6$.

2. $\frac{dy}{dx} = 3x^2 - 8x$; when $x = 1$, $y = 0$.

3. $\frac{dy}{dx} = 6\sqrt{x}$; when $x = 4$, $y = 11$.

4. $\frac{dy}{dx} = \frac{1}{2}y$; when $x = 0$, $y = 1$.

5. $\frac{dy}{dx} = 4y^2$; when $x = 2$, $y = 1$.

6. Find the equation of and sketch the curve that passes through the point $(2, -1)$ and has at every point $\frac{dy}{dx} = \frac{5-x}{y-3}$.

7. At every point of a certain curve $dy/dx = xy^2$. The curve goes through the point $(2, 1)$. Find its equation and sketch it.

8. What curve passing through $(1, 3)$ has at every point $\frac{dy}{dx} = \frac{5-x}{y}$?

9. Find the equation of and sketch the curve that passes through the point $(1, 2)$ and has at every point $\frac{dy}{dx} = -\frac{2xy}{x^2+1}$.

10. What curve passing through the point $(4, 2)$ cuts every member of the family of hyperbolas $x^2 - y^2 = k$ at right angles? HINT: Through any point (x, y) (except the origin) there passes one and only one of these hyperbolas, and its slope is $dy/dx = x/y$. The required curve must then have $dy/dx = -y/x$.

11. Find the equation of the curve passing through the point (4, 2) and intersecting all of the hyperbolas $xy = k$ at right angles. See hint in Prob. 10.

12. Sketch several members of the family of ellipses $2x^2 + 3y^2 = a^2$. Find the equation of the curve that passes through the point (4, 8) and cuts all of these ellipses at right angles. See hint in Prob. 10.

13. What family of curves has the property that each one cuts all of the hyperbolas $xy = k$ at right angles?

14. Determine a family of curves such that each one cuts every member of the family of circles $x^2 + y^2 - 4x + 6y = k$ at right angles. Sketch both sets of curves.

15. Find the equation of the curve that passes through (2, 2) and has at every point $\dfrac{dy}{dx} = \dfrac{xy - x}{y}$.

16. At every point of a certain curve $d^2y/dx^2 = 2x$. The curve passes through (3, 6) and its tangent at this point has an inclination of 45°. What is the equation of this curve?

17. By the use of certain principles of mechanics it can be shown that a cantilever beam of length l carrying a uniformly distributed load of w lb. per linear foot is deflected into a curve such that at every point $EI \dfrac{d^2y}{dx^2} = -\frac{1}{2}w(l - x)^2$ where E and I are constants whose values depend upon the size and material of the beam. Find the equation of this elastic curve of the beam, given that $y = 0$ and $dy/dx = 0$ when $x = 0$. Compute the maximum deflection (this is the value of y when $x = l$). See Fig. 79.

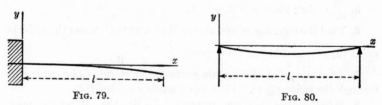

FIG. 79.   FIG. 80.

18. As in Prob. 17 for the case of a simple beam supported at the ends (Fig. 80). In this case the equation is

$$EI \frac{d^2y}{dx^2} = \frac{1}{2}wx(l - x);$$

$dy/dx = 0$ when $x = \frac{1}{2}l$, and $y = 0$ when $x = 0$. Compute the maximum deflection, which in this case is the value of y when $x = \frac{1}{2}l$.

84. Physical problems. The compound interest law.— In many physical problems, the law governing the time rate of change of a function Q is known. The value of Q for a particular value (or values) of t is observed. With this information one can often, by integration, derive the relation between Q and t and thus compute the value of Q corresponding to any value of t.

Of particular interest is the case in which the rate at which Q is changing at any instant is proportional to the value at Q at that instant.

Example

The rate at which a certain substance in a solution is decomposing at any instant is known to be proportional to the amount of it present in the solution at that instant. Initially there are 27 g. and 3 hr. later it is found that 8 g. are left. How much will be left after another hour?

Solution

If Q is the amount present at any time t, we are given that

$$\frac{dQ}{dt} = kQ; \qquad \text{also} \qquad \begin{cases} Q = 27 \text{ when } t = 0; \\ Q = 8 \text{ when } t = 3. \end{cases}$$

Separating the variables and integrating we have

$$\frac{dQ}{Q} = k\, dt$$
$$\log Q = kt + \log C$$
$$Q = Ce^{kt}.$$

Since $Q = 27$ when $t = 0$, we find $C = 27$. Hence,

$$Q = 27e^{kt}.$$

The value of k may be found from the condition that $Q = 8$ when $t = 3$. Thus,

$$8 = 27e^{3k}$$
$$e^{3k} = \tfrac{8}{27}$$
$$e^k = \tfrac{2}{3}.$$

Since $e^{kt} = (e^k)^t$ and $e^k = \tfrac{2}{3}$, we have finally

$$Q = 27(\tfrac{2}{3})^t.$$

At the end of another hour $t = 4$ and

$$Q = 27(\tfrac{2}{3})^4 = 5\tfrac{1}{3} \text{ g.}$$

The graphical picture showing how Q decreases with increasing t is presented in Fig. 81.   It has the familiar form of the exponential curve

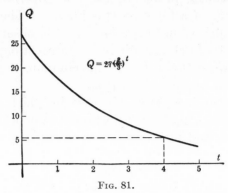

$$Q = 27(\tfrac{2}{3})^t$$

$y = a^{-x}$ where $a > 1$.   The relation could of course be written in the form $Q = 27(\tfrac{3}{2})^{-t}$.

When a quantity Q increases at a rate which is at every instant proportional to the value of Q, it is said to increase according to the *compound interest law*.   This is the way in which an amount of money would increase if the interest were added *continuously* instead of at the end of each year or other interest period.

Example

A sum of \$100 is invested at an interest rate of 6 per cent per annum compounded continuously.   What is the amount at the end of 10 years? Compare the situation with the cases in which it is compounded annually and semiannually.

Solution

Let A be the amount at any time t.   Then $A = 100$ when $t = 0$ and we must find A when $t = 10$.   At any instant, A is increasing at a rate of $0.06A$ dollars per year; *i.e.*,

$$\frac{dA}{dt} = 0.06A.$$

Separating the variables and integrating we have

$$\frac{dA}{A} = 0.06 \, dt$$

$$\log A = 0.06 \, t + C.$$

Since $A = 100$ when $t = 0$, $C = \log 100$; hence,

$$\log A = 0.06t + \log 100$$
$$\log \frac{A}{100} = 0.06t$$
$$A = 100e^{0.06t}.$$

This relation gives the amount A at any time t; taking $t = 10$ we have

$$A]_{t=10} = 100e^{0.6} = \$182.21.$$

Using tables it is found that the amount would be \$179.08 if compounded annually and \$180.61 if compounded semiannually. If the amount were computed on the assumption of compounding monthly, daily, hourly, etc., the results would approach closer and closer to that

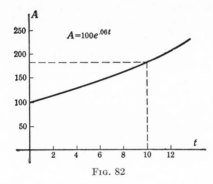

FIG. 82

obtained above as the length of the interest period approached zero. The graph of the relation between A and t is the exponential curve shown in Fig. 82.

PROBLEMS

1. In a chemical reaction a substance A is being transformed into another substance B at a rate that is proportional to the amount of A remaining untransformed. Starting with 36 g. of A it is found that 25 g. remain after 2 hr. How much will remain at the end of 4 hr.?

2. Bacteria multiply at a rate proportional to the number present. If the original number N_1 doubles in 3 hr., in how many hours will there be $6N_1$?

3. A sum of money is invested at 3 per cent per annum compounded continuously. In how many years will the original amount be doubled?

4. A sum of \$1,600 is invested at 4 per cent per annum compounded continuously for 8 years. What is the final amount? Compare the result with that obtained when it is compounded semiannually.

5. A war bond costing \$75 is worth \$100 at the end of 10 years. Show that the interest rate is slightly less than 2.9 per cent compounded continuously.

6. Assume that radium decomposes at a rate proportional to the amount present, and that an original amount Q_0 is reduced to $\frac{1}{2}Q_0$ in 1,500 years. What percentage of Q_0 remains at the end of 300 years?

7. A cylindrical tank containing 100 gal. of water stands on end. There is a small leak at the bottom. The rate at which water escapes is proportional to the square root of the depth (and hence proportional to the square root of the volume present, since the cross section is constant). If 10 gal. leaks out the first day, how much will leak out the next day; the fifth day?

8. A tank contains 1,000 gal. of brine in which there are 800 lb. of dissolved salt. Pure water is run into the tank at 16 gal. per minute and the mixture, which is kept uniform by stirring, is withdrawn at the same rate. How many lb. of salt remain after 25 min.?

Hint: Let P be the number of lb. of salt present at the end of t min. The number of lb. of salt in each gallon of mixture is then $P/1,000$, and in withdrawing 16 gal. per minute one withdraws

$$\frac{P}{1000} \times 16 = \frac{2P}{125} \text{ lb. of salt per minute.}$$

Thus P is *decreasing* at $2P/125$ lb. per minute, or

$$\frac{dP}{dt} = -\frac{2P}{125}.$$

The initial condition is, of course, $P = 800$ when $t = 0$.

9. In Prob. 8, find the number of minutes required to reduce the salt concentration to 0.25 lb. per gallon.

10. Solve Prob. 8 if pure water is run in at 20 gal. per minute, the mixture being withdrawn at 16 gal. per minute. Hint: In this case, after t min. the tank contains $(1,000 + 4t)$ gal., and if P is the number of lb. of salt present there are $\dfrac{P}{1,000 + 4t}$ lb. of salt per gallon.

11. A tank contains 1,000 gal. of brine in which there are 600 lb. of dissolved salt. Pure water is run into the tank at 16 gal. per minute and the mixture is withdrawn at 12 gal. per minute. In how many minutes will the salt concentration be reduced to 0.1 lb. per gallon?

12. A tank initially contains 400 gal. of brine in which there are 100 lb. of dissolved salt. A brine containing 0.6 lb. of salt per gallon is run into the tank at a rate of 5 gal. per minute and the mixture, kept uniform by stirring, runs out at the same rate. Determine the amount of salt in the tank at the end of 40 min. Hint: Let P be the number of pounds of salt in the tank at the end of t min.　The rate at which salt is entering is

$$0.6 \text{ lb. per gallon} \times 5 \text{ gal. per minute} = 3 \text{ lb. per minute.}$$

The rate at which salt is leaving the tank is

$$\frac{P}{400} \text{ lb. per gallon} \times 5 \text{ gal. per minute} = \frac{P}{80} \text{ lb. per minute.}$$

Then

$$\frac{dP}{dt} = 3 - \frac{P}{80} \text{ lb. per minute.}$$

13. A tank contains 25 gal. of water and 25 gal. of alcohol mixed together.　Alcohol is run in at 5 gal. per minute while the mixture is withdrawn at 3 gal. per minute.　The mixture is kept uniform by stirring.　In how many minutes will the contents be 75 per cent alcohol? HINT: Let W be the number of gallons of water present at any time.

14. Assume that the rate at which a body cools in air is proportional to the difference between its temperature and that of the surrounding atmosphere.　A body originally at 80° cools down to 60° in 20 min., the air temperature being 40°.　What will be its temperature after another 40 min.?

15. The temperature of a body drops from 100 to 80° in 3 hr. when surrounded by air having a temperature of 20°.　Assuming the law of cooling stated in the preceding problem, in how long will the temperature of the body be reduced to 30°?

85. Rectilinear motion.　The projectile.—If a particle whose weight is W lb. is acted on by a resultant force of F lb., it is known that an acceleration is produced in the direction of the applied force.　The relation between the magnitudes of the applied force, the weight of the particle, and the acceleration produced (in feet per second per second) is experimentally found to be

$$F = \frac{W}{g} a.$$

In this equation g is a constant whose value is 32.2.　The quantity W/g is called the *mass* of the particle.

In many simple problems involving rectilinear motion, both the force F and the weight W are known.　The acceleration can then be obtained from the above relation. And, since $a = dv/dt = d^2s/dt^2$, one can, by two integrations, obtain expressions for the velocity and displacement of the particle in terms of the time.

Example

From a point 30 ft. above the ground, a small lead ball is thrown vertically upward with an initial velocity of 60 ft. per second. Find its velocity and distance *from the ground* at the end of t sec.

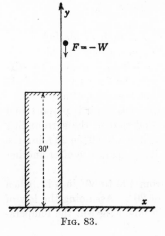

FIG. 83.

Solution (Fig. 83)

The only force acting on the ball while in the air (neglecting air resistance) is its own weight which acts vertically *downward*. If we take the upward direction as positive we have

$$-W = \frac{W}{g} a;$$
$$a = -g$$

or

$$\frac{dv}{dt} = -g.$$

Integrating we obtain

$$v = -gt + C_1.$$

Since $v = +60$ when $t = 0$, $C_1 = 60$; hence, at any time,

$$v = 60 - gt.$$

Replacing v by dy/dt and integrating again, we have

$$y = 60t - \tfrac{1}{2}gt^2 + C_2.$$

Since $y = +30$ when $t = 0$, $C_2 = 30$; hence, at any time,

$$y = 30 + 60t - \tfrac{1}{2}gt^2.$$

In the more general problem, the projectile is fired with initial velocity v_0 at an angle α with the horizontal as indicated in Fig. 84. The motion in this case is not rectilinear. However, the only force acting on the projectile while it is in the air (neglecting air resistance) is again its own weight, which of course acts vertically downward.

Choosing axes as indicated in the figure, we may write our fundamental relation in the form

$$F_x = \frac{W}{g} a_x, \qquad F_y = \frac{W}{g} a_y.$$

Substituting 0 for F_x and $-W$ for F_y and solving for the components of the acceleration, we have

$$a_x = 0, \qquad a_y = -g.$$

Integrating and evaluating the constants we find that, at any time t,

$$v_x = v_0 \cos \alpha, \qquad v_y = v_0 \sin \alpha - gt.$$

Integrating again and evaluating the constants we have

$$x = (v_0 \cos \alpha)t, \qquad y = (v_0 \sin \alpha)t - \tfrac{1}{2}gt^2.$$

The details are left to the student as an exercise. The last

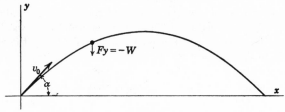

FIG. 84.

two equations may of course be regarded as parametric equations of the path followed by the projectile.

PROBLEMS

1. From the top of a building 50 ft. high, a stone is thrown vertically upward with initial velocity 80 ft. per second. Express its velocity and distance above the ground at any time t as functions of t. Find the greatest height reached by the projectile.

2. From a point 800 ft. above the ground a small heavy particle i thrown vertically downward with initial velocity 60 ft. per second. Derive expressions for its velocity and distance from the ground at any time t. With what velocity does it strike the ground?

3. Derive expressions for the velocity and position at any time t of a body dropped from a height of h ft. above the earth. Show that its

velocity when it strikes the earth will be $\sqrt{2gh}$ if the air resistance is neglected.

4. A ball is thrown horizontally with initial velocity v_0 ft. per second as shown in Fig. 85. Show that if air resistance is negligible it travels in a path whose parametric equations, with axes as shown, are

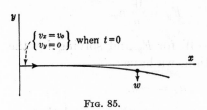

$$x = v_0 t; \qquad y = -\tfrac{1}{2}gt^2.$$

FIG. 85.

HINT: Start with the equations $F_x = 0$; $F_y = -w$. From these equations deduce that $a_x = 0$ and $a_y = -g$. Then integrate twice, evaluating the constants from the initial conditions $v_x = v_0$, $v_y = 0$, $x = 0$, and $y = 0$, when $t = 0$.

5. An airplane at an elevation of 12,000 ft. is moving horizontally at a speed of 220 ft. per second when a bomb is released. How far will the bomb travel horizontally before striking the ground if air resistance is negligible? HINT: First show that the equations of Prob. 4 apply.

6. Derive the equations given on page 191 for the path of a projectile that is fired with initial velocity v_0 at an angle α with the horizontal. By eliminating the parameter t, show that the path is a parabola.

7. A particle of weight w is projected vertically downward with an initial velocity of 40 ft. per second through a fluid. If the resistance of the fluid to the motion is kv^2 where $k = \frac{1}{64} w$, derive an expression for the velocity of the particle at any time. Discuss the way in which this velocity varies, and show, in particular, that it approaches a limiting value of 8 ft. per second. HINT: The weight w of the particle acts downward while the resistance kv^2 acts upward. The resultant force is then $w - kv^2$, and if we take downward as positive we have

$$\frac{w}{g}\frac{dv}{dt} = w - kv^2.^*$$

8. Solve Prob. 7 for the case in which the initial velocity of the particle is zero. Show that in this case the velocity of the particle increases as time goes on and again approaches 8 ft. per second as a limiting value.

9. A particle of weight w falls from rest in a medium in which the resistance to motion is equal to kv. Derive an expression for its velocity at any time. Show that as time goes on the velocity approaches a limiting value of w/k.

* The buoyant force of the fluid is neglected here. If, for example, the specific gravity of the fluid is 0.1 that of the particle, then there is an additional upward (buoyant) force of $0.1w$. The right-hand member of the equation would then be $0.9w - kv^2$.

10. A body is projected horizontally with initial velocity v_0 through a medium in which the resisting force is proportional to the velocity of the body. Show that the velocity will decrease according to the law $v_x = v_0 e^{-kt}$ and that the horizontal distance moved in t sec. is

$$x = \frac{v_0}{k}(1 - e^{-kt}).$$

11. Suppose that an automobile of weight W starts from rest and is supplied by the motor with a *constant* driving force F. If the resistance to motion is proportional to the velocity show that the car will gain speed according to the law

$$v = \frac{F}{k}\left(1 - e^{-\frac{gkt}{W}}\right).$$

12. A bullet is fired horizontally from a point A with velocity v_0. The air resistance may be assumed to be horizontal and equal to $-kv_x^2$. Derive expressions for v_x and v_y in terms of t. Find also the horizontal and vertical distances x and y of the bullet from A at any time t.

13. A block weighing 200 lb. is propelled along a rough horizontal surface, starting from rest, by a horizontal force of 40 lb. There is a frictional resistance of 30 lb. between the block and the surface. The resistance of the medium is equal to $2v$ where v is the velocity of the block. Derive expressions for the velocity and displacement of the block in terms of t. HINT: $F = 40 - 30 - 2v$.

14. A man and parachute together weigh 225 lb. and the air resistance is assumed to be $\frac{1}{4}v^2$ where v is the velocity of descent in ft. per second. If $v = 80$ ft. per second downward when the parachute is opened, show that at any subsequent time the velocity is given by the equation

$$\frac{v - 30}{v + 30} = \frac{5}{11}e^{-\frac{gt}{15}}.$$

Show that v approaches 30 ft. per second as a limiting value.

15. Assume in Prob. 14 that the air resistance is $10v$ instead of $\frac{1}{4}v^2$. For this case derive an expression for the velocity at any time and find the limiting velocity. In how many seconds would the velocity be reduced to 25 ft. per second?

CHAPTER XVI

TRIGONOMETRIC INTEGRALS

86. Introduction.—Many problems of the integral calculus lead either directly or indirectly to integrals involving powers of the trigonometric functions. Using the fundamental identities and the double- and half-angle formulas, one can often transform such integrals into forms in which the standard integration formulas can be applied. Thus, none of the formulas applies directly to $\int \cos^3 x \, dx$; however,

$$
\begin{aligned}
\int \cos^3 x \, dx &= \int \cos^2 x \cos x \, dx \\
&= \int (1 - \sin^2 x) \cos x \, dx \\
&= \int \cos x \, dx - \int \sin^2 x \cos x \, dx \\
&= \sin x - \tfrac{1}{3} \sin^3 x + C.
\end{aligned}
$$

In this chapter we shall consider only the types of trigonometric integrals which arise often in the later applications and for which simple rules for integration can be given.

87. $\int \sin^m x \cos^n x \, dx$.—Simple rules can be given for handling this integral if one of the exponents is a positive *odd* integer or if both exponents are positive *even* integers. Since the treatments are entirely different, they will be given separately.

CASE I. *One of the exponents a positive odd integer.*— This case can always be handled by the procedure just used on $\int \cos^3 x \, dx$. Suppose for example that m is odd. One can then take out $\sin x \, dx$ as dv, leaving an *even* exponent for $\sin x$; then, using the relation

$$
\sin^2 x = 1 - \cos^2 x
$$

he can obtain a series of terms of the form

$$
\int \cos^q x \sin x \, dx
$$

which can be integrated by the formula for $\int v^n dv$.

Example

$\int \sin^3 x \cos^4 x \, dx$

Solution

Since the exponent of sin x is a positive odd integer, we proceed as follows:

$$\int \sin^3 x \cos^4 x \, dx = \int \cos^4 x \sin^2 x \sin x \, dx$$
$$= \int \cos^4 x (1 - \cos^2 x) \sin x \, dx$$
$$= \int \cos^4 x \sin x \, dx - \int \cos^6 x \sin x \, dx$$
$$= -\frac{\cos^5 x}{5} + \frac{\cos^7 x}{7} + C.$$

The student should notice carefully that this procedure will always apply if one of the exponents is a *positive odd integer* no matter what the other exponent may be—any positive or negative integer or fraction, or zero.

CASE II. *Both exponents positive even integers.*—The integration can be accomplished in this case by changing over to multiple angles. For this purpose the following formulas, which the student can easily derive, are used:

$$\sin^2 x = \tfrac{1}{2}(1 - \cos 2x).$$
$$\cos^2 x = \tfrac{1}{2}(1 + \cos 2x).$$
$$\sin x \cos x = \tfrac{1}{2} \sin 2x.$$

Example 1

$\int \cos^2 x \, dx.$

Solution

$$\int \cos^2 x \, dx = \int \tfrac{1}{2}(1 + \cos 2x) dx$$
$$= \tfrac{1}{2}\int dx + \tfrac{1}{2}\int \cos 2x \, dx$$
$$= \tfrac{1}{2}x + \tfrac{1}{4} \sin 2x + C.$$

Example 2

$\int \sin^2 x \cos^2 x \, dx.$

Solution

$$\int \sin^2 x \cos^2 x \, dx = \tfrac{1}{4}\int \sin^2 2x \, dx$$
$$= \tfrac{1}{4}\int \tfrac{1}{2}(1 - \cos 4x) dx$$
$$= \tfrac{1}{8}x - \tfrac{1}{32} \sin 4x + C.$$

PROBLEMS

1. $\int \sin^3 x \, dx.$

2. $\int \cos^3 \frac{1}{2}x \, dx.$

3. $\int \sin^5 x \, dx.$

4. $\int \cos^5 2x \, dx.$

5. $\int \sin^7 x \, dx.$

6. $\int \cos^7 x \, dx.$

7. $\int \sin x \cos^5 x \, dx.$

8. $\int \sin^3 2\theta \cos^3 2\theta \, d\theta.$

9. $\int \sin^3 x \cos^2 x \, dx.$

10. $\int \sin^2 x \cos^3 x \, dx.$

11. $\int \sin^5 x \cos^5 x \, dx.$

12. $\int \sqrt{\sin x} \cos^3 x \, dx.$

13. $\int \tan^3 x \, dx.$

14. $\int \sin^4 x \cos^3 x \, dx.$

15. $\int \sin x \sec^2 x \, dx.$

16. $\int \tan \theta \sec^3 \theta \, d\theta.$

17. $\int \frac{\sec^4 x \, dx}{\csc^3 x}.$

18. $\int \frac{\sin^3 x \, dx}{\sqrt{\cos x}}.$

19. $\int \sin^2 x \, dx.$

20. $\int \cos^2 \frac{1}{2}\theta \, d\theta.$

21. $\int \sin^4 x \, dx.$

22. $\int \cos^4 x \, dx.$

23. $\int \sin^6 x \, dx.$

24. $\int \cos^6 \frac{1}{2}x \, dx.$

25. $\int \sin^2 \frac{1}{2}\theta \cos^2 \frac{1}{2}\theta \, d\theta.$

26. $\int \sin^2 x \cos^4 x \, dx.$

27. $\int \sin^4 x \cos^4 x \, dx.$

28. $\int \sin^4 x \cos^2 x \, dx.$

29. $\int (\sin x + \cos x)^2 dx.$

30. $\int (1 + \sin 2x)^2 dx.$

31. $\int (\cos 2x + \cos x)^2 dx.$

32. $\int (\sqrt{\sin x} + 2 \cos x)^2 dx.$

33. $\int \sin x \sin 2x \, dx.$

34. $\int \tan^2 x \cos^3 x \sin x \, dx.$

35. $\int \sin x \cos x \cos^4 2x \, dx.$

36. $\int \sin^2 \frac{1}{2}\theta \cos^2 \theta \, d\theta.$

37. $\int \cos^4 \theta \tan^2 \theta \, d\theta.$

38. From the relation $\cos 2\theta = \cos^2 \theta - \sin^2 \theta$, show that $\cos^2 \theta = \frac{1}{2}(1 + \cos 2\theta)$ and $\sin^2 \theta = \frac{1}{2}(1 - \cos 2\theta)$.

88. $\int \sec^n x \, dx$ or $\int \csc^n x \, dx$.—If n is any *positive even integer* the integration can be performed as indicated in the following example:

Example
$\int \sec^6 x\, dx$

Solution

We may take out $\sec^2 x\, dx$ as dv and transform the remainder into a polynomial in $\tan x$; thus,

$$\begin{aligned}
\int \sec^6 x\, dx &= \int \sec^4 x\, \sec^2 x\, dx \\
&= \int (1 + \tan^2 x)^2\, \sec^2 x\, dx \\
&= \int (1 + 2\tan^2 x + \tan^4 x)\, \sec^2 x\, dx \\
&= \int \sec^2 x\, dx + 2\int \tan^2 x\, \sec^2 x\, dx + \int \tan^4 x\, \sec^2 x\, dx \\
&= \tan x + \tfrac{2}{3}\tan^3 x + \tfrac{1}{5}\tan^5 x + C.
\end{aligned}$$

If n is a positive *odd* integer, a method called *integration by parts* may be employed. This method will be discussed in the next chapter.

89. $\int \tan^n x\, dx$ or $\int \cot^n x\, dx.$—If n is any *positive integer,* these types can be reduced to forms which are easily integrated by the use of the relations:

$$\tan^2 x = \sec^2 x - 1.$$
$$\cot^2 x = \csc^2 x - 1.$$

Example
$$\begin{aligned}
\int \tan^4 x\, dx &= \int \tan^2 x(\sec^2 x - 1)dx \\
&= \int \tan^2 x\, \sec^2 x\, dx - \int \tan^2 x\, dx \\
&= \tfrac{1}{3}\tan^3 x - \int (\sec^2 x - 1)dx \\
&= \tfrac{1}{3}\tan^3 x - \tan x + x + C.
\end{aligned}$$

90. $\int \tan^m x\, \sec^n x\, dx$ or $\int \cot^m x\, \csc^n x\, dx.$—We shall consider here only two cases.

Case I. *Exponent of sec x a positive even integer.*—In this case one may take out $\sec^2 x\, dx$ as dv and transform the remainder into a polynomial in $\tan x$.

Example
$\int \tan^3 x\, \sec^4 x\, dx.$

Solution

Since the exponent of $\sec x$ is a positive *even* integer, we may proceed as follows:

$$\int \tan^3 x \sec^4 x \, dx = \int \tan^3 x \sec^2 x \sec^2 x \, dx$$
$$= \int \tan^3 x(1 + \tan^2 x) \sec^2 x \, dx$$
$$= \int \tan^3 x \sec^2 x \, dx + \int \tan^5 x \sec^2 x \, dx$$
$$= \tfrac{1}{4} \tan^4 x + \tfrac{1}{6} \tan^6 x + C.$$

CASE II. *Exponent of tan x a positive odd integer.*—In this case one can take out sec x tan x dx as dv and transform the remainder into a polynomial in sec x.

Example

$$\int \sec^3 x \tan^3 x \, dx$$

Solution

Since the exponent of tan x is a positive *odd* integer, we proceed as follows:

$$\int \sec^3 x \tan^3 x \, dx = \int \sec^2 x \tan^2 x \sec x \tan x \, dx$$
$$= \int \sec^2 x (\sec^2 x - 1) \sec x \tan x \, dx$$
$$= \int \sec^4 x \sec x \tan x \, dx - \int \sec^2 x \sec x \tan x \, dx$$
$$= \tfrac{1}{5} \sec^5 x - \tfrac{1}{3} \sec^3 x + C.$$

It is of course possible that a given integral could be handled by either of these procedures. Thus, $\int \sec^4 x \tan^3 x \, dx$ could be found by either method, since the exponent of sec x is even and that of tan x is odd. On the other hand, *neither* of the procedures could be used on $\int \sec^3 x \tan^2 x \, dx$.

PROBLEMS

1. $\displaystyle\int \tan^2 x \, dx.$

2. $\displaystyle\int \tan^3 x \, dx.$

3. $\displaystyle\int \cot^2 \tfrac{1}{2}\theta \, d\theta.$

4. $\displaystyle\int \cot^3 2\theta \, d\theta.$

5. $\displaystyle\int \tan^4 \theta \, d\theta.$

6. $\displaystyle\int \cot^4 \tfrac{1}{2}x \, dx.$

7. $\displaystyle\int \tan^5 2x \, dx.$

8. $\displaystyle\int \sec^2 \tfrac{1}{2}x \, dx.$

9. $\displaystyle\int \sec^4 \tfrac{1}{2}x \, dx.$

10. $\displaystyle\int \sec^6 4x \, dx.$

11. $\displaystyle\int \frac{dx}{\sin^2 x}.$

12. $\displaystyle\int \frac{dx}{\cos^4 x}.$

13. $\displaystyle\int \sec^2 x \tan^3 x \, dx.$

14. $\displaystyle\int \csc^2 x \cot^3 x \, dx.$

15. $\int \sec^6 x \tan x \, dx.$

16. $\int \sec^4 2x \tan^4 2x \, dx.$

17. $\int \sec^2 \theta \tan^4 \theta \, d\theta.$

18. $\int \sec^6 2x \tan^2 2x \, dx.$

19. $\int \sec x \tan^3 x \, dx.$

20. $\int \csc^3 x \cot^3 x \, dx.$

21. $\int \sec^5 x \tan^3 x \, dx.$

22. $\int \tan^5 x \sec x \, dx.$

23. $\int \sec^3 x \tan^5 x \, dx.$

24. $\int \tan^5 x \sec^4 x \, dx.$

25. $\int \sin 2x \sec^6 x \, dx.$

26. $\int \dfrac{\sin^2 x}{\cos^4 x} \, dx.$

27. $\int \sin 2x \cos x \tan^2 x \, dx.$

28. $\int \sqrt{\tan x} \sec^4 x \, dx.$

29. $\int (\tan x + \cot x)^2 dx.$

30. $\int (2 \sec x + 3 \tan x)^2 dx.$

31. By adding the two equalities

$$\sin (A + B) = \sin A \cos B + \cos A \sin B$$
$$\sin (A - B) = \sin A \cos B - \cos A \sin B,$$

we obtain the relation

$$\sin A \cos B = \tfrac{1}{2}[\sin (A + B) + \sin (A - B)].$$

If we let $A = mx$ and $B = nx$, this becomes

$$\sin mx \cos nx = \tfrac{1}{2}[\sin (m + n)x + \sin (m - n)x].$$

Use this result to show that if $m \neq n$,

$$\int \sin mx \cos nx \, dx = -\tfrac{1}{2} \left[\frac{\cos (m + n)x}{m + n} + \frac{\cos (m - n)x}{m - n} \right] + C.$$

32. By adding the two equalities

$$\cos (A + B) = \cos A \cos B - \sin A \sin B$$
$$\cos (A - B) = \cos A \cos B + \sin A \sin B,$$

we obtain the relation

$$\cos A \cos B = \tfrac{1}{2}[\cos (A + B) + \cos (A - B)].$$

If we let $A = mx$ and $B = nx$, this becomes

$$\cos mx \cos nx = \tfrac{1}{2}[\cos (m + n)x + \cos (m - n)x].$$

Use this result to show that if $m \neq n$,

$$\int \cos mx \cos nx \, dx = \tfrac{1}{2} \left[\frac{\sin (m + n)x}{m + n} + \frac{\sin (m - n)x}{m - n} \right] + C.$$

33. By proceeding as in Prob. 32 after *subtracting* the first two equalities, show that if $m \neq n$,

$$\int \sin mx \sin nx \, dx = \tfrac{1}{2} \left[-\frac{\sin (m + n)x}{m + n} + \frac{\sin (m - n)x}{m - n} \right] + C.$$

In the following problems use the results of Probs. 31 to 33:

34. $\int \sin 6x \cos 2x \, dx.$ **35.** $\int \sin 4x \cos 3x \, dx.$

36. $\int \cos 4x \cos 2x \, dx.$ **37.** $\int \sin 8x \sin 3x \, dx.$

CHAPTER XVII

METHODS OF INTEGRATION

91. Introduction.—A study of integration is largely a study of methods of transforming various types of integrands into forms in which the fundamental integration formulas can be applied. One of the most useful devices for this purpose is that of substituting a new variable. Consider as an example

$$\int \sqrt{4 - x^2}\, dx.$$

The integration cannot be performed directly by any of the standard formulas. Let us, then, transform the integrand into a rational trigonometric function by letting

$$x = 2 \sin \theta.$$

Since if $x = 2 \sin \theta$, $dx = 2 \cos \theta\, d\theta$, we have, upon substituting,

$$
\begin{aligned}
\int \sqrt{4 - x^2}\, dx &= \int \sqrt{4 - 4 \sin^2 \theta}\, 2 \cos \theta\, d\theta \\
&= 4\int \cos^2 \theta\, d\theta \\
&= 4\int \tfrac{1}{2}(1 + \cos 2\theta)d\theta \\
&= 2\theta + \sin 2\theta + C.
\end{aligned}
$$

Having thus performed the integration in terms of θ, we can change the result back into terms of x as follows:
Since $x = 2 \sin \theta$,

$$\sin \theta = \frac{x}{2}.$$

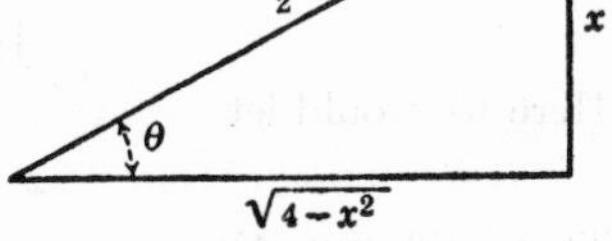

Fig. 86.

The relation between θ and x is therefore represented by the triangle shown in Fig. 86. From it,

$$\sin 2\theta = 2 \sin \theta \cos \theta$$

$$= 2 \cdot \frac{x}{2} \cdot \frac{\sqrt{4 - x^2}}{2}.$$

Finally then,

$$\int \sqrt{4 - x^2}\, dx = 2 \arcsin \frac{x}{2} + \frac{x \sqrt{4 - x^2}}{2} + C.$$

92. Trigonometric substitutions.—In various applications we shall frequently encounter integrands of the following types:

$$x^m \sqrt{a^2 - x^2}; \qquad x^m \sqrt{a^2 + x^2}; \qquad x^m \sqrt{x^2 - a^2}$$

where m is a positive or negative integer. Such integrands can be transformed into rational trigonometric functions as follows:

> If $\sqrt{a^2 - x^2}$ occurs, let $x = a \sin \theta$.
> If $\sqrt{a^2 + x^2}$ occurs, let $x = a \tan \theta$.
> If $\sqrt{x^2 - a^2}$ occurs, let $x = a \sec \theta$.

If the resulting trigonometric integral is of a type previously discussed, the integration can be performed and the result changed back into terms of x as illustrated in the preceding article.

The student is warned against the rather common error of merely substituting $d\theta$ for dx. *One must always substitute for dx its value in terms of θ and $d\theta$.*

Example

$$\int x^3 \sqrt{5 + x^2}\, dx.$$

Here we would let

$$x = \sqrt{5} \tan \theta.$$

Then, *differentiating,*

$$\frac{dx}{d\theta} = \sqrt{5} \sec^2 \theta;$$

$$dx = \sqrt{5} \sec^2 \theta\, d\theta.$$

Making the substitutions we have

$$\int x^3 \sqrt{5 + x^2}\, dx = \int (\sqrt{5}\tan\theta)^3 \sqrt{5 + 5\tan^2\theta}\ (\sqrt{5}\sec^2\theta\,d\theta)$$
$$= 25\sqrt{5}\int \tan^3\theta \sec^3\theta\,d\theta.$$

The integration can be performed by the methods of Chap. XVI, and the result can then be changed back into terms of x. The reason for this particular substitution is of course the fact that if $x = \sqrt{5}\tan\theta$, then

$$\sqrt{5 + x^2} = \sqrt{5 + 5\tan^2\theta} = \sqrt{5}\sqrt{1 + \tan^2\theta} = \sqrt{5}\sec\theta.$$

PROBLEMS

1. Derive a formula for $\int \dfrac{dv}{\sqrt{v^2 - a^2}}$. *Formula* (16)

2. Derive a formula for $\int \sqrt{a^2 - v^2}\,dv$.

3. $\int \dfrac{x^3 dx}{\sqrt{9 + x^2}}$.

4. $\int \dfrac{dx}{x^2 \sqrt{a^2 + x^2}}$.

5. $\int \dfrac{dx}{x^2 \sqrt{9x^2 + 25}}$.

6. $\int \dfrac{dx}{x^4 \sqrt{8 + x^2}}$.

7. $\int \dfrac{\sqrt{x^2 + 16}}{x^4}\,dx$.

8. $\int x^3 \sqrt{4 + x^2}\,dx$.

9. $\int x^2 \sqrt{25 - x^2}\,dx$.

10. $\int x^3 \sqrt{4 - x^2}\,dx$.

11. $\int x^3 \sqrt{5 - 2x^2}\,dx$.

12. $\int \dfrac{\sqrt{4 - 9x^2}}{x^2}\,dx$.

13. $\int \dfrac{dx}{x^2 \sqrt{7 - 4x^2}}$.

14. $\int \dfrac{x^3 dx}{\sqrt{a^2 - x^2}}$.

15. $\int \dfrac{dx}{\sqrt{5x^2 - x^4}}$.

16. $\int \dfrac{dt}{t \sqrt{16 - t^2}}$.

17. $\int \dfrac{\sqrt{x^2 - 1}}{x}\,dx$.

18. $\int \dfrac{\sqrt{4x^2 - 9}}{x}\,dx$.

19. $\int z^3 \sqrt{z^2 - 16}\,dz$.

20. $\int x^3 \sqrt{4x^2 - 25}\,dx$.

21. $\int \dfrac{\sqrt{y^2 - 4}}{y^4}\,dy$.

22. $\int \dfrac{\sqrt{3x^2 - 16}}{x^4}\,dx$.

23. $\int \dfrac{x^3 dx}{\sqrt{x^2 - 9}}$.

24. $\int \dfrac{x^3 dx}{\sqrt{4x^2 - 7}}$.

25. $\int \dfrac{du}{u \sqrt{u^2 - a^2}}$.

26. $\int \dfrac{dx}{x \sqrt{3x^2 - 5}}$.

27. $\int \dfrac{dx}{x^2 \sqrt{4x^2 - 9}}.$

28. $\int \dfrac{dx}{x^2 \sqrt{x^2 - 6}}.$

29. $\int \dfrac{dx}{x^3 \sqrt{x^2 - 1}}.$

30. $\int x(9 - x^2)^{\frac{3}{2}}dx.$

31. $\int x \sqrt{(x^2 - 16)^3} \, dx.$

32. $\int x^3(9 - 4x^2)^{\frac{3}{2}}dx.$

33. $\int \dfrac{dx}{\sqrt{x^2 + 2x + 5}}.$

34. $\int x \sqrt{3 - 2x - x^2} \, dx.$

35. $\int \dfrac{x^2 dx}{\sqrt{(a^2 - x^2)^3}}.$

36. $\int \dfrac{x^2 dx}{\sqrt{(x^2 + a^2)^3}}.$

93. Algebraic substitutions.—If the integrand contains one radical of the form

$$\sqrt[n]{ax + b}$$

it may be rationalized by the substitution

$$\sqrt[n]{ax + b} = z.$$

Example
$$\int x \sqrt{3x + 5} \, dx.$$

Solution

Let

$$\sqrt{3x + 5} = z;$$

then

$$3x + 5 = z^2 \quad \text{and} \quad 3 \, dx = 2z \, dz \quad \text{or} \quad dx = \tfrac{2}{3}z \, dz.$$

We have then

$$\int x \sqrt{3x + 5} \, dx = \int \left(\frac{z^2 - 5}{3}\right) \cdot z \cdot \tfrac{2}{3}z \, dz$$

$$= \frac{2}{9}\int (z^4 - 5z^2)dz$$

$$= \frac{2}{9}\left(\frac{z^5}{5} - \frac{5z^3}{3}\right) + C.$$

If we now replace z by $\sqrt{3x + 5}$ and simplify, we obtain the final result:

$$\int x \sqrt{3x + 5} \, dx = \frac{2}{135}(3x + 5)^{\frac{3}{2}}(9x - 10) + C.$$

The student should verify this result by differentiation.

94. Substitutions in general.—The transformations just studied constitute some of the most useful ones; they do not by any means exhaust the possibilities. One is of course free at any time to make any change of variable that he pleases. If the integration can be performed in terms of the new variable, the result can easily be changed back into terms of the original variable.

A considerable amount of ingenuity is required in the matter of choosing a substitution that will simplify a given integral. The following examples will give the student some idea of the many possibilities.

1. The substitution $e^x = z$ reduces

$$\int \frac{dx}{e^x - 1} \quad \text{to} \quad \int \frac{dz}{z^2 - z}.$$

2. The substitution $\tan \frac{1}{2}x = z$ reduces

$$\int \frac{dx}{\sin x - 4 \cos x - 4} \quad \text{to} \quad \int \frac{dz}{z - 4}.$$

3. The substitution $x = 1/z$ reduces

$$\int \frac{dx}{x^2 \sqrt{a^2 + x^2}} \quad \text{to} \quad - \int \frac{z\, dz}{\sqrt{1 + a^2 z^2}}.$$

PROBLEMS

1. $\int 8x \sqrt{1 + 4x}\, dx.$

2. $\int x \sqrt{2 - 3x}\, dx.$

3. $\int \frac{4x + 5}{\sqrt{2x - 3}}\, dx.$

4. $\int \frac{6x + 9}{\sqrt{2x + 5}}\, dx.$

5. $\int \frac{\sqrt{x}\, dx}{\sqrt{x} - 2}.$

6. $\int \frac{2\sqrt{x} - 3}{\sqrt{x} - 3}\, dx.$

7. $\int \frac{\sqrt{3 + x}}{x - 6}\, dx.$

8. $\int \frac{dx}{\sqrt{2x + 7} + 12}.$

9. $\int x \sqrt[3]{2x + 9}\, dx.$

10. $\int \frac{2x - 4}{\sqrt[3]{3x + 6}}\, dx.$

11. $\int \frac{x^2 + 5}{\sqrt[3]{x + 5}}\, dx.$

12. $\int x^5 \sqrt{2x^3 + 4}\, dx.$

13. $\int x^3 \sqrt{x^2 + 5}\, dx.$

14. $\int \frac{dx}{\sqrt[3]{x} + \sqrt{x}}.$

15. $\int \dfrac{\sqrt{x-4}}{x\sqrt{x}}\,dx.$ HINT: Let $x = 4\sec^2\theta.$

16. $\int \dfrac{dx}{x\sqrt{x}\sqrt{9-x}}\cdot$ HINT: Let $x = 9\sin^2\theta.$

17. $\int \dfrac{dx}{x\sqrt{6x-x^2}}\cdot$ HINT: Let $x = 6\sin^2\theta.$

18. $\int \dfrac{dx}{x\sqrt{x^2-8x}}\cdot$ HINT: Let $x = 8\sec^2\theta.$

19. $\int \dfrac{dx}{x\sqrt{2ax-x^2}}\cdot$ 　　　　**20.** $\int \dfrac{dx}{x\sqrt{x^2-2ax}}\cdot$

21. $\int \dfrac{x^{\frac{3}{2}}dx}{\sqrt{x^2+4x}}\cdot$ HINT: Let $x = 4\tan^2\theta.$

22. $\int \sqrt{4-\sqrt{x}}\,dx.$ 　　　　**23.** $\int \dfrac{e^x(e^x+4)}{e^x-2}\,dx.$

24. Show that if one lets

$$\tan\frac{x}{2} = z; \quad i.e., \quad x = 2\arctan z,$$

then

$$dx = \frac{2\,dz}{1+z^2},$$
$$\sin x = \frac{2z}{1+z^2},$$
$$\cos x = \frac{1-z^2}{1+z^2}.$$

Use the substitution indicated in Prob. 24 in the following problems:

25. $\int \dfrac{dx}{\sin x - 2\cos x - 2}\cdot$ 　　**26.** $\int \dfrac{\cos x\,dx}{1+\cos x}\cdot$

27. $\int \dfrac{dx}{\sin x + \tan x}\cdot$ 　　　　**28.** $\int \dfrac{dx}{2+\sin x}\cdot$

95. Integration by parts.—One of the most useful aids to integration is the process known as *integration by parts*. The necessary formula is obtained from that for the differential of a product. If u and v are differentiable functions of x then

$$d(uv) = u\,dv + v\,du.$$

Integrating both sides with respect to x, we may write

$$uv = \int u\,dv + \int v\,du.$$

Rearranging this result, we have the formula for integration by parts,

$$\int u \, dv = uv - \int v \, du.$$

In order to use this formula we must regard the given integrand as the product of a function u and the differential dv of another function v. No general rule for thus breaking the integrand into two parts can be given. One usually takes as much of it as he can readily integrate as dv and calls the remainder u.

Example
$$\int xe^x dx$$

Solution

We cannot perform the integration by previous methods. However we *can* integrate $e^x dx$. We may therefore regard the integrand as being of the form $u \, dv$ where,

$$u = x \quad \text{and} \quad dv = e^x dx.$$

Differentiating u to obtain du and integrating dv to obtain v, we have

$$du = dx \quad \text{and} \quad v = e^x.$$

Using the formula for integration by parts, we obtain

$$\int xe^x dx = xe^x - \int e^x dx$$
$$= xe^x - e^x + C$$

A wrong choice of u and dv may lead to a more complicated integral. Suppose, for instance, that in the example just solved we had let

$$u = e^x \qquad dv = x \, dx;$$
then,
$$du = e^x dx \qquad v = \tfrac{1}{2}x^2.$$

Applying the formula, we have

$$\int xe^x dx = \tfrac{1}{2}x^2 e^x - \tfrac{1}{2}\int x^2 e^x dx.$$

This relation is of course true, but it is readily seen that the second integral is more difficult to handle than the original one.

In some cases it may be necessary to apply the formula more than once. Thus, if one starts with

$$\int x^2 e^x dx,$$

the first application of the formula, letting $u = x^2$ and $dv = e^x dx$, leads to an integral of the form

$$\int x e^x dx.$$

This integral may in turn be evaluated by parts as in the previous example.

In certain cases it may be necessary to use the procedure illustrated by the following:

Example
$$\int e^x \sin x \, dx.$$

Solution
Let

$$u = e^x \qquad dv = \sin x \, dx;$$
$$du = e^x dx \qquad v = - \cos x.$$

Hence,

(1) $$\int e^x \sin x \, dx = -e^x \cos x + \int e^x \cos x \, dx.$$

The integral obtained on the right-hand side is not simpler than the original one. However, we may apply integration by parts to it letting

$$u = e^x, \qquad dv = \cos x \, dx,$$
$$du = e^x dx, \qquad v = \sin x.$$

Substituting in (1) we obtain

$$\int e^x \sin x \, dx = -e^x \cos x + e^x \sin x - \int e^x \sin x \, dx.$$

Transposing, we have

$$2\int e^x \sin x \, dx = e^x(\sin x - \cos x) + C'$$
$$\int e^x \sin x \, dx = \frac{e^x}{2} (\sin x - \cos x) + C.$$

PROBLEMS

1. $\int x e^{-x} dx.$ 　　　　2. $\int x a^x dx.$

3. $\int x^2 e^{2x} dx.$ 　　　　4. $\int x^2 a^x dx.$

5. $\int \log x\, dx.$ **6.** $\int x^2 \log x\, dx.$

7. $\int \log^2 x\, dx.$ **8.** $\int t \sin t \cos t\, dt.$

9. $\int x \cos 2x\, dx.$ **10.** $\int \theta^2 \sin 2\theta\, d\theta.$

11. $\int \arcsin x\, dx.$ **12.** $\int \arccos \tfrac{1}{2}x\, dx.$

13. $\int \arctan x\, dx.$ **14.** $\int x \arctan x\, dx.$

15. $\int x^3 \arctan \tfrac{1}{2}x\, dx.$ **16.** $\int x^2 \operatorname{arccot} x\, dx.$

17. $\int e^x \sin \tfrac{1}{2}x\, dx.$ **18.** $\int e^x \cos 2x\, dx.$

19. $\int e^{2x} \sin 4x\, dx.$ **20.** $\int x \tan^2 x\, dx.$

21. $\int \dfrac{x}{\cos^2 x}\, dx.$ **22.** $\int \dfrac{x}{\sin^2 2x}\, dx.$

23. $\int \sin x \sin 3x\, dx.$ **24.** $\int \sec^2 x\, dx.$

25. $\int \csc^3 x\, dx.$ **26.** $\int x \sin^2 x\, dx.$

27. $\int \sin \sqrt{x}\, dx.$ **28.** $\int \cos \sqrt{x}\, dx.$

HINT: First let $\sqrt{x} = z.$

29. $\int \arcsin \sqrt{x}\, dx.$ **30.** $\int \sqrt{x} \arctan \sqrt{x}\, dx.$

31. $\int \sin x \sqrt{1 + \cos^2 x}\, dx.$ **32.** $\int (x + e^x)^2 dx.$

HINT: First let $\cos x = \tan \theta.$

33. $\int (2x + \cos x)^2 dx.$ **34.** $\int \dfrac{3x + 4 \sin 2x}{\cos^2 x}\, dx.$

35. $\int \sec^5 x\, dx.$ **36.** $\int \sec^3 x \tan^2 x\, dx.$

37. Show that $\int x^m \log x\, dx = x^{m+1} \left[\dfrac{\log x}{m + 1} - \dfrac{1}{(m + 1)^2} \right].$

38. Show that $\int e^{ax} \sin bx\, dx = \dfrac{e^{ax}(a \sin bx - b \cos bx)}{a^2 + b^2}.$

39. Show that $\int e^{ax} \cos bx\, dx = \dfrac{e^{ax}(a \cos bx + b \sin bx)}{a^2 + b^2}.$

96. Integration of rational fractions.

Any rational fraction in which the numerator is *not* of lower degree than the denominator can be reduced, by performing the indicated division, to a simple polynomial plus a fraction in which the numerator *is* of lower degree than the denominator. Thus by actual division,

$$\frac{x^4 + 2x^3 - 5x^2 - 8x + 16}{x^3 - x^2 - 4x + 4} = x + 3 + \frac{2x^2 + 4}{x^3 - x^2 - 4x + 4}.$$

If one has such a fraction to integrate, his first step is to perform the division. Since the polynomial thus obtained is easily integrated, we need consider here only the integration of the remaining fraction in which the numerator is of *lower* degree than the denominator.

The integration of such a fraction is carried out by breaking it up into a sum of several simpler fractions called *partial fractions*. Thus, in the above example, it will be shown that

$$\frac{2x^2 + 4}{x^3 - x^2 - 4x + 4} \equiv \frac{1}{x + 2} + \frac{3}{x - 2} - \frac{2}{x - 1}.$$

The first step in thus breaking a given fraction up into partial fractions is to *factor the denominator* into its prime factors. The rest of the procedure depends upon the nature of the factors obtained. We shall consider only three cases.

Case I. *Factors of denominator all linear and each occurring only once.*—Corresponding to each factor of the form $px + q$ assume a fraction of the form

$$\frac{A}{px + q}.$$

In the example just discussed, the factors of the denominator are $(x + 2)$, $(x - 2)$, and $(x - 1)$. Hence we assume that for proper values of A, B, and C, which are yet to be determined,

$$\frac{2x^2 + 4}{x^3 - x^2 - 4x + 4} \equiv \frac{A}{x + 2} + \frac{B}{x - 2} + \frac{C}{x - 1}.$$
$$\equiv \frac{A(x - 2)(x - 1) + B(x + 2)(x - 1) + C(x + 2)(x - 2)}{(x + 2)(x - 2)(x - 1)}.$$

The denominators are identical; hence, the fractions will be identical if we determine A, B, and C, so that

$$2x^2 + 4 \equiv A(x - 2)(x - 1) + B(x + 2)(x - 1)$$
$$+ C(x + 2)(x - 2)$$
$$\equiv (A + B + C)x^2 + (-3A + B)x$$
$$+ (2A - 2B - 4C).$$

Two polynomials in x are equal for all values of x if, and only if, the coefficients of like powers of x are equal. Equating these coefficients we have

$$A + B + C = 2.$$
$$-3A + B = 0.$$
$$2A - 2B - 4C = 4.$$

Solving these equations, we find

$$A = 1, \qquad B = 3, \qquad C = -2.$$

Hence,

$$\frac{2x^2 + 4}{x^3 - x^2 - 4x + 4} \equiv \frac{1}{x + 2} + \frac{3}{x - 2} - \frac{2}{x - 1}.$$

The result may of course be checked by combining the three fractions on the right into a single fraction.

A somewhat simpler method of finding the values of A, B, and C is as follows: If

$$2x^2 + 4 \equiv A(x - 2)(x - 1) + B(x + 2)(x - 1)$$
$$+ C(x + 2)(x - 2)$$

for *all* values of x, then they must certainly be equal for any particular values of x that we may care to choose. Substituting for x the values 2, -2, and 1 successively, we find

$$12 = 4B, \qquad \text{or} \qquad B = 3.$$
$$12 = 12A, \qquad \text{or} \qquad A = 1.$$
$$6 = -3C, \qquad \text{or} \qquad C = -2.$$

It is obvious that we may substitute *any* three values of x that we please and obtain three equations in the unknowns A, B, and C. The above values were chosen so that each equation would contain only *one* of the unknowns.

CASE II. *Factors of denominator all linear but some repeated.*—If a linear factor $px + q$ occurs r times in the denominator, one must assume r fractions corresponding to it; the denominators of these fractions are $(px + q)$, $(px + q)^2$, $\cdots$, $(px + q)^r$. Thus, if the factors of the denominator are

$$(x - 3)^2 \quad \text{and} \quad (x - 1),$$

the corresponding partial fractions are

$$\frac{A}{x - 3} + \frac{B}{(x - 3)^2} + \frac{C}{x - 1}$$

where A, B, and C are to be determined as in the previous case.

Example

Evaluate $\displaystyle\int \frac{x^2 + 6x - 1}{(x - 3)^2(x - 1)} \, dx$.

Solution

Assume

$$\frac{x^2 + 6x - 1}{(x - 3)^2(x - 1)} \equiv \frac{A}{(x - 3)} + \frac{B}{(x - 3)^2} + \frac{C}{x - 1}$$

$$\equiv \frac{A(x - 3)(x - 1) + B(x - 1) + C(x - 3)^2}{(x - 3)^2(x - 1)}.$$

Equating numerators we have

$$x^2 + 6x - 1 \equiv A(x - 3)(x - 1) + B(x - 1) + C(x - 3)^2.$$

Let $x = 1$: $6 = 4C$ or $C = \frac{3}{2}$.
Let $x = 3$: $26 = 2B$ or $B = 13$.
Let $x = 0$: $-1 = 3A - B + 9C$ or $A = -\frac{1}{2}$.

Hence,

$$\int \frac{(x^2 + 6x - 1)dx}{(x - 3)^2(x - 1)} = -\frac{1}{2} \int \frac{dx}{x - 3} + 13 \int \frac{dx}{(x - 3)^2} + \frac{3}{2} \int \frac{dx}{x - 1}$$

$$= -\frac{1}{2} \log (x - 3) - \frac{13}{x - 3} + \frac{3}{2} \log (x - 1) + C$$

$$= \log \sqrt{\frac{(x - 1)^3}{x - 3}} - \frac{13}{x - 3} + C.$$

CASE III. *Denominator contains some irreducible quadratic factors.*—Corresponding to each factor of the form $ax^2 + bx + c$ we assume a fraction of the form

$$\frac{Ax + B}{ax^2 + bx + c}.$$

Example

Evaluate $\displaystyle\int \frac{(8x^2 + 3)dx}{(x^2 + x + 1)(x - 2)}$.

Partial Solution

Assume

$$\frac{8x^2 + 3}{(x^2 + x + 1)(x - 2)} \equiv \frac{Ax + B}{x^2 + x + 1} + \frac{C}{x - 2}.$$
$$\equiv \frac{Ax(x - 2) + B(x - 2) + C(x^2 + x + 1)}{(x^2 + x + 1)(x - 2)}.$$

Equating numerators we have

$$8x^2 + 3 \equiv Ax(x - 2) + B(x - 2) + C(x^2 + x + 1).$$

Let $x = 2$: $35 = 7C$ or $C = 5$.
Let $x = 0$: $3 = -2B + C$ or $B = 1$.
Let $x = 1$: $11 = -A - B + 3C$ or $A = 3$.

We have then

$$\int \frac{(8x^2 + 3)dx}{(x^2 + x + 1)(x - 2)} = \int \frac{(3x + 1)dx}{x^2 + x + 1} + \int \frac{5\ dx}{x - 2}.$$

PROBLEMS

1. $\displaystyle\int \frac{x\ dx}{x - 3}$.

2. $\displaystyle\int \frac{(2x + 5)dx}{x - 1}$.

3. $\displaystyle\int \frac{(7 - 2x)dx}{3x - 5}$.

4. $\displaystyle\int \frac{(x^3 + 1)dx}{x - 1}$.

5. $\displaystyle\int \frac{(x + 7)dx}{x^2 + 2x - 8}$.

6. $\displaystyle\int \frac{(3x + 4)dx}{x^2 + 5x + 6}$.

7. $\displaystyle\int \frac{(x^2 + x + 1)dx}{x^2 - 7x + 10}$.

8. $\displaystyle\int \frac{(x - 6)dx}{x^2 - x}$.

9. $\displaystyle\int \frac{(6x^2 - 23x + 9)dx}{x^3 - 4x^2 + 3x}$.

10. $\displaystyle\int \frac{dx}{x^3 - 3x^2 + 2x}$.

11. $\displaystyle\int \frac{(x^2 - 17x + 22)dx}{(x - 1)(x - 3)(x + 2)}$.

12. $\displaystyle\int \frac{(3x - 1)dx}{(x - 4)(2x + 1)(x - 1)}$.

13. $\displaystyle\int \frac{x^3 dx}{(x + 1)(x^2 - 4)}$.

14. $\displaystyle\int \frac{(x^3 + x + 1)dx}{x(x - 1)(x - 2)(x - 3)}$.

15. $\int \dfrac{dv}{v^2 - a^2}.$ *Formula* (15)

16. $\int \sec \theta \, d\theta = \int \dfrac{\cos \theta \, d\theta}{1 - \sin^2 \theta}.$ *Formula* (17)

HINT: Let $\sin \theta = x.$

17. $\int \csc \theta \, d\theta.$

18. $\int \dfrac{dx}{2e^x - 1}.$

19. $\int \dfrac{(x - 1 - 2x^2)dx}{(x - 1)^2(x - 3)}.$

20. $\int \dfrac{(3x + 4)dx}{(x + 2)^2(x - 6)}.$

21. $\int \dfrac{dx}{x^2(x^2 - 4)}.$

22. $\int \dfrac{(x^5 - 2)dx}{x^4 - 2x^3}.$

23. $\int \dfrac{dx}{x^3 - 10x^2 + 33x - 36}.$

24. $\int \dfrac{(-3x^2 + 7x - 16)dx}{x^3 - 5x^2 + 7x - 3}.$

25. $\int \sec^3 \theta \, d\theta = \int \dfrac{\cos \theta \, d\theta}{(1 - \sin^2 \theta)^2}.$

HINT: Let $\sin \theta = x.$

26. $\int \csc^3 \theta \, d\theta.$

27. $\int \dfrac{(x^2 + 9x + 29)dx}{(x - 4)(x^2 + 2x + 3)}.$

28. $\int \dfrac{(2x^2 + 6x - 1)dx}{x^3 + x^2 + x}.$

29. $\int \dfrac{(6x^3 - 19x^2 + 23x - 28)dx}{(x - 1)(x - 4)(x^2 + x + 4)}.$

30. $\int \dfrac{(15 - 5x + 10x^2 - x^3)dx}{x^2(x^2 + 5)}.$

31. $\int \dfrac{(5x^2 - 20x + 1)dx}{(x^2 + 4)(2x^2 + x + 1)}.$

32. $\int \dfrac{(5x^3 + 10x^2 - 4x - 43)dx}{(3x^2 - x + 7)(x^2 + x + 5)}.$

33. $\int \dfrac{dx}{x^3 - 8}.$

34. $\int \dfrac{dx}{x^4 - 16}.$

35. $\int \dfrac{(4x^3 + 23x^2 - 14x + 52)dx}{x^4 + 6x^3 + 14x^2 + 36x + 48}.$

CHAPTER XVIII

THE DEFINITE INTEGRAL

97. Definition of area under a curve.—In this chapter we shall consider the problem of computing the area bounded by a curve whose equation is $y = f(x)$, the x-axis, and the ordinates at $x = a$ and $x = b$. Considering at first the case in which $f(x)$ is positive throughout the interval we define this *area under the curve* as follows (Fig. 87):

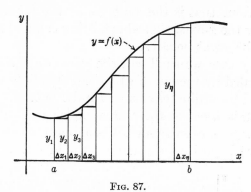

Fig. 87.

1. Divide the interval from $x = a$ to $x = b$ into any number n of parts, and denote the directed lengths of these subintervals by Δx_1, Δx_2, Δx_3, $\cdots$, Δx_n.

2. Denote the ordinates at the left-hand ends of these intervals by y_1, y_2, y_3, $\cdots$, y_n.

3. Denote the sum of the areas of the rectangles having the Δx's as bases and the y's as altitudes by A'; then

$$A' = y_1\Delta x_1 + y_2\Delta x_2 + y_3\Delta x_3 + \cdots + y_n\Delta x_n.$$

4. Now let each Δx approach zero. The number of rectangles increases beyond bound while, simultaneously, the area of each one approaches zero. The *limit* of their sum,

215

if it exists, is the required area.   Denoting it by A, we have

$$A = \lim_{\substack{\Delta x_i \to 0 \\ n \to \infty}} (y_1 \Delta x_1 + y_2 \Delta x_2 + y_3 \Delta x_3 + \cdots + y_n \Delta x_n).$$

If $f(x)$ is positive throughout the interval from $x = a$ to $x = b$, as shown in Fig. 87, then all the y's are positive. Also, if $b > a$ all the Δx's are positive.   For if the points of division on the x-axis are denoted by $x_1 (= a)$, x_2, x_3, x_4, etc., then the directed length Δx_i is equal to $x_{i+1} - x_i$, which is positive.   In this case, then, every term in the above sum is positive and A is positive.

If $f(x)$ is negative throughout the interval and $b > a$, then A as defined above is negative.   And finally, if $f(x)$ is positive over part of the interval and negative over part, then A has a value that is the *algebraic sum* of the areas above and below the x-axis, that above being counted as positive and that below as negative.

In every case we shall call the value of A the *algebraic area* bounded by the curve whose equation is $y = f(x)$, the x-axis, and the ordinates at $x = a$ and $x = b$.   We may also refer to this area as the "area under the curve" from $x = a$ to $x = b$, even though it is actually under the curve only if $f(x)$ is positive throughout the interval.

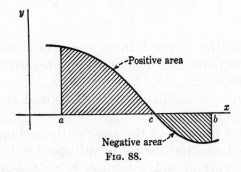

Fig. 88.

There will be a limited number of cases in which we shall want to compute the *arithmetic area*, this being the total area bounded by the curve, the x-axis, and the two ordinates, all of it being regarded as positive.   In a case such as that shown in Fig. 88 this would be done by computing A for the part from $x = a$ to $x = c$ and for the part from $x = c$ to $x = b$ separately and adding the absolute values of the two results.

It is intuitively evident that in setting up our definition of the area A we could have taken the right-hand ordinate for each Δx interval as the altitude of the rectangle, instead of the left-hand ordinate.   The definition will be stated in a more general form in Art. 101.

98. Notation.—In order to have a brief way of writing the sum encountered in the preceding section, we define the symbol

$$\sum_{i=1}^{n} y_i \Delta x_i$$

to stand for the sum of all terms that can be formed from $y_i \Delta x_i$ by letting the *index* i take successively all integral values from 1 to n inclusive; *i.e.*, by definition,

$$\sum_{i=1}^{n} y_i \Delta x_i \equiv y_1 \Delta x_1 + y_2 \Delta x_2 + y_3 \Delta x_3 + \ldots + y_n \Delta x_n.$$

Using this convenient notation we may express our definition of the algebraic area under the curve $y = f(x)$ from $x = a$ to $x = b$ in the form

$$A = \lim_{\Delta x_i \to 0} \sum_{i=1}^{n} y_i \Delta x_i.$$

99. Computation of the area.—In a few simple cases it is possible to compute the area by following the above definition.   For convenience we divide the interval into n *equal* parts, express the sum of the areas of the rectangles as a function of n, and find the limit of this function as $n \to \infty$.

The following two formulas, which can be proved by induction, are necessary in connection with the next example and some of the problems of the following set.

(1) $1^2 + 2^2 + 3^2 + \cdots + k^2 = \dfrac{k(k+1)(2k+1)}{6}.$

(2) $1^3 + 2^3 + 3^3 + \cdots + k^3 = \dfrac{k^2(k+1)^2}{4}.$

Example

Compute the area under the parabola $y = x^2$ from $x = 0$ to $x = 3$.

Solution (Fig. 89)

1. Dividing the interval from $x = 0$ to $x = 3$ into n equal parts, we have $\Delta x = 3/n$.

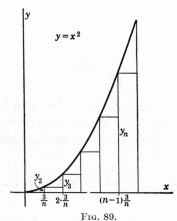

$y = x^2$

FIG. 89.

2. The ordinates are

$$y_1 = 0, \qquad y_2 = \left(\frac{3}{n}\right)^2, \qquad y_3 = \left(2 \cdot \frac{3}{n}\right)^2, \cdots, \qquad y_n = \left(\overline{n-1} \cdot \frac{3}{n}\right)^2.$$

3. $A' = \Delta x(y_1 + y_2 + y_3 + \cdots + y_n)$

$= \dfrac{3}{n}\left[0 + \left(\dfrac{3}{n}\right)^2 + 2^2\left(\dfrac{3}{n}\right)^2 + 3^2\left(\dfrac{3}{n}\right)^2 + \cdots + (n-1)^2\left(\dfrac{3}{n}\right)^2\right]$

$= \dfrac{27}{n^3}[1^2 + 2^2 + 3^2 + \cdots + (n-1)^2].$

4. $A = \lim\limits_{n \to \infty} \dfrac{27}{n^3}[1^2 + 2^2 + 3^2 + \cdots + (n-1)^2]$

$= \lim\limits_{n \to \infty} \dfrac{27}{n^3}\left[\dfrac{(n-1)(n)(2n-1)}{6}\right]$

$= \lim\limits_{n \to \infty} \dfrac{27}{6}\left[\dfrac{2n^3 - 3n^2 + n}{n^3}\right]$

$= 9.$

PROBLEMS

In each of the following problems first sketch the curve whose equation is given.   Then shade the area A "under the curve" in the specified interval, and state whether the value of A is positive or negative:

  1. $y = 6x - x^2$; $x = 1$ to $x = 5$.

  2. $y = x^2 - 4x$; $x = -1$ to $x = 3$.

  3. $y = \sin x$; $x = \frac{1}{2}\pi$ to $x = \pi$.

  4. $y = \cos^2 x$; $x = 0$ to $x = \pi$.

  5. $y = 5x^2 - x^3$; $x = -1$ to $x = 4$.

  6. $y = x^3 - 4x^2$; $x = 1$ to $x = 3$.

  7. $y = \sqrt{25 - x^2}$; $x = 0$ to $x = 4$.

  8. $y = 9x - x^3$; $x = -2$ to $x = 2$.

  9. $x^2y + 3y = 12$; $x = -3$ to $x = 1$.

  10. $x^2y - 5y = 5x$; $x = -1$ to $x = 2$.

  11. Redraw Fig. 89 using the right-hand ordinate for each Δx interval as the altitude of the rectangle, instead of the left-hand ordinate. Express the sum of the areas of these rectangles as a function of n and find the limit as $n \to \infty$.   HINT: In this case the first ordinate is equal to $(3/n)^2$ instead of zero, and the last one is $\left(n \cdot \dfrac{3}{n}\right)^2$.

  12. Compute the area under the curve $y = x^3$ in the interval from $x = 0$ to $x = 4$.   Draw the figure and show the rectangles used.

100. Computation of area by integration.

—We shall now show that the area under a curve can be found by a process involving integration, and thus arrive at a simple method of computing the limit of a sum of the type just discussed. For this purpose we let $y = f(x)$ be the equation of the curve (Fig. 90), and for the present we assume that $f(x)$ is continuous and increasing over the interval from $x = a$ to $x = b$.   We then proceed as follows:

Think of the area under the curve as being "generated" by an ordinate of variable length which starts at $x = a$ and moves to the right, its upper end remaining always on the curve.   The area generated when the moving ordinate has reached any point x is a quantity which depends upon x; i.e., it is a function of x.   Call this function $A(x)$.   We shall now show that $A(x)$ *is a function whose derivative with respect to x is $f(x)$*, and that, consequently, $A(x)$ *can be found by integrating $f(x)$.*

In order to find the derivative of $A(x)$ with respect to x we let x increase by an amount Δx, form the quotient $\Delta A/\Delta x$, and then let $\Delta x \to 0$. From Fig. 90 we see that the

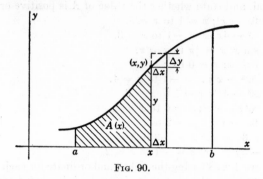

FIG. 90.

increment ΔA in area corresponding to an increment Δx in x is more than $y\,\Delta x$ and less than $(y + \Delta y)\Delta x$; *i.e.*,

$$y\,\Delta x < \Delta A < (y + \Delta y)\Delta x.$$

Dividing by Δx we obtain the inequality

$$y < \frac{\Delta A}{\Delta x} < y + \Delta y.$$

When $\Delta x \to 0$, Δy also approaches zero if $f(x)$ is a continuous function. Then

$$\lim_{\Delta x \to 0} \frac{\Delta A}{\Delta x} = \frac{dA}{dx} = y = f(x).$$

This equation states that for any position of the moving ordinate, the instantaneous *rate* at which area is being generated is equal to the value of y at that instant. This is intuitively evident. Suppose, for example, that at a certain place the ordinate is 8 in.; then obviously, at this position, area is being generated at a rate of 8 sq. in. per inch moved by the ordinate in the x-direction.

Since $dA/dx = y$, or

(1) $$\frac{dA}{dx} = f(x),$$

we can find $A(x)$ by integration. Let $\phi(x)$ be a function obtained by integrating $f(x)$; then

(2) $A(x) = \int f(x)dx = \phi(x) + C.$

The value of A corresponding to the starting point $x = a$ is zero; hence,

$$0 = \phi(a) + C \qquad \text{or} \qquad C = -\phi(a).$$

Replacing C by $-\phi(a)$ in (2) we have the expression for the area from $x = a$ to any other point x:

(3) $A(x) = \phi(x) - \phi(a).$

Finally, the area under the curve from $x = a$ to $x = b$ is found by replacing x by b in the right-hand member of (3):

(4) $A = \phi(b) - \phi(a).$

Example

To find the area under the curve $y = x^2$ from $x = 1$ to $x = 3$, we have

$$\int x^2 dx = \frac{x^3}{3};$$

$x^3/3$ is the function $\phi(x)$ in the above derivation. Its value when $x = 3$ is 9; its value when $x = 1$ is $\frac{1}{3}$. Then

$$A = 9 - \tfrac{1}{3} = 8\tfrac{2}{3}.$$

If the curve is drawn with 1 in. equal to 1 unit on each axis then the area under the curve from $x = 1$ to $x = 3$ is exactly $8\frac{2}{3}$ sq. in.

If $f(x)$ is *decreasing* throughout the interval, the derivation is the same as above except that the inequality signs are reversed. If $f(x)$ has any finite number of maximum and minimum points in the interval from $x = a$ to $x = b$, the interval can be subdivided into parts such that $f(x)$ is either increasing, decreasing, or remaining constant throughout each part, as indicated in Fig. 91. The derivation can then be applied to each part.

Finally, we state the following:

RULE: *In order to compute the algebraic area bounded by the continuous curve whose equation is $y = f(x)$, the x-axis, and the ordinates at $x = a$ and $x = b$, proceed as follows:*

Step 1. Find $\int f(x)dx$ in the usual way, obtaining a function $\phi(x)$. The constant of integration may be omitted.

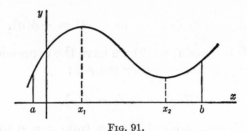

FIG. 91.

Step 2. Find the values of $\phi(x)$ when $x = b$, and when $x = a$, and subtract the latter from the former. This difference is equal to the algebraic area.

We shall use the symbol

$$\int_a^b f(x)dx$$

to denote the operation indicated in the two steps above; i.e.,

$$\int_a^b f(x)dx \; = \; \phi(x)\Big]_a^b \; = \; \phi(b) \; - \; \phi(a).$$

This symbol is called the *definite integral of $f(x)$ from $x = a$ to $x = b$.* The numbers a and b are called the *lower limit* and *upper limit*, respectively, of the definite integral.

Example 1

The algebraic area bounded by the curve $y = \dfrac{12x}{x^2 + 3}$, the x-axis, and the ordinates at $x = 0$ and $x = 4$ is given by

$$A = \int_0^4 \frac{12x}{x^2 + 3}\, dx = 6 \log (x^2 + 3)\Big]_0^4 = 6 \log 19 - 6 \log 3$$
$$= 6 \log \tfrac{19}{3} = 6(1.8458) = 11.07.$$

The logarithms are, of course, *natural* logarithms.   The area, which is shown in Fig. 92, is 11.07 sq. in. if the unit on each axis is 1 in.

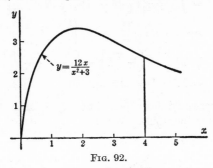

FIG. 92.

Example 2

The algebraic area bounded by the curve $y = \sin x$, the x-axis, and the ordinates at $x = 0$ and $x = \frac{3}{2}\pi$ is given by (Fig. 93):

$$\int_0^{\frac{3\pi}{2}} \sin x \, dx = -\cos x \Big]_0^{\frac{3\pi}{2}} = (-\cos \tfrac{3}{2}\pi) - (-\cos 0)$$
$$= 0 - (-1) = 1.$$

This is the *algebraic* area.   If one wanted the *arithmetic* area, one would evaluate separately the integrals

$$\int_0^{\pi} \sin x \, dx$$

and

$$\int_{\pi}^{\frac{3\pi}{2}} \sin x \, dx,$$

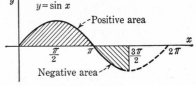

FIG. 93.

and then add the absolute values of the results.   The student may verify that these integrals have the values $+2$ and -1, respectively. The arithmetic area is then 3 sq. units.

The area enclosed by two curves can often be computed as indicated in the following:

Example 3

Find the area enclosed by the curves $y = \dfrac{8}{x^2 + 4}$ and $4y = x^2$.

Solution (Fig. 94)

The curves intersect at $(\pm 2, 1)$.   If A is the area enclosed by them, then

$$A = \text{area } ABCDE - \text{area } ABODE$$

$$= \int_{-2}^{2} \frac{8}{x^2 + 4}\, dx - \int_{-2}^{2} \frac{x^2}{4}\, dx$$

$$= 4 \arctan \frac{x}{2}\Big]_{-2}^{2} - \frac{x^3}{12}\Big]_{-2}^{2}$$

$$= 4\left[\frac{\pi}{4} - \left(-\frac{\pi}{4}\right)\right] - \left[\frac{8}{12} - \left(-\frac{8}{12}\right)\right]$$

$$= 2\pi - \tfrac{4}{3} = 4.95 \text{ sq. units.}$$

The same answer could have been obtained by integrating from 0 to 2 and then doubling the result. Why?

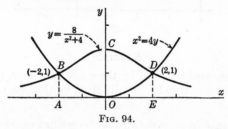

Fig. 94.

When the integration leads to an inverse trigonometric function, as it does in the above example, one should always use the *principal values*. Thus

$$\int_{-1}^{+1} \frac{dx}{\sqrt{1 - x^2}} = \arcsin x\Big]_{-1}^{+1} = \arcsin(+1)$$
$$- \arcsin(-1).$$

Referring to Fig. 49, page 103, the student should recall that we were dealing with the principal branch AB of function $y = \arcsin x$ when we found that $D_x y = \dfrac{1}{\sqrt{1 - x^2}}.$ If we confine ourselves to this branch then

$$\arcsin(+1) = \tfrac{1}{2}\pi \qquad \text{and} \qquad \arcsin(-1) = -\tfrac{1}{2}\pi$$
$$(\textbf{not } \tfrac{3}{2}\pi).$$

The value of the above definite integral is then

$$\tfrac{1}{2}\pi - (-\tfrac{1}{2}\pi) = \pi.$$

Of course, we could use the branch on which

$$\arcsin(+1) = \tfrac{5}{2}\pi$$

and arcsin $(-1) = \frac{3}{2}\pi$, but nothing would be gained by doing this.

PROBLEMS

1. Make a sketch similar to Fig. 90 but showing a function $f(x)$ that is *decreasing* throughout the interval from $x = a$ to $x = b$. Write out for this case the proof that $dA/dx = f(x)$.

2. Show that the difference between ΔA and $dA (= y\, dx)$ in Fig. 90 is an infinitesimal of higher order than Δx when $\Delta x \to 0$.

In each of the following cases compute the algebraic area bounded by the given curve, the x-axis, and the given ordinates. Sketch the curve and shade the required area:

3. $y = \frac{1}{2}x^2 + x; x = 1, x = 4.$

4. $y = 5x - x^2; x = 0, x = 4.$

5. $y = 3x + x^2; x = -3, x = 0.$

6. $y = x^2 - 8x + 15; x = 2, x = 5.$

7. $y = x^2 - 2x + 2; x = -1, x = 3.$

8. $y = 9x - x^3; x = -3, x = 3.$

9. $y = x^3 - 8x; x = 0, x = 2.$

10. $4y = x^3 - x^2 - 20x; x = -4, x = 0.$

11. $y = 2\sqrt{x}; x = 0, x = 9.$

12. $y = \log x; x = 1, x = e.$

13. $y = 2\sin 3x; x = 0, x = \frac{1}{3}\pi.$

14. $y = \sin^2 x; x = 0, x = \pi.$

15. $y = 4\cos^2 \frac{1}{2}x; x = 0, x = \pi.$

16. $y = 2\sin^3 \frac{1}{2}x; x = 0, x = \pi.$

17. $y = \sin x + \cos x; x = 0, x = \frac{1}{2}\pi.$

18. $xy = 4; x = 1, x = 3.$

19. $y = \dfrac{3}{\sqrt{x}}; x = 1, x = 9.$

20. $y = x\sqrt{16 - x^2}; x = 0, x = 4.$

21. $x^2y + y - 5 = 0; x = 0, x = 3.$

22. $x^2y + 4y = 8x; x = 0, x = 2.$

23. $x^2y - 4y = 15; x = 3, x = 5.$

24. $y = \dfrac{8}{\sqrt{4 - x^2}}; x = 0, x = 1.$

25. $y = 4xe^{-x}; x = 0, x = 2.$

In each of the following cases compute the total area (in the arithmetic sense) enclosed by the two given curves; draw the figure and shade the area found:

26. $2y = x^2; y^2 = 16x.$

27. $x^2 = 6y; x^2 = 12y - 9.$

28. $y = 8x - x^2; y = 2x.$

29. $y = 8x - x^2; 3y = x^2.$

30. $x^2y + 2y = 3x; 4y = x^2.$

31. $x^2y + 2y = 6x; 3y = x.$

32. $x^2y + 3y + 6x = 0$; $2y = 5x - 2x^2$.

33. $4y = x^2(5 - x)$; $y = (x - 2)^2$.

34. Compute the area bounded by the curves $y = e^x$, $y = e^{-x}$, and the line $x = 2$.

35. Compute the area bounded by the curves $y = \sin x$ and $y = \cos x$ between two successive points of intersection.

36. The algebraic area bounded by the curve $x = f(y)$, the y-axis, and the horizontal lines ca and db (Fig. 95) is obviously given by

$$\int_{y=c}^{y=d} x \, dy.$$

Compute the shaded area in the figure, the equation of the curve being $x = 2y^2 - \frac{1}{2}y^3$.

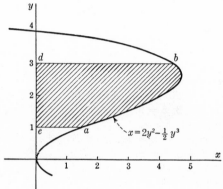

Fig. 95.

37. Evaluate $\int_{y=0}^{y=4} x \, dy$ where $x = y^2 - 4y$. Draw the graph of this equation and interpret your result as an area. Explain why the result is negative. See Prob. 36.

In each of the following cases compute the total area (in the arithmetic sense) enclosed by the two given curves. Use the method suggested by Prob. 36:

38. $x = y^2(4 - y)$; $x = 4y - y^2$.

39. $x = y^2 + 3y$; $x = 3 + y$.

40. $x = y(1 + y)(2 - y)$; $x = 2(1 + y)(2 - y)$.

101. The Fundamental Theorem.—In defining the area under a curve we might have proceeded somewhat more generally as follows:

1. Divide the interval from $x = a$ to $x = b$ into n subintervals, and denote their directed lengths by Δx_1, Δx_2, $\cdots$, Δx_n (Fig. 96).

2. Select any point x_1 in the first interval, any point x_2 in the second, $\cdot\ \cdot\ \cdot$, any point x_n in the last.

3. Form the sum

$$\sum_{i=1}^{n} f(x_i)\Delta x_i \equiv f(x_1)\Delta x_1 + f(x_2)\Delta x_2 + \cdot\ \cdot\ \cdot + f(x_n)\Delta x_n.$$

This is the sum of the areas of the n rectangles shown in Fig. 96 having $\Delta x_1,\ \Delta x_2,\ \cdot\ \cdot\ \cdot\ ,\ \Delta x_n$ as bases.

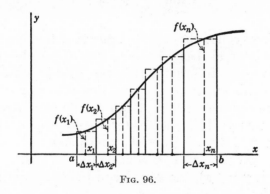

FIG. 96.

4. Then, if A is the algebraic area under the curve,

$$A = \lim_{\Delta x_i \to 0} [f(x_1)\Delta x_1 + f(x_2)\Delta x_2 + \cdot\ \cdot\ \cdot + f(x_n)\Delta x_n]$$

or

$$A = \lim_{\Delta x_i \to 0} \sum_{i=1}^{n} f(x_i)\Delta x_i.$$

We have already shown, however, that

$$A = \int_a^b f(x)dx.$$

Combining these two results we may state the theorem that is known as the *Fundamental Theorem* of the integral calculus, namely,

$$\lim_{\Delta x_i \to 0} \sum_{i=1}^{n} f(x_i)\Delta x_i = \int_a^b f(x)dx.$$

This theorem, which enables one to calculate the limit of a sum of the above type by integration, is of great importance. In the next several chapters we shall see that many important physical as well as geometrical problems can be solved by expressing the quantity to be computed as the limit of such a sum, and then evaluating it by integration. The quantity

$$\lim_{\Delta x_i \to 0} \sum_{i=1}^{n} f(x_i) \Delta x_i$$

is sometimes called the definite integral of the function $f(x)$ over that interval (from $x = a$ to $x = b$), which is divided into subintervals in forming the sum. We shall frequently encounter this quantity in connection with physical problems in which we are not at all interested in finding the area under a curve. It is important to remember, however, that we can always, if we wish, interpret it as being equal to the algebraic area bounded by the curve whose equation is $y = f(x)$, the x-axis, and the ordinates at $x = a$ and $x = b$.

102. Some properties of the definite integral.—In this section we shall discuss briefly several important properties of the definite integral.

A. The sign.—If each of the quantities $f(x_i)\Delta x_i$ is positive then their sum is certainly positive and the limit of their sum is positive. Similarly, if each of the quantities is negative, their sum must be negative. From this we deduce that:

1. *If $f(x)$ is* **positive** *throughout the interval from $x = a$ to $x = b$, and $a < b$, then the value of $\int_a^b f(x)dx$ is certainly* **positive.**

2. *If $f(x)$ is* **negative** *throughout the interval from $x = a$ to $x = b$, and $a < b$, then the value of $\int_a^b f(x)dx$ is certainly* **negative.**

B. Interchange of limits.—It is easy to show that

$$\int_a^b f(x)dx = - \int_b^a f(x)dx;$$

for, if
$$\int f(x)dx = \phi(x),$$
then

$$\int_a^b f(x)dx = \phi(b) - \phi(a) \qquad \text{while} \qquad \int_b^a f(x)dx$$
$$= \phi(a) - \phi(b).$$

With respect to the sum $\Sigma f(x_i)\Delta x_i$ we may regard the interchanging of limits as reversing the sign of each of the Δx's. (We regard Δx_i as a directed quantity having the same sign as the directed segment from the lower to the upper limit.)

C. Subdividing the interval.—It is sometimes necessary to divide the interval from $x = a$ to $x = b$ into two parts, one running from a to k and the other from k to b. It is easy to show that

$$\int_a^k f(x)dx + \int_k^b f(x)dx = \int_a^b f(x)dx;$$

for, if
$$\int f(x)dx = \phi(x),$$
then we have

$$[\phi(k) - \phi(a)] + [\phi(b) - \phi(k)] = \phi(b) - \phi(a).$$

It should be observed that k need not be inside the interval from a to b as long as $f(x)$ is continuous over the entire interval.*

103. Change of limits corresponding to change of variable.—We have seen that in order to perform an integration it is sometimes necessary to make a change of variable. With a definite integral one can avoid the trouble of changing the result back into terms of the original variable by making a corresponding change in the limits.

Example

Evaluate $\displaystyle\int_0^4 \sqrt{16 - x^2}\, dx.$

Solution

Let $x = 4 \sin \theta$: The integration is over the x-interval from $x = 0$ to $x = 4$. The corresponding interval for the new variable θ is found from the relation $x = 4 \sin \theta$:

---

* Continuity of $f(x)$ is not necessary for the existance of its definite integral, but so far we have considered only continuous functions.

Putting $x = 4$:

$$4 = 4 \sin \theta, \quad \sin \theta = 1, \quad \theta = \tfrac{1}{2}\pi.$$

Putting $x = 0$:

$$0 = 4 \sin \theta, \quad \sin \theta = 0, \quad \theta = 0.$$

The θ interval that corresponds to $x = 0$ to $x = 4$ is then $\theta = 0$ to $\theta = \tfrac{1}{2}\pi$; hence,

$$\int_0^4 \sqrt{16 - x^2}\, dx = 16 \int_0^{\frac{1}{2}\pi} \cos^2 \theta\, d\theta = 4\pi.$$

PROBLEMS

1. Why can one be certain that the value of $\int_3^5 (2 - x)dx$ is negative without evaluating it?

2. Under what conditions will $\int_a^b x^2 dx$ be negative?

3. Show that:

$$\int_{-a}^a f(x)dx = 2 \int_0^a f(x)dx \text{ if } f(x) \text{ is an } even \text{ function.}$$

$$\int_{-a}^a f(x)dx = 0 \text{ if } f(x) \text{ is an } odd \text{ function.}$$

[$f(x)$ is an even function if $f(-x) \equiv f(x)$; it is odd if $f(-x) \equiv -f(x)$.]

4. Show that $\int_{-a}^a \sin x\, dx = 0$, and interpret the result geometrically. Show also that $\int_{-a}^a \cos x\, dx = 2 \int_0^a \cos x\, dx.$

Evaluate each of the following limits, the sum being taken over the given interval:

5. $\displaystyle \lim_{\Delta x_i \to 0} \sum_{i=1}^n 4 \sec^2 x_i \Delta x_i; \ x = 0 \text{ to } \tfrac{1}{4}\pi.$

6. $\displaystyle \lim_{\Delta x_i \to 0} \sum_{i=1}^n x_i \log x_i \Delta x_i; \ x = 1 \text{ to } e.$

7. $\displaystyle \lim_{\Delta x_i \to 0} \sum_{i=1}^n 3 \cos^2 x_i \Delta x_i; \ x = 0 \text{ to } \tfrac{1}{2}\pi.$

8. $\displaystyle \lim_{\Delta x_i \to 0} \sum_{i=1}^n (2 + \sqrt{x_i})^2 \Delta x_i; \ x = 1 \text{ to } 4.$

Evaluate the following definite integrals:

9. $\displaystyle \int_0^4 (x + 2\sqrt{x})^2 dx.$ **10.** $\displaystyle \int_{\frac{\pi}{6}}^{\frac{\pi}{2}} \sin^3 x\, dx.$

11. $\int_0^{\frac{\pi}{2}} \sin^3 x \cos^2 x \, dx.$
12. $\int_0^{\frac{\pi}{4}} \tan^4 \theta \, d\theta.$

13. $\int_{\frac{\pi}{4}}^{\frac{\pi}{3}} \frac{\sec \theta \, d\theta}{\sin \theta}.$
14. $\int_0^4 \frac{4 \, dy}{\sqrt[3]{16 - 2y}}.$

15. $\int_9^{16} \frac{\sqrt{y} \, dy}{y - 4}.$
16. $\int_1^6 \frac{x \, dx}{\sqrt{x + 3}}.$

17. $\int_0^3 x^3 \sqrt{9 - x^2} \, dx.$
18. $\int_0^4 x^3 \sqrt{9 + x^2} \, dx.$

19. $\int_0^2 x^2 \sqrt{4 - x^2} \, dx.$
20. $\int_1^2 \frac{\sqrt{x^2 - 1} \, dx}{x}.$

21. $\int_{-a}^a \sqrt{a^2 - x^2} \, dx.$
22. $\int_4^7 \frac{x \, dx}{(x - 3)^{\frac{3}{2}}}.$

23. $\int_0^1 \frac{x^3 dx}{\sqrt{x^2 + 1}}.$
24. $\int_0^1 3y e^y dy.$

25. $\int_0^{\frac{\pi}{2}} x \sin x \, dx.$
26. $\int_1^4 \log x \, dx.$

27. Sketch the curve whose equation is $y^2 = x^2(4 - x)$, and compute the area enclosed by it.

28. Compute the area of the circle $x^2 + y^2 = 25$.

29. Show that the area of the ellipse $\frac{x^2}{a^2} + \frac{y^2}{b^2} = 1$ is πab.

30. Compute the area bounded by the hyperbola $\frac{x^2}{a^2} - \frac{y^2}{b^2} = 1$ and the line $x = 2a$.

104. Parametric equations.—The area bounded by the curve $y = f(x)$, the x-axis, and the ordinates at $x = a$ and $x = b$ is given by the value of $\int_a^b y \, dx$. If the curve is defined by the parametric equations,

$$y = g(t), \qquad x = h(t);$$

then

$$dx = h'(t) dt,$$

and

$$\int_{x=a}^{x=b} y \, dx = \int_{t=t_1}^{t=t_2} g(t) \cdot h'(t) dt$$

where the limits t_1 and t_2 are the values of t corresponding to $x = a$ and $x = b$, respectively. They may be obtained from the equation $x = h(t)$.

Example

Compute the area of the ellipse $x = a \cos \theta$, $y = b \sin \theta$.

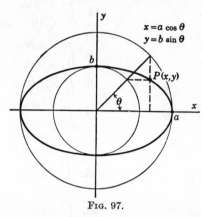

$x = a \cos \theta$
$y = b \sin \theta$

$P(x, y)$

FIG. 97.

Solution (Fig. 97)

Taking advantage of the symmetry of the curve we may find the area in the first quadrant and multiply by 4; hence,

$$A = 4 \int_{x=0}^{x=a} y \, dx$$

$$= 4 \int_{\theta=\frac{\pi}{2}}^{\theta=0} (b \sin \theta)(-a \sin \theta) d\theta$$

$$= 4ab \int_{0}^{\frac{\pi}{2}} \sin^2 \theta \, d\theta$$

$$= \pi ab.$$

105. Improper integrals.—The definite integrals thus far encountered have had finite limits, and we have considered only cases in which the integrand $f(x)$ is continuous over the interval. It is frequently necessary to consider definite integrals in which these conditions are not satisfied. Such integrals are called *improper integrals*.

We shall consider first the case in which the interval of integration is not finite. Values are assigned to such integrals by the following definitions:

(1) $\int_{a}^{\infty} f(x) dx$ *means* $\lim\limits_{h \to \infty} \int_{a}^{h} f(x) dx.$

(2) $\int_{-\infty}^{a} f(x)dx$ *means* $\displaystyle\lim_{h \to -\infty} \int_{h}^{a} f(x)dx.$

(3) $\int_{-\infty}^{\infty} f(x)dx$ *means* $\int_{-\infty}^{0} f(x)dx + \int_{0}^{\infty} f(x)dx.$

The two integrals on the right in definition (3) are, of course, to be evaluated in accordance with definitions (1) and (2).

In case the limit exists, the improper integral is said to be *convergent;* if the limit does not exist, the integral has no value and in this case it is said to be *divergent.*

Example 1

Evaluate $\displaystyle\int_{0}^{\infty} \frac{dx}{(x+1)^2}.$

Solution

We shall integrate from 0 to h thus obtaining a function of h; then we shall examine the behavior of this function when $h \to \infty$.

$$\int_{0}^{h} \frac{dx}{(x+1)^2} = -\frac{1}{x+1}\Big]_{0}^{h} = -\frac{1}{h+1} + 1.$$

$$\lim_{h \to \infty} \left(1 - \frac{1}{h+1}\right) = 1.$$

Hence,
$$\int_{0}^{\infty} \frac{dx}{(x+1)^2} = 1.$$

The geometrical interpretation of the result is shown in Fig. 98.   The

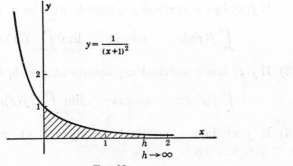

FIG. 98.

area under the curve $y = \dfrac{1}{(x+1)^2}$ from $x = 0$ to $x = h$ is

$$1 - \frac{1}{h+1}.$$

As the point h moves indefinitely far to the right, this area continually increases and approaches 1 square unit as a limit.

Example 2

Evaluate $\displaystyle\int_2^\infty \frac{dx}{x}.$

Solution

As in example 1 we shall integrate from 2 to h and then examine the behavior of the resulting function of h as $h \to \infty$.

$$\int_2^h \frac{dx}{x} = \log x \Big]_2^h = \log h - \log 2.$$

In this case

$$\lim_{h \to \infty} (\log h - \log 2) = \infty.$$

The integral has no value and is said to be divergent. The result means that the area bounded by the curve $y = 1/x$, the x-axis, and the ordinates at $x = 2$ and $x = h$ increases beyond bound as the ordinate at $x = h$ moves farther and farther to the right.

The second kind of improper integral to be considered is that in which the integrand $f(x)$ is not continuous over the interval of integration $(a \leqq x \leqq b)$. We shall confine our attention to the case in which the graph of $f(x)$ has one vertical asymptote in this interval, and we set up the following definitions, it being assumed that $a < b$:

(1) If $f(x)$ has a vertical asymptote at $x = a$, then

$$\int_a^b f(x)dx \qquad means \qquad \lim_{\epsilon \to 0} \int_{a+\epsilon}^b f(x)dx.$$

(2) If $f(x)$ has a vertical asymptote at $x = b$, then

$$\int_a^b f(x)dx \qquad means \qquad \lim_{\epsilon \to 0} \int_a^{b-\epsilon} f(x)dx.$$

(3) If $f(x)$ has a vertical asymptote at $x = k$ where $a < k < b$, then

$$\int_a^b f(x)dx \qquad means \qquad \int_a^k f(x)dx + \int_k^b f(x)dx.$$

In each case the integral is said to be *convergent* if the limit exists, and *divergent* if it does not exist. The two integrals on the right in definition (3) are of course to be evaluated in accordance with definitions (1) and (2). These must both be convergent in order that an integral of type (3) may have a value.

Example 1

Evaluate $\int_0^4 \dfrac{dx}{\sqrt{x}}$.

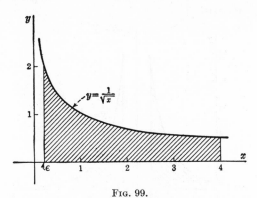

FIG. 99.

Solution (Fig. 99)

The function $1/\sqrt{x}$ has a vertical asymptote at $x = 0$. We therefore integrate from ϵ to 4, thus obtaining a function of ϵ, and then find the limit of this function (if it exists) when $\epsilon \to 0$.

$$\int_\epsilon^4 \frac{dx}{\sqrt{x}} = \int_\epsilon^4 x^{-\frac{1}{2}}dx = 2\sqrt{x}\,\Big]_\epsilon^4 = 4 - 2\sqrt{\epsilon}.$$

$$\lim_{\epsilon \to 0} (4 - 2\sqrt{\epsilon}) = 4.$$

The value of the integral is then 4.

Example 2

Evaluate $\int_0^2 \dfrac{dx}{(x-1)^2}$.

Solution (Fig. 100)

The curve $y = 1/(x-1)^2$ has a vertical asymptote at $x = 1$. In accordance with definition (3) above, we must integrate from 0 to $1 - \epsilon$, thus obtaining a function of ϵ, and then find the limit of this function as $\epsilon \to 0$. Next we must integrate from $1 + \epsilon$ to 2 and find the limit of this result as $\epsilon \to 0$. If the limits exist, their sum is the value of the given integral. If either or both of the limits are nonexistent, the integral has no value.

$$\int_0^{1-\epsilon} \frac{dx}{(x-1)^2} = \frac{1}{\epsilon} - 1.$$

$$\lim_{\epsilon \to 0} \left(\frac{1}{\epsilon} - 1 \right) = \infty.$$

It is evident, without considering the part from $1 + \epsilon$ to 2, that the integral does not exist.

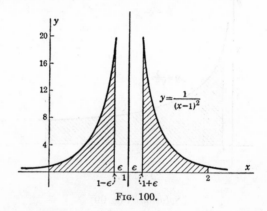

FIG. 100.

The student should observe that if we had proceeded carelessly, not noticing the discontinuity in the integrand, we should have obtained

$$\int_0^2 \frac{dx}{(x-1)^2} = -\frac{1}{x-1} \Big]_0^2 = -2.$$

This result is obviously incorrect. For we are integrating from left to right and the integrand is positive; the value of the integral would therefore have to be positive—if there were any value at all.

It can be shown that if

$$\int f(x)dx = \phi(x)$$

where $\phi(x)$ is *continuous* over the interval $a \leqq x \leqq b$, then the integral can be evaluated in the usual way; *i.e.*, without using ϵ. The proof for the various cases can be carried out as indicated below for the case in which $f(x)$ is continuous over the interval except for a vertical asymptote at $x = k$

where $a < k < b$. In this case

$$\int_a^b f(x)dx = \lim_{\epsilon \to 0} \int_a^{k-\epsilon} f(x)dx + \lim_{\epsilon \to 0} \int_{k+\epsilon}^b f(x)dx$$

$$= \lim_{\epsilon \to 0} [\phi(k - \epsilon) - \phi(a)]$$

$$+ \lim_{\epsilon \to 0} [\phi(b) - \phi(k + \epsilon)].$$

Because of the assumed continuity of $\phi(x)$,

$$\lim_{\epsilon \to 0} \phi(k - \epsilon) = \lim_{\epsilon \to 0} \phi(k + \epsilon) = \phi(k).$$

We have then

$$\int_a^b f(x)dx = \phi(k) - \phi(a) + \phi(b) - \phi(k) = \phi(b) - \phi(a).$$

Example

Evaluate $\int_1^{10} \dfrac{dx}{\sqrt[3]{x - 2}}$.

Solution

The function $\dfrac{1}{\sqrt[3]{x - 2}}$ has a vertical asymptote at $x = 2$, but

$$\int \frac{dx}{\sqrt[3]{x - 2}} = \int (x - 2)^{-\frac{1}{3}} dx = \tfrac{3}{2}(x - 2)^{\frac{2}{3}}$$

which is a continuous function over the interval $1 \leqq x \leqq 10$. We may then evaluate the integral in the usual way:

$$\int_1^{10} \frac{dx}{\sqrt[3]{x - 2}} = \tfrac{3}{2}(x - 2)^{\frac{2}{3}} \Big]_1^{10} = \tfrac{3}{2}(4) - \tfrac{3}{2}(1) = 4\tfrac{1}{2}.$$

PROBLEMS

Evaluate each of the following improper integrals or show that it is divergent. Draw the figure in each case:

1. $\int_4^\infty \dfrac{dx}{3x - 2}$.

2. $\int_2^\infty \dfrac{dx}{x^2}$.

3. $\int_1^\infty \dfrac{dx}{\sqrt{x}}$.

4. $\int_{-\infty}^\infty 4xe^{-x^2}dx$.

5. $\int_0^\infty e^{-\frac{1}{2}x}dx$.

6. $\int_{-\infty}^0 e^x dx$.

7. $\int_0^\infty xe^{-x}dx$.

8. $\int_0^\infty \cos x \, dx$.

9. $\int_{-\infty}^{\infty} \frac{dx}{x^2 + 4}$.

10. $\int_0^{\infty} \frac{8x\, dx}{x^2 + 3}$.

11. $\int_3^{\infty} \frac{4x\, dx}{x^2 - 3}$.

12. $\int_2^{\infty} \frac{dx}{x(x - 1)}$.

13. $\int_0^2 \frac{dx}{\sqrt{x}}$.

14. $\int_1^5 \frac{dx}{x - 1}$.

15. $\int_4^8 \frac{dx}{\sqrt{x - 4}}$.

16. $\int_{-1}^2 \frac{dx}{x^2}$.

17. $\int_0^{\frac{\pi}{2}} \tan \theta\, d\theta$.

18. $\int_{-2}^2 \frac{t\, dt}{\sqrt{4 - t^2}}$.

19. $\int_0^3 \frac{x\, dx}{\sqrt{9 - x^2}}$.

20. $\int_0^4 \frac{x\, dx}{\sqrt{4 - x}}$.

21. $\int_{-2}^2 \frac{dx}{\sqrt[3]{2x + 4}}$.

22. $\int_0^a \frac{dx}{\sqrt{a^2 - x^2}}$.

23. $\int_0^a \frac{x^2 dx}{\sqrt{a^2 - x^2}}$.

24. $\int_2^4 \frac{dx}{\sqrt{x^2 - 4}}$.

25. Show that $\int_1^{\infty} \frac{dx}{x^n} = \frac{1}{n - 1}$ if $n > 1$, and that the integral is divergent if $n \lessgtr 1$.

26. Compute the area "bounded" by the curve $y = \frac{12}{x^2 + 6}$ and the x-axis.

27. Sketch the curve $y^2(4 - x) = x^3$ and compute the area "bounded" by it and the line $x = 4$.

28. Find the area of a circle using the parametric equations $x = r \cos \theta$, $y = r \sin \theta$.

29. Find the area enclosed by the four-cusped hypocycloid whose parametric equations are $x = a \cos^3 \theta$, $y = a \sin^3 \theta$.

30. Find the area bounded by the x-axis and one arch of the cycloid whose parametric equations are $x = a(\theta - \sin \theta)$, $y = a(1 - \cos \theta)$.

CHAPTER XIX

FURTHER APPLICATIONS OF THE DEFINITE INTEGRAL

106. Introduction.—In this chapter we shall consider the problems of computing areas bounded by curves whose equations are given in polar coordinates, volumes of certain kinds of solids, lengths of curves, and areas of surfaces of revolution.

In each case we shall define the quantity to be found as the limit of a sum of the type just studied. We shall then be able to carry out the computation by means of the Fundamental Theorem.

107. Area in polar coordinates.—In rectangular coordinates we have considered the problem of finding the area bounded by the curve $y = f(x)$, the x-axis, and the ordinates at $x = a$ and $x = b$. The corresponding problem in polar coordinates is that of determining the area bounded by the curve $\rho = f(\theta)$ and the two radii vectors $\theta = \theta_1$, and $\theta = \theta_2$. In Fig. 101 this is the area bounded by the curve and the lines OA and OB.

The procedure is analogous to that used in rectangular coordinates: We divide the θ-interval

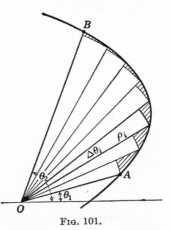

Fig. 101.

from θ_1 to θ_2 into n subintervals having the directed magnitudes $\Delta\theta_1, \Delta\theta_2, \cdots, \Delta\theta_n$. We then draw the corresponding radii vectors, denoting their directed lengths by $\rho_1, \rho_2,$ $\cdots, \rho_n$, and draw the circular arcs as shown.

239

Recalling that the area of a circular sector having radius r and central angle α is $\frac{1}{2}r^2\alpha$, we write down the following expression for the sum of the areas of the circular sectors:

$$A' = \tfrac{1}{2}\rho_1{}^2\Delta\theta_1 + \tfrac{1}{2}\rho_2{}^2\Delta\theta_2 + \cdots + \tfrac{1}{2}\rho_n{}^2\Delta\theta_n.$$

We now define* the area bounded by the curve and the lines OA and OB to be equal to the limit of this sum when each $\Delta\theta \to 0$ and $n \to \infty$; i.e.,

$$A = \lim_{\Delta\theta_i \to 0} \sum_{i=1}^{n} \tfrac{1}{2}\rho_i{}^2\Delta\theta_i.$$

This limit, by virtue of the Fundamental Theorem, is equal to the value of $\int_{\theta=\theta_1}^{\theta=\theta_2} \frac{1}{2}\rho^2 d\theta$, it being understood of course that we are to replace ρ by $f(\theta)$ before performing the integration. We have then the following:

Theorem: *The area bounded by the curve whose polar equation is $\rho = f(\theta)$ and the two radii vectors $\theta = \theta_1$ and $\theta = \theta_2$ is given by*

$$A = \tfrac{1}{2} \int_{\theta_1}^{\theta_2} \varrho^2 d\theta.$$

It should be observed that the question of whether the area lies above or below the "x-axis" has nothing to do with the sign of A in this case. If ρ is real throughout the interval, then the integrand, ρ^2, is positive. Consequently, *A is positive if the integration is in the counterclockwise sense; i.e., if $\theta_1 < \theta_2$.* If $\theta_1 > \theta_2$, ρ being real, the value of the integral will be negative.

Example 1

Find the area that is common to the circle $\rho = 3 \cos \theta$ and the cardioid $\rho = 1 + \cos \theta$.

---

* We have already given a definition of area bounded by a curve, in terms of a sum of rectangles. It will probably be intuitively evident to the student that this new definition, which is more convenient when polar coordinates are involved, would yield the same numerical measure for the same area.

Solution (Fig. 102)

The curves intersect at the origin and at $\left(\dfrac{3}{2},\ \pm\dfrac{\pi}{3}\right)$. The required area is twice the area bounded by OA, arc AB of the cardioid, and arc BO of the circle. The area bounded by the radii vectors OA and OB and

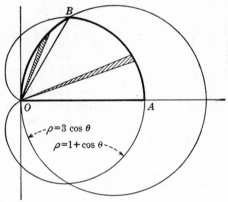

FIG. 102.

arc AB of the cardioid is given by

$$\tfrac{1}{2}\int_0^{\frac{\pi}{3}} \rho^2 d\theta = \tfrac{1}{2}\int_0^{\frac{\pi}{3}} (1 + \cos\theta)^2 d\theta = \frac{\pi}{4} + \frac{9}{16}\sqrt{3}.$$

The area bounded by radius vector OB and arc OB of the circle is given by

$$\tfrac{1}{2}\int_{\frac{\pi}{3}}^{\frac{\pi}{2}} \rho^2 d\theta = \tfrac{1}{2}\int_{\frac{\pi}{3}}^{\frac{\pi}{2}} 9\cos^2\theta\, d\theta = \frac{9\pi}{24} - \frac{9}{16}\sqrt{3}.$$

Adding these areas, and doubling the result, we find that $A = \tfrac{5}{4}\pi = 3.93$ sq. units.

The student may think of the area as being generated by revolving the little shaded "area element" shown in the figure. From θ to 0 to $\theta = \tfrac{1}{3}\pi$ the outer end of the element is on arc AB of the cardioid; from $\theta = \tfrac{1}{3}\pi$ to $\theta = \tfrac{1}{2}\pi$ the outer end is an arc BO of the circle.

Example 2

Compute the entire area bounded by the curve $\rho = a \sin 3\theta$.

Solution (Fig. 103)

If we wish, we may compute the area of one leaf by integrating from $\theta = 0$ to $\tfrac{1}{3}\pi$, and then multiply by 3:

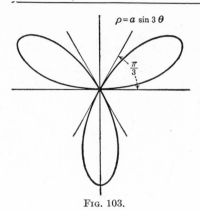

$$A = 3 \cdot \tfrac{1}{2} \int_0^{\frac{\pi}{3}} \rho^2 d\theta$$

$$= \frac{3a^2}{2} \int_0^{\frac{\pi}{3}} \sin^2 3\theta \, d\theta$$

$$= \frac{3a^2}{4} \int_0^{\frac{\pi}{3}} (1 - \cos 6\theta) d\theta$$

$$= \frac{3a^2}{4} \left[\theta - \tfrac{1}{6} \sin 6\theta \right]_0^{\frac{\pi}{3}}$$

$$= \frac{\pi a^2}{4}.$$

FIG. 103.

We could have obtained the entire area by integrating from $\theta = 0$ to π; thus

$$A = \tfrac{1}{2} \int_0^{\pi} a^2 \sin^2 3\theta \, d\theta = \frac{\pi a^2}{4}.$$

What area would be obtained by integrating from $\theta = \tfrac{1}{3}\pi$ to $\tfrac{2}{3}\pi$? Would the result be positive or negative? Why?

PROBLEMS

1. Sketch the curve $\rho = 4 \sin 3\theta$ and shade the area obtained by evaluating $\tfrac{1}{2} \int_0^{\frac{\pi}{2}} \rho^2 d\theta$.

2. Sketch the curve $\rho = a \cos 3\theta$ and shade the area obtained by evaluating $\tfrac{1}{2} \int_0^{\frac{\pi}{2}} \rho^2 d\theta$.

3. Which of the following integrals gives the entire area enclosed by the curve $\rho = 2 \cos 3\theta$? $2 \cdot \tfrac{1}{2} \int_0^{\frac{\pi}{2}} \rho^2 d\theta$; $2 \cdot \tfrac{1}{2} \int_0^{\pi} \rho^2 d\theta$; $6 \cdot \tfrac{1}{2} \int_0^{\frac{\pi}{3}} \rho^2 d\theta$.

4. Sketch the cardioid $\rho = a(1 + \cos \theta)$. Which ones of the following integrals give its entire area? $4 \cdot \tfrac{1}{2} \int_0^{\frac{\pi}{2}} \rho^2 d\theta$; $2 \cdot \tfrac{1}{2} \int_0^{\pi} \rho^2 d\theta$; $\tfrac{1}{2} \int_0^{2\pi} \rho^2 d\theta$.

5. If $\rho = 2 \sin 3\theta$, is the value of $\int_\pi^{2\pi} \rho^2 d\theta$ positive or negative?

6. Sketch the circle $\rho = a \sin \theta$. Is its entire area given by $\tfrac{1}{2} \int_0^{\pi} \rho^2 d\theta$ or $\tfrac{1}{2} \int_0^{2\pi} \rho^2 d\theta$?

Sketch each of the following curves, and compute the entire area enclosed by it:

7. $\rho = 4 \cos \theta$.

8. $\rho = a(1 + \sin \theta)$.

9. $\rho = a \sin 2\theta$.

10. $\rho = 2 \cos 3\theta$.

11. $\rho = 3 \sin 3\theta$.

12. $\rho^2 = a^2 \sin 2\theta$.

13. $\rho^2 = 4 \cos 2\theta$.

14. $\rho = 2 + \sin \theta$.

15. $\rho = 3 - \cos \theta$.

16. $\rho = 4 \sqrt{\sin \theta}$.

17. Compute the area inside the small loop of the limacon whose equation is $\rho = 1 - 2 \cos \theta$.

18. Sketch the lemniscate $\rho^2 = a^2 \cos 2\theta$, noting that in the interval $\dfrac{\pi}{4} < \theta < \dfrac{3\pi}{4}$ there is no real value of ρ. Evaluate $\frac{1}{2} \int_{\frac{\pi}{4}}^{\frac{\pi}{2}} \rho^2 d\theta$ and explain this negative result.

19. Find the area common to the two circles $\rho = a$ and $\rho = 2a \sin \theta$.

20. Find the area common to the circle $\rho = 3 \sin \theta$ and the cardioid $\rho = \sin \theta + 1$.

21. Find the area that is inside the lemniscate $\rho^2 = 8 \cos 2\theta$ and outside the circle $\rho = 2$.

22. Find the area bounded by the parabola $\rho \sin^2 \theta = \cos \theta$ and the line $\rho \cos \theta = 1$.

23. Find the area that is inside the cardioid $\rho = 4(1 + \cos \theta)$ and outside the circle $\rho = 8 \cos \theta$.

24. Find the area that is inside the circle $\rho = a \sin \theta$ and outside the cardioid $\rho = a(1 - \sin \theta)$.

25. Find the area enclosed by the curve whose equation in rectangular coordinates is

$$(x^2 + y^2)^2 = a^2(x^2 - y^2).$$

26. The area of the circle shown in Fig. 104 is equal to the sum of the areas of the n concentric rings. Show from this that the area is given by the formula

$$A = \int_0^r 2\pi x \, dx.$$

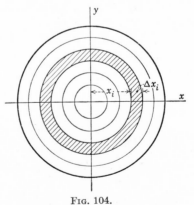

Fig. 104.

108. Volumes of solids of revolution. Disk method.—

If the area bounded by the curve $y = f(x)$, the x-axis, and the ordinates at $x = a$ and $x = b$ is revolved about the x-axis, a volume is generated. The magnitude of the volume may be defined as follows (Fig. 105):

1. Divide the interval from $x = a$ to $x = b$ into n sub-intervals precisely as was done in defining the area under a curve, and draw the corresponding rectangles.

2. Each rectangle, having base Δx_i and height y_i, when revolved about the x-axis, generates a cylindrical disk of radius y_i and thickness Δx_i. Since the volume of a right circular cylinder of radius r and height h is $\pi r^2 h$, the volume of the disk is $\pi y_i^2 \Delta x_i$.

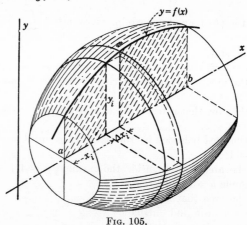

Fig. 105.

3. The sum of the volumes of the n disks is

$$\sum_{i=1}^{n} \pi y_i^2 \Delta x_i = \pi y_1^2 \Delta x_1 + \pi y_2^2 \Delta x_2 + \cdots + \pi y_n^2 \Delta x_n.$$

4. If V is the required volume of the solid then, by definition,

$$V = \lim_{\Delta x_i \to 0} \sum_{i=1}^{n} \pi y_i^2 \Delta x_i.$$

This limit, in accordance with the Fundamental Theorem, is equal to the value of $\int_{x=a}^{x=b} \pi y^2 dx$, it being understood, of course, that we are to replace y by $f(x)$ before performing the integration. We have then the following:

Theorem: *If the area bounded by the curve whose equation is $y = f(x)$, the x-axis, and the ordinates at $x = a$ and $x = b$*

is revolved about the x-axis, the volume generated is given by

$$V = \pi \int_a^b y^2 dx.$$

If y is real throughout the interval, then the integrand, y^2, is positive. Consequently, *V will be positive if we integrate from left to right; i.e., if* $a < b$.

In a similar way one can show that, if the area bounded by the curve $x = f(y)$, the y-axis, and the lines $y = c$ and $y = d$ is revolved about the y-axis, the volume generated is given by the formula

$$V = \pi \int_c^d x^2 dy.$$

Example

Compute the volume generated by revolving the area bounded by the y-axis and the parabola $y^2 - 4y + 2x - 5 = 0$ about the y-axis.

Solution (Fig. 106)

Putting $x = 0$ and solving for y, we find that the parabola crosses the y-axis at $y = -1$ and $y = 5$. When the area that is shaded in the

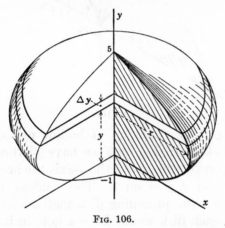

Fig. 106.

figure is revolved about the y-axis it generates the solid shown. It is useful to think of each strip of area as generating a disk of radius x and thickness Δy or dy and thus having a volume equal to $\pi x^2 dy$. The entire volume is

$$V = \pi \int_{-1}^5 x^2 dy = \frac{\pi}{4} \int_{-1}^5 (5 + 4y - y^2)^2 dy = \frac{324\pi}{5}.$$

The student must not use the above formulas blindly. In each problem he should first sketch the curve so as to show the area to be revolved and the axis of revolution. He should then draw a typical "strip" of the area as is done in Fig. 105 in order to see clearly the radius and thickness of the disk generated. In some of the problems of the next set the area is to be revolved about a line that is not a coordinate axis. In such cases one must be particularly careful in analyzing the situation.

109. The cylindrical shell method.—The volume of a solid of revolution may sometimes be computed more easily

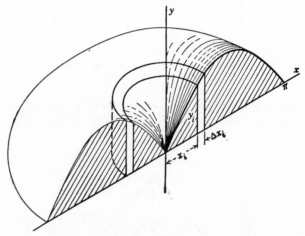

Fig. 107.

by regarding it as made up of hollow cylindrical shells instead of disks. In Fig. 107 we have pictured the solid generated by revolving about the y-axis the area under one arch of the curve $y = \sin x$. The student will observe that if we used the preceding disk method for computing the volume, each disk would have a hole in it that would have to be taken into consideration; i.e., each "disk" would really be a *washer*.

A simpler procedure results from letting each vertical strip of area generate a hollow cylindrical shell of inside radius x, height y, and thickness Δx. The volume of such a shell is nearly equal to $(2\pi x) \cdot y \cdot \Delta x$. (If the cylindrical shell were cut along an element and rolled out, it would approximate a flat plate with length $2\pi x$, width y, and thickness Δx.) The sum of the volumes of the shells generated by the n strips of area is then given approximately by

$$\sum_{i=1}^{n} 2\pi x_i y_i \Delta x_i.$$

We may use the limit of this sum as an alternate definition of the volume generated:*

$$V = \lim_{\Delta x_i \to 0} \sum_{i=1}^{n} 2\pi x_i y_i \Delta x_i = 2\pi \int_a^b xy \, dx.$$

The limits refer to the x-interval, which is divided into subintervals in forming the strips of area, and we must, of course, replace y by $f(x)$ before performing the integration. In Fig. 107 it is the area under the curve $y = \sin x$ in the interval from $x = 0$ to $x = \pi$ that is revolved. We have then

$$V = 2\pi \int_0^\pi xy \, dx$$
$$= 2\pi \int_0^\pi x \sin x \, dx$$
$$= 2\pi \Big[-x \cos x + \sin x \Big]_0^\pi$$
$$= 2\pi^2 = 19.74 \text{ cu. units.}$$

When the axis of revolution is a line other than the y-axis, a corresponding change must, of course, be made in the formula. The student must draw the figure for each problem and analyze the situation carefully.

PROBLEMS

1. The area bounded by the x-axis and the upper half of the circle $x^2 + y^2 = 25$ is revolved about the x-axis. Compute the volume of the sphere generated. Use disk method.

* It can be shown that this definition will give the same measure, when applied to the same volume, as the preceding definition which employed disks.

2. Find the volume of the sphere generated by revolving the area bounded by the y-axis and the right-hand half of the circle $x^2 + y^2 = a^2$ about the y-axis. Use shell method.

3. The area bounded by the curve $y = 2\sqrt{x}$, the x-axis, and the line $x = 9$ is revolved about the x-axis. Compute the volume generated.

4. Compute the volume of a parabolic reflector that is 12 in. in diameter and 8 in. deep.

5. Find the volume of the cone generated when the area bounded by the line $y = hx/r$, the y-axis, and the line $y = h$ is revolved about the y-axis. Use disk method.

6. Compute the volume generated by revolving the area bounded by the x-axis and one arch of the curve $y = \sin x$ about the x-axis.

7. The area under the curve $y = \cos x$ in the interval from $x = 0$ to $\frac{1}{2}\pi$ is revolved about the y-axis. Compute the volume generated.

8. The area under the curve $y = \tan x$ in the interval from $x = 0$ to $\frac{1}{4}\pi$ is revolved about the x-axis. Compute the volume generated.

9. The area under the curve $y = 2\sin \frac{1}{2}x$ in the interval from $x = 0$ to 2π is revolved about the y-axis. Find the volume generated.

10. Compute the volume of the ellipsoid generated when the area bounded by the x-axis and the upper half of the ellipse $9x^2 + 25y^2 = 225$ is revolved about the x-axis.

11. Compute the volume of the ellipsoid generated when the area bounded by the y-axis and the right-hand half of the ellipse $\dfrac{x^2}{a^2} + \dfrac{y^2}{b^2} = 1$ is revolved about the y-axis.

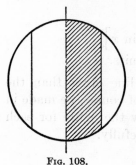

12. A cylindrical hole 6 in. in diameter is drilled through a solid sphere whose diameter is 10 in. Find the volume removed from the sphere if the axis of the hole passes through its center. Hint: Revolve the shaded area shown in Fig. 108 about the y-axis.

13. The radius of a solid sphere is 6 in. A cylindrical hole is to be drilled through the sphere, the axis of the hole passing through its center. What must be the radius of the hole if half the volume of the sphere is to be removed?

Fig. 108.

14. Compute the volume generated by revolving the area under the curve $y = \dfrac{8}{x^2 + 4}$, in the interval from $x = 0$ to 2, about the y-axis.

15. Compute the volume generated by revolving the area under the curve $y = \dfrac{9}{6 - x^2}$, in the interval from $x = 0$ to 2, about the y-axis.

16. The area under the curve $y = e^{-x}$ in the interval $x = 0$ to ∞ is revolved about the x-axis. Compute the volume generated. Note that this is an improper integral.

17. Solve Prob. 16 for the case in which this area is revolved about the y-axis.

18. The area under the curve $xy = 1$ in the interval from $x = 0$ to 2 is revolved about the y-axis. Compute the volume generated. Use both methods and note that the integrals involved are improper.

19. The area bounded by the x-axis and the parabola $y = 4x - x^2$ is revolved about the y-axis through an arc of $120°$. Compute the volume generated.

20. A certain solid can be generated by revolving the area bounded by the y-axis and the parabola $y^2 = 2x + 4$ about the y-axis through an angle of $90°$. What is its volume?

21. The area enclosed by the hypocycloid whose parametric equations are $x = a \cos^3 \theta$, $y = a \sin^3 \theta$ is revolved about the y-axis. Find the volume generated.

22. The area under the curve $y = \log x$ in the interval from $x = 1$ to $x = e$ is revolved about the y-axis. Compute the volume generated using both methods.

23. Compute the volume generated by revolving the area between the line $y = 1$ and the curve $y = 2 \sin x$, in the interval from $x = \frac{1}{6}\pi$ to $\frac{5}{6}\pi$, about the line $y = 1$; about the x-axis.

24. The area under the curve $y = e^x$ in the interval from $x = -1$ to 1 is revolved about the line $x = -1$. Find the volume generated.

25. The area common to the circles $x^2 + y^2 = 16$ and $x^2 + y^2 = 8x$ is revolved about their common chord. Find the volume generated.

26. The area enclosed by the curve $xy = 2$ and the line $2x + 2y = 9$ is revolved about the y-axis. Compute the volume generated.

27. Compute the volume of the solid generated by revolving one arch of the cycloid $x = a(\theta - \sin \theta)$, $y = a(1 - \cos \theta)$ about the x-axis.

28. Solve Prob. 27 for the case in which the area is revolved about the y-axis. Use the cylindrical shell method.

29. The area "bounded" by the curve $y = \dfrac{8}{x^2 + 4}$ and the x-axis is revolved about the x-axis. Compute the volume generated.

30. The area above the x-axis bounded by the circle $x^2 + y^2 = r^2$, and the lines $y = x$ and $y = -x$, is revolved about the y-axis. Compute the volume generated. Note that this is the volume common to a sphere and a cone. Use the cylindrical shell method.

*31. Compute the volume bounded by the xy-plane, the paraboloid $x^2 + y^2 = az$, and the cylinder $x^2 + y^2 = a^2$. Use both methods.

*Students who have not studied solid analytic geometry may defer those

32. Compute the volume common to the sphere $x^2 + y^2 + z^2 = 6$ and the paraboloid $x^2 + y^2 = z$.   HINT: Revolve the area common to the circle $x^2 + z^2 = 6$ and the parabola $z = x^2$ about the z-axis.   Use cylindrical shell method.

33. Find the volume generated by revolving the circle $x^2 + y^2 = 2rx$ about the y-axis.

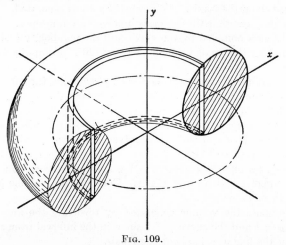

FIG. 109.

34. Compute the volume of the torus generated by revolving the circle $(x - R)^2 + y^2 = r^2$ (Fig. 109) about the y-axis.   HINT: Use cylindrical shell method, and after setting up the integral let $x - R = t$.

110. Solids with known parallel cross sections.—The

disk method amounts essentially to regarding the solid of revolution as made up of the thin slices into which it could be divided by passing planes perpendicular to its axis. For this type of solid each slice is a circular disk having radius y, which in general varies with x, since $y = f(x)$. The area of the face of a slice is πy^2, and we multiply this by Δx to obtain its volume (Fig. 110).

The method can obviously be extended to a larger class of solids.   Consider, for example, the conoid shown in Fig. 111.   Its base is the circle $x^2 + y^2 = r^2$, and its "vertex" is a line segment parallel to the base and at a

problems in this set and the next that involve equations of surfaces until they have read Chap. XXIV.

distance h above it.   The length of this segment is $2r$.   The surface is generated by an *element* that moves so as to intersect both the circle and this line segment and remain parallel to the yz-plane.

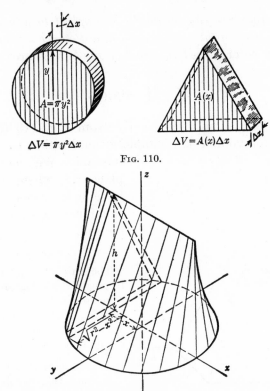

$$A = \pi y^2$$

$$\Delta V = \pi y^2 \Delta x$$

$$A(x)$$

$$\Delta V = A(x)\Delta x$$

FIG. 110.

FIG. 111.

At a distance x from the yz-plane, the section of this solid is a triangle whose base is $2\sqrt{r^2 - x^2}$ and whose altitude is the constant h.   The area of this section, expressed in terms of x, is

$$A(x) = h\sqrt{r^2 - x^2}.$$

If we multiply this by Δx, we have approximately the volume of the slice shown:

$$\Delta V = A(x)\Delta x = h\sqrt{r^2 - x^2}\,\Delta x.$$

The volume of the solid is the limit of the sum of such slices when each $\Delta x \to 0$; *i.e.*,

$$v = \int_a^b A(x)dx = \int_{-r}^r h \sqrt{r^2 - x^2}\, dx = \tfrac{1}{2}\pi r^2 h.$$

This procedure can obviously be applied to any solid for which the area of the cross section at a distance x from a fixed plane can be expressed in terms of x. If this area is $A(x)$, then,

$$V = \int_a^b A(x)dx.$$

The student should see clearly from Fig. 110 that this formula for volume is a simple generalization of the disk method. We merely replace πy^2, where $y = f(x)$, by a more general expression for the area of the cross section.

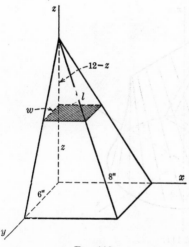

Fig. 112.

Example

The base of a pyramid is a rectangle whose sides are 8 in. and 6 in., respectively. Its altitude is 12 in., the vertex being directly above one corner of the base. Compute its volume.

Solution (Fig. 112)

We may think of the solid as consisting of thin slices made by planes parallel to the base. At a distance z above the base the section is a rectangle. We first find its dimensions, l and w, in terms of z. From similar triangles:

$$\frac{l}{12 - z} = \frac{8}{12} \quad \text{or} \quad l = \tfrac{2}{3}(12 - z);$$

$$\frac{w}{12 - z} = \frac{6}{12} \quad \text{or} \quad w = \tfrac{1}{2}(12 - z).$$

The area of the section, *expressed in terms of z*, is then

$$A(z) = lw = \tfrac{1}{3}(12 - z)^2.$$

The volume of the pyramid is

$$\int_0^{12} A(z)dz = \tfrac{1}{3}\int_0^{12} (12 - z)^2 dz = 192 \text{ cu. in.}$$

PROBLEMS

1. The base of a right pyramid is a rectangle whose sides are 5 in. and 3 in., respectively, and its altitude is 9 in. Express the area of the section at a distance z above its base in terms of z. Compute its volume.

2. The base of a triangular pyramid is a right triangle whose legs are $AC = 6$ in. and $BC = 10$ in. Its vertex is directly above C and the altitude is 16 in. Express the area of the section at a distance z above the base in terms of z. Compute its volume.

3. Find the volume bounded by the three coordinate planes and the plane $3x + 4y + 2z = 12$.

4. A solid has the circle $x^2 + y^2 = 25$ for a base. The sections parallel to the yz-plane are squares. Sketch the solid and compute its volume.

5. Compute the volume of an elliptical conoid whose base is the ellipse $x^2 + 2y^2 = 12$ and whose altitude is 10.

6. Find the volume bounded by the paraboloid $9z = 4x^2 + 9y^2$ and the plane $z = 4$.

7. Compute the volume bounded by the surface $x^2 + 4y^2 = 4 - z$ and the planes $z = 0$ and $z = 3$.

8. Compute the volume bounded by the paraboloid $2x = 4y^2 + 9z^2$ and the plane $x = 9$.

9. Find the volume cut from the paraboloid $4y^2 + z^2 + x = 16$ by the plane $x = 12$.

10. The axes of two circular cylinders having radius r intersect at right angles. Find the common volume. HINT: Fig. 113 shows the upper half of the required volume. First observe that the section in the xy-plane is a square whose side is $2r$, and that sections parallel to this are smaller squares. Show that at a distance z above the xy-plane the side of the square is $2\sqrt{r^2 - z^2}$.

11. Compute the volume of an ellipsoid whose semiaxes are $a = 6$, $b = 5$, and $c = 4$.

12. Derive a formula for the volume of the ellipsoid whose equation is
$$\frac{x^2}{a^2} + \frac{y^2}{b^2} + \frac{z^2}{c^2} = 1.$$

13. A wedge is cut from a tree 6 ft. in diameter by first making a horizontal saw cut halfway through the trunk and then making a second cut inclined at 45° to the horizontal and meeting the first one along a diameter of the section. Compute the volume of the wedge.

14. A solid right circular cylinder with radius 8 in. and height 14 in. is cut by a plane that passes through a diameter of the lower base and is tangent to the upper base. Find the volume of the smaller piece.

15. The radius of a hemispherical vat is 5 ft. and it contains oil to a depth of 4 ft. Find the volume of the oil.

16. Compute the volume of the segment cut from a sphere of radius 6 in. by two parallel planes whose distances from the center are 2 in. and 4 in., respectively.

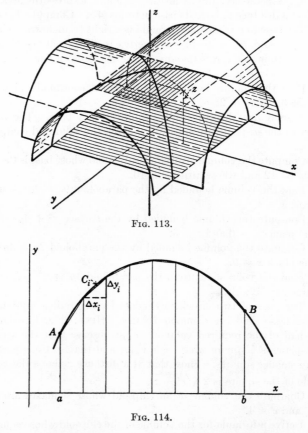

Fig. 113.

Fig. 114.

111. Length of a curve.—The length s of a curve such as arc AB in Fig. 114 is defined as the limit approached by the sum of the lengths of the n chords drawn as shown, when n increases indefinitely in such a way that the length of each chord approaches zero.

The length of the ith chord is

$$C_i = \sqrt{(\Delta x_i)^2 + (\Delta y_i)^2}.$$

Our definition can then be written in the form

$$s = \lim_{\Delta x_i \to 0} \sum_{i=1}^{n} \sqrt{(\Delta x_i)^2 + (\Delta y_i)^2}$$

$$= \lim_{\Delta x_i \to 0} \sum_{i=1}^{n} \sqrt{1 + \left(\frac{\Delta y_i}{\Delta x_i}\right)^2} \, \Delta x_i.$$

Using the Theorem of Mean Value and the Fundamental Theorem, we arrive at the formula*

$$(1) \qquad s = \int_{x=a}^{x=b} \sqrt{1 + \left(\frac{dy}{dx}\right)^2} \, dx.$$

An alternate formula that can be used conveniently if we have $x = f(y)$, where y is the independent variable, is, of course,

$$(2) \qquad s = \int_{y=c}^{y=d} \sqrt{1 + \left(\frac{dx}{dy}\right)^2} \, dy.$$

Finally, a third form, which is particularly convenient when the equation of the curve is given by the parametric equations $x = g(t)$, $y = h(t)$, is

$$(3) \qquad s = \int \sqrt{(dx)^2 + (dy)^2}.$$

In using this form we replace dx by $g'(t)dt$ and dy by $h'(t)dt$. The limits are of course the values of t corresponding to the end points of the arc whose length is to be computed.

The quantity $\sqrt{(dx)^2 + (dy)^2}$ or $\sqrt{1 + (dy/dx)^2} \, dx$ is the *differential* of the arc length s. It serves as an approximation to the increment Δs in the arc, corresponding to an increment Δx or dx in x, just as the differential $dy = f'(x)dx$ serves as an approximation to Δy.

* The details will be omitted.

The corresponding formula for length of arc in polar coordinates can be obtained by applying to (3) the usual transformation equations. Letting

$$x = \rho \cos \theta \qquad \text{and} \qquad y = \rho \sin \theta,$$

and assuming that $\rho = F(\theta)$, we have

$$dx = -\rho \sin \theta \, d\theta + \cos \theta \, d\rho;$$
$$dy = \rho \cos \theta \, d\theta + \sin \theta \, d\rho.$$

The result of substituting these expressions for dx and dy in (3) is

(4) $$s = \int \sqrt{(d\rho)^2 + \rho^2 (d\theta)^2}.$$

If θ is to be regarded as the independent variable this may be put into the convenient form

(5) $$s = \int_{\theta_1}^{\theta_2} \sqrt{\varrho^2 + \left(\frac{d\varrho}{d\theta}\right)^2} \, d\theta.$$

An easy method of remembering formula (4) is indicated in Fig. 115. It shows that a small element of arc is

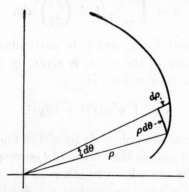

FIG. 115.

approximately equal to the hypotenuse of a right triangle with one side equal to $\rho \, d\theta$ and the other equal to $d\rho$.

Example 1

Compute the length of the parabola $y = \frac{1}{2}x^2$ from $x = 0$ to $x = 1$.

Solution

$$y = \tfrac{1}{2}x^2$$

$$\frac{dy}{dx} = x;$$

$$s = \int_0^1 \sqrt{1 + \left(\frac{dy}{dx}\right)^2}\, dx = \int_0^1 \sqrt{1 + x^2}\, dx$$

$$= \int_0^{\frac{\pi}{4}} \sec^3 \theta\, d\theta \qquad \text{(letting } x = \tan \theta)$$

$$= \tfrac{1}{2}[\sec \theta \tan \theta + \log (\sec \theta + \tan \theta)]_0^{\frac{\pi}{4}}$$
$$= \tfrac{1}{2}[\sqrt{2} + \log (\sqrt{2} + 1)]$$
$$= 1.148.$$

Example 2

Compute the length of one arch of the cycloid $x = a(\theta - \sin \theta)$, $y = a(1 - \cos \theta)$.

Solution

$$dx = a(1 - \cos \theta)\, d\theta; \qquad dy = a \sin \theta\, d\theta.$$
$$\sqrt{(dx)^2 + (dy)^2} = a \sqrt{(1 - \cos \theta)^2 + \sin^2 \theta}\, d\theta$$
$$= a \sqrt{2 - 2 \cos \theta}\, d\theta$$
$$= 2a \sin \tfrac{1}{2}\theta\, d\theta$$

$$s = \int_0^{2\pi} 2a \sin \tfrac{1}{2}\theta\, d\theta = 8a.$$

Example 3

Compute the perimeter of the circle $\rho = 2a \sin \theta$.

Solution (Fig. 116)

$$\frac{d\rho}{d\theta} = 2a \cos \theta.$$

$$s = \int_0^{\pi} \sqrt{4a^2 \sin^2 \theta + 4a^2 \cos^2 \theta}\, d\theta$$

$$= 2a \int_0^{\pi} d\theta = 2\pi a.$$

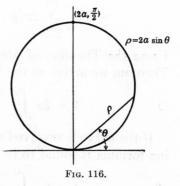

FIG. 116.

112. Area of a surface of revolution.

—Let the curve, together with the n chords shown in Fig. 117, be revolved about the x-axis. The curve generates a surface of revolution while each chord generates the lateral surface of a frustum of a cone. The area of the surface is defined as the limit approached by the sum of the lateral areas of the frustums when $n \to \infty$ in such a way that every $\Delta x \to 0$.

It will be recalled that the lateral area of a frustum is obtained by multiplying its mean circumference by its

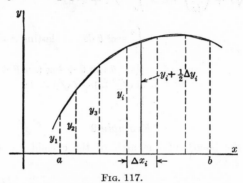

Fig. 117.

slant height. Thus, the area of the ith frustum is

$$2\pi(y_i + \tfrac{1}{2}\Delta y_i) \sqrt{(\Delta x_i)^2 + (\Delta y_i)^2}.$$

The surface area is then given by

$$A = \lim_{\Delta x_i \to 0} \sum_{i=1}^{n} 2\pi(y_i + \tfrac{1}{2}\Delta y_i) \sqrt{(\Delta x_i)^2 + (\Delta y_i)^2}$$

$$= \lim_{\Delta x_i \to 0} \sum_{i=1}^{n} 2\pi(y_i + \tfrac{1}{2}\Delta y_i) \sqrt{1 + \left(\frac{\Delta y_i}{\Delta x_i}\right)^2} \, \Delta x_i.$$

Using the Theorem of Mean Value and the Fundamental Theorem we arrive at the formula*

(1) $$A = 2\pi \int_{x=a}^{x=b} y \sqrt{1 + \left(\frac{dy}{dx}\right)^2} \, dx.$$

If the curve is revolved about the y-axis, the corresponding formula is found to be

(2) $$A = 2\pi \int_{x=a}^{x=b} x \sqrt{1 + \left(\frac{dy}{dx}\right)^2} \, dx.$$

* The details are rather complicated and will be omitted.

In either (1) or (2) we may replace $\sqrt{1 + (dy/dx)^2}\, dx$ by $\sqrt{1 + (dx/dy)^2}\, dy$. If we use ds to denote either of these expressions for the differential of arc we may write (1) and (2), respectively, as

$$A = 2\pi \int y\, ds \quad \text{and} \quad A = 2\pi \int x\, ds.$$

The corresponding formulas in polar coordinates are obtained by replacing y by $\rho \sin \theta$ or x by $\rho \cos \theta$ and using $\sqrt{\rho^2 + (d\rho/d\theta)^2}\, d\theta$ for ds.

Example

Compute the area of the spherical surface generated by revolving the upper half of the circle $x^2 + y^2 = r^2$ about the x-axis.

Solution

$$\frac{dy}{dx} = -\frac{x}{y}.$$

$$ds = \sqrt{1 + \left(\frac{dy}{dx}\right)^2}\, dx = \sqrt{1 + \frac{x^2}{y^2}}\, dx = \frac{r}{y}\, dx.$$

$$A = 2\pi \int_{x=-r}^{x=r} y\, ds$$

$$= 2\pi \int_{-r}^{r} y\left(\frac{r}{y}\, dx\right)$$

$$= 2\pi r \int_{-r}^{r} dx$$

$$= 4\pi r^2.$$

PROBLEMS

In each of the following cases compute the length of the arc as indicated:

1. $y = x^{\frac{3}{2}}$; from $x = 0$ to $x = \frac{7}{3}$.

2. $y = \log \cos x$; from $x = 0$ to $x = \frac{1}{3}\pi$.

3. $y = 2\left(e^{\frac{x}{4}} + e^{-\frac{x}{4}}\right)$; from $x = 0$ to $x = 4$.

4. $y = \frac{a}{2}\left(e^{\frac{x}{a}} + e^{-\frac{x}{a}}\right)$; from $x = 0$ to $x = x_1$.

5. $y = 2\sqrt{x}$; $x = 0$ to $x = 3$.
HINT: After setting up the integral, let $x = \tan^2 \theta$.

6. $y = x^2$; $x = 0$ to $x = 1$.

7. $y = 2e^{\frac{1}{2}x}$; $x = 0$ to $x = 2$.

8. $y = \frac{x^3}{3} + \frac{1}{4x}$; $x = 1$ to $x = 3$.

9. Find the perimeter of the cardioid $\rho = a(1 + \cos \theta)$.

10. Sketch the curve $\rho = 4 \sin^3 \tfrac{1}{3}\theta$ for $\theta = 0$ to $\tfrac{3}{2}\pi$ and compute the length of this arc.

11. Find the perimeter of the four-cusped hypocycloid whose equation is $x^{\frac{2}{3}} + y^{\frac{2}{3}} = a^{\frac{2}{3}}$.

12. Solve Prob. 11 using the parametric equations: $x = a \cos^3 \theta$, $y = a \sin^3 \theta$.

13. Set up an integral whose value is equal to the length of one arch of the curve $y = \sin x$.

14. Compute the area of the surface generated by revolving the arc of the parabola $y = x^2$ from $x = 0$ to $x = 3$ about the y-axis.

15. The parabolic reflector of an automobile headlight is 12 in. in diameter and 4 in. deep. What is its area?

16. Compute the area of the surface generated by revolving the four-cusped hypocycloid $x^{\frac{2}{3}} + y^{\frac{2}{3}} = a^{\frac{2}{3}}$ about the x-axis.

17. Solve Prob. 16 using the parametric equations: $x = a \cos^3 \theta$, $y = a \sin^3 \theta$.

In each of the following cases compute the area of the surface generated as indicated:

18. By revolving one arch of the curve $y = \sin x$ about the x-axis.

19. By revolving the arc of the curve $y = \log x$ from $x = 0$ to $x = 1$ about the y-axis.

20. By revolving the arc of the curve $y = e^x$ for which $x < 0$ about the x-axis.

21. By revolving one arch of a cycloid about its base.

22. By revolving the upper half of the circle $\rho = 2a \cos \theta$ about the polar axis.

23. By revolving the upper half of the cardioid $\rho = a(1 + \cos \theta)$ about the polar axis.

24. By revolving the circle $\rho = 2a \cos \theta$ about the 90-270° line.

25. Derive a formula for the surface area of a torus.

26. Show that the area of a zone of altitude h on a sphere of radius r is equal to $2\pi rh$. Thus show that it is equal to the lateral area of a right circular cylinder having the same radius as the sphere and height equal to the altitude of the zone.

113. Mean value of a function.—The average, or arithmetic mean, of a set of n numbers is found by dividing their sum by n. Thus the average of the numbers 6, 12, 14, 13, and 10 is

$$\frac{6 + 12 + 14 + 13 + 10}{5} = 11.$$

In scientific work it is often necessary to assign "weights"

to the numbers, the weights indicating the relative importance of the numbers in the calculation. Thus if the
temperature in a room should be maintained at 60° for
8 hr., then at 45° for 4 hr., and then at 20° for 3 hr., the time
average of the temperature would be

$$\frac{60(8) + 45(4) + 20(3)}{8 + 4 + 3} = 48°.$$

This is not the arithmetic mean of the numbers 60, 45, and
20, but is a *weighted average*, the weights being the numbers
8, 4, and 3.

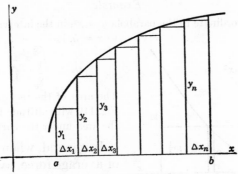

FIG. 118.

Consider now a function $y = f(x)$ defined over the interval
from $x = a$ to $x = b$. In order to arrive at a proper
definition of its average or mean value over this interval we
proceed as follows (Fig. 118): The quantity

$$\frac{y_1(\Delta x_1) + y_2(\Delta x_2) + \cdots + y_n(\Delta x_n)}{\Delta x_1 + \Delta x_2 + \cdots + \Delta x_n}$$

is a weighted average of the n ordinates, $y_1, y_2, \cdots, y_n$,
the weights being the Δx's. The numerator in this expression is equal to the sum of the areas of the n rectangles
shown, while the denominator is equal to the length $b - a$
of the interval.

Suppose now that the number of ordinates selected in the
interval is allowed to increase indefinitely in such a way that
each $\Delta x \to 0$. The limit of the numerator is the area under

the curve, and the denominator remains equal to $b - a$. It is natural then that we should define the *mean ordinate to the curve*, or the *mean value of $f(x)$ relative to x*, over the interval from $x = a$ to $x = b$, by the equation

$$y_m = \frac{\int_a^b f(x)dx}{b - a}.$$

Geometrically, this mean value of y is equal to the height of a rectangle having $b - a$ as its base, and having its area equal to that under the curve.

Example

The mean ordinate to the parabola $y = x^2$, in the interval from $x = 1$ to $x = 5$, is

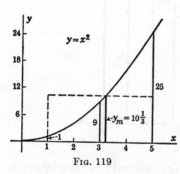

Fig. 119

$$y_m = \frac{\int_1^5 x^2 dx}{5 - 1} = 10\tfrac{1}{3}.$$

The area of the rectangle shown in Fig. 119 with altitude $10\tfrac{1}{3}$ is equal to the area under the curve.

In general, when one speaks of average force, average temperature, average speed, etc., he is referring to the mean value as here defined (with respect to time, distance, or some other variable that is either specified or implied). Suppose, for example, that the speed in feet per minute of a moving object varies in accordance with the equation

$$v = 3 \sqrt{t} + 2.$$

The average value of v over the time interval from $t = 0$ to 9 min. is

$$\frac{\int_0^9 v\, dt}{9 - 0} = \frac{\int_0^9 (3 \sqrt{t} + 2)dt}{9} = \frac{72}{9} = 8 \text{ ft. per minute.}$$

Here, the numerator is the distance traveled in the 9-min. interval. The average speed that we have found is a speed which, if maintained constantly for 9 min., would result

in the same distance.   Geometrically, the value of $\int_0^9 v\,dt$
is the area under the speed-time graph (Fig. 120).   Observe
that the area of the little shaded element in the figure is the
product of an instantaneous value of v and a small time
interval Δt, and that it therefore represents a distance Δs.
The area under the speed-time curve accordingly represents

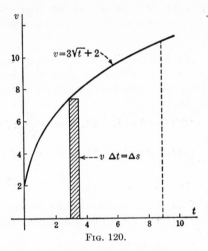

$v = 3\sqrt{t} + 2$

$v\,\Delta t = \Delta s$

FIG. 120.

the total distance traversed by the moving object in the
given time interval.*

In later applications we shall see that the area under a
curve may represent various important physical quantities,
and it is for this reason that the problem of computing such
an area is of fundamental importance in scientific work.

PROBLEMS

In each of the following cases sketch the curve whose equation is given
and compute the mean ordinate in the given interval:

* We may regard the speed v as a scalar quantity that is positive when
the particle is moving one way and negative when it is moving the other
way along its path.   Then the algebraic area under the curve gives the
algebraic distance traversed.   The average value of v is the speed (plus or
minus) that would result in the same algebraic distance in the same time.
Thus if $v = a \sin t$, the average value of v in the interval from $t = 0$ to 2π
is zero.

1. $y = 4 \sin x$; $x = 0$ to π.   **2.** $y = \sqrt{x}$; $x = 0$ to 10.

3. $y = \sqrt{25 - x^2}$; $x = -5$ to 5.   **4.** $y = \cos^2 x$; $x = 0$ to π.

5. $y = 2 \sin^3 \frac{1}{2}x$; $x = 0$ to 2π.   **6.** $y = x^2 - 3x$; $x = 0$ to 3.

7. $y = 4x^2 - x^3$; $x = -1$ to 3.   **8.** $y = \dfrac{4x}{x^2 + 1}$; $x = 0$ to 4.

9. What is the mean value of the function $\sin^3 x$ over the interval from $x = 0$ to 2π?

10. Show that if $f(x)$ is a *linear* function over the interval from $x = a$ to $x = b$, then its mean value is equal to one-half the sum of $f(a)$ and $f(b)$.

In each of the following cases it is assumed that a quantity Q varies with the time t in accordance with the given equation. In each case sketch the curve over the given interval and compute the mean value of Q:

11. $Q = (2 + \sqrt{t})^2$; $t = 0$ to 1.   **12.** $Q = \dfrac{12t}{t^2 + 3}$; $t = 0$ to 5.

13. $Q = \dfrac{6}{\sqrt[3]{8 - 2t}}$; $t = 0$ to 4.   **14.** $Q = \dfrac{t}{t + 3}$; $t = 1$ to 6.

15. $Q = \dfrac{9t}{(t - 3)^{\frac{3}{2}}}$; $t = 4$ to 7.   **16.** $Q = \frac{1}{3}t^3 \sqrt{9 - t^2}$; $t = 0$ to 3.

17. The speed of an object, in feet per minute, varies in accordance with the equation $v = \frac{1}{4}t^2(8 - t)$. Compute the average speed for the interval $t = 0$ to 6.

18. The speed of a particle, in feet per minute, varies in accordance with the equation $v = \dfrac{4t}{\sqrt{t + 2}}$. Compute the average speed for the interval $t = 2$ to 14.

19. The speed of a particle, in feet per minute, varies in accordance with the equation $v = \frac{16}{3}t - \frac{1}{2}t^2$. Show that the mean value of v over the interval $t = 0$ to 16 is zero and interpret this result.

20. A particle moves on the x-axis so that its speed in feet per second is given by $v = 6\pi \cos^3 \frac{1}{2}\pi t$. Find the mean value of v over the interval $t = 0$ to 3. Describe the motion.

CHAPTER XX

APPROXIMATE INTEGRATION

114. Introduction.—In many cases we are unable to find the value of $\int_a^b f(x)dx$ by the usual method, either because we do not have an analytical expression for the function $f(x)$, or because we cannot perform the integration.* In such a case we may approximate the value of the definite integral by making the graph of the function $f(x)$ and measuring the area under it by any means available.

Example

The length of one arch of the curve $y = \sin x$ is given by the value of

$$\int_0^\pi \sqrt{1 + \cos^2 x}\, dx.$$

This integration cannot be performed in terms of functions with which the student is familiar. The value of the definite integral is, however, equal to the area under the curve

$$y = \sqrt{1 + \cos^2 x}$$

in the interval from 0 to π. This curve might be plotted on rectangular coordinate paper and the area determined approximately by counting squares.

In the present chapter we shall develop two formulas for approximating the value of $\int_a^b f(x)dx$. Another method, using infinite series, will be given in Chap. XXVIII.

115. The trapezoidal rule.—One convenient method of making the approximation is as follows:

Divide the interval from $x = a$ to $x = b$ into a convenient

---

* It can be shown that if $f(x)$ is *continuous* the integral always exists in the sense that there is a function $\phi(x)$ whose derivative is $f(x)$. It may be, however, that $\phi(x)$ cannot be expressed as a finite combination of the elementary functions that we have studied.

number n of *equal* parts, construct the trapezoids as indicated in Fig. 121, and take the sum of their areas as an approximation to the area under the curve.

We may denote the lengths of the $n + 1$ ordinates by $y_0, y_1, \cdots , y_n$ and the sum of the areas of the trapezoids

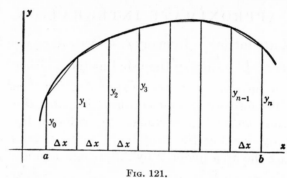

Fig. 121.

by A_T.   Then

$$A_T = \tfrac{1}{2}(y_0 + y_1)\Delta x + \tfrac{1}{2}(y_1 + y_2)\Delta x$$
$$+ \cdots + \tfrac{1}{2}(y_{n-1} + y_n)\Delta x,$$

or

$$A_T = \Delta x[\tfrac{1}{2}y_0 + y_1 + y_2 + \cdots + y_{n-1} + \tfrac{1}{2}y_n].$$

The accuracy of the approximation depends of course upon the number of intervals used and upon the character of the function $f(x)$.

Example

Evaluate approximately $\int_0^{2.5} \sqrt{16 - x^3}\, dx$ taking $n = 5$.

Solution (Fig. 122)

If we divide the interval from $x = 0$ to $x = 2.5$ into 5 equal parts, the length of each part is $\Delta x = 0.5$. Computing the necessary ordinates we construct the following table:

x	0	0.5	1.0	1.5	2.0	2.5
y	4	3.98	3.87	3.55	2.83	0.61

The above trapezoidal formula then gives:

$$A = 0.5[\tfrac{1}{2}(4) + 3.98 + 3.87 + 3.55 + 2.83 + \tfrac{1}{2}(0.61)] = 8.27.$$

Whether or not we are justified in giving the result to three significant figures is not immediately apparent. From the figure it is evident that our approximation is somewhat smaller than the actual value of the

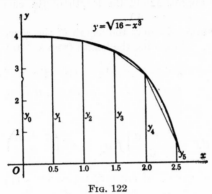

Fig. 122

integral. A better approximation, and a rough estimate of the error in our present approximation, could be obtained by repeating the calculation using $n = 10$.

PROBLEMS

In each of the following cases evaluate the given integral by using the trapezoidal rule with the given value of n, and also by integration:

1. $\displaystyle\int_1^7 x^2 dx;\ n = 6.$ 2. $\displaystyle\int_2^5 \sqrt{x^2 + 6}\, dx;\ n = 6.$

3. $\displaystyle\int_0^4 x\sqrt{4 + x^2}\, dx;\ n = 8.$ 4. $\displaystyle\int_2^7 \frac{dx}{x};\ n = 10.$

5. $\displaystyle\int_0^{\frac{\pi}{2}} \sin\theta\, d\theta;\ n = 9.$ 6. $\displaystyle\int_0^2 e^{-x}\, dx;\ n = 4.$

In each of the following cases evaluate the given integral using the trapezoidal rule with the given value of n:

7. $\displaystyle\int_1^5 \sqrt{\tfrac{1}{2}x^3 + 4}\, dx;\ n = 4.$ 8. $\displaystyle\int_1^6 \sqrt{x^2 + 3x}\, dx;\ n = 5.$

9. $\displaystyle\int_1^5 \frac{x^2 dx}{\sqrt{x^2 + 8}};\ n = 4.$ 10. $\displaystyle\int_1^4 x\sqrt{x^3 + 6}\, dx;\ n = 6.$

11. $\displaystyle\int_0^{\frac{\pi}{2}} \sqrt{\sin\theta}\, d\theta;\ n = 9.$ 12. $\displaystyle\int_0^{\frac{\pi}{4}} \sqrt{2 + \sin^2\theta}\, d\theta;\ n = 5.$

13. $\int_0^2 e^{-x^2}dx; n = 10.$ **14.** $\int_0^{\frac{\pi}{2}} \dfrac{d\theta}{\sqrt{2 - \cos^2 \theta}}; n = 6.$

15. $\int_0^{\frac{\pi}{2}} \sqrt{1 + \cos^2 x}\ dx; n = 9.$ **16.** $\int_0^{\frac{\pi}{4}} \sqrt{\tan \theta}\ d\theta; n = 5.$

17. Compute approximately the length of the curve $y = \frac{1}{6}x^3$ from $x = 1$ to $x = 4$ Use $n = 6$.)

18. Compute approximately the length of the curve $y = \cos x$ from $x = 0$ to $x = 2\pi$. (In finding the length from $x = 0$ to $\frac{1}{2}\pi$ use $n = 9$.)

116. The prismoid formula.—By direct integration it can be shown that *if $f(x)$ is a polynomial in x of degree 3 or less*, then

$$(1) \quad \int_a^b f(x)\ dx = \frac{b - a}{6}\left[f(a) + 4f\left(\frac{a + b}{2}\right) + f(b)\right].$$

In this equation $f(a)$, of course, represents the value of the integrand when $x = a$, $f(b)$ is its value when $x = b$, and $f\left(\dfrac{a + b}{2}\right)$ is its value when the value of x is half-way between a and b.

Example

The values of the function $3x - \frac{1}{3}x^2$ when $x = 1$, 3, and 5, are, respectively $\frac{8}{3}$, 6, and $\frac{20}{3}$. Consequently,

$$\int_1^5 (3x - \tfrac{1}{3}x^2)dx = \frac{5 - 1}{6}\left[\tfrac{8}{3} + 4(6) + \tfrac{20}{3}\right] = \frac{200}{9}.$$

The geometrical interpretation is given by **Fig. 123**. *Assuming that $f(x)$ is a polynomial in x of degree 3 or less,* then: The area under the curve $y = f(x)$ in the interval from $x = a$ to $x = b$ is given exactly by the formula

$$(2) \qquad A = \frac{b - a}{6}\left[y_a + 4y_{\frac{a+b}{2}} + y_b\right].$$

If $f(x)$ is not a polynomial in x, or if it is not of degree 3 or less, then (2) gives an approximation to the area by giving exactly the area under the parabola

$$y = Ax^2 + Bx + C$$

that passes through the points P, Q, and R (Fig. 123). It may be remarked that the area under any cubic curve through P, Q, and R, in the interval from $x = a$ to $x = b$, is equal to that under the parabola.

We at first prove (1) for the case of an interval from $x = -h$ to $x = h$, the mid-point being at $x = 0$. Letting

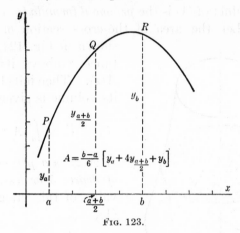

Fig. 123.

$f(x) = Ax^3 + Bx^2 + Cx + D$, we have

$$\int_{-h}^{h} (Ax^3 + Bx^2 + Cx + D)dx = \frac{2Bh^3}{3} + 2\,Dh.$$

Also, in this case,

$$
\begin{aligned}
f(-h) &= -Ah^3 + Bh^2 - Ch + D; \\
4f(0) &= \qquad\qquad\qquad\quad 4D; \\
f(h) &= Ah^3 + Bh^2 + Ch + D.
\end{aligned}
$$

Adding these and multiplying by $\dfrac{b-a}{6}$, which in this case is equal to $2h/6$ or $h/3$, we obtain the result:

$$\frac{2h}{6}[f(-h) + 4f(0) + f(h)] = \frac{2Bh^3}{3} + 2Dh.$$

This proves (1) for the case of an interval that is bisected by the origin. The proof for the general case follows immediately because, by letting $x = x' + \frac{1}{2}(a + b)$, we can translate the axes so that the new origin is at the mid-point of the interval. The equation $y = Ax^3 + Bx^2 + Cx + D$ takes the form $y = Ax^3 + B'x^2 + C'x + D'$, and the new interval is of the type for which we have just proved the theorem.

A by-product of (1) is the *prismoid formula* for computing volumes. Let the area of the cross section of the solid

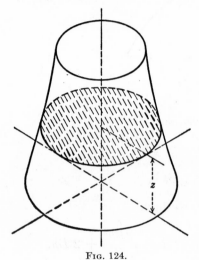

shown in Fig. 124, at a distance z above its base, be $A(z)$. Then if its height is h, its volume is given by

$$V = \int_0^h A(z)dz.$$

If $A(z)$ is a polynomial in z of degree 3 or less, then the value of this integral is, by (1),

$$V = \frac{h}{6} (A_B + 4A_M + A_T)$$

Fig. 124.

where A_B, A_M, and A_T denote the cross-sectional areas at the bottom, mid-section, and top, respectively.

Example

For the sphere shown in Fig. 125, $A_B = A_T = 0$ and $A_M = \pi r^2$. Since $h = 2r$ we have

$$V = \frac{2r}{6} [0 + 4(\pi r^2) + 0] = \tfrac{4}{3}\pi r^3.$$

The result is necessarily exact because at a distance z above the bottom section, the cross-sectional area is given by

$$A(z) = \pi(2rz - z^2).$$

Thus $A(z)$ is a polynomial in z of degree 2.

For solids not satisfying the specified conditions, the **prismoid** formula gives an approximation to the volume.

It is used by engineers for estimating the volumes of such irregular solids as one encounters, for example, in making cuts and fills in road building.

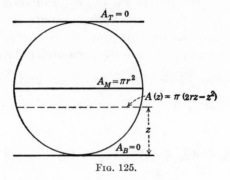

FIG. 125.

117. Simpson's rule.—Another method of approximating the area under the curve whose equation is $y = f(x)$, from $x = a$ to $x = b$, is as follows:

1. Divide the interval from $x = a$ to $x = b$ into an *even* number of equal parts. Denote the lengths of the $n + 1$ ordinates by $y_0, y_1, \cdots, y_n$, as indicated in Fig. 126.

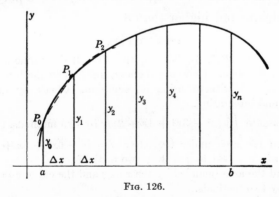

FIG. 126.

2. Take as an approximation to the area under the curve in the first *two* strips, the quantity

$$\frac{2\,\Delta x}{6}\,(y_0 + 4y_1 + y_2).$$

This is exactly the area under the parabola

$$y = Ax^2 + Bx + C$$

determined by the points P_0, P_1, P_2, and shown dotted in the figure. The procedure then amounts to substituting an arc of a parabola for this part of the curve.

3. Similarly, approximate the area under the curve in the next two strips by $\dfrac{\Delta x}{3} (y_2 + 4y_3 + y_4)$ and continue this process. Finally, adding together these approximations, we have

$$A_s = \frac{\Delta x}{3} [(y_0 + 4y_1 + y_2) + (y_2 + 4y_3 + y_4) + \cdots$$
$$+ (y_{n-2} + 4y_{n-1} + y_n)],$$

or

$$A_s = \frac{\Delta x}{3} [y_0 + 4y_1 + 2y_2 + 4y_3 + 2y_4 + \cdots$$
$$+ 4y_{n-1} + y_n].$$

From previous considerations it is clear that this formula will give the value of $\int_a^b f(x)dx$ *exactly*, if $f(x)$ is a polynomial in x of degree not higher than 3.

PROBLEMS

1. The points $P(1, 6)$, $Q(3, 8)$, and $R(5, 2)$ determine a parabola $y = Ax^2 + Bx + C$. Compute the area under it in the interval from $x = 1$ to $x = 5$ without using its equation. Check by finding its equation and integrating.

2. Evaluate $\int_0^2 (x^3 - 3x^2 + 4x + 2)dx$ by two methods.

3. Find the area under the curve $y = x^3 - 6x^2 + 8x + 4$ in the interval from $x = -1$ to $x = 3$ by two methods.

4. Find the area bounded by the x-axis and the curve $y = (x + 2)^2 (2 - x)$ by two methods.

5. Show that the prismoid formula gives exactly the volume of a right circular cone or cylinder.

6. Use the prismoid formula to find the volume common to two right circular cylinders of radius r whose axes intersect at right angles.

7. An automobile headlight is in the form of a paraboloid of revolution. It is 8 in. in diameter and 6 in. deep. Show that the prismoid formula will give its volume exactly, and then use this formula to compute the volume.

8. Approximate the volume generated by revolving about the x-axis the area under the curve $y = \sin x$ in the interval from $x = 0$ to π, using the prismoid formula. Why is the result not exact?

9. The area bounded by the x-axis and the curve $y = 4x - x^2$ is revolved about the y-axis. Set up an integral for the volume generated using the cylindrical shell method. Evaluate the integral by two methods.

10. Show that the prismoid formula will give exactly the volume of an ellipsoid with semiaxes a, b, and c, and then use this formula to compute the volume.

11. Show that the prismoid formula will give exactly the volume bounded by the xy-plane and the paraboloid $x^2 + 4y^2 + 2z = 16$, and then use this formula to compute the volume.

Evaluate each of the following integrals using Simpson's rule with the given value of n:

12. $\int_1^5 \sqrt{130 - x^3}\, dx$; $n = 4$. **13.** $\int_2^8 \sqrt[3]{4 + x^2}\, dx$; $n = 6$.

14. $\int_2^6 \dfrac{x\, dx}{\sqrt{5 + x^3}}$; $n = 4$. **15.** $\int_1^7 \dfrac{x^2 dx}{\sqrt[3]{x^2 + 6}}$; $n = 6$.

16. $\int_0^{\frac{\pi}{2}} \sqrt{2 + \cos^2 \theta}\, d\theta$; $n = 6$. **17.** $\int_0^{\frac{\pi}{2}} \sqrt{\sin x}\, dx$; $n = 6$.

18. $\int_0^2 e^{-x^2} dx$; $n = 10$. **19.** $\int_0^2 x^2 e^{-x^2} dx$; $n = 10$.

In each of the following cases use Simpson's rule to approximate the area under the curve determined by the given experimental data:

20.

x	1	2	3	4	5	6	7
y	2.76	4.84	7.24	8.35	6.28	5.84	5.21

21.

x	2	4	6	8	10
y	1.40	2.83	3.34	5.76	8.22

22.

x	1	2	3	4	5	6	7
y	12.2	14.4	22.4	37.3	44.3	36.2	28.8

In each of the following cases the areas of the cross sections of a solid are given.   Compute the volume:

23.

z (ft.)	0	2	4	6	8	10	12
A (sq. ft.)	4.6	6.8	12.2	16.4	14.2	11.6	8.6

24.

x (in.)	0	1	2	3	4	5	6
A (sq. in.)	1.46	2.84	3.36	3.84	4.12	4.68	5.12

CHAPTER XXI

FIRST MOMENT. CENTROID

118. Introduction.—The moment of a force with respect to a point is defined as the product of the magnitude of the force and the perpendicular distance from the point to its line of action. Fig. 127 shows a system of three parallel forces acting upon a body. The total moment of the system with respect to point O is

$$\Sigma M \ = \ 4(10) \ + \ 7(5) \ + \ 9(8) \ = \ 147 \text{ in.-lb.}$$

If we divide this total moment by the sum of the three forces, we have

$$\frac{\Sigma M}{\Sigma F} = \frac{\text{sum of moments}}{\text{sum of forces}} = \frac{147 \text{ in.-lb.}}{23 \text{ lb.}} = 6.4 \text{ in.}$$

This is the distance from O to the line of action of the resultant of the three forces; *i.e.*, the three given forces could be replaced by a single force of 23 lb. at a distance of 6.4 in. from O and the moment with respect to O (and in fact with respect to any point in the plane) would be unaltered. This resultant force is shown dotted in the figure. The student should observe that the quantity

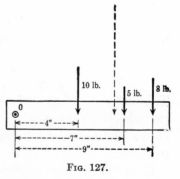

Fig. 127.

$$\frac{4(10) \ + \ 7(5) \ + \ 9(8)}{10 + 5 + 8} = 6.4$$

is a *weighted average* of the distances 4, 7, and 9, the weights being the magnitudes of the forces concentrated at the respective points.

275

As a further example, consider the system of four particles shown in Fig. 128, and let the numbers represent their respective weights in pounds. These weights constitute a system of parallel (downward) forces, and the total moment with respect to the y-axis is

$$\Sigma M_y = 5(4) + 2(7) + 7(8) + 6(5) = 120 \text{ in.-lb.}$$

Here, the weights are the numbers in parentheses and the other numbers are the corresponding "moment arms," which are assumed to be in inches.

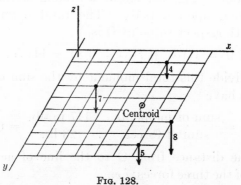

FIG. 128.

If we divide this total moment by the sum of the weights and denote the result by $\bar{x}$, we have

$$\bar{x} = \frac{\Sigma M_y}{\Sigma W} = \frac{120 \text{ in.-lb.}}{24 \text{ lb.}} = 5 \text{ in.}$$

This may be regarded as the average distance of the particles from the y-axis. Actually, it is a *weighted average* of the distances, the "weights" being the weights of the particles.

If we similarly compute the total moment with respect to the x-axis, divide by the total weight, and denote the result by $\bar{y}$, we have

$$\bar{y} = \frac{\Sigma M_x}{\Sigma W} = \frac{3(7) + 1(4) + 8(5) + 6(8)}{7 + 4 + 5 + 8}$$

$$= \frac{113 \text{ in.-lb.}}{24 \text{ lb.}} = 4.7 \text{ in.}$$

The point having coordinates $(\bar{x}, \bar{y})$ is called the *centroid* or *center gravity* of the system of particles. In certain respects the system is equivalent to a single particle of weight 24 lb. located at this point. The idea can be extended in an obvious way to three dimensions.

In the next section we shall consider the problem of locating the *centroid* or *center of gravity* or *center of mass* of a solid. Such a body may be regarded as consisting of a large number of minute particles—and its center of mass is the centroid of this system in the sense discussed above. In the gravitational system of units the *mass* of a particle is its weight divided by the constant g. We shall use the Greek letter δ to denote the *mass per unit volume*.

119. First moment and centroid of the mass of a body.— We must first define what is called the *first moment of the mass of a body with respect to a plane*. For convenience in formulating the definition we shall use the solid shown in Fig. 129 as the body and the yz-plane as the plane. (The solid is one octant of the ellipsoid $\dfrac{x^2}{25} + \dfrac{y^2}{16} + \dfrac{z^2}{16} = 1$.)

We set up the definition as follows:

1. Divide the solid into n slices by passing planes parallel to the given plane (the yz-plane in this case). Denote the masses of the slices by $\Delta m_1, \Delta m_2, \cdots, \Delta m_n$.

2. Multiply the mass of each slice by the distance of the slice from the given plane, and add the quantities so obtained. In this case the distances are $x_1, x_2, \cdots, x_n$, so we form the sum*

$$\sum_{i=1}^{n} x_i \Delta m_i.$$

(If one thinks of the weight of a slice as a downward force

---

* It is immaterial whether x_i stands for the distance from the yz-plane to the *nearer* face of the slice or to the farther face or to an intermediate point. It can be shown that the limit obtained in the next step (when $\Delta x_i \to 0$) is the same. Corresponding statements will apply in several similar situations in this chapter and the next.

proportional to its mass, then we are essentially multiplying each force by its "moment arm.")

3. Determine the limit of this sum when the thickness of each slice approaches zero and $n \to \infty$. *This limit is the required moment.* If we denote it by M_{yz}, then

$$M_{yz} = \lim_{\Delta x_i \to 0} \sum_{i=1}^{n} x_i \Delta m_i = \int x \, dm.$$

Here, dm denotes the differential of mass, it being understood that it refers to a slice taken as indicated in step 1.

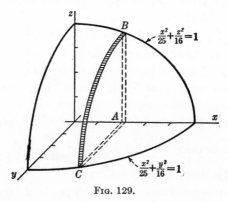

Fig. 129.

Applying the above definition also to the other coordinate planes, we have, finally,

$$M_{yz} = \int x \, dm; \qquad M_{xz} = \int y \, dm; \qquad M_{xy} = \int z \, dm.$$

In each case the symbol dm refers to a slice that is taken parallel to the plane denoted by the subscripts.

If we divide each of these three moments by the entire mass of the body, we obtain the three coordinates of the *centroid* or *center of* mass:

$$\bar{x} = \frac{\int x \, dm}{m}; \qquad \bar{y} = \frac{\int y \, dm}{m}; \qquad \bar{z} = \frac{\int z \, dm}{m}.$$

In the first of the above integrals dm must be expressed in terms of x and dx. Thus, if the area of the cross section at a distance x from the yz-plane is $A(x)$, then the volume of a slice is $dv = A(x)dx$ and its mass is $dm = \delta \cdot A(x)dx$ where δ is the mass per unit volume. In the second integral we similarly express dm as $\delta \cdot A(y)dy$, and in the third as $\delta \cdot A(z)dz$.

Example

Locate the centroid of the (homogeneous) solid bounded by the coordinate planes and the surface $\dfrac{x^2}{25} + \dfrac{y^2}{16} + \dfrac{z^2}{16} = 1$.

Solution (Fig. 129)

The volume of the slice shown is $\frac{1}{4}\pi \cdot AB \cdot AC \cdot dx$ where AB and AC must be expressed in terms of x. The equation of the trace of the surface in the xz-plane is $\dfrac{x^2}{25} + \dfrac{z^2}{16} = 1$. Solving this for z in terms of x we have

$$AB = \tfrac{4}{5}\sqrt{25 - x^2}.$$

Using the trace in the xy-plane, we similarly find that

$$AC = \tfrac{4}{5}\sqrt{25 - x^2}.$$

The mass of the slice is then

$$dm = \delta \cdot dv = \frac{4\delta\pi}{25}(25 - x^2)dx.$$

We multiply the mass of the slice by its distance x from the yz-plane and integrate from $x = 0$ to $x = 5$:

$$M_{yz} = \int x\,dm = \int_0^5 x \cdot \frac{4\delta\pi}{25}(25 - x^2)dx$$
$$= \frac{4\delta\pi}{25}\int_0^5 (25x - x^3)dx = 25\pi\delta.$$

The mass of the body, obtained by the slice method or by using the formula $v = \frac{4}{3}\pi abc$ for the volume of an ellipsoid, is $\frac{40}{3}\pi\delta$. Then

$$\bar{x} = \frac{M_{yz}}{m} = \frac{25\pi\delta}{\frac{40}{3}\pi\delta} = 1\tfrac{7}{8}.$$

The student may show, by using slices parallel to the xz-plane, that $\bar{y} = 1\frac{1}{2}$ and, by using slices parallel to the xy-plane, that $\bar{z} = 1\frac{1}{2}$. The coordinates of the center of mass are then $(1\frac{7}{8}, 1\frac{1}{2}, 1\frac{1}{2})$.

If the *volumes* of the slices were used instead of their masses, the *centroid of the volume* would be obtained. For a homogeneous solid such as we have assumed above, the centroid of the volume coincides with that of the mass.

It can be shown that if a homogeneous solid has a plane of symmetry, its center of mass lies on that plane. In the case of a solid of revolution the centroid lies on the axis of revolution. The above procedure can be used to determine the one unknown coordinate.

Example

Find the center of gravity of a solid homogeneous right circular cone of the radius r and height h.

Solution (Fig. 130)

Taking the cone in the position shown, we have $\bar{y} = \bar{z} = 0$. To find

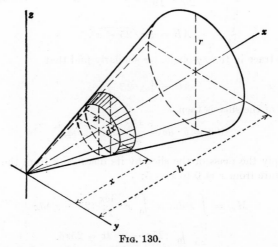

Fig. 130.

$\bar{x}$ we divide the solid into slices parallel to the yz-plane. Then

$$dm = \delta \pi z^2 dx.$$

$$\int x \, dm = \delta \pi \int_0^h xz^2 dx.$$

But

$$\frac{z}{x} = \frac{r}{h}, \quad \text{hence} \quad z^2 = \frac{r^2 x^2}{h^2}.$$

We have then

$$\int x \, dm = \frac{\delta \pi r^2}{h^2} \int_0^h x^3 dx$$

$$= \frac{\delta \pi r^2 h^2}{4}.$$

Dividing this by the mass of the cone ($= \frac{1}{3}\pi r^2 h \delta$), we find that

$$\bar{x} = \tfrac{3}{4}h.$$

The centroid is then on the axis of the cone at a distance of $\frac{3}{4}h$ from the vertex—or at a distance of $\frac{1}{4}h$ from the base.

The equation $\bar{x} = M_{yz}/m$ implies also, of course, that

$$M_{yz} = m \cdot \bar{x}.$$

Thus when one *knows* the location of the centroid, he can find M_{yz} by merely multiplying the mass of the body by $\bar{x}$. Similar statements apply in regard to M_{xy} and M_{xz}. If a solid is built up of simple parts whose individual centroids are known, the center of gravity of the composite body can easily be found.

Example

A solid cylindrical steel rod is tapered to a conical point as indicated in Fig. 131.   Locate its center of gravity.

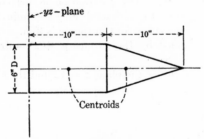

FIG. 131.

Solution

Let the plane of the left-hand end of the cylinder be the yz-plane. Then to find $\bar{x}$ we must compute M_{yz} and divide by the entire mass of the rod.

For the cylindrical part we obviously have $\bar{x} = 5$ in.; hence,

$$(M_{yz})_{\text{cyl.}} = (\pi \cdot 3^2 \cdot 10 \cdot \delta)(5) = 450\pi\delta.$$

The distance from the yz-plane to the centroid of the conical part is $10 + \frac{1}{4}(10) = 12.5$ in., so that for this part

$$(M_{yz})_{\text{cone}} = (\tfrac{1}{3}\pi \cdot 3^2 \cdot 10 \cdot \delta)(12.5) = 375\pi\delta.$$

Adding these, we have for the entire body

$$M_{yz} = 450\pi\delta + 375\pi\delta = 825\pi\delta.$$

Dividing this by the mass of the entire body, we find that

$$\bar{x} = \frac{M_{yz}}{m} = \frac{825\pi\delta}{120\pi\delta} = 6\tfrac{7}{8} \text{ in.}$$

PROBLEMS

In Probs. 1 to 13 locate the center of mass of the given solid, it being assumed that the solid is homogeneous so that δ is a constant:

1. A rectangular parallelepiped with edges a, b, and c.

2. A pyramid whose base is a square 6 in. on a side, the vertex being 12 in. above the center of the base.

3. A pyramid whose base is a rectangle 4 in. by 6 in., the vertex being 10 in. above the center of the base.

4. A pyramid whose base is a square 6 in. on a side, the vertex being 12 in. above one corner of the base.

5. The solid bounded by the coordinate planes and the plane $\dfrac{x}{a} + \dfrac{y}{b} + \dfrac{z}{c} = 1$.

6. A conoid of height h whose base is the circle $x^2 + y^2 = r^2$.

7. A right elliptical cone whose altitude is 18 in. and whose base is an ellipse with semiaxes 6 in. and 4 in.

8. A solid hemisphere. (*Ans.* $\tfrac{3}{8} r$ from plane surface.)

9. The spherical cap cut from a solid sphere of radius 5 in. by a plane whose distance from the center of the sphere is 3 in.

10. The solid bounded by the surface $y^2 + z^2 = 6x$ and the plane $x = 6$.

11. The solid bounded by the plane $z = 12$ and the surface

$$z = 16 - x^2 - 4y^2.$$

12. The solid bounded by the yz-plane and the right-hand half of the ellipsoid $\dfrac{x^2}{a^2} + \dfrac{y^2}{b^2} + \dfrac{z^2}{c^2} = 1$.

13. The solid generated by revolving the area under the curve $y = \sqrt{x}$ in the interval from $x = 0$ to $x = 9$ about the x-axis.

14. A water tank consists of a right circular cylinder with its axis vertical, to which is attached a hemispherical bottom. The diameter of the cylinder is 8 ft. and its height is 10 ft. How far below the surface is the center of gravity of the water when the tank is full? Use result of Prob. 8.

15. Locate the centroid of a solid homogeneous "top" whose upper part is a hemisphere 2.5 in. in diameter and whose lower part is a right circular cone of diameter 2.5 in. and height 4 in. Use results of Prob. 8 and example on page 280.

16. A wooden buoy consists of two solid right circular cones with common radius of 1.5 ft. The altitude of the upper cone is 1 ft. and that of the bottom cone is 4 ft. Locate the centroid.

17. A cylindrical hole of radius 3 in. is drilled through a solid copper hemisphere of radius 5 in., the axis of the hole coinciding with that of the hemisphere. Locate the centroid of the remaining solid. HINT: Use the shell method and observe that the height of the centroid of a shell is $\frac{1}{2}y$ so that $M = \int \frac{1}{2}y \cdot 2\pi xy\delta\, dx$.

18. The area under the curve $y = \sin x$ in the interval from $x = 0$ to π is revolved about the y-axis. Find the centroid of the volume generated. See hint in Prob. 17.

19. A solid homogeneous right circular cylinder of radius r and height h is cut by a plane that passes through a diameter of the lower base and is tangent to the upper base. Find the centroid of the smaller piece.

20. The density of a solid hemisphere varies directly as the distance from its plane surface. Locate its center of mass. HINT: At a distance x from the plane surface (yz-plane) the mass per unit volume is kx.

21. Locate the center of mass of a solid right circular cone if the density varies directly as the distance from the vertex. HINT: Using Fig. 130, $\delta = kx$.

22. A piece of wire is bent into the form of a quadrant of a circle of radius 6 in. Locate its center of gravity. HINT: The mass of a piece of length $ds = r\, d\theta$ is $\delta \cdot r\, d\theta$. Multiply this by x, which is equal to $r \cos\theta$, and integrate from $\theta = 0$ to $\frac{1}{2}\pi$ to determine M_{yz}. See Fig. 132.

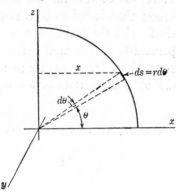

FIG. 132.

120. First moment and centroid of a plane area.—The

first moment of a plane area with respect to a line l in its plane may be defined as follows (Fig. 133):

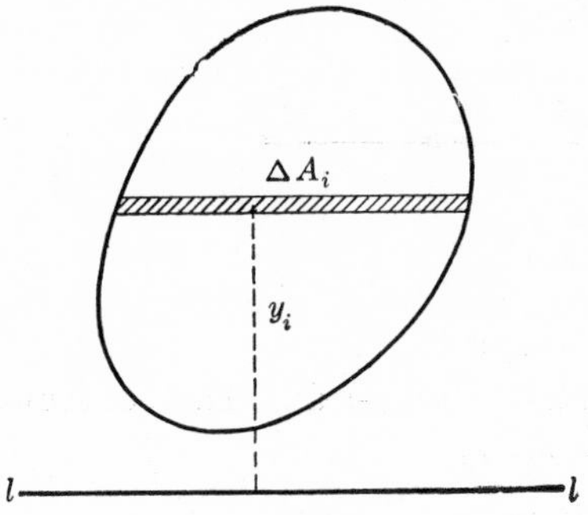

1. Divide the area into n strips by drawing lines parallel to l. Denote the areas of the strips by ΔA_1, $\Delta A_2, \cdots, \Delta A_n$.

2. Multiply the area of each strip by the distance of the strip from the line l, and add the quantities so ob-

FIG. 133.

tained.   Thus, if the distances are $y_1, y_2, \cdots, y_n$, we form
the sum

$$\sum_{i=1}^{n} y_i \Delta A_i.$$

3. Determine the limit of this sum when the width of
each strip approaches zero and $n \to \infty$. *This limit is the
required moment.*   Denoting it by M_l we have

$$M_l = \lim_{\Delta A_i \to 0} \sum_{i=1}^{n} y_i \Delta A_i = \int y \, dA.$$

Here, dA stands for the differential of area, it being understood that it refers to a strip parallel to l.   In general, we
shall refer the given area to a coordinate system and shall be
primarily concerned with computing its moments with
respect to the coordinate axes.   In such cases we replace
dA by $y \, dx$ or $x \, dy$ or an appropriate similar expression.

Example

Find M_y for the area bounded by the curves $y^2 = 4x$ and $x^2 = 4y$

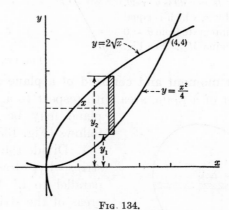

FIG. 134.

Solution (Fig. 134)

We divide the area into strips parallel to the y-axis.   Then, as shown
in the figure,

$$dA = (y_2 - y_1)dx = (2\sqrt{x} - \tfrac{1}{4}x^2)dx.$$

Multiplying dA by the distance x of the strip from the y-axis, we have

$$x \, dA = x(2 \sqrt{x} - \tfrac{1}{4}x^2)dx.$$

The integral from $x = 0$ to $x = 4$ gives the required moment:

$$M_y = \int_0^4 x(2 \sqrt{x} - \tfrac{1}{4}x^2)dx = 9\tfrac{3}{5}.$$

The coordinates of the centroid of an area are defined by the equations

$$\bar{x} = \frac{\int x \, dA}{A}; \qquad \bar{y} = \frac{\int y \, dA}{A}.$$

In each case dA refers to a strip parallel to the proper coordinate axis.

Example

For the area shown Fig. 134 we found that

$$M_y = \int x \, dA = 9\tfrac{3}{5}.$$

The student may verify that in this case $A = 5\tfrac{1}{3}$.   Then

$$\bar{x} = \frac{\int x \, dA}{A} = \frac{9\tfrac{3}{5}}{5\tfrac{1}{3}} = 1\tfrac{4}{5}.$$

By similarly using strips parallel to the x-axis one finds that

$$\int y \, dA \text{ or } M_x$$

has the same value as M_y, so that $\bar{y} = \bar{x}$. The centroid of this area is then the point $(1\tfrac{4}{5}, 1\tfrac{4}{5})$.

The student should observe that if the area of each strip is expressed in square inches and its distance from the axis in inches, then the moment is in *inches cubed*. When we divide this by the area, we obtain a linear distance that may be regarded as the *average distance of the area from the line*. Physically, the centroid of an area is the limiting position of the center of gravity of a thin plate whose shape is that of the area, as the thickness approaches zero.

It can be shown that, if an area has a line of symmetry, its centroid lies on that line. Thus in the above case the area is symmetrical with respect to the line $y = x$ and the point $(1\tfrac{4}{5}, 1\tfrac{4}{5})$ is on this line. Any symmetry that an area possesses may be used in locating its centroid.

Example

Locate the centroid of a semicircle.

Solution (Fig. 135)

Because of symmetry the centroid is on the y-axis; *i.e.*, $\bar{x} = 0$. To find $\bar{y}$ we first compute M_x, using strips parallel to the x-axis. The

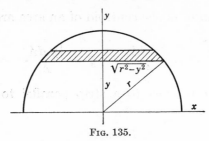

FIG. 135.

area of such a strip is

$$dA = 2\sqrt{r^2 - y^2}\, dy.$$
$$y\, dA = 2y\sqrt{r^2 - y^2}\, dy.$$
$$M_x = \int y\, dA = \int_0^r 2y\sqrt{r^2 - y^2}\, dy = \tfrac{2}{3}r^3.$$
$$\bar{y} = \frac{M_x}{A} = \frac{\tfrac{2}{3}r^3}{\tfrac{1}{2}\pi r^2} = \frac{4r}{3\pi} = 0.424r.$$

The coordinates of the centroid are then $(0,\ 0.424r)$.

121. Composite areas.—The relation $\bar{x} = M_y/A$ implies that $M_y = A \cdot \bar{x}$. Thus, if one *knows* the location of the centroid of an area, he can find M_y by multiplying the area by $\bar{x}$. Similarly, $M_x = A \cdot \bar{y}$.

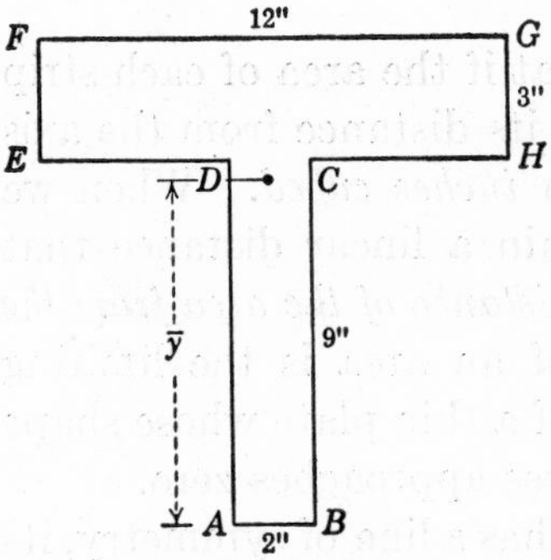

In connection with the computation of stresses in beams and columns, it is necessary to locate the centroid of the area of the cross section. Such sections are often composed of simple parts whose individual centroids are known from symmetry or previous computations. In such cases the centroid of the composite area can be located easily.

FIG. 136.

Example

Find the centroid of the area shown in Fig. 136.

Solution

The figure is composed of two rectangles, the centroid of each being at its geometrical center. Thus the distance from AB to the centroid of $ABCD$ is $4\frac{1}{2}$ in., and the distance from AB to the centroid of $EFGH$ is $(9 + 1\frac{1}{2}) = 10\frac{1}{2}$ in. Taking moments with respect to AB, we have

$$\text{Moment of rectangle } ABCD = (2)(9)(4\tfrac{1}{2}) = 81 \text{ in.}^3$$
$$\text{Moment of rectangle } EFGH = (12)(3)(10\tfrac{1}{2}) = \underline{378} \text{ in.}^3$$
$$\text{Total moment with respect to } AB = \overline{459} \text{ in.}^3$$

The total area is 54 sq. in. If we denote the distance from AB to the centroid of the composite area by $\bar{y}$, then

$$\bar{y} = \frac{459 \text{ in.}^3}{54 \text{ in.}^2} = 8\tfrac{1}{2} \text{ in.}$$

122. Computation of moment using strips perpendicular to axis.

—If we follow the above definitions, we shall always use strips parallel to the y-axis when finding M_y and parallel to the x-axis when finding M_x. It is possible, however, to compute the value of M with respect to a line by using strips that are *perpendicular* instead of parallel to the line. This is desirable in cases where it leads to a simpler integral.

Example

Compute M_x for the area under one arch of the curve $y = \sin x$.

Solution (Fig. 137)

Ordinarily we should use strips *parallel* to the x-axis. In this case, however, we would have $dA = (\pi - 2 \arcsin y)dy$. We avoid this rather complicated expression by taking strips *perpendicular* to the x-axis as

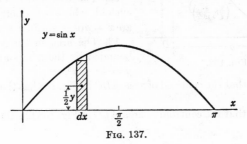

$y = \sin x$

FIG. 137.

shown. The area of a strip is $dA = y\,dx = \sin x\,dx$. *The strip is a rectangle having its centroid at a distance $\tfrac{1}{2}y$ from the x-axis.* The value of M_x for this one strip, which we may denote by dM_x, is

$$dM_x = y\,dx \cdot \tfrac{1}{2}y = \tfrac{1}{2}y^2 dx.$$

We have then
$$M_x = \int_0^\pi \tfrac{1}{2}y^2 dx$$
$$= \tfrac{1}{2}\int_0^\pi \sin^2 x\,dx = \frac{\pi}{4}.$$

PROBLEMS

In each of the following cases locate the centroid of the specified area:

1. The area bounded by the parabola $y^2 = 10x$ and the line $x = 5$.

2. The area bounded by the x-axis, the parabola $y^2 = 6x$, and the line $x = 6$. (First quadrant.)

3. The area in the first quadrant bounded by the coordinate axes and the circle $x^2 + y^2 = 36$.

4. The area in the first quadrant bounded by the coordinate axes and the ellipse $\dfrac{x^2}{a^2} + \dfrac{y^2}{b^2} = 1$.

5. The area bounded by the coordinate axes and the line
$$3x + 4y = 24.$$

6. The area enclosed by the parabolas $y^2 = 8x$ and $x^2 = 8y$.

7. The area bounded by the parabola $y^2 = 16x$ and the line $y = 2x$.

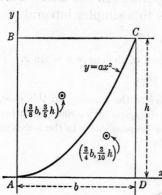

FIG. 138.

8. The area in the first quadrant bounded by the curves $y = x^4$ and $y = 4x^2$.

9. The area bounded by the parabola $y^2 = 4x$ and the line $y = 2x - 4$.

10. The area under the curve $y = \cos x$ from $x = 0$ to $\tfrac{1}{2}\pi$.

11. The area under the curve $y = \sin x$ from $x = 0$ to π.

12. The area under one arch of the cycloid whose parametric equations are $x = a(\theta - \sin\theta), y = a(1 - \cos\theta)$.

13. The area in the first quadrant bounded by the x-axis and the curve $y = 4x - x^3$.

14. Show that the centroid of area ADC in Fig. 138 has the coordinates $(\tfrac{3}{4}b, \tfrac{3}{10}h)$.

15. Show that the centroid of area ABC in Fig. 138 has the coordinates $(\tfrac{3}{8}b, \tfrac{3}{5}h)$.

In each of the following cases locate the centroid of the given area by giving its distances from the lower left-hand corner:

16. The area shown in Fig. 139a.

17. The area shown in Fig. 139b.

18. The area shown in Fig. 139c.

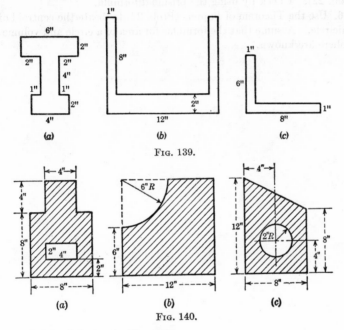

Fig. 139.

(a)   (b)   (c)

Fig. 140.

(a)   (b)   (c)

19. The shaded area in Fig. 140a.

20. The shaded area in Fig. 140b.

21. The shaded area in Fig. 140c.

22. Prove the Theorem of Pappus: *If an area that lies entirely on one side of a line is revolved about the line, the volume of the solid generated is equal to the product of the area and the circumference of the path traveled by its centroid.*

HINT: Using Fig. 141, note that

$$V = \int 2\pi y \, dA = 2\pi \int y \, dA,$$

and that

$$\int y \, dA = \bar{y} \cdot A.$$

Hence

$$V = 2\pi \bar{y} A.$$

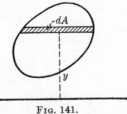

Fig. 141.

23. Using the Theorem of Pappus (Prob. 22) derive a formula for the volume of a torus of radius R whose cross section has a radius r.

24. Using the Theorem of Pappus (Prob. 22) derive a formula for the volume of a right circular cone. HINT: Revolve a right triangle having legs $AC = r$ and $BC = h$ about BC.

25. The height of a frustum of a cone is 10 in. and the radii of its bases are 8 in. and 12 in. Compute its volume using the Theorem of Pappus (Prob. 22). Check by using the prismoid formula.

26. Use the Theorem of Pappus (Prob. 22) to locate the centroid of a semicircle. Assume that the formulas for area of a circle and volume of a sphere are known.

CHAPTER XXII

SECOND MOMENT. RADIUS OF GYRATION

123. Second moment of area.—The definition of the *second moment* or *moment of inertia* of a plane area with respect to a line in its plane differs from that of the first moment only in one respect; namely, the area of each strip is multiplied by the *square* of its distance from the line instead of by the first power of this distance. The second moments with respect to the x- and y-axes are denoted by I_x and I_y, respectively. Thus

$$I_x = \int y^2 dA, \qquad I_y = \int x^2 dA,$$

where dA in each case refers to the area of a strip that is parallel to the axis indicated by the subscript.

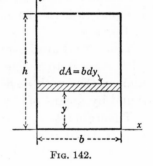

FIG. 142.

Example 1

Compute the second moment of the area of a rectangle with respect to one side.

Solution (Fig. 142)

Choosing axes as shown in the figure, we have

$$dA = b\, dy;$$
$$y^2 dA = y^2 b\, dy;$$
$$I_x = \int y^2 dA = \int_0^h y^2 b\, dy = \frac{bh^3}{3}.$$

Example 2

Compute the second moment of the area of a circle with respect to a diameter.

Solution (Fig. 143)

$$dA = 2y\, dx;$$
$$x^2 dA = 2x^2 y\, dx = 2x^2 \sqrt{r^2 - x^2}\, dx;$$
$$I_y = \int x^2 dA = \int_{-r}^r 2x^2 \sqrt{r^2 - x^2}\, dx = \frac{\pi r^4}{4}.$$

291

This result could have been obtained by finding the value of I for the area in the first quadrant and multiplying by 4.

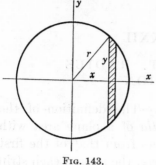

FIG. 143.

If an area has a line of symmetry its *first* moment with respect to that line is zero. This results from the fact that the directed distance y_i in the sum $\Sigma y_i \Delta A_i$ is positive for the strips on one side and negative for those on the other, and the corresponding parts cancel. The situation is entirely different in the case of *second* moment. In the sum $\Sigma (y_i)^2 \Delta A_i$ the factor $(y_i)^2$ is always *positive*. The second moment of an area with respect to a line of symmetry is equal to *twice* the value of I for the part lying on one side of this line.

124. The Parallel-axis Theorem.—When the value of I with respect to a line through the centroid of an area is known, that with respect to any line parallel to this can be found by means of the following:

Theorem: *If I_g is the second moment of an area A with respect to a line through its centroid and I_l is the second moment with respect to a line l parallel to this, then*

$$I_l = I_g + Ad^2,$$

where d is the distance between the two lines.

The proof of this theorem, using the notation indicated in Fig. 144, is as follows:

$$\begin{aligned}
I_l &= \int y^2 \cdot dA \\
&= \int (y' + d)^2 dA \\
&= \int y'^2 dA + 2d \int y' dA + d^2 \int dA \\
&= I_g + 0 + Ad^2.
\end{aligned}$$

Here, the value of $\int y' dA = M_g$ is the *first moment* of the area with respect to line g. Its value is zero because this line goes through the centroid. $(M_g = \bar{y}' \cdot A$ and $\bar{y}' = 0.)$

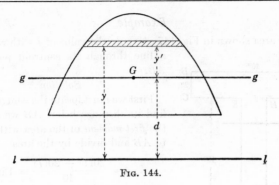

FIG. 144.

Example

We have already found that the value of I for the area of a circle with respect to a diameter is $\dfrac{\pi r^4}{4}$. If we want the value with the respect to a tangent line, we have (Fig. 145),

$$I_t = I_x + A \cdot r^2$$
$$= \frac{\pi r^4}{4} + \pi r^2 \cdot r^2 = \frac{5\pi r^4}{4}.$$

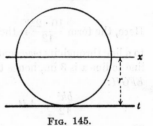

FIG. 145.

125. Composite areas.—Of great importance in connection with the computation of stresses in beams and columns is the second moment of the area of the cross section of the beam or column with respect to a line called the *neutral axis* of the section. The section often consists of rectangular parts. The value of I for a rectangle with sides b and h, with respect to a line through its centroid parallel to side b, is (Fig. 146)

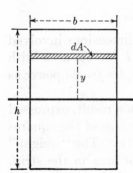

FIG. 146.

$$I = \int_{-\frac{h}{2}}^{\frac{h}{2}} y^2(b\,dy) = \frac{by^3}{3}\Bigg]_{-\frac{h}{2}}^{\frac{h}{2}} = \frac{bh^3}{12}.$$

One may use this result and the Parallel-axis Theorem, in finding the value of I for a composite area.

Example

For the area shown in Fig. 147 compute the value of I with respect to a line through its centroid parallel to AB.

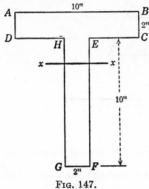

Fig. 147.

Solution

First we must locate the centroid. To find its distance below AB we compute the *first moment* of the area with respect to AB and divide by the area. Thus

$$\bar{y} = \frac{20(1) + 20(7)}{40} = 4 \text{ in.}$$

The line x is then 4 in. below AB. The value of I_x for rectangle $ABCD$ is equal to

$$\frac{bh^3}{12} + Ad^2 = \frac{10 \cdot 2^3}{12} + 20(3)^2$$
$$= 186.67 \text{ in}^4.$$

Here, the term $\dfrac{10 \cdot 2^3}{12}$ is the value of I for rectangle $ABCD$ with respect to a line through its *own* centroid parallel to AB. The distance from this line to line x is 3 in., hence the term $20(3)^2$. Similarly, for the rectangle *EFGH*:

$$\frac{bh^3}{12} + Ad^2 = \frac{2 \cdot 10^3}{12} + 20(3)^2 = 346.67 \text{ in.}^4$$

The centroid of rectangle *EFGH* is 3 in. *below* line x, but, since we use the *square* of the distance, we may ignore the negative sign. Adding the two results we have for the entire area:

$$I_x = 186.67 + 346.67 = 533.3 \text{ in.}^4$$

126. Radius of gyration.—If all the dimensions involved are expressed in inches, the value of I for an area with respect to a line is expressed in *inches to the fourth power* as indicated in the above example.

If we divide I by the area A we obtain a result, expressed in *inches squared*, that is a weighted average of the squares of the distances of the strips from the line. The "weight" given to each distance is the amount of area in the strip. The square root of this average, which is in inches, is called the *radius of gyration of the area with respect to the line.* Denoting it by k, we have

$$k = \sqrt{\frac{I}{A}} \qquad \text{or} \qquad I = Ak^2.$$

Example

For the area shown in Fig. 147 we have found that $I = 533.3$ in^4. The area is 40 sq. in. so that

$$k = \sqrt{\frac{533.3 \text{ in.}^4}{40 \text{ in.}^2}} = 3.65 \text{ in.} \qquad \text{(approximately)}$$

The radius of gyration of the area with respect to the line is 3.65 in. The value of I_x is equal to the entire area (40 sq. in.) multiplied by the *square* of this distance, and is thus the same as if all the area were concentrated at this distance from the line.

PROBLEMS

In Prob. 1 to 6 find both I_x and I_y for the given area:

1. The area bounded by the parabola $y^2 = 5x$ and the line $x = 5$.

2. The area bounded by the ellipse $\dfrac{x^2}{a^2} + \dfrac{y^2}{b^2} = 1$.

3. The area bounded by the x-axis and the parabola $y = 4 - x^2$.

4. The area bounded by the curve $y = x^3$, the x-axis, and the line $x = 2$.

5. The area bounded by the coordinate axes, the curve $y = e^x$, and the line $x = 1$.

6. The area under the curve $y = \cos x$ in the interval from $x = 0$ to $\frac{1}{2}\pi$.

7. Compute I_y for the area under the curve $y = \dfrac{8}{x^2 + 4}$ in the interval from $x = 0$ to 2.

8. Compute I_y for the area bounded by the x-axis and the curve $y = 4x - x^2$.

9. Find the value of I for the area of a circle with respect to a tangent line without using the Parallel-axis Theorem.

10. Compute I_x for the area under one arch of the curve $y = \sin x$, using strips that are perpendicular to the x-axis. HINT: Such a strip is a rectangle, and in accordance with the result of example 1, page 291, its second moment is $bh^3/3$ or $y^3 dx/3$. Therefore $I = \frac{1}{3}\displaystyle\int_0^\pi y^3 dx$.

11. Show that I_x for the area of the right triangle with vertices at $(0, 0)$, $(b, 0)$, and $(0, h)$, is $bh^3/12$.

12. Show that I_b for the area of any triangle with base b and altitude h is $bh^3/12$.

13. Find the value of I for the area of a triangle of base b and altitude h with respect to a line through its centroid parallel to the base.   HINT: Compute I with respect to the base (Prob. 12) and use the Parallel-axis Theorem.

14. The sides of a rectangle are 3 in. and 4 in.   Compute the second moment of its area with respect to a diagonal.

15. An isosceles trapezoid has bases 12 in. and 6 in., and its altitude is 4 in.   Find the second moment of its area with respect to the longer base.

16. The shaded area in Fig. 148a represents the cross section of a hollow column.   Compute the value of I for this area with respect to a line through its centroid parallel to a side of the square.

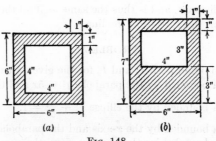

FIG. 148.

17. The shaded area in Fig. 148b represents the cross section of a hollow column.   Locate its centroid, draw a line through this point parallel to the 6 in. sides, and find the second moment of the area with respect to this line.

In each of the following cases compute the second moment of the given area with respect to lines AA' and BB' which go through its centroid:

18. The area of Fig. 149a.
19. The area of Fig. 149b.
20. The area of Fig. 149c.

21. Suppose that an area is symmetrical with respect to the x-axis. What general statement can be made about the values of its first and second moments with respect to this axis?

22. The first moment of the area of the circle $x^2 + y^2 = r^2$ with respect to the x-axis is zero, that of the bottom half canceling that of the top half.   Why is this not also true of the second moment?

23. Find the radius of gyration of the area of a rectangle having sides b and h, with respect to side b.

24. Find the radius of gyration of the area of a circle with respect to a diameter.

25. The area of the cross section of a 9-in. American Standard *I*-beam is 10.22 sq. in. The radii of gyration with respect to its two axes of symmetry are 3.30 in. and 0.84 in., respectively. Compute the corresponding values of *I*.

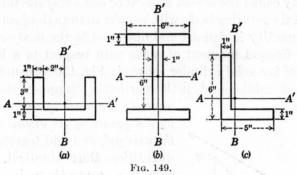

FIG. 149.

26. Same as Prob. 25 for the 15-in. beam. In this case the area of the cross section is 21.85 sq. in., and the radii of gyration are 5.61 and 1.18 in.

127. Second moment of mass with respect to a plane.—

The second moment of the mass of a body with respect to a plane is defined in the same way as the first moment, the only difference being that the mass of each slice is multiplied by the *square* of its distance from the plane instead of by the first power of this distance. This quantity is not itself of physical importance. It is used, however, in finding the second moment of a mass with respect to a line—and this latter quantity is of fundamental importance in the dynamics of rotating bodies.

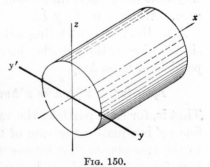

FIG. 150.

Suppose, for example, that a solid cylinder is held with its axis horizontal as indicated in Fig. 150 and then released to swing as a pendulum about the fixed axis yy'. Let it be required to determine the rotational velocity of the cylinder when it passes through the lowest position and the pull which it exerts upon the supports at that instant.   These are problems of mechanics which we shall not solve here.   We wish merely to point out that in order to solve them one must know the value of a quantity called the *second moment* or *moment of inertia* of the mass of the rotating body with respect to the axis of rotation. This quantity is defined and discussed in the next section.

128. Second moment of mass with respect to a line.— Think of the solid cylinder shown in Fig. 150 as being composed of millions of little particles.   Suppose that we

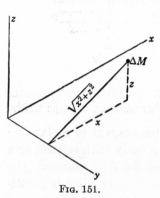

FIG. 151.

multiply the mass of each particle by the square of its distance from the axis yy', and add together the quantities thus obtained.   The resulting quantity is called the *second moment* or *moment of inertia* of the mass of the body with respect to the line yy'.   More precisely, the second moment is the *limit* approached by this sum when the number of particles is increased indefinitely in such a way that the largest dimension of each particle approaches zero.   We denote it by I_y.

A method of calculating this quantity results from the simple observation, made clear by Fig. 151, that for *any* particle of mass Δm,

$$I_y = (x^2 + z^2)\Delta m = x^2\Delta m + z^2\Delta m = I_{yz} + I_{xy}.$$

That is, for each particle, the value of I with respect to the line yy' is equal to the sum of the values of I with respect to the two planes that intersect in this line.   Since this is true for each particle, it is true for the sum of n particles and for the limit of the sum.   We have, then, the following:

Theorem: *The second moment of the mass of a body with respect to a line is equal to the sum of its second moments with respect to any two planes that intersect at right angles along this line.*

In the case of the cylinder shown in Fig. 150 the value of I_{yz} can be found easily by dividing it into slices parallel

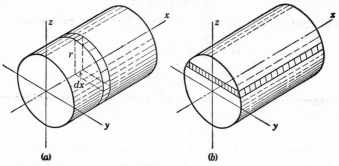

(a)   (b)

FIG. 152.

to the yz-plane. Thus (Fig. 152a),

$$I_{yz} = \int x^2 dm = \int_0^h x^2 \cdot \delta\pi r^2 dx = \frac{\delta\pi r^2 h^3}{3} = \tfrac{1}{3}mh^2.$$

Similarly, using slices parallel to the xy-plane (Fig. 152b),

$$I_{xy} = \int z^2 dm = \int_{-r}^r z^2 \cdot \delta 2 \sqrt{r^2 - z^2}\, h\, dz$$

$$= 4\delta h \int_0^r z^2 \sqrt{r^2 - z^2}\, dz$$

$$= 4\delta h r^4 \int_0^{\frac{\pi}{2}} \sin^2 \theta \cos^2 \theta\, d\theta$$

$$\text{(letting } z = r \sin \theta\text{)}$$

$$= \frac{\delta\pi r^4 h}{4} = \tfrac{1}{4}mr^2.$$

Adding the results, we have

$$I_y = \tfrac{1}{3}mh^2 + \tfrac{1}{4}mr^2.$$

129. Solids of revolution.—For a solid of revolution, the value of I with respect to the axis of revolution can be found by the cylindrical shell method.

Example

A solid cylinder of radius r and height h is generated by revolving a rectangle about one side as shown in Fig. 153. The strip shown generates a cylindrical shell for which

$$dm = \delta \cdot 2\pi xh\, dx.$$

This mass lies at a distance x from the axis of revolution (z-axis), so that for it the second moment is

$$x^2 \cdot \delta \cdot 2\pi x h \, dx.$$

The integral from $x = 0$ to $x = r$ gives I_z for the entire cylinder:

$$I_z = \int_0^r x^2 \cdot \delta \cdot 2\pi x h \, dx$$
$$= 2\pi h \delta \int_0^r x^3 dx = \frac{\pi r^4 h \delta}{2}.$$

It is convenient to express the result in terms of the mass m of the cylinder. Since $m = \pi r^2 h \delta$, we have

$$I = \tfrac{1}{2} m r^2.$$

Another method of computing the second moment with respect to the axis of revolution, is to divide the solid into

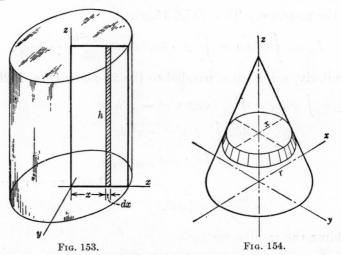

FIG. 153.   FIG. 154.

disks by passing planes perpendicular to this axis. Each disk is a circular cylinder, and by virtue of the above result its second moment is $\tfrac{1}{2}(\Delta m) r^2$ where Δm is its mass.

Example

By passing planes parallel to the xy-plane, the solid cone shown in Fig. 154 is divided into disks. The mass of a disk is

$$\Delta m = \delta \cdot \pi x^2 dz.$$

For this disk the value of I_z is

$$\tfrac{1}{2}(\Delta m) x^2 = \tfrac{1}{2}(\delta \pi x^2 dz) x^2 = \tfrac{1}{2} \delta \pi x^4 dz.$$

The integral from $z = 0$ to $z = h$ gives the required moment:

$$I_z = \tfrac{1}{2}\delta\pi \int_0^h x^4 dz.$$

To express x in terms of z, we use similar triangles:

$$\frac{x}{r} = \frac{h-z}{h} \qquad \text{or} \qquad x = \frac{r}{h}(h-z).$$

Finally then,

$$I_z = \frac{\delta\pi r^4}{2h^4} \int_0^h (h-z)^4 dz$$

$$= \frac{\delta\pi r^4}{2h^4} \cdot \frac{h^5}{5} = \tfrac{1}{10}(\pi r^2 h \delta)r^2.$$

If we replace $\tfrac{1}{3}\pi r^2 h \delta$ by m we can write the result in the form

$$I_z = \tfrac{3}{10}mr^2.$$

The problem could also of course be solved by the cylindrical shell method.

130. The Parallel-axis Theorem.—When the second moment of the mass of a solid with respect to a line through its centroid is known, that with respect to any line parallel to this can be found by means of the following:

Theorem: *If I_g is the second moment of the mass of a solid with respect to a line through its centroid and I_l is the second moment with respect to a line l parallel to this, then*

$$I_l = I_g + md^2$$

where m is the mass of the solid and d is the distance between the two lines.

PROOF: Take the plane determined by l and g as the xy-plane and let the y-axis coincide with g as shown in Fig. 155. Then for any particle of mass Δm in the body,

$$I_l = [z^2 + (x+d)^2]\Delta m$$
$$= (z^2 + x^2)\Delta m + (2d)x\,\Delta m + d^2\Delta m.$$

Let us now sum these three terms separately for all the particles in the body. We have

$$\Sigma(x^2 + z^2)\Delta m = I_g; \qquad 2d\Sigma x\,\Delta m = 0; \qquad d^2\Sigma\,\Delta m = md^2.$$

The theorem follows immediately from these results. It should be observed that $\Sigma x\,\Delta m = 0$ only because the line g passes through the centroid of the body.

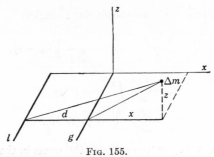

Fig. 155.

131. Radius of gyration.—Suppose that the value of I for the mass of a body with respect to a line be divided by the mass m of the body. The result may be regarded as a weighted average of the squares of the distances of the particles from the line. The square root of this average is called the *radius of gyration* of the mass with respect to the line. It represents the distance from the line at which *all* of the mass could be considered concentrated without changing its value of I. Denoting it by k, we have

$$k = \sqrt{\frac{I}{m}}.$$

Consider, as an example, the case of the solid cylinder. We have already found that, with respect to its axis, $I = \frac{1}{2}mr^2$. Dividing by m and taking the square root, we have

$$k = \frac{r}{\sqrt{2}} = 0.707r.$$

That is, the value of I for this mass is the same as if all the mass were concentrated at a distance of about $0.7r$ from the axis.

The moment of inertia with respect to the axis of rotation of an irregular rotating part such as a crankshaft, flywheel, or connecting rod, is often specified most conveniently by stating its radius of gyration or "equivalent radius." The value of I is computed from this by means of the relation

$$I = mk^2.$$

There are experimental methods of determining I or k for such irregular bodies. They involve such procedures, for example, as using the body as a compound pendulum or torsion pendulum, the value of I or k being computed from the observed periods of the motion.

132. Polar second moment of area.—Corresponding to the second moment of the mass of a cylinder with respect to its axis we have, in two dimensions, the second moment of the area of a circle with respect to its center. It can be defined as follows: Divide the circle into n concentric rings; multiply the area in each ring by the square of the distance of the ring from the center; add the quantities so obtained, and find the limit of this sum when the width of each ring approaches zero and $n \to \infty$. The result is (Fig. 156)

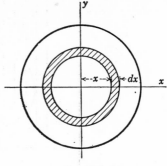

Fig. 156.

$$I_0 = \lim_{\Delta x_i \to 0} \sum_{i=1}^{n} (x_i)^2 (2\pi x_i \Delta x_i) = \int_0^r x^2 (2\pi x \, dx) = \frac{\pi r^4}{2}.$$

This quantity is often called the *polar moment of inertia* of the area of the circle. It is used in calculating the shearing stress produced in a circular shaft when it is subjected to a twisting moment or torque—as is the case when it is transmitting power.

A general definition of the second moment of a plane area with respect to a point in its plane is suggested by Fig. 157. We let ΔA denote a rectangular area element having dimensions Δx and Δy. We multiply the area of each such element by the square of its distance from the origin and add, thus obtaining a sum in which each term has the form $(x^2 + y^2)\Delta A$. We then take the limit of this sum when each Δx and each Δy approaches zero. This double summation leads to a *double integral* and its consideration will be postponed until the topic of multiple integrals is studied (Chap. XXVI).

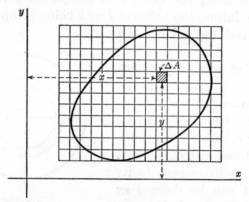

FIG. 157.

We wish at present to point out, however, that for each element of area

$$(x^2 + y^2)\Delta A = x^2 \Delta A + y^2 \Delta A.$$

From this it can be shown that

$$I_0 = I_x + I_y.$$

The second moment of a plane area with respect to a point in its plane is equal to the sum of its second moments with respect to any two lines that lie in the plane and intersect at right angles at this point.

Example

We have already found that for the area of the circle $x^2 + y^2 = r^2$, $I_x = I_y = \pi r^4 / 4$. Using the above theorem, we have

$$I_0 = I_x + I_y = \frac{\pi r^4}{4} + \frac{\pi r^4}{4} = \frac{\pi r^4}{2}.$$

This checks with the result obtained above by dividing the circle into rings.

PROBLEMS

In Probs. 1 to 6 compute the second moment of the mass of the given solid (assumed to be homogeneous) with respect to the given line:

1. A right circular cone with respect to its axis using the cylindrical shell method.

2. A sphere with respect to a diameter using both the shell and disk methods.

3. A right circular cylinder with respect to an element.

4. The ellipsoid whose surface has the equation $\dfrac{x^2}{a^2} + \dfrac{y^2}{b^2} + \dfrac{z^2}{c^2} = 1$, with respect to the x-axis.

5. A cube with respect to an edge.

6. A right pyramid with square base of side a and altitude h, with respect to a line through its apex perpendicular to its base.

7. Compute I_x for the mass of the solid generated when the area under the curve $y = 2\sqrt{x}$ in the interval from $x = 0$ to 4 is revolved about the x-axis.

8. Compute I_x for the mass of the solid generated when the area under one arch of the curve $y = \sin x$ is revolved about the x-axis. Use the disk method.

9. A solid is generated by revolving the area under the curve $y = 4 - x^2$ in the interval from $x = 0$ to 2 about the y-axis. Compute the second moment of its mass with respect to the y-axis.

10. Show that the second moment of the mass of a long thin rod with respect to an axis through one end perpendicular to the rod is approximately $\frac{1}{3}ml^2$ where l is its length. Explain why this is not the exact value. HINT: Let the rod lie along the x-axis and show that $I_{yz} = \frac{1}{3}ml^2$. Then $I_y = I_{yz} + I_{xy}$ but I_{xy} is comparatively small. Why?

11. Find the second moment of the mass of a solid right circular cone with respect to a diameter of its base. HINT: Add the value of I with respect to the plane of the base to one-half the value of I with respect to the axis of the cone. Why?

12. Find the second moment of the mass of a solid right circular cone with respect to a line through its apex perpendicular to its axis. See hint in Prob. 11 and use a similar method.

13. A solid sphere rotates about an axis tangent to its surface. Compute the second moment of its mass with respect to this axis.

14. A rectangular slab 2 ft. long, 1 ft. wide, and 2 in. thick rotates about one of the 2-in. edges. Compute the second moment of its mass with respect to this axis.

15. The two faces of a triangular slab 2 in. thick are right triangles having legs $AC = 2$ ft. and $BC = 1$ ft. Compute the second moment of its mass with respect to the 2-in. edge through C.

16. The dimensions of a flat rectangular slab of mass m are b ft. and h ft. Show that with respect to axes that pass through g and A, respectively, perpendicular to the faces of the slab, we have (Fig. 158a)

$$I_g = \frac{m}{12}\,(b^2 + h^2);$$

$$I_A = \frac{m}{12}\,(b^2 + 4h^2).$$

17. A flat slab consists of a 2-ft. square surmounted by a semicircle and containing a hole 1 ft. square as shown in Fig. 158c. The semicircular part weighs 6 lb. and the weight of the remainder is 9 lb. Compute the second moment of this mass with respect to an axis through A

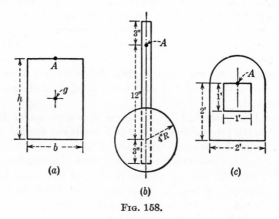

(a)

(b)

(c)

FIG. 158.

perpendicular to the faces of the slab. HINT: Use the results of Prob. 16. Divide weight by $g(= 32.2)$ to find mass.

18. A pendulum consists of a slender rod to which is attached a solid disk as shown in Fig. 158b. The rod is 18 in. long and weighs 3 lb. The axis of rotation passes through A perpendicular to the plane of the paper. Compute the moment of inertia of the mass with respect to this axis and find the corresponding radius of gyration. HINT: Use result of Prob. 10 on pieces of rod above and below A. Use result of example on p. 299 and the Parallel-axis Theorem on disk. Use all dimensions in feet if mass is found by dividing weight by 32.2 (ft./sec.²).

19. If a body rotates about a fixed axis, its kinetic energy is $\frac{1}{2}I\omega^2$ where I is the second moment of its mass with respect to that axis and ω is its angular velocity. A sphere and a disk having the same mass and radius rotate about their geometrical axes at the same speed. Compare their kinetic energies.

20. A flywheel 9 ft. in diameter weighs 4.5 tons and its radius of gyration with respect to its axis of rotation is 3.8 ft. Compute the corresponding value of I.

21. An ellipse has semiaxes a and b. Compute the second moment of its area with respect to its center.

22. Find the second moment of the area of a square with respect to one corner.

23. Find the second moment of the area of a rectangle with respect to its center.

24. A hollow steel shaft has internal diameter 6 in. and external diameter 8 in. Compute the polar second moment of the area of its cross section.

25. A hollow steel shaft with outside radius r has its inside radius equal to $\frac{1}{2}r$. Show that the polar second moment of the area of its cross section is equal to $\frac{15}{16}$ of that of a solid shaft of radius r.

CHAPTER XXIII

LIQUID PRESSURE. WORK

133. Fluid pressure.—Using the equilibrium principle of statics, it can be shown that the pressure at any point in a liquid is the same in all directions. It can furthermore be demonstrated that at a depth of h ft. below the free surface of a liquid that weighs w lb. per cubic foot the pressure is

$$p = wh \text{ lb. per square foot.}$$

The pressure (per unit area) thus increases *linearly* with increasing depth, the rate of increase being equal to the

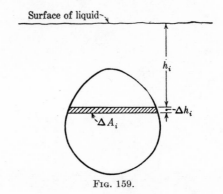

Fig. 159.

weight per cubic unit of the liquid. In this chapter we shall always use the term pressure to mean the *force per unit area*.

134. Resultant force on a plane vertical wall.—We consider now the problem of computing the resultant force exerted on one side of a flat plate by a liquid in which it is submerged vertically. The procedure is as follows (Fig. 159):

308

1. Divide the submerged area into n strips parallel to the liquid surface and denote their areas by ΔA_1, ΔA_2, $\cdots$, ΔA_n.

2. Multiply the area of each strip by the pressure at a point in this strip, and add the quantities so obtained; *i.e.*, form the sum

$$\sum_{i=1}^{n} (wh_i)\Delta A_i.$$

3. Find the limit of this sum when the width of each strip approaches zero and $n \to \infty$. This limit is, by definition, the resultant force against the area. Thus (Fig. 159)

$$F = \lim_{\Delta h_i \to 0} \sum_{i=1}^{n} wh_i \Delta A_i = \int wh \, dA.$$

Example

Find the magnitude of the resultant force against the face of the dam shown in Fig. 160 when the water is 12 ft. deep.

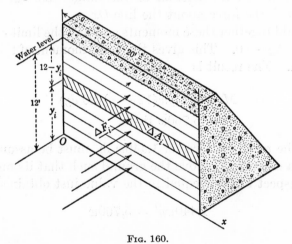

Fig. 160.

Solution

The area of a strip is

$$dA = 20 \, dy \qquad \text{(sq. ft.)}.$$

With our choice of a coordinate system the depth of the strip below the water surface is $(12-y)$ ft., and the pressure at this depth is

$$w(12-y) \qquad \text{(lb. per square foot)}.$$

The force against the strip is then

$$wh \, dA \,=\, w(12 \,-\, y)(20 \, dy) \qquad \text{(lb.)}.$$

Finally, the total or *resultant* force against the face of the dam is

$$F \,=\, \int_0^{12} w(12 \,-\, y)(20 \, dy)$$
$$=\, 1440w \,=\, 1440(62.4) \,=\, 89{,}900 \text{ lb}.$$

135. Center of pressure.—The forces ΔF_1, ΔF_2, $\cdots$, ΔF_n of the water against the strips of area in Fig. 160 constitute a system of parallel forces. To determine completely the resultant of such a system we must know not only its magnitude, which we have already found, but also its position; *i.e.*, we must find the height y' above the ground at which the resultant force of 89,900 lb. must be assumed to act. This may be found as follows:

1. Multiply the magnitude of each force ΔF_i by its distance above the bottom of the dam. This gives the *moment* of the force about the line Ox.

2. Add together these moments and find the limit of their sum as $\Delta y_i \rightarrow 0$. This gives the total moment of the force system. The result is

$$M \,=\, \int_0^{12} yw(12 \,-\, y)(20 \, dy)$$
$$=\, 5{,}760w \text{ ft.-lb.}$$

3. The resultant force of 1,440w lb. must be assumed to act at a distance y' above the ground such that its moment with respect to Ox is equal to the value just obtained; *i.e.*,

$$1{,}440wy' \,=\, 5{,}760w$$

or

$$y' \,=\, 4 \text{ ft}.$$

It is clear that the water tends both to push the dam back and to turn it over. We have found that, with respect to both of these items, the effect is the same as that of a concentrated force of 89,900 lb. applied at a point 4 ft. above

the base.   The point of application of this resultant force
is called the *center of pressure*.

136. The general case of a submerged plane surface.—
Consider a submerged thin plate whose plane makes an
angle α with the plane of the liquid surface and intersects
this surface in a line PP'.   In Fig. 161 this line is perpendicular to the paper and is
represented by point P.

The resultant force of the
liquid against one side of the
plate is normal to this surface and we state now two
general theorems concern-
ing its magnitude and
position.

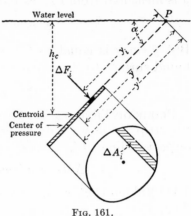

Fig. 161.

Theorem I: *The magnitude of the resultant force is
equal to the product of the
area and the pressure at its
centroid.   That is,*

$$F = wh_cA,$$

where h_c *denotes the depth of the centroid below the free surface
of the liquid.*

Theorem II: *The distance from the line PP' to the center
of pressure, measured along the plane of the plate, is*

$$y' = \frac{k^2}{\bar{y}},$$

*where k is the radius of gyration of the area with respect to the
line PP' and $\bar{y}$ is the distance from PP' to the centroid.*

The proofs of these theorems are given below, some
details being left to the student.

PROOF OF THEOREM I: Dividing the area into strips and
noting that the depth of ith strip is $y_i \sin \alpha$ we have, for the
force on this strip,

$$\Delta F_i = w(y_i \sin \alpha)\Delta A_i.$$

The total force on the plate is, then,

$$F = \int wy \sin \alpha \, dA$$
$$= w \sin \alpha \int y \, dA.$$

The value of $\int y \, dA$ is the first moment of the area of the plate with respect to PP' and is of course equal to $\bar{y}A$ where $\bar{y}$ is measured from PP' as indicated in the figure.   Hence,

$$F = w \sin \alpha \, \bar{y}A.$$

But $\bar{y} \sin \alpha$ is equal to the vertical distance h_c from the liquid surface to the centroid; consequently,

$$F = wh_cA.$$

PROOF OF THEOREM II: Multiplying the force against the ith strip by y_i we obtain the moment of this force with respect to line PP'.   Thus,

$$\Delta M_i = y_i(wy_i \sin \alpha \, \Delta A_i).$$

The total moment of the force system with respect to PP' is, then,

$$M = w \sin \alpha \int y^2 dA.$$

But $\int y^2 dA$ is the second moment of the area of the plate with respect to PP' and is equal to Ak^2 where k is the corresponding radius of gyration.   Consequently,

$$M = w \sin \alpha \, Ak^2.$$

The resultant force, whose magnitude was obtained in Theorem I, must act at a distance y' from PP' so that its moment with respect to PP' is equal to the value just obtained; *i.e.*,

$$(w \sin \alpha \, \bar{y}A)y' = w \sin \alpha \, Ak^2.$$

Solving for y' we have

$$y' = \frac{k^2}{\bar{y}}.$$

Example

Find the magnitude and position of the resultant force against the dam shown in Fig. 160, using the above general theorems.

Solution

The depth of the centroid is 6 ft. and the pressure at this point is $6w$ lb. per square foot. The area is 240 sq. ft. The resultant force is, then,

$$F = 240(6w) = 1,440w \text{ lb.}$$

The value of k^2, with respect to the water line, is

$$k^2 = \frac{I}{A} = \frac{\dfrac{20(12^3)}{3}}{240} = 48.$$

The distance of the center of pressure below the surface of the water is

$$y' = \frac{k^2}{\bar{y}} = \frac{48}{6} = 8 \text{ ft.}$$

PROBLEMS

1. A rectangular plate is 4 ft. long and 2 ft. wide. It is submerged vertically in water with the upper 4-ft. edge parallel to and 3 ft. below

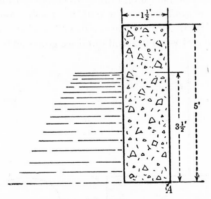

Fig. 162.

the surface. Find the magnitude and position of the resultant force against one side of the plate both with and without using Theorems I and II.

2. A rectangular plate is l ft. long and h ft. wide. It is submerged vertically in a liquid with an edge of length l in the surface. Show that the depth of the center of pressure is $\frac{2}{3}h$ both with and without using Theorem II.

3. Fig. 162 shows the cross section of a retaining wall that is subjected on one side to the pressure of a mixture of mud, sand, and water to a depth of $3\frac{1}{2}$ ft. Assuming the action of this mixture to be equivalent to that of a liquid weighing 110 lb. per cubic foot. compute the force

against a section of the wall 10 ft. long.   Find the moment of this force
with respect to the edge of the wall through A.   This moment measures
the tendency of the force to overturn the wall.

4. The edges of a triangular plate are 5, 5, and 6 ft.   It is submerged
vertically in water with the 6-ft. edge in the water surface.   Find the
force against one side both with and without using Theorem I.

5. The edges of a cubical box are each 6 ft.   The box contains liquid
concrete weighing 250 lb. per cubic foot to a depth of 3 ft.   Find the
magnitude and position of the resultant force against one side.

6. Suppose that in Prob. 5 the side is held in place by four screws,
one at each corner.   Compute the tensile forces in these screws.

7. A cylindrical tank 4 ft. in diameter and 6 ft. long has its axis
horizontal.   It is half full of oil weighing 50 lb. per cubic foot.   Find
the force exerted against one end both with and without using Theorem I.

8. A circular gate in the vertical face of a dam is 4 ft. in diameter.
Find the force on it when the water level is 3 ft. above the top of the
gate.

9. The cross section of an oil tank is an ellipse with major and minor
axes 6 and 4 ft., respectively.   The tank has its axis and the major axis
of the ends horizontal.   Find the force on the upper half and on the
lower half of one end when it is full of oil weighing 50 lb. per cubic foot.

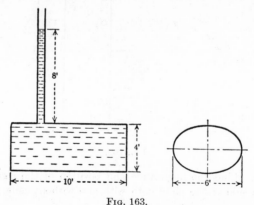

Fig. 163.

10. Find the force against one end of the elliptical tank shown in
Fig. 163.

11. A trough 6 ft. long has a trapezoidal cross section as shown in
Fig. 164.   Find the magnitude and position of the resultant force against
the vertical end $ABCD$ when the trough is full of water.

12. Find the magnitude and position of the resultant force against
the sloping side $BEFD$ of the trough shown in Fig. 164 when it is full of
water.

13. The two sloping sides of a triangular trough 12 ft. long are inclined at 45° to the horizontal.   Find the force on these sides and also on the ends when the water is 2 ft. deep.

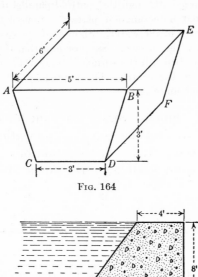

FIG. 164

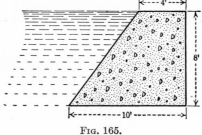

FIG. 165.

14. Find the magnitude and the position of the resultant force of the water against the face of the dam shown in Fig. 165.   Show that the vertical component of this force is equal to the weight of the wedge of water resting on the dam.   The length of the dam is 20 ft.

15. An opening in a dam has the form shown in Fig. 166.   Where should a single horizontal prop be placed if it is to hold in place a plate which covers the opening?   What compressive force would be exerted on the prop?

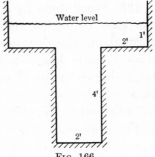

FIG. 166.

16. Show that the relation $y' = k^2/\bar{y}$ may also be written in the form $y' = I/M$ where I and M denote, respectively, the second and first moments of the area.

17. Show that the location of the center of pressure is given by the equation $y' = \bar{y} + \dfrac{k^2}{\bar{y}}$ where k denotes the radius of gyration of the area with respect to an axis through the centroid parallel to PP' (Fig. 161).

18. Suppose that a rectangular plate is submerged vertically with edge b in the surface of the water. Show that the center of pressure is at a depth $\tfrac{2}{3}h$ below the surface. Suppose now that the plate be pushed farther and farther beneath the surface. Show that the center of pressure remains below the centroid but approaches the centroid as the depth increases indefinitely.

137. Work.—Suppose that a constant force of F lb. acts upon a body and that the point of application of the force moves a distance d ft. in the direction of the force.   The product of the magnitude of the force and the distance

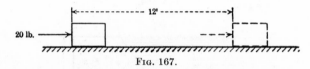

Fig. 167.

moved is called the *work* done by the force on the body during the motion.   Denoting it by U, we have

$$U = Fd \text{ ft.-lb.}$$

Thus, the work done by the 20 lb.-force indicated in Fig. 167 in pushing the block a distance of 12 ft. is $20(12) = 240$ ft.-lb.

138. Work done by a variable force.—We consider now the case in which the force does not remain constant throughout the distance interval but varies according to some definite law, say $F = f(x)$, from a value F_1 at the beginning to a value F_2 at the end of the interval.   The way in which the force varies might be represented graphically as indicated in Fig. 168.

The work done by the variable force in the interval from $x = a$ to $x = b$ may be calculated as follows:

1. Divide the interval into n subintervals having directed lengths $\Delta x_1, \Delta x_2, \cdots, \Delta x_n$.

2. Multiply the length of each subinterval by the value of the force at some point in this interval and add the quantities so obtained; *i.e.*, form the sum

$$\sum_{i=1}^{n} f(x_i)\Delta x_i.$$

3. Find the limit of this sum when each $\Delta x \to 0$ and $n \to \infty$. By definition, this limit is the work done by the variable

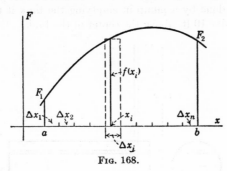

FIG. 168.

force. Thus

$$U = \lim_{\Delta x_i \to 0} \sum_{i=1}^{n} f(x_i)\Delta x_i = \int_a^b f(x)dx.$$

It is immediately evident that the work done is represented geometrically by the (algebraic) area under the force-displacement graph in the interval from $x = a$ to $x = b$.

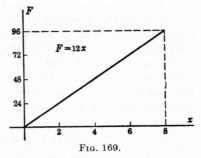

FIG. 169.

Example 1

The force required to stretch a spring is directly proportional to the elongation, the force being 12 lb. when it is stretched 1 in. Find the work done in stretching it 8 in. beyond its free length.

Solution

As the spring is stretched, the applied force varies linearly from 0 to 96 lb. as indicated in Fig. 169. When it has been stretched x in. the force at that instant is $F = 12x$ lb.   The work done is, then,

$$U = \int_0^8 12x\, dx = 384 \text{ in.-lb.}$$

It should be observed that this result may also be obtained by multiplying the total elongation of the spring by the value of the force at the mid-point of the stretch.   Why?

Example 2

The tank shown in Fig. 170 is full of oil weighing 50 lb. per cubic foot. Find the work done by a pump in emptying the tank if the oil is discharged at a point 10 ft. above the center of the tank.

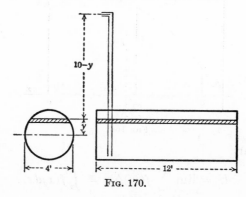

FIG. 170.

Solution

We may divide the oil into a large number of slices as indicated in the figure.   The force required to lift a slice is equal to its weight.   The work done on each slice is the product of this force and the distance through which the slice must be lifted.   Hence, taking a slice at a distance y from the x-axis (assumed through the center of one end) we have
Weight of slice $= 2 \sqrt{4 - y^2}\,(12)(50)dy = 1{,}200 \sqrt{4 - y^2}\, dy$.
Distance to be lifted $= 10 - y$.
Work done on slice $= 1{,}200 \sqrt{4 - y^2}\,(10 - y)dy$.
The total work done is obtained by integrating this expression between limits that cover all the slices; $i.e.$, from $y = -2$ to $y = +2$.   Thus,

$$U = 1{,}200 \int_{-2}^{+2} \sqrt{4 - y^2}\,(10 - y)dy$$
$$= 24{,}000\pi \text{ ft.-lb.}$$

The student should observe that it would not be permissible to integrate from 0 to 2 and double the result.   Why?

PROBLEMS

1. A certain spring requires a force of 12 lb. to stretch it $\frac{1}{2}$ in. Find the work done in stretching it 3 in. beyond its free length.

2. The free length of a spring is 12 in. A force of 8 lb. is required to stretch it 1 in. How much work is done in stretching it from a length of 14 in. to a length of 16 in.?

3. The spring on a bumping post in a freight yard is compressed 1 in. by a force of 36,000 lb. Find the work done in compressing it $\frac{1}{2}$ in.

4. A force $F = f(x)$ acts on a body in the direction of its motion from $x = a$ to $x = b$. Give an appropriate definition of the *average* value of F (with respect to x) over the interval, and explain the physical significance of this average force.

5. A force F(lb.) acts on a body in the direction of its motion and varies in magnitude in accordance with the law $F = 4\sqrt{x}$ where x is the distance moved (ft.). Make the graph showing how F varies with x and calculate the work done in the interval from $x = 1$ to $x = 9$ ft. Find the average value of F over this interval. See Prob. 4.

6. Same as Prob. 5 for the case in which $F = \dfrac{3x}{\sqrt{x+4}}$, the interval being from $x = 0$ to $x = 5$ ft.

7. Same as Prob. 5 for the case in which $F = 8 \sin \pi x/2$, the interval being from $x = 0$ to $x = 4$ ft.

8. A cable 80 ft. long and weighing 4 lb. per foot hangs from a windlass. Find the work done in winding it up.

9. A cable weighing 5 lb. per foot is wound on a drum and supports a weight of 1,400 lb. If the weight is originally 100 ft. below the drum, find the work done in lifting it 60 ft.

10. A cistern has the form of a right circular cylinder 6 ft. in diameter and 12 ft. deep. It contains water to a depth of 8 ft. Find the work done in emptying the cistern if the pump lifts the water to a point 2 ft. above the ground. Show that the result is the same as if the mass of water were concentrated at its centroid.

11. Find the work done in pumping half of the oil from the tank in Example 2, page 318.

12. A tank has the form of a right circular cylinder 4 ft. in diameter and 12 ft. long. It lies with its axis horizontal, and is filled with oil weighing 50 lb. per cubic foot. Find the work done in emptying the tank if the oil is pumped to a point 8 ft. above the center of the tank.

13. The cross section of a cylindrical tank 12 ft. long is an ellipse with axes 6 ft. and 4 ft., respectively. The tank lies with its axis and the major axis of the end horizontal and is full of oil weighing 50 lb. per cubic foot. Find the work done in emptying the tank if the oil is pumped to a point 4 ft. above its center.

14. Solve Prob. 13 if the tank is initially half full of oil.

15. A hemispherical vat 8 ft. in diameter is full of a liquid weighing 60 lb. per cubic foot. Find the work done in pumping the liquid to a point 4 ft. above the top of the vat.

16. A hemispherical vat 10 ft. in diameter is filled with a liquid weighing 60 lb. per cubic foot. Find the work done in lowering the level 3 ft. if the liquid is discharged 5 ft. above the top of the vat.

17. A vat consists of a right circular cylinder to which is attached a hemispherical bottom. The cylinder is 6 ft. in diameter and 4 ft. high and the vat is filled with a liquid weighing 50 lb. per cubic foot. Find the work done in pumping the liquid to the top of the vat.

18. A volume v_1 of air at pressure p_1 is confined in a cylindrical chamber fitted with a piston. The air is then allowed to expand (or is compressed) by moving the piston, and the final volume and pressure are v_2 and p_2. Show that the work done by the gas is

$$U = \int_{v_1}^{v_2} p \, dv.$$

HINT: The force on the piston is pA where A is its area. Then $U = \int F \, dx = \int pA \, dx$ and $A \, dx = dv$.

19. A quantity of gas having a volume of 60 cu. in. and pressure of 40 lb. per square inch is allowed to expand in a cylinder as described in Prob. 18 until its volume is doubled. Compute the work done by the gas on the piston assuming that the law $pv = k$ applies.

20. Compute the work done in compressing 300 cu. ft. of air at a pressure of 20 lb. per square inch to a volume of 40 cu. ft. assuming that the law $pv = k$ applies. See Prob. 18.

21. Compute the work done in compressing 240 cu. ft. of air at a pressure of 15 lb. per square inch to a volume of 30 cu. ft. assuming that the law $pv^n = k$ applies with $n = 1.4$. See Prob. 18.

CHAPTER XXIV

SOLID ANALYTIC GEOMETRY

139. Rectangular coordinates in space.—In this chapter we shall present the fundamentals of three-dimensional analytic geometry, stressing particularly those topics that are essential to the following chapters on partial derivatives and multiple integrals.

We shall use the rectangular coordinate system illustrated by Fig. 171. It consists of three mutually perpendicular *axes* upon which positive directions are chosen as indicated

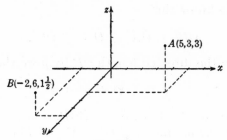

Fig. 171.

by the arrowheads. The plane determined by the x- and y-axes is called the *xy-coordinate plane, etc.* We locate a point in space by giving its directed distances from the three coordinate planes, writing them in the order (x, y, z).

The coordinate planes divide space into eight octants which are characterized by the signs of the coordinates. The octant in which all three coordinates are positive is called the *first* octant. The others are not usually numbered. In Fig. 171, A is in the first octant; B is in the octant in which the coordinates have the signs $(- + +)$.

140. Length and direction of the radius vector OP.—The directed segment OP drawn from the origin to any point

321

$P(x, y, z)$ is called the *radius vector* of P. In order to compute its length we note that OP may be regarded as a diagonal of a rectangular box whose edges have the lengths $OA = x$, $OB = y$, and $OC = z$ (Fig. 172). From solid

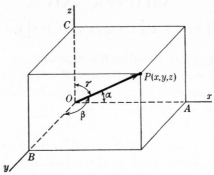

Fig. 172.

geometry we know that

$$\overline{OP}^2 = \overline{OA}^2 + \overline{OB}^2 + \overline{OC}^2.$$

If we denote the directed length OP by ρ we then have

$$\varrho = \sqrt{x^2 + y^2 + z^2}.$$

The angles $\alpha = \angle AOP$, $\beta = \angle BOP$, and $\gamma = \angle COP$ are called the *direction angles* of OP. Each of these is a positive angle not greater than 180°. The cosines of these direction angles are called the *direction cosines* of OP. They are

$$\cos \alpha = \frac{OA}{OP} = \frac{x}{\rho};$$

$$\cos \beta = \frac{OB}{OP} = \frac{y}{\rho};$$

$$\cos \gamma = \frac{OC}{OP} = \frac{z}{\rho}.$$

If we square the direction cosines, and add, we have

$$\cos^2 \alpha + \cos^2 \beta + \cos^2 \gamma = \frac{x^2 + y^2 + z^2}{\rho^2} = \frac{\rho^2}{\rho^2} = 1.$$

The sum of the squares of the direction cosines of OP is equal to one.

If P is in the first octant its coordinates are all positive. In this case the direction cosines of OP are all positive and

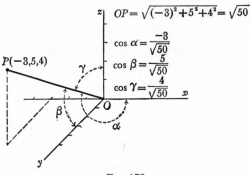

$$OP = \sqrt{(-3)^2 + 5^2 + 4^2} = \sqrt{50}$$

$$\cos \alpha = \frac{-3}{\sqrt{50}}$$

$$\cos \beta = \frac{5}{\sqrt{50}}$$

$$\cos \gamma = \frac{4}{\sqrt{50}}$$

Fig. 173.

its direction angles are all less than 90°. If P has one or more negative coordinates the corresponding direction cosines are negative. The direction angles having negative cosines are between 90 and 180° (including the latter value). A typical case is shown in Fig. 173.

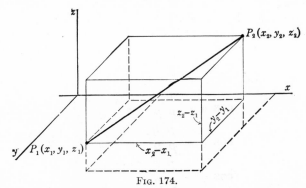

Fig. 174.

141. The distance formula.—Let $P_1(x_1, y_1, z_1)$ and $P_2(x_2, y_2, z_2)$ be any two points. As shown in Fig. 174, the segment P_1P_2 may be regarded as a diagonal of a rectangular box whose edges have the lengths $x_2 - x_1$, $y_2 - y_1$, and $z_2 - z_1$, respectively. If we denote the undirected distance between the points by d, we have immediately

$$d = \sqrt{(x_2 - x_1)^2 + (y_2 - y_1)^2 + (z_2 - z_1)^2}.$$

142. Direction cosines of any directed line.—Let l (Fig. 175) be any directed line and let P_1 and P_2 be two points on it such that the directed segment P_1P_2 is positive.   Through P_1 draw auxiliary axes P_1x', P_1y', and P_1z' parallel to, and having the same positive directions as the x-, y-, and z-axes, respectively.   Then the *direction angles* of l are

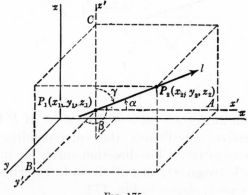

Fig. 175.

α, β, and γ as shown in the figure.   The directed segment P_1P_2 is positive and its length is

$$d = \sqrt{(x_2 - x_1)^2 + (y_2 - y_1)^2 + (z_2 - z_1)^2}.$$

The direction cosines of l are then

$$\cos \alpha = \frac{P_1A}{P_1P_2} = \frac{x_2 - x_1}{d};$$

$$\cos \beta = \frac{P_1B}{P_1P_2} = \frac{y_2 - y_1}{d};$$

$$\cos \gamma = \frac{P_1C}{P_1P_2} = \frac{z_2 - z_1}{d}.$$

Since d is positive, each of these direction cosines is positive or negative depending upon the sign of the numerator. The effect of reversing the positive direction on l is to change the signs of all the direction cosines—and to replace the direction angles by their supplements.

If we square the direction cosines of l, and add, we have the relation

$$\cos^2 \alpha + \cos^2 \beta + \cos^2 \gamma = 1.$$

143. Direction numbers.—If a point moves from A to B along the line shown in Fig. 176, it moves 6 units in the positive x-direction, 3 units in the negative y-direction, and 2 units in the positive z-direction.   The numbers 6, -3, and 2, written in the form

$$6 : -3 : 2$$

may be used to define the *direction* of the line.   They fix its direction by indicating that for every 6 units moved in the x-direction a point traveling along the line must move -3 units in the y-direction and 2 units in the z-direction. Any set of three numbers proportional to these would serve equally well.   Thus, the numbers

$$12 : -6 : 4 \qquad \text{or} \qquad -6 : 3 : -2$$

also define the direction of the line determined by A and B. More generally, if $P_1(x_1, y_1, z_1)$ and $P_2(x_2, y_2, z_2)$ are any two points on a line l then the direction of l is fixed by the *direction numbers*

$$x_2 - x_1 : y_2 - y_1 : z_2 - z_1.$$

Any set of three numbers that can be obtained from these by multiplying all of them by the same nonzero constant k is also a set of direction numbers.

It is obvious that any set of three numbers, not all zero, may be regarded in the above way as defining the direction of a line in space.   It can easily be shown that the direction cosines of a line l having direction numbers $a : b : c$ are

$$\cos \alpha = \frac{a}{\pm \sqrt{a^2 + b^2 + c^2}},$$

$$\cos \beta = \frac{b}{\pm \sqrt{a^2 + b^2 + c^2}},$$

$$\cos \gamma = \frac{c}{\pm \sqrt{a^2 + b^2 + c^2}};$$

where the signs of the denominators are all plus or all minus depending upon which direction on the line is chosen as positive.

Example

If the positive direction on the line shown in Fig. 176 is from A to B, the corresponding direction cosines are

$$\cos \alpha = \frac{6}{+\sqrt{6^2 + (-3)^2 + 2^2}} = +\frac{6}{7};$$

$$\cos \beta = \frac{-3}{+7} = -\frac{3}{7};$$

$$\cos \gamma = \frac{2}{+7} = +\frac{2}{7}.$$

The positive sign was chosen for the radical because α and γ are obviously less than 90° and their cosines are positive.

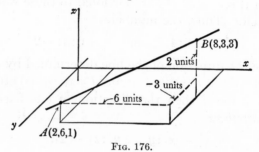

Fig. 176.

PROBLEMS

1. In each of the following, plot the point P and draw the radius vector OP; find its length and direction cosines:

(a) $P(6, 3, 2)$.   (b) $P(-4, 0, 3)$.   (c) $P(6, 6, -3)$.

2. For a certain radius vector OP, $\cos \alpha = \frac{2}{3}$ and $\cos \beta = \frac{1}{3}$. Find two possible values for $\cos \gamma$ and draw the figure.

3. In each of the following cases plot the given points, draw the line joining them, and find its length and direction numbers:

(a) $P(2, 4, 3)$ $Q(8, 1, 1)$.   (b) $A(-3, -3, 1)$ $B(4, 1, 5)$.

4. Draw each of the following triangles, and show that it is a right triangle:

(a) $A(0, 5, 1)$ $B(3, 7, 4)$ $C(6, 1, 5)$.
(b) $A(-4, 0, 5)$ $B(4, 1, 8)$ $C(6, 6, 1)$.

5. Find the coordinates of the point on the z-axis that is equidistant from $A(-2, 6, 1)$ and $B(5, 3, 4)$.

6. A point $P(x, y, z)$ moves so that its distance from $A(-2, 5, 2)$ is always equal to its distance from $B(6, 1, 6)$. Find the equation of the surface on which its moves and describe the surface.

7. Find the equation of the surface all points of which are at a distance of 6 units from the point $(6, 0, 0)$.

8. A point $P(x, y, z)$ moves so that its distance from $F(0, 0, 5)$ is always equal to its distance from the xy-plane. Find the equation of its locus. Sketch this surface.

9. A line goes through $A(-4, 6, 1)$ and has direction numbers $2: -2:1$. What are the coordinates of the point where this line pierces the yz-plane; the xz-plane?

10. Draw each of the following lines. Find its direction numbers and direction cosines. The positive direction in each case is from the first point to the second.

(a) $A(2, 6, 1)$ $B(7, 3, -3)$.   (b) $A(-3, -2, 1)$ $B(4, 2, 5)$.

11. Two of the direction angles of a certain line are $\alpha = 45°$ and $\beta = 60°$. What are its direction cosines if the positive direction is such that γ is an acute angle?

12. A line goes through $P(4, 7, 2)$ and makes equal angles with the coordinate axes. What are the coordinates of the points at which it pierces the coordinate planes?

144. Angle between two directed lines.—Let l_1 and l_2 be two directed lines in space. The angle between them may

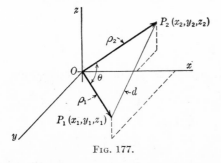

Fig. 177.

be defined as follows: From the origin draw radii vectors OP_1 and OP_2 parallel to l_1 and l_2, respectively, and having their positive directions. The angle P_1OP_2 is then the angle between l_1 and l_2. The cosine of this angle can be found by using the cosine law (Fig. 177).

Let $OP_1 = \rho_1$, $OP_2 = \rho_2$, and $P_1P_2 = d$.   Then

$$d^2 = \rho_1{}^2 + \rho_2{}^2 - 2\rho_1\rho_2 \cos \theta.$$

Solving this for $\cos \theta$ we have

$$\cos \theta = \frac{\rho_1{}^2 + \rho_2{}^2 - d^2}{2\rho_1\rho_2}.$$

But

$$\rho_1{}^2 = x_1{}^2 + y_1{}^2 + z_1{}^2; \qquad \rho_2{}^2 = x_2{}^2 + y_2{}^2 + z_2{}^2;$$
$$d^2 = (x_2 - x_1)^2 + (y_2 - y_1)^2 + (z_2 - z_1)^2.$$

Substituting these expressions into the numerator of the above expression, we find that

$$\cos \theta = \frac{x_1x_2 + y_1y_2 + z_1z_2}{\rho_1\rho_2}$$

$$= \frac{x_1}{\rho_1} \cdot \frac{x_2}{\rho_2} + \frac{y_1}{\rho_1} \cdot \frac{y_2}{\rho_2} + \frac{z_1}{\rho_1} \cdot \frac{z_2}{\rho_2}.$$

Now if the direction angles of OP_1 are α_1, β_1, γ_1, and those of OP_2 are α_2, β_2, γ_2 it is obvious that $x_1/\rho_1 = \cos \alpha_1$, $x_2/\rho_2 = \cos \alpha_2$, $y_1/\rho_1 = \cos \beta_1$, etc.   Making these substitutions we have, finally,

$$\cos \theta = \cos \alpha_1 \cos \alpha_2 + \cos \beta_1 \cos \beta_2 + \cos \gamma_1 \cos \gamma_2.$$

The lines are mutually perpendicular if and only if $\theta = 90°$.   Since $\cos 90° = 0$, the condition for perpendicularity is

$$\cos \alpha_1 \cos \alpha_2 + \cos \beta_1 \cos \beta_2 + \cos \gamma_1 \cos \gamma_2 = 0.$$

In terms of the direction numbers $a_1:b_1:c_1$ and $a_2:b_2:c_2$ of the two lines, the formula for $\cos \theta$ is

$$\cos \theta = \pm \frac{a_1a_2 + b_1b_2 + c_1c_2}{\sqrt{a_1{}^2 + b_1{}^2 + c_1{}^2} \sqrt{a_2{}^2 + b_2{}^2 + c_2{}^2}},$$

where the plus or minus sign is to be used depending upon the choice of positive directions on the lines.   In terms of direction numbers the condition for perpendicularity is

$$a_1a_2 + b_1b_2 + c_1c_2 = 0.$$

145. Normal equation of a plane.—A plane may be determined by specifying the length and direction of the normal ON drawn from the origin to the plane. In Fig. 178 let the directed length $ON = p$, and let the direction angles of ON be α, β, and γ.

We wish now to determine the equation of the plane in terms of these data. For this purpose we let P (x, y, z) be any point in the plane. We denote the directed length OP

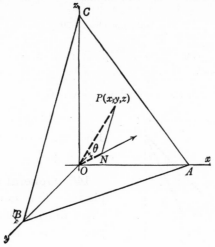

FIG. 178.

by ρ and let the direction angles of OP be α_1, β_1, and γ_1. Then, if θ is the angle between the directed segments OP and ON, the triangle OPN is a right triangle in which

$$OP \cos \theta = ON,$$

or

$$\rho \cos \theta = p.$$

Using the known formula for $\cos \theta$ we can write this in the form

$$\rho(\cos \alpha_1 \cos \alpha + \cos \beta_1 \cos \beta + \cos \gamma_1 \cos \gamma) = p.$$

Now since

$$\rho \cos \alpha_1 = x, \qquad \rho \cos \beta_1 = y, \qquad \text{and} \qquad \rho \cos \gamma_1 = z,$$

we have

(1) $$x \cos \alpha + y \cos \beta + z \cos \gamma = p.$$

This is the *normal form* of the equation of a plane. It can be used for writing down the equation of a plane when the length and direction of its normal ON are known.

Example

Find the equation of the plane through $N(-6, 3, 6)$ perpendicular to ON.

Solution (Fig. 179)

In this case

$$ON = p = \sqrt{(-6)^2 + 3^2 + 6^2} = 9;$$
$$\cos \alpha = -\tfrac{2}{3}; \qquad \cos \beta = \tfrac{1}{3}; \qquad \cos \gamma = \tfrac{2}{3}.$$

The normal form of the required equation is then

$$-\tfrac{2}{3}x + \tfrac{1}{3}y + \tfrac{2}{3}z = 9.$$

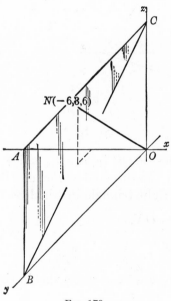

FIG. 179.

This can, of course, be reduced to

$$2x - y - 2z + 27 = 0.$$

146. General equation of a plane.—The normal form of the equation of a plane is of first degree in x, y, and z. Every plane has an equation of this form so we can say that every plane has an equation that is of first degree. We can easily prove, conversely, that every equation of first degree in x, y, and z represents a plane. In fact we have the following:

Theorem: *The locus of every equation of the form*

(2) $$Ax + By + Cz + D = 0,$$

in which A, B, and C are not all zero, is a plane. Furthermore, the **normal** *to the plane has direction numbers $A:B:C$.*

The proof is as follows: Without altering the locus of (2) we may divide by $\pm \sqrt{A^2 + B^2 + C^2}$. We thus obtain the equation

$$\frac{A}{\pm \sqrt{A^2 + B^2 + C^2}} x + \frac{B}{\pm \sqrt{A^2 + B^2 + C^2}} y$$

$$+ \frac{C}{\pm \sqrt{A^2 + B^2 + C^2}} z + \frac{D}{\pm \sqrt{A^2 + B^2 + C^2}} = 0.$$

Comparing this last equation with the normal form (1) we see that its locus, and hence that of (2), is a plane whose normal has the direction cosines:

$$\cos \alpha = \frac{A}{\pm \sqrt{A^2 + B^2 + C^2}};$$

$$\cos \beta = \frac{B}{\pm \sqrt{A^2 + B^2 + C^2}};$$

$$\cos \gamma = \frac{C}{\pm \sqrt{A^2 + B^2 + C^2}}.$$

It follows that the numbers $A : B : C$ are direction numbers of the normal.

Example

Find the equation of the plane through $A(2, 6, 1)$ perpendicular to the line $P(-3, 1, 2)\ Q(4, -3, 6)$.

Solution

The direction numbers of PQ are $7 : -4 : 4$, and, since PQ is a normal to the required plane, these numbers can be used as the coefficients of x, y, and z in its equation; *i.e.*, the equation is

$$7x - 4y + 4z + D = 0$$

where D is determined by the condition that the plane goes through $A(2, 6, 1)$. Thus

$$7(2) - 4(6) + 4(1) + D = 0 \qquad \text{or} \qquad D = +6.$$

The required equation is then

$$7x - 4y + 4z + 6 = 0.$$

If one or more of the coefficients A, B, and C has the value zero, the plane is parallel to the corresponding axis or axes. Thus the equation $4x + 5y = 7$ represents a plane parallel to the z-axis; the equation $4x = 7$ represents a plane parallel to both the y- and z-axes and consequently parallel to the yz-plane.

147. Angle between two planes.—When two planes intersect there are two supplementary angles of intersection. As indicated in Fig. 180 these are equal, respectively, to the corresponding two angles between the normals. Thus the problem of finding the angle between two planes is reduced to that of finding the angle between two lines, namely, their

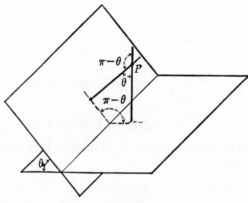

FIG. 180.

normals. If the equations of the planes are

$$\begin{cases} A_1 x + B_1 y + C_1 z + D_1 = 0 \\ A_2 x + B_2 y + C_2 z + D_2 = 0, \end{cases}$$

then the normals have the direction numbers

$$A_1 : B_1 : C_1 \qquad \text{and} \qquad A_2 : B_2 : C_2.$$

The angle between these normals, and consequently that between the planes, is given by the formula

$$\cos \theta = \pm \frac{A_1 A_2 + B_1 B_2 + C_1 C_2}{\sqrt{A_1^2 + B_1^2 + C_1^2} \sqrt{A_2^2 + B_2^2 + C_2^2}}.$$

The condition for perpendicularity of the planes is

$$A_1 A_2 + B_1 B_2 + C_1 C_2 = 0.$$

The planes are parallel if and only if their normals are parallel, in which case the direction numbers of the normals are proportional. The condition for parallelism of the planes is then

$$\frac{A_1}{A_2} = \frac{B_1}{B_2} = \frac{C_1}{C_2}.$$

PROBLEMS

1. Draw each of the following triangles and show that it is a right triangle; find the cosine of the angle at A:

(a) $A(0, 5, 1)$ $B(6, 3, 5)$ $C(6, 2, 4)$.

(b) $A(-1, 4, 3)$ $B(5, -2, 5)$ $C(0, 4, 0)$.

(c) $A(-4, 0, 2)$ $B(5, 1, 6)$ $C(8, 6, -2)$.

2. A line l_1 is drawn from the origin to $P(4, -2, 4)$, and from P a line l_2 is drawn so as to make equal angles with the coordinate axes. Draw the figure and find the cosine of the angle between l_1 and l_2.

3. What relation must exist between the direction cosines of two lines if the lines are to be parallel?

4. A force of 36 lb. acts along the line OP drawn from the origin to $P(7, 4, 4)$. Find the component of this force in the direction of a line making equal angles with the coordinate axes.

5. Write the equation of the plane for which $\alpha = 60°$, $\beta = 45°$, $\gamma = 60°$, $p = 4$.

6. Find the equation of the plane that satisfies the given conditions:

(a) Passes through $P(4, -2, 1)$ and is perpendicular to the radius vector OP.

(b) Passes through the mid-point of the line segment $A(-2, 5, 1)$ $B(6, 1, 5)$ and is perpendicular to AB.

(c) Passes through the points $A(-2, 1, 1)$, $B(4, 5, 3)$ and $C(2, 1, 2)$.

7. Find the point on the y-axis that is equidistant from the two points $A(1, -4, 4)$ and $B(7, 6, 2)$.

8. Find the cosine of the acute angle between the two given planes:

(a) $2x - y + 2z - 10 = 0$; $4x + y + z - 7 = 0$.

(b) $3x + 4y = 16$; $4y - 2z = 5$.

9. The base of a right pyramid 12 in. high is a rectangle 8 in. long and 6 in. wide. Find the angle between two of its faces.

10. Show that the direction numbers $a:b:c$ of a line that is perpendicular to each of two nonparallel lines l_1 and l_2 having direction numbers $a_1:b_1:c_1$ and $a_2:b_2:c_2$, respectively, are

$$a:b:c = \begin{vmatrix} b_1 & c_1 \\ b_2 & c_2 \end{vmatrix} : \begin{vmatrix} c_1 & a_1 \\ c_2 & a_2 \end{vmatrix} : \begin{vmatrix} a_1 & b_1 \\ a_2 & b_2 \end{vmatrix}.$$

HINT: The condition that l is perpendicular to both l_1 and l_2 is that $aa_1 + bb_1 + cc_1 = 0$ and $aa_2 + bb_2 + cc_2 = 0$.   Solve these equations for a/c and b/c using determinants.

11. Show that the direction numbers of the line of intersection of the two planes

$$\begin{cases} A_1x + B_1y + C_1z + D_1 = 0 \\ A_2x + B_2y + C_2z + D_2 = 0 \end{cases}$$

are

$$\begin{vmatrix} B_1 & C_1 \\ B_2 & C_2 \end{vmatrix} : \begin{vmatrix} C_1 & A_1 \\ C_2 & A_2 \end{vmatrix} : \begin{vmatrix} A_1 & B_1 \\ A_2 & B_2 \end{vmatrix}.$$

HINT: The line of intersection is perpendicular to the normals to both planes.   See Prob. 10.

12. Find the equation of the plane that passes through $P(1, 3, 2)$ and is perpendicular to the planes $2x + y - z + 12 = 0$ and

$$x - y + z + 4 = 0.$$

HINT: The plane must be perpendicular to their line of intersection.

148. Equations of a line in space.—We have seen that the locus of any linear equation is x, y, and z is a plane.   We

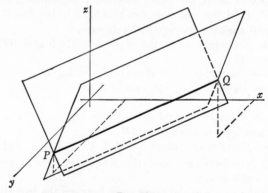

FIG. 181.

shall now see that a *line* in space may be defined by *two* such equations.   Consider the equations

$$(1) \qquad \begin{cases} A_1x + B_1y + C_1z + D_1 = 0 \\ A_2x + B_2y + C_2z + D_2 = 0. \end{cases}$$

Each of these represents a plane, and let it now be assumed that these planes intersect along a line PQ as shown in Fig. 181.   The first equation is satisfied by the coordinates of all points on the one plane and by no other points. Similarly, the second is satisfied by the coordinates of all points on the second plane and by no other points. Consequently, *the line of intersection of the planes is the locus of all points whose coordinates satisfy* **both** *equations*. The two equations therefore define this line. They are the *general equations* of the line.

If we eliminate z between equations (1), we obtain an equation in x and y. This is the equation of the plane through the line PQ perpendicular to the xy-plane. Similarly, if we eliminate y (or x) we obtain the equation of the plane through PQ perpendicular to the xz- (or yz-) plane. A pair of such equations constitute the *projection form* of the equations of a line.

Example

The equations $\begin{cases} 4x + 7y - 64 = 0 \\ 2x - 7z + 3 = 0 \end{cases}$ define the line PQ shown in Fig. 182. The first equation is that of the plane through PQ perpendicular

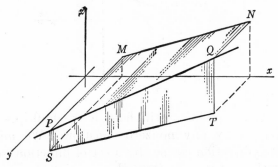

Fig. 182.

to the xy-plane. The second is that of the plane through PQ perpendicular to the xz-plane. ST and MN are the projections of PQ on these coordinate planes.

149. The symmetric form.—A line may be determined by specifying the coordinates of two points on it or by giving the coordinates of one point on it and its direction numbers. From such data its equations can easily be written down in the *symmetric form*, which we shall now derive.

Let $P_1(x_1, y_1, z_1)$ be one point on a line l (Fig. 183) whose direction angles are α, β, and γ. Let $P(x, y, z)$ be any other point on the line, and denote the directed distance P_1P by d. Then

$$\cos \alpha = \frac{x - x_1}{d}; \qquad \cos \beta = \frac{y - y_1}{d}; \qquad \cos \gamma = \frac{z - z_1}{d}.$$

If we solve each of these equations for d and equate the values so obtained, we have the equations

$$\frac{x - x_1}{\cos \alpha} = \frac{y - y_1}{\cos \beta} = \frac{z - z_1}{\cos \gamma}.$$

These equations constitute the *symmetric form* of the equations of a line.

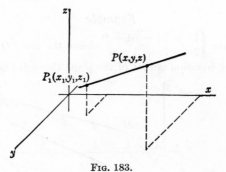

FIG. 183.

The above equalities still hold if we multiply all the denominators by any nonzero constant. We may thus replace the direction cosines by a set of direction numbers. The equations of the line through the point (x_1, y_1, z_1) with direction numbers $a:b:c$ are then

$$\frac{x - x_1}{a} = \frac{y - y_1}{b} = \frac{z - z_1}{c}.$$

This is also called the symmetric form.

If a line is determined by two points we may first find its direction numbers and then write its equations in the above form.

Example

Find the symmetric and projection equations of the line through $A(2, 2, 4)$ and $B(8, 6\frac{1}{2}, 2\frac{1}{2})$.

Solution (Fig. 184)

Direction numbers of the line are $6 : 4\frac{1}{2} : -1\frac{1}{2}$ or $4 : 3 : -1$. The

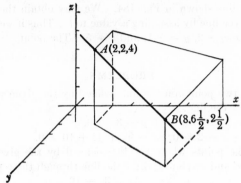

Fig. 184.

symmetric equations are then

$$\frac{x-2}{4} = \frac{y-2}{3} = \frac{z-4}{-1}.$$

The equation $\dfrac{x-2}{4} = \dfrac{y-2}{3}$ reduces to $3x - 4y + 2 = 0$; the equation $\dfrac{x-2}{4} = \dfrac{z-4}{-1}$ reduces to $x + 4z - 18 = 0$. The projection form of the equations is then

$$\begin{cases} 3x - 4y + 2 = 0 \\ x + 4z - 18 = 0. \end{cases}$$

These equations represent the two projecting planes shown in the figure.

150. The parametric form.—If we let t denote the value of each of the three fractions in the symmetric form, we may write

$$\frac{x - x_1}{a} = t; \qquad \frac{y - y_1}{b} = t; \qquad \frac{z - z_1}{c} = t.$$

Solving these equations for x, y, and z, respectively, we obtain the equations

$$x = x_1 + at; \qquad y = y_1 + bt; \qquad z = z_1 + ct.$$

These are *parametric* equations of the line, t being the parameter.

Example

The equations

$$x = 2 + 4t, \qquad y = 2 + 3t, \qquad z = 4 - t.$$

represent the line shown in Fig. 184. We may obtain the coordinates of a point on the line by assigning a value to t. Thus if we let $t = -1$, we find that $x = -2$, $y = -1$, and $z = 5$. The point $(-2, -1, 5)$ is on the line.

PROBLEMS

1. Locate two points on the line defined by the given pair of equations and draw the line:

(a) $x + 3y + z = 18$; $2x + y - 3z = 6$.

(b) $x - y + z - 2 = 0$; $8x - 9y + 4z + 10 = 0$.

2. Find the points where the line defined by the given equations pierces the xy- and xz-planes; draw the line through these points:

(a) $6x - y + 3z = 18$; $2x - 3y - 3z + 10 = 0$.

(b) $x + y - z = 2$; $x + 3y + z = 10$.

3. Find the direction cosines of the line defined by the equations $2x - 3y - 2z + 11 = 0$, $x - 6y + 2z + 10 = 0$, if the positive direction is such that γ is acute.

4. Write symmetric equations of the line satisfying the given conditions; reduce the equations to the projection form:

(a) Through $(2, 1, 6)$; direction numbers $4 : 3 : -2$.

(b) Through $(3, 0, -4)$; direction numbers $-1 : 2 : 2$.

(c) Through $(-2, -5, -2)$ and $(4, -1, 2)$.

(d) Through $(-2, 0, 0)$ and $(4, 5, 3)$.

5. Find equations of the line through the given point perpendicular to the given plane:

(a) $A(8, 10, 8)$; $x + y + 2z = 6$.

(b) $P(2, 1, 4)$; $4x - 3y + 2z = 12$.

6. Find the angle between the lines $\dfrac{x - 2}{4} = \dfrac{y - 1}{7} = \dfrac{z}{-4}$ and $\dfrac{x}{3} = \dfrac{y - 1}{4} = \dfrac{z + 4}{-5}$.

7. Show that the lines $\dfrac{2x - 10}{3} = \dfrac{1 - y}{5} = \dfrac{z + 4}{6}$ and

$$\frac{x - 1}{4} = \frac{5y + 10}{-6} = \frac{2 - z}{2}$$

are mutually perpendicular.

8. At what point does the line $\dfrac{2x - 9}{6} = \dfrac{y - 3}{1} = \dfrac{z - 5}{4}$ pierce the plane $2x + 3y + 3z - 12 = 0$?

9. Draw the line whose parametric equations are $x = 2 - 3t$, $y = 1 + 4t$; $z = 6 - t$. Find its projection equations.

10. Find the equation of the plane through $P(-4, 6, 1)$ perpendicular to the line whose projection equations are $x - 2z + 2 = 0$ and

$$2y + z + 5 = 0.$$

151. The sphere. Cylindrical surfaces.—In general, the locus of an equation in x, y, and z is a surface, and we have already seen that if the equation is *linear* the surface is a *plane*.

It is obvious that the equation $x^2 + y^2 + z^2 = r^2$ represents a sphere with center at the origin and radius r— for it is satisfied by the coordinates of those points, and only those points, whose distance from the origin is r. More generally, it can easily be shown that the equation of the sphere with center at (h, k, l) and radius r is

$$(x - h)^2 + (y - k)^2 + (z - l)^2 = r^2.$$

This is called the *standard* equation of the sphere. By performing the indicated operations on the left-hand member, the equation can be reduced to the *general* form:

$$x^2 + y^2 + z^2 + Gx + Hy + Iz + K = 0.$$

A surface generated by a line which moves so that it is always parallel to a fixed line and always intersects a fixed curve is called a *cylindrical surface* or *cylinder*. Any position of the generating line is called an *element* of the cylinder, and the curve is called a *directrix*.

Consider now the equation

$$y^2 = 4x.$$

In the xy-plane the graph of this equation is the parabola shown in Fig. 185. Now let a cylindrical surface be generated by a line which moves so that it always intersects this parabola and remains parallel to the z-axis.   It is easy to show that the equation $y^2 = 4x$ is satisfied by the coordinates of every point on this surface.   Thus, let $P(x, y, z)$ be any point on the surface and let $P'(x, y, 0)$ be the projection of P on the xy-plane.   Then, if the coordinates of P' satisfy the equation $y^2 = 4x$, those of P must do likewise because *both points have the same x- and y- coordinates*.   Conversely, every point whose coordinates satisfy the equation lies on the surface.   *The equation $y^2 = 4x$ is then the equation of the surface.*

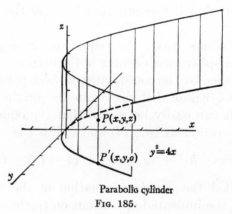

Parabolic cylinder
Fig. 185.

Observe that the parabola in the xy-plane is the locus of points whose coordinates satisfy the *two* equations $y^2 = 4x$ and $z = 0$.   This is the *trace* of the surface in the xy-plane. The upper parabola shown in the figure is the section of the surface cut by a plane parallel to the xy-plane and 4 units above it.   All points on this parabola satisfy the *two* equations $y^2 = 4x$ and $z = 4$.

By applying the above method of reasoning to the general case of an equation $\varphi(x, y) = 0$ we may prove the following:

Theorem: *If an equation that represents a surface does not contain the variable z, then the surface is a cylinder with elements parallel to the z-axis.   Its directrix is the curve in the xy-plane, which is the locus of the given equation.*

Similarly, if the variable x (or y) is absent, the locus is a

cylindrical surface whose elements are parallel to the
x- (or y-) axis.

152. The ellipsoid.—The surface defined by the equation

$$\frac{x^2}{a^2} + \frac{y^2}{b^2} + \frac{z^2}{c^2} = 1$$

is called an *ellipsoid* (Fig. 186).   By putting $z = 0$ we find
that the trace of the surface in the xy-plane is the ellipse

$$\frac{x^2}{a^2} + \frac{y^2}{b^2} = 1.$$

If we put $z = k$, we find that sections parallel to the

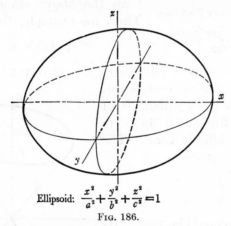

Ellipsoid: $\dfrac{x^2}{a^2} + \dfrac{y^2}{b^2} + \dfrac{z^2}{c^2} = 1$

FIG. 186.

xy-plane are also ellipses.   Similar considerations apply in
regard to the xz- and yz-planes.

If any two of the three constants a, b, and c are equal, the
surface is an ellipsoid of revolution, which is sometimes
called a *spheroid*.   Such a surface could be generated by
revolving an ellipse about its major or minor axis.   Finally,
if $a = b = c$, the surface is a sphere.

153. The elliptic paraboloid.—The surface defined by the
equation

$$\frac{x^2}{a^2} + \frac{y^2}{b^2} = z$$

is an elliptic paraboloid (Fig. 187). Sections parallel to

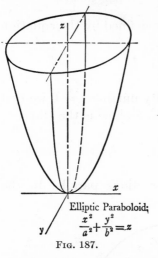

Elliptic Paraboloid;
$$\frac{x^2}{a^2}+\frac{y^2}{b^2}=z$$
FIG. 187.

and above the xy-plane are
ellipses. Sections parallel to the
other coordinate planes are parabolas. If $a = b$, the elliptic sections are circles and the surface is
a paraboloid of revolution. Such
a paraboloid could be generated
by revolving a parabola about its
axis.

The equation of the paraboloid
is often encountered in forms other
than the above standard form.
Thus, for example, the equation

$$x^2 + 4y^2 = 6 - z$$

represents an elliptic paraboloid whose vertex is at $z = 6$,
and which opens downward.
Its trace in the xy-plane is of
course the ellipse $x^2 + 4y^2 = 6$.

154. The elliptic cone.—The
locus of the equation

$$\frac{x^2}{a^2} + \frac{y^2}{b^2} - \frac{z^2}{c^2} = 0$$

is an elliptic cone (Fig. 188). Its
trace in the xy-plane is the "point
ellipse" $\dfrac{x^2}{a^2} + \dfrac{y^2}{b^2} = 0$. Sections
parallel to the xy-plane are
ellipses. Its trace in each of the
other coordinate planes is a pair
of lines through the origin; sections parallel to these coordinate
planes are hyperbolas.

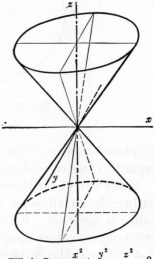

Elliptic Cone: $\dfrac{x^2}{a^2}+\dfrac{y^2}{b^2}-\dfrac{z^2}{c^2}=0$
FIG. 188.

If $a = b$, the elliptic sections are circles and the surface is a circular cone. It could be generated by revolving

a line having the equations $z = mx$, $y = 0$ about the z-axis.

155. Curves in space.—Consider the two equations

$$\begin{cases} x^2 + y^2 - 4z = 0 \\ x - y + 2z = 12. \end{cases}$$

The locus of the first equation is a paraboloid while that of the second is a plane that intersects the paraboloid in a curve. The points whose coordinates satisfy *both* equations are those lying on this curve. *We may therefore regard the above pair of equations as the equations of this curve in space.*

We may project this space curve onto the xy-plane by dropping a perpendicular from each point of the curve to the plane. These perpendiculars or projectors form a cylindrical surface whose equation is obtained by eliminating z between the given equations. In the above case the equation of this *projecting cylinder* is

$$x^2 + y^2 + 2x - 2y - 24 = 0.$$

The projecting cylinders on the xz- and yz-planes can be obtained similarly by eliminating y and x, respectively. A curve in space is often defined by giving the equations of two of its projecting cylinders. This corresponds to our method of defining a line in space by giving the equations of two of its projecting planes.

156. Parametric equations of a space curve.—We have already seen that the line through (x_1, y_1, z_1) with direction numbers $a:b:c$ has the parametric equations

$$x = x_1 + at, \qquad y = y_1 + bt, \qquad z = z_1 + ct.$$

In each of these equations the right-hand member is a *linear* function of t.

In general, the three equations

$$x = f_1(t), \qquad y = f_2(t), \qquad z = f_3(t)$$

are parametric equations of a *curve* in space, t being the parameter. The result of eliminating t between the first two equations is the xy-projecting cylinder of the curve, and the other projecting cylinders are similarly obtained. As an example, consider the equations

$$x = 4 \cos t, \qquad y = 4 \sin t, \qquad z = \tfrac{2}{3}t.$$

When $t = 0$, we have $x = 4$, $y = 0$, $z = 0$. These are the

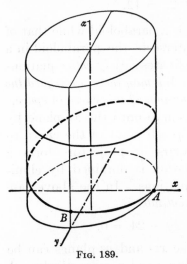

coordinates of point A in Fig. 189. If we let $t = \tfrac{1}{2}\pi$, we have $x = 0$, $y = 4$, $z = \tfrac{1}{3}\pi$. The corresponding point is B in the figure. By continuing in this manner we may plot the curve as shown.

If we eliminate t between the first two of the given equations, we have the relation

$$x^2 + y^2 = 16.$$

Since the x- and y-coordinates of every point on the curve satisfy this equation, the curve must lie upon this cylinder.

FIG. 189.

It is called a *circular helix* and its parametric equations have the general form

$$x = a \cos t, \qquad y = a \sin t, \qquad z = bt.$$

PROBLEMS

1. Find the equation of the sphere satisfying the following conditions:

(a) Center at $(2, 0, 0)$, radius 2.

(b) Having the points $(-4, 5, 1)$ and $(4, 1, 7)$ as ends of a diameter.

(c) Center at $(4, 2, 5)$ and tangent to the xy-plane.

2. Sketch the following cylindrical surfaces:

(a) $x^2 + y^2 = 6x.$ (b) $z = 4 - x^2.$ (c) $y^2 + z^2 = 9.$

Sketch the following surfaces:

3. $z = x^2 + 4y^2.$

4. $x^2 + y^2 = 12 - z.$

5. $x^2 + y^2 = z^2.$

6. $y^2 + z^2 + x = 6.$

7. $x^2 - y + 4z^2 = 0.$

8. $4(y^2 + z^2) = x^2.$

9. $\dfrac{x^2}{25} + \dfrac{y^2}{9} + \dfrac{z^2}{9} = 1.$

10. $x^2 + 2y^2 + 3z^2 = 36.$

11. $x^2 + 4y^2 + 4z^2 = 8x.$

12. $x^2 + y^2 + z^2 = 4z.$

In each of the following cases draw the curve defined by the given pair of equations:

13. $x^2 + y^2 + z^2 = 25$; $x^2 + y^2 = 9$.
14. $x^2 + y^2 + z^2 = 36$; $x^2 + y^2 = 6x$.
15. $x^2 + y^2 + z^2 = 32$; $x^2 + y^2 = 4z$.
16. $x^2 + y^2 = 10x$; $2z = x$.
17. $x = 5 \sin t$; $y = 4 \cos t$; $z = \frac{1}{2}t$.
18. $x = 4 \cos^2 t$; $y = 4 \sin^2 t$; $z = t^2$.

157. Cylindrical coordinates.—The student is familiar with the fact that the equation of a certain curve may be simpler in polar than in rectangular coordinates. Similarly, the equation of a certain surface may be simpler when

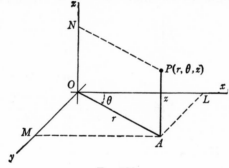

Fig. 190.

a coordinate system other than the rectangular system is employed. In this section and in the following one, we shall discuss briefly the *cylindrical* and *spherical* coordinate systems. Both of these coordinate systems are used extensively in the study of various advanced topics in mathematics and mathematical physics.

Let P be a point in space whose rectangular coordinates are (x, y, z), and let A be the foot of the perpendicular from P to the xy-plane. Let (r, θ) be the polar coordinates in the xy-plane of A.* Then the three numbers (r, θ, z) are called the *cylindrical coordinates* of P.

---

* We use (r, θ) instead of (ρ, θ) here because we still wish to denote the radius vector OP by ρ.

The relations that enable one to change the coordinates of a point or the equation of a surface from rectangular to cylindrical coordinates are easily seen from Fig. 190 to be:

$$x = r \cos \theta; \qquad y = r \sin \theta; \qquad z = z.$$

Those for making the reverse transformation are equally obvious.

Example

The equation $x^2 + y^2 - z^2 = 0$, which represents a circular cone, becomes $r^2 - z^2 = 0$ or $z = \pm r$ in cylindrical coordinates. Similarly, the equation $x^2 + y^2 + z^2 = 16$ becomes $r^2 + z^2 = 16$.

158. Spherical coordinates.—Let P be a point in space whose rectangular coordinates are (x, y, z), and let A be the

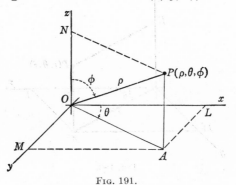

Fig. 191.

foot of the perpendicular from P to the xy-plane. Then, as shown in Fig. 191, let

$$OP = \rho; \qquad \text{angle } LOA = \theta; \qquad \text{angle } NOP = \phi.$$

The three numbers $(\rho,\ \theta,\ \phi)$ are the *spherical coordinates* of P. This coordinate system is similar to that used in locating a point on the earth's surface by means of longitude and latitude. The angle θ corresponds to the longitude and ϕ to the colatitude, the latitude being the angle AOP.

In the spherical coordinate system, θ may have any positive or negative value; ϕ is identical with the direction angle γ and is restricted to positive values not greater than $180°$. It is customary to restrict ρ to positive values, but if we wish we may agree to interpret negative values of ρ as we did in dealing with polar coordinates in the plane.

The relations that enable one to transform the coordinates of a point or the equation of a surface from rectangular to spherical coordinates are easily found. Noting that

$$OA = NP = \rho \sin \phi,$$

while $ON = \rho \cos \phi$, we deduce immediately that

$$x = \rho \sin \phi \cos \theta;$$
$$y = \rho \sin \phi \sin \theta;$$
$$z = \rho \cos \phi.$$

Example

The equation $x^2 + y^2 = 4z$ represents a paraboloid of revolution. Upon making the above substitutions we obtain its equation in spherical coordinates as follows:

$$\rho^2 \sin^2 \phi \ (\cos^2 \theta + \sin^2 \theta) = 4 \rho \cos \phi;$$
$$\rho \sin^2 \phi = 4 \cos \phi;$$
$$\rho = 4 \cos \phi \csc^2 \phi.$$

PROBLEMS

1. Find the rectangular coordinates of the point whose spherical coordinates are:

(a) $(8, 60°, 45°)$.   (b) $(6, \pi, \tfrac{1}{2}\pi)$.   (c) $(\sqrt{12}, \tfrac{1}{2}\pi, \tfrac{3}{4}\pi)$.

2. Find spherical and cylindrical coordinates for the points whose rectangular coordinates are:

(a) $(4, 4, 2)$.   (b) $(-2, 2, 0)$.   (c) $(0, 0, -5)$.

3. Sketch the locus in cylindrical coordinates of each of the following equations:

(a) $r = 4$.   (b) $r = 2 \cos \theta$.   (c) $\theta = \tfrac{1}{4}\pi$.

4. Describe the locus in spherical coordinates of each of the following equations:

(a) $\rho = 2$.   (b) $\theta = \tfrac{3}{4}\pi$.   (c) $\phi = \tfrac{1}{6}\pi$.

Transform each of the following equations into cylindrical coordinates; sketch the locus:

5. $x^2 + y^2 = 8$.   **6.** $x^2 + y^2 = 4y$.

7. $x^2 + y^2 + z^2 = 14$.   **8.** $xy = 2$.

9. $x^2 + y^2 + z^2 = 6z$.   **10.** $x^2 + y^2 = 4z^2$.

Transform each of the following equations into spherical coordinates; sketch the locus:

11. $x^2 + y^2 + z^2 = 16.$ 12. $x^2 + y^2 = 5.$

13. $x^2 + y^2 + z^2 = 4z.$ 14. $x^2 + y^2 + z^2 = 6x.$

15. $x^2 + y^2 = 4z^2.$ 16. $6z = x^2 + y^2.$

17. Sketch the space curve defined by the equations $x^2 + y^2 + z^2 = 16$, $x^2 + y^2 = 4x$. What are the equations of this curve in cylindrical coordinates; in spherical coordinates?

18. Same as Prob. 17 for the curve whose equations are $x^2 + y^2 = 9$, and $z = \frac{1}{2}x$.

CHAPTER XXV

PARTIAL DERIVATIVES

159. Functions of two or more variables.—We use the abbreviation $z = f(x, y)$ to mean that z is a function of the two variables x and y. We also use symbols such as $f(x, y)$, $g(x, y)$, and $\varphi(x, y)$ to denote specific functions of x and y. Thus if we were concerned in a particular discussion with the two functions $(x^3y + 3y^2)$ and $(4xy - 2y)$, it might be convenient to call the first function $f(x, y)$ and the second $g(x, y)$. The notation is of course easily extended to the case of a function of more than two variables.

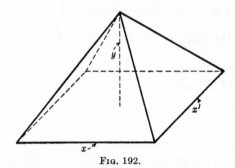

Fig. 192.

Example

Figure 192 shows a right pyramid having a square base of side x and altitude y. Its volume v is a function of x and y; *i.e.*,

$$v = f(x, y) = \tfrac{1}{3}x^2y.$$

The total area A of its surface is another function of x and y, and it is easy to show that this function is

$$A = g(x, y) = x^2 + x \sqrt{x^2 + 4y^2}.$$

The ideas of single-valuedness, continuity, etc., which have been discussed for functions of one variable, are easily extended. Thus z is a *single-valued* function of x and y if

349

there is just *one* value of z for each admissible pair of values of x and y. The function is *continuous* at the point (x_1, y_1) if it has a value $f(x_1, y_1)$ at this point and if, furthermore, the value of $f(x, y)$ is arbitrarily near $f(x_1, y_1)$ for all points (x, y) that are sufficiently near (x_1, y_1).

160. Partial derivatives.—Consider the single-valued function $z = f(x, y)$. Corresponding to a given pair of values of x and y there is a definite value of z. Suppose now that we let x change by an amount Δx, keeping y fixed. The change in the value of z is, of course,

$$\Delta z = f(x + \Delta x, y) - f(x, y).$$

If we divide Δz by Δx, we have

$$\frac{\Delta z}{\Delta x} = \frac{f(x + \Delta x, y) - f(x, y)}{\Delta x}.$$

This quantity measures the average rate of change of z relative to x over the interval Δx. If we now let $\Delta x \to 0$ and denote the limit of the fraction by $\left(\dfrac{dz}{dx}\right)_y$ or $\dfrac{\partial z}{\partial x}$, we have

$$\left(\frac{dz}{dx}\right)_y \text{ or } \frac{\partial z}{\partial x} = \lim_{\Delta x \to 0} \frac{f(x + \Delta x, y) - f(x, y)}{\Delta x}.$$

This limit, if it exists, is called the *partial derivative of z with respect to x*. Its value, for any given pair of values of x and y, is the instantaneous rate of change of z relative to x when y is held constant. Similarly, the rate of change of z with respect to y when x is held constant is

$$\left(\frac{dz}{dy}\right)_x \text{ or } \frac{\partial z}{\partial y} = \lim_{\Delta y \to 0} \frac{f(x, y + \Delta y) - f(x, y)}{\Delta y}.$$

The usual formulas can, of course, be used in finding these derivatives. One merely treats y as a constant when taking the derivative of $f(x, y)$ with respect to x, and treats x as a constant when differentiating with respect to y. The symbols $\partial f/\partial x$, $\partial f/\partial y$, and f_x, f_y are also used to denote partial derivatives of $f(x, y)$. Thus if one writes

$$f(x, y) = x^2 y + 4y^3,$$

then one might write

$$\frac{\partial f}{\partial x} \text{ or } f_x = 2xy; \qquad \frac{\partial f}{\partial y} \text{ or } f_y = x^2 + 12y^2.$$

The following examples should make clear the physical interpretation of the partial derivative.

Example 1

For any pair of values of x and y, the formula

$$A = x^2 + x\sqrt{x^2 + 4y^2}$$

gives the surface area of the pyramid shown in Fig. 192. Find the values of $\partial A/\partial x$ and $\partial A/\partial y$ when $x = 6$ in. and $y = 4$ in.

Solution

$$A = x^2 + x\sqrt{x^2 + 4y^2};$$

$$\frac{\partial A}{\partial x} = 2x + [x \cdot \tfrac{1}{2}(x^2 + 4y^2)^{-\frac{1}{2}}(2x) + \sqrt{x^2 + 4y^2} \cdot 1]$$

$$= 2x + \frac{x^2}{\sqrt{x^2 + 4y^2}} + \sqrt{x^2 + 4y^2}$$

$$= 2x + \frac{2x^2 + 4y^2}{\sqrt{x^2 + 4y^2}}.$$

$$\frac{\partial A}{\partial x}\bigg]_{(6,\,4)} = 12 + \frac{72 + 64}{10} = 25.6.$$

This result means that when $x = 6$ in. and $y = 4$ in., the surface area increases at a rate of 25.6 sq. in. *per inch of increase in x if y is held constant.* Similarly,

$$\frac{\partial A}{\partial y} = 0 + x \cdot \tfrac{1}{2}(x^2 + 4y^2)^{-\frac{1}{2}}(8y)$$

$$= \frac{4xy}{\sqrt{x^2 + 4y^2}}.$$

$$\frac{\partial A}{\partial y}\bigg]_{(6,\,4)} = \tfrac{96}{10} = 9.6.$$

This means that if x is held fixed, the surface area increases with y at a rate of 9.6 *sq. in. per inch.*

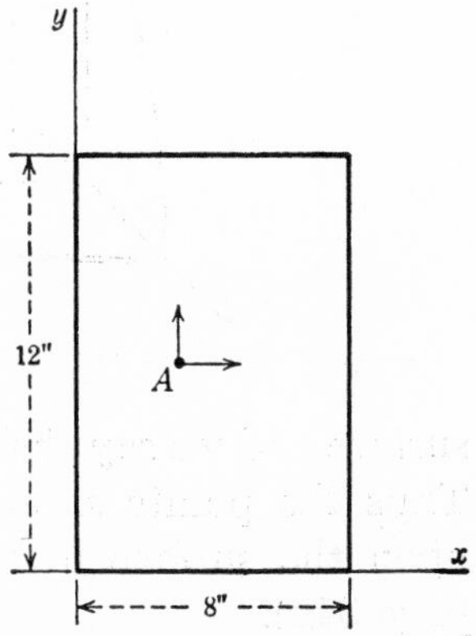

Example 2

The temperature in degrees centigrade at any point (x, y) on the plate shown in Fig. 193 is given by

$$T = \tfrac{1}{4}xy^2 + 2x.$$

Find the values of $\partial T/\partial x$ and $\partial T/\partial y$ at the point $A(3, 6)$.

FIG. 193.

Solution

$$\frac{\partial T}{\partial x} = \tfrac{1}{4}y^2 + 2$$

$$\frac{\partial T}{\partial x}\bigg]_{(3,\,6)} = 11 \qquad \text{(degrees per inch)}.$$

The result means that at A the temperature increases at a rate of 11 deg. per inch moved along the plate in the x-direction. Similarly,

$$\frac{\partial T}{\partial y} = \tfrac{1}{2}xy$$

$$\frac{\partial T}{\partial y}\bigg]_{(3,\,6)} = 9 \qquad \text{(degrees per inch)}.$$

Thus, in the y-direction the temperature increases at a rate of 9 deg. per inch at the point A.

161. Geometrical interpretation.—In general, the points whose coordinates satisfy the relation $z = f(x, y)$ lie upon a

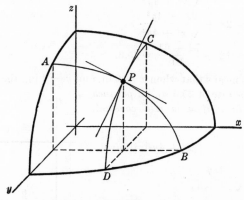

FIG. 194.

surface and we say that the equation *represents* this surface. Thus the points satisfying the relation $4z = x^2 + 3y^2$ lie upon the surface of an elliptic paraboloid (see Fig. 187, page 342).

In order to obtain geometrical interpretations of $\partial z/\partial x$ and $\partial z/\partial y$, let P (Fig. 194) be a point on the surface whose equation is $z = f(x, y)$. Through P pass a plane parallel to the xz-plane thus cutting the curve APB from the surface. The points on this curve satisfy the *two* equations

$$z = f(x, y); \qquad y = k.$$

It is obvious that as a point moves along this curve its
z-coordinate varies with x while *its y-coordinate remains
constant.* It is easy to see that the rate of change of z with
respect to x at P, which we have denoted by $\partial z/\partial x$, is equal
to the slope of the tangent line to this curve at P. Similarly, the value of $\partial z/\partial y$ at P is equal to the slope of the
tangent line to the curve CPD. These slopes are, of course,
positive or negative depending upon whether z increases or
decreases as x (or y) increases.

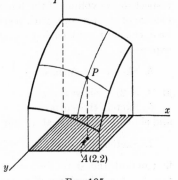

In order to bring together
the physical and geometrical
interpretations we give the
following:

Example

Let the temperature at any point
of a plate 3 ft. square be given by the
equation

$$T = 48 - \tfrac{4}{3}x^2 - 3y^2 \qquad \text{(degrees)}$$

where the coordinate system is taken
as shown in Fig. 195. At every

Fig. 195.

point of the plate we may erect an ordinate whose length represents the
temperature at that point and consider the surface that passes through
the upper ends of these ordinates. Thus at $A(2, 2)$ we have $T = 30\tfrac{2}{3}$
deg. and the corresponding point on the surface is P. Now

$$\frac{\partial T}{\partial x} = -\tfrac{8}{3}x; \qquad \frac{\partial T}{\partial x}\bigg]_{(2,\,2)} = -5\tfrac{1}{3} \ \text{(degrees per foot).}$$

$$\frac{\partial T}{\partial y} = -6y; \qquad \frac{\partial T}{\partial y}\bigg]_{(2,\,2)} = -12 \ \text{(degrees per foot).}$$

Physically, these derivatives represent the rates of change of the temperature (with respect to the distance moved along the plate) in the
x- and y-directions, respectively. Geometrically, they represent the
slopes of the two curves drawn on the surface as shown.

PROBLEMS

1. The volume of the pyramid shown in Fig. 192 is $v = \tfrac{1}{3}x^2y$.
Find the value of $\partial v/\partial x$ and $\partial v/\partial y$ when $x = 9$ in. and $y = 12$ in.
Explain the physical meaning of each result.

2. If two sides and the included angle of a triangle are x, y, and θ, then its area is $A = \frac{1}{2}xy \sin \theta$. Find the value of $\partial A/\partial x$ when $x = 12$ in., $y = 8$ in., and $\theta = \frac{1}{6}\pi$. Interpret the result physically, giving the units in which it is expressed.

3. The temperature at any point (x, y, z) in a body is given by the formula

$$T = x^2 + 3y^2 - 6z.$$

Evaluate $\partial T/\partial x$, $\partial T/\partial y$, and $\partial T/\partial z$ at $(2, 1, 2)$ and interpret the results. Assume that T is in degrees centigrade and x, y, and z are in inches.

4. A quantity of gas is confined in a cylinder that is fitted with a piston. Its volume can be changed by moving the piston, and the pressure, volume, and absolute temperature are connected by the relation $pv = ct$ where c is a constant. Find the rate of change of the pressure with respect to the volume if the temperature is held constant and the rate of change of the pressure with respect to the temperature if the volume is held constant. In each case give units in which the rate might be expressed.

5. Sketch the surface $\dfrac{x^2}{16} + \dfrac{y^2}{9} = 4 - z$. Evaluate $\partial z/\partial x$ and $\partial z/\partial y$ at $(4, 3, 2)$. Show the geometrical meanings of these derivatives.

6. Sketch the surface $4z = x^2 + y^2$. Evaluate $\partial z/\partial y$ at $(2, 4, 5)$ and show its geometrical meaning.

7. Sketch the part of the ellipsoid $\dfrac{x^2}{6} + \dfrac{y^2}{3} + \dfrac{z^2}{2} = 1$ that lies in the first octant and show the curves cut from it by the planes $x = 1$ and $y = 1$. Find the slopes of these curves at $P(1, 1, 1)$.

In each of the following problems find $\partial z/\partial x$ and $\partial z/\partial y$:

8. $z = x^3 - 4x^2y^2 + 8y^2$.   **9.** $z = x^3 + 5x^2y + 2y^3 + 6$.

10. $z = \dfrac{y^2}{y - 4x}$.   **11.** $z = \dfrac{x - y}{x^2 + y^2}$.

12. $z = \log (x^2 + y^2)$.   **13.** $z = \arctan \left(\dfrac{y}{x}\right)$.

14. $z = x \cos (xy)$.   **15.** $z = xe^{\frac{y}{x}}$.

16. $z = xe^y + ye^x$.   **17.** $z = e^{(x-y)} - x^2y$.

In each of the following problems find $\partial z/\partial x$ and $\partial z/\partial y$ using the method of implicit differentiation:

18. $x^2 + 4y^2 + z^2 = 16$.   **19.** $xy + z^2 = 6$.

20. $z^2 = \dfrac{x^2}{4} + \dfrac{y^2}{9}$.   **21.** $\dfrac{x^2}{a^2} + \dfrac{y^2}{b^2} + \dfrac{z^2}{c^2} = 1$.

22. $x^2z + 4z^2 = 8y$.   **23.** $x^2 + y^2 + z^2 = a^2$.

24. If $z = \dfrac{x^2 - y^2}{xy}$, verify that $x\dfrac{\partial z}{\partial x} + y\dfrac{\partial z}{\partial y} = 0$.

25. If $z = \dfrac{x^3 - y^3}{xy}$, verify that $x\dfrac{\partial z}{\partial x} + y\dfrac{\partial z}{\partial y} = z$.

26. If $u = \dfrac{yz + x^2}{xz}$, verify that $x\dfrac{\partial u}{\partial x} + y\dfrac{\partial u}{\partial y} + z\dfrac{\partial u}{\partial z} = 0$.

27. From the point $(1, 2, 2)$ on the sphere $x^2 + y^2 + z^2 = 9$, a line is drawn tangent to the sphere and parallel to the xz-plane. What are its equations?

28. A parabola is defined by the two equations $z = 2x^2 + y^2$, $y = 2$. Write the equations of the tangent line to this curve at $P(1, 2, 6)$.

162. Tangent plane and normal line.—Let $P(x_1, y_1, z_1)$ be any point on the surface whose equation is $z = f(x, y)$. The equation of any plane through P can be written in the form

$$(1) \qquad z - z_1 = A(x - x_1) + B(y - y_1).$$

That this equation represents a plane through P, no matter what values are assigned to A and B, is clear from the fact

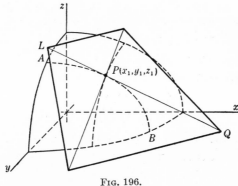

Fig. 196.

that it is of first degree in x, y, and z and is satisfied by the coordinates of P.

We wish now to determine A and B so that the above equation will represent the *tangent plane* to the surface at P. We do this as follows (Fig. 196):

The plane $y = y_1$ cuts the curve APB from the surface, and at P the slope of this curve is equal to the value of $\partial z/\partial x$. This same plane $(y = y_1)$ cuts a line LPQ from the

plane determined by (1). This line has the equations
$y = y_1$ and $z - z_1 = A(x - x_1)$, and its slope is therefore
equal to A. In order that the plane be tangent to the
surface, this line must be tangent to the curve APB at P.
This means that A must be equal to the value of $\partial z/\partial x$ at P.

By taking the section made by the plane $x = x_1$ one can
show in a similar way that B must be equal to the value
of $\partial z/\partial y$ at P. The equation of the tangent plane to the
surface is then

$$(2) \qquad z - z_1 = \left(\frac{\partial z}{\partial x}\right)_P (x - x_1) + \left(\frac{\partial z}{\partial y}\right)_P (y - y_1).$$

The line through P perpendicular to the tangent plane is
called the *normal line* to the surface. It is shown in solid
analytic geometry that the coefficients A, B, and C in the
equation

$$Ax + By + Cz + D = 0$$

are direction numbers of the *normal* to the plane represented
by the equation.* If (2) were written in this form, the
coefficients of x, y, and z would be $\left(\dfrac{\partial z}{\partial x}\right)_P$, $\left(\dfrac{\partial z}{\partial y}\right)_P$, and -1,
respectively. Hence the normal to the surface at P has
the direction numbers

$$\left(\frac{\partial z}{\partial x}\right)_P : \left(\frac{\partial z}{\partial y}\right)_P : -1.$$

The equations of the line through $P(x_1, y_1, z_1)$ with direction numbers $a:b:c$ are shown in solid analytic geometry
to be†

$$\frac{x - x_1}{a} = \frac{y - y_1}{b} = \frac{z - z_1}{c}.$$

Hence the equations of the normal line to the surface at
P are

$$(3) \qquad \frac{x - x_1}{\left(\dfrac{\partial z}{\partial x}\right)_P} = \frac{y - y_1}{\left(\dfrac{\partial z}{\partial y}\right)_P} = \frac{z - z_1}{-1}.$$

* See page 330.
† See page 336.

Example

Find the equations of tangent plane and normal line to the sphere $x^2 + y^2 + z^2 = 17$ at $P(3, -2, 2)$.

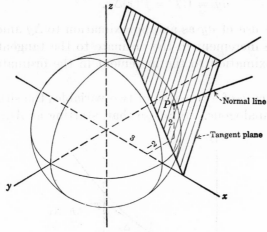

Fig. 197.

Solution (Fig. 197)

$$\frac{\partial z}{\partial x} = -\frac{x}{z}; \qquad \frac{\partial z}{\partial x}\bigg]_{3,-2,2} = -\tfrac{3}{2}.$$

$$\frac{\partial z}{\partial y} = -\frac{y}{z}; \qquad \frac{\partial z}{\partial y}\bigg]_{3,-2,2} = 1.$$

The equation of the tangent plane is, then,

$$z - 2 = -\tfrac{3}{2}(x - 3) + 1(y + 2),$$

or

$$3x - 2y + 2z = 17.$$

The equations of the normal line are

$$\frac{x - 3}{-\tfrac{3}{2}} = \frac{y + 2}{1} = \frac{z - 2}{-1},$$

or

$$\begin{cases} 2x + 3y = 0 \\ y + z = 0. \end{cases}$$

163. The total differential.—In Chap. XIII we called the quantity $dy = f'(x)\Delta x$ the *differential* of the function $y = f(x)$. This differential was useful in finding approximately the change in the value of $f(x)$ caused by a small change Δx in x.　As shown in Fig. 198,

$$\Delta y = CB = f(x + \Delta x) - f(x)$$

while

$$dy = CT = f'(x)\Delta x.$$

Thus the use of dy as an approximation to Δy amounts to using the increment in the ordinate to the tangent line as an approximation to the increment in the ordinate to the curve.

In the case of a function of two variables the situation is entirely analogous.　Suppose that, starting at $A(x_1, y_1, z_1)$

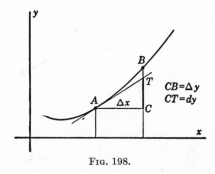

$$CB = \Delta y$$
$$CT = dy$$

Fig. 198.

on the surface $z = f(x, y)$, we let x and y change by small amounts Δx and Δy, respectively.　The change produced in the value of the function z, as shown in Fig. 199, is

$$\Delta z = CB = f(x_1 + \Delta x, y_1 + \Delta y) - f(x_1, y_1).$$

As an approximation to Δz we may use the part represented by CT, *which is the increment in the ordinate to the tangent plane.*　The equation of this plane is

$$z - z_1 = \left(\frac{\partial z}{\partial x}\right)_A (x - x_1) + \left(\frac{\partial z}{\partial y}\right)_A (y - y_1).$$

If we let $x - x_1 = \Delta x$ and $y - y_1 = \Delta y$, we have

$$CT = \left(\frac{\partial z}{\partial x}\right)_A \Delta x + \left(\frac{\partial z}{\partial y}\right)_A \Delta y.$$

It is intuitively evident that CT is a good approximation to

Δz if Δx and Δy are sufficiently small and the partial derivatives are not both zero. It can be shown that if $\partial z/\partial x$ and $\partial z/\partial y$ are continuous in the neighborhood of A then the increment Δz is given exactly by the expression:

$$\Delta z = \left(\frac{\partial z}{\partial x}\right)_A \Delta x + \left(\frac{\partial z}{\partial y}\right)_A \Delta y + \epsilon \sqrt{(\Delta x)^2 + (\Delta y)^2},$$

where ϵ represents a quantity that approaches 0 when Δx and $\Delta y \to 0$. The proof is best deferred to a course in

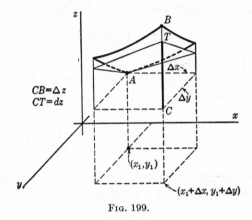

FIG. 199.

advanced calculus and will not be given here. The result means that the quantity

$$\left(\frac{\partial z}{\partial x}\right)_A \Delta x + \left(\frac{\partial z}{\partial y}\right)_A \Delta y$$

differs from Δz only by an amount $\epsilon \sqrt{(\Delta x)^2 + (\Delta y)^2}$, which is an infinitesimal of higher order than Δx and Δy when these increments approach zero. This approximation is often called the *principal part* of the increment Δz. It is also called the *total differential* of the function z and is denoted by dz. Thus, by definition,

$$dz = \frac{\partial z}{\partial x} \Delta x + \frac{\partial z}{\partial y} \Delta y.$$

It is customary to define the increments of the independent variables by the equations $dx = \Delta x$ and $dy = \Delta y$ and to replace Δx and Δy in the above expression by dx and dy, respectively. Finally, whether x and y are independent variables or not we define the total differential of the function $z = f(x, y)$ to be

$$dz = \frac{\partial z}{\partial x}\, dx + \frac{\partial z}{\partial y}\, dy.$$

Here it is to be understood that $dx = \Delta x$ and $dy = \Delta y$ if x and y are independent variables. However if, for example, $x = g(t)$ and $y = h(t)$ where t is independent, then

$$dx = g'(t)\, dt$$

and $dy = h'(t)\, dt$ where $dt = \Delta t$.

The total differential of a function of three or more variables is similarly defined. Thus if $U = f(x, y, z)$, the quantity

$$dU = \frac{\partial U}{\partial x}\, dx + \frac{\partial U}{\partial y}\, dy + \frac{\partial U}{\partial z}\, dz$$

gives approximately the change in U caused by changes dx, dy, and dz in the variables x, y, and z.

Example

The metal in a cylindrical can is $\frac{1}{64}$ in. thick on top, bottom, and sides. The inside dimensions are $r = 4$ in., $h = 8$ in. Find approximately the volume of the metal.

Solution

The volume of metal is equal to the amount by which the volume of a cylinder increases when its radius changes from 4 to $4\frac{1}{64}$ in. and its height from 8 to $8\frac{1}{32}$ in. Why?

$$V = \pi r^2 h,$$

$$dV = \frac{\partial V}{\partial r}\, dr + \frac{\partial V}{\partial h}\, dh$$

$$= 2\pi h r\, dr + \pi r^2 dh.$$

Taking $r = 4$, $h = 8$, $dr = \frac{1}{64}$, $dh = \frac{1}{32}$, we have

$$dV = 64\pi\left(\tfrac{1}{64}\right) + 16\pi\left(\tfrac{1}{32}\right)$$

$$= \tfrac{3}{2}\pi \text{ cu. in.}$$

PROBLEMS

In each of the following cases find the equations of the tangent plane and normal line to the given surface at the given point:

1. $4z = x^2 + y^2$; $(2, 2, 2)$.

2. $z = x^2 + y^2 - 4$; $(1, 1, -2)$.

3. $z = 8 - x^2 - 2y^2$; $(2, 1, 2)$.

4. $x^2 + y^2 + z^2 = 38$; $(5, 2, 3)$.

5. $xyz = 16$; $(4, 2, 2)$.

6. $\dfrac{x^2}{16} + \dfrac{y^2}{8} + \dfrac{z^2}{4} = 1$; $(-2, 2, 1)$.

7. Show that the equation of the tangent plane to the sphere $x^2 + y^2 + z^2 = a^2$ at a point $P(x_1, y_1, z_1)$ on its surface is

$$x_1 x + y_1 y + z_1 z = a^2.$$

8. Show that if $z = x^2 y$, then $dz = 2xy\, dx + x^2 dy$. Use this result to find approximately the value of $(5.06)^2 \cdot (1.95)$.

9. Find the differential of the function $x^2 y^3$. Use the result to calculate approximately $(5.96)^2 (2.04)^3$.

10. Find the total differential of the function $U = xyz$. Multiply out $(x + dx)(y + dy)(z + dz)$. What terms constitute the difference between ΔU and dU?

Find the total differentials of the following functions:

11. $z = x^2 + 6xy^2 + 2y$.

12. $U = xyz + 4x^2 z^2$.

13. $w = \dfrac{z}{xy}$.

14. $z = \dfrac{y}{\sqrt{x^2 + y^2}}$.

15. $A = \frac{1}{2}xy \sin \theta$.

16. $z = \log \sqrt{x^2 + y^2}$.

17. $Q = x^2 + y^2 - 2xy \cos \theta$.

18. $z = \dfrac{x}{y} + \sqrt{xy}$.

19. A metal box is 6 ft. long, 4 ft. wide, and 3 ft. deep. The thickness of the metal is 0.05 ft. Find approximately the volume of metal in the box.

20. The inside diameter and height of a can are found by measurement to be 5.0 in. and 12.6 in., respectively. If there is a possible error of 0.05 in. in each measurement, what is approximately the greatest possible error in the computed volume?

21. The specific gravity of a solid is found from the formula

$$s = \frac{A}{A - w}$$

where A and w are its weight in air and water, respectively. If the readings are $A = 6.4$ lb., $w = 2.8$ lb., with possible errors of 0.05 lb. in each, what is the corresponding possible error in s?

22. Two sides of a triangle are 16 ft. and 24 ft. with possible errors of 0.1 ft. The included angle is 30° with a possible error of 0.2°. What is the maximum error in the computed area?

23. A triangle is found to have sides 64 ft. and 50 ft., with included angle 42°. If there is an uncertainty of 0.5 ft. in each side and 0.5° in the angle, what is the corresponding uncertainty in the computed area?

24. The sine of the acute angle A in a right triangle is determined by measuring the opposite side a and hypotenuse c and dividing. If $a = 4.64$ in. and $c = 9.36$ in., with a possible error of 0.01 in. in each, compute $\sin A$ and find the corresponding possible error.

25. Show that the relative error in the computed volume of a rectangular box is equal to the sum of the relative errors in the measurements of its three edges; *i.e.*,

$$\frac{dv}{v} = \frac{dx}{x} + \frac{dy}{y} + \frac{dz}{z}.$$

26. If the measurements of radius and height of a right circular cone are subject to errors of 2 per cent and 1 per cent, respectively, what is the corresponding percentage error in the computed volume?

27. The value of a function of the form $kx^m y^n$ is computed from measurements of x and y. Show that the relative error in the value of the function is equal to m times the relative error in x plus n times the relative error in y.

164. Total derivatives.—We have studied the equation $z = f(x, y)$ for the case in which x and y represent independent variables. Let us now consider the relation defined by the *two* equations

$$z = f(x, y); \qquad y = g(x).$$

Here, z is a function of x and y while y in turn is a function of x. Thus z is really a function of the single (independent) variable x, and we may develop a formula for the rate of change of z relative to x.

If x is given an increment Δx, then y which depends upon x changes by some corresponding amount Δy. The change produced in z is given by

$$\Delta z = \frac{\partial z}{\partial x} \Delta x + \frac{\partial z}{\partial y} \Delta y + \epsilon \sqrt{(\Delta x)^2 + (\Delta y)^2}.$$

(This expression for Δz was given on page 359 but the proof has been omitted.)　If we divide Δz by Δx and then let $\Delta x \to 0$, we obtain the formula

$$\frac{dz}{dx} = \frac{\partial z}{\partial x} + \frac{\partial z}{\partial y} \cdot \frac{dy}{dx}.$$

This derivative is called the *total derivative* of z with respect to x.　Its physical interpretation is given by the following:

Example

The volume of the pyramid shown in Fig. 192 is $v = \frac{1}{3}x^2y$.　Assume that x and y are both allowed to vary, not independently, but subject to the relation $y = 3\sqrt{x} + 2$.　We then have

$$v = \tfrac{1}{3}x^2y; \qquad y = 3\sqrt{x} + 2.$$

The total derivative of v with respect to x is

$$\begin{aligned}
\frac{dv}{dx} &= \frac{\partial v}{\partial x} + \frac{\partial v}{\partial y} \cdot \frac{dy}{dx} \\
&= \tfrac{2}{3}xy + \tfrac{1}{3}x^2 \cdot \tfrac{3}{2}x^{-\frac{1}{2}} \\
&= \tfrac{2}{3}xy + \tfrac{1}{2}x^{\frac{3}{2}}.
\end{aligned}$$

Let us assign to x the value $x = 4$ in.　From the above relation between x and y we find that $y = 8$ in.　The corresponding value of dv/dx is

$$\frac{dv}{dx}\bigg]_{x=4} = \tfrac{64}{3} + 4 = 25\tfrac{1}{3}.$$

The result means that if x is allowed to vary, and if y is not held constant but is also allowed to vary in accordance with the relation $y = 3\sqrt{x} + 2$, then when $x = 4$ in. v is increasing at a rate of $25\tfrac{1}{3}$ cu. in. per inch of change in x.　It will be recalled that $\partial v/\partial x$ measures the rate of change of v relative to x *if y is held constant*.

Consider now the relation defined by the equations

$$z = f(x, y); \qquad x = g(t); \qquad y = h(t).$$

The equations really define z as a function of the single variable t and we may develop a formula for the rate of change of z relative to t.　For this purpose we proceed as before but divide Δz by Δt instead of by Δx.　We thus get

$$\frac{\Delta z}{\Delta t} = \frac{\partial z}{\partial x} \cdot \frac{\Delta x}{\Delta t} + \frac{\partial z}{\partial y} \cdot \frac{\Delta y}{\Delta t} + \epsilon \sqrt{\left(\frac{\Delta x}{\Delta t}\right)^2 + \left(\frac{\Delta y}{\Delta t}\right)^2}.$$

If we now let $\Delta t \to 0$, we obtain the formula

$$\frac{dz}{dt} = \frac{\partial z}{\partial x} \cdot \frac{dx}{dt} + \frac{\partial z}{\partial y} \cdot \frac{dy}{dt}.$$

The extension to cases in which more variables are involved is obvious. One of the uses of this total derivative is in connection with problems involving time rates. Suppose, for example, that $U = f(x,\ y,\ z)$ and that at a certain instant x, y, and z are changing at time rates dx/dt, dy/dt, and dz/dt, respectively. The corresponding time rate of change of U is given by

$$\frac{dU}{dt} = \frac{\partial U}{\partial x} \cdot \frac{dx}{dt} + \frac{\partial U}{\partial y} \cdot \frac{dy}{dt} + \frac{\partial U}{\partial z} \cdot \frac{dz}{dt}.$$

165. Directional derivatives.—Let the temperature at any point of the plate shown in Fig. 200 be given by the equation

$$T = f(x,\ y).$$

We have already seen that the value of $\partial T/\partial x$ at any point $P(x,\ y)$ represents the rate of change of the temperature with respect to the distance moved along the plate—say in degrees per inch—in the x-direction. Similarly, $\partial T/\partial y$ measures the corresponding rate in the y-direction. We wish now to derive an expression for the rate of change of T with respect to the distance moved *in any direction*. We proceed as follows:

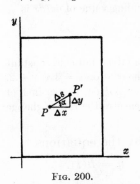

Fig. 200.

Suppose that we move from P to P', this representing a displacement Δx in the x-direction and Δy in the y-direction. The distance moved along the plate is

$$PP' = \Delta s = \sqrt{(\Delta x)^2 + (\Delta y)^2},$$

and the direction is determined by the angle α that PP' makes with the positive x-direction. The change in the value of T corresponding to the displacement from P to P' is

$$\Delta T = \frac{\partial T}{\partial x} \Delta x + \frac{\partial T}{\partial y} \Delta y + \epsilon \sqrt{(\Delta x)^2 + (\Delta y)^2}.$$

If we divide ΔT by the distance moved along the plate, we have

$$\frac{\Delta T}{\Delta s} = \frac{\partial T}{\partial x} \frac{\Delta x}{\Delta s} + \frac{\partial T}{\partial y} \frac{\Delta y}{\Delta s} + \epsilon \sqrt{\left(\frac{\Delta x}{\Delta s}\right)^2 + \left(\frac{\Delta y}{\Delta s}\right)^2}.$$

But $\Delta x/\Delta s = \cos \alpha$ and $\Delta y/\Delta s = \sin \alpha$. Making these substitutions and letting P' approach P along the line PP', we have

(1) $$\frac{dT}{ds} = \frac{\partial T}{\partial x} \cos \alpha + \frac{\partial T}{\partial y} \sin \alpha.$$

This is the *directional derivative* of T in the direction α.

Example

If $T = 3xy + 2y$, where x and y are in inches and T is in degrees, then

$$\frac{\partial T}{\partial x} = 3y; \qquad \frac{\partial T}{\partial y} = 3x + 2.$$

At the point (2, 2) we have $\partial T/\partial x = 6$ and $\partial T/\partial y = 8$ (degrees per inch). If we take $\alpha = 45°$, we have for this direction

$$\frac{dT}{ds} = 6 \frac{\sqrt{2}}{2} + 8 \frac{\sqrt{2}}{2} = 7 \sqrt{2} = 9.9 \quad \text{(degrees per inch)}.$$

We may investigate dT/ds for maximum and minimum values at a fixed point on the plate by taking its derivative with respect to α:

$$\frac{d}{d\alpha}\left(\frac{dT}{ds}\right) = \frac{\partial T}{\partial x} (-\sin \alpha) + \frac{\partial T}{\partial y} \cos \alpha.$$

Setting this equal to zero and solving for α, we get

$$\tan \alpha = \frac{\dfrac{\partial T}{\partial y}}{\dfrac{\partial T}{\partial x}}.$$

The numerically largest value of dT/ds occurs when α has this value, and from (1) it is found that this greatest value of dT/ds is

$$\left.\frac{dT}{ds}\right|_{\text{max.}} = \sqrt{\left(\frac{\partial T}{\partial x}\right)^2 + \left(\frac{\partial T}{\partial y}\right)^2}.$$

This greatest rate of change of T is called the *gradient* of the temperature at the point.

Example

In the last example we had at the point $(2, 2)$:

$$\frac{\partial T}{\partial x} = 6; \qquad \frac{\partial T}{\partial y} = 8.$$

At this point the maximum rate of change of the temperature is

$$\left.\frac{dT}{ds}\right|_{\text{max.}} = \sqrt{6^2 + 8^2} = 10 \text{ deg. per inch.}$$

This maximum rate occurs in the direction given by

$$\tan \alpha = \frac{\dfrac{\partial T}{\partial y}}{\dfrac{\partial T}{\partial x}} = \frac{8}{6} = \frac{4}{3}.$$

We may consider now a more abstract situation. If $z = f(x, y)$, then the quantity

$$\frac{dz}{ds} = \frac{\partial z}{\partial x} \cos \alpha + \frac{\partial z}{\partial y} \sin \alpha$$

is the *directional derivative* of z in the direction α. Its value measures the rate of change of z with respect to the distance moved in the xy-plane, for the particular direction chosen. If we interpret the equation $z = f(x, y)$ as representing a surface, then the directional derivative represents the slope of a line drawn tangent to the surface and having the direction α as shown in Fig. 201. The numerically greatest value of dz/ds at a given point is called the *gradient* of the function at the point. Its value is

$$\left.\frac{dz}{ds}\right|_{\text{max.}} = \sqrt{\left(\frac{\partial z}{\partial x}\right)^2 + \left(\frac{\partial z}{\partial y}\right)^2}.$$

This can be interpreted geometrically as the slope of the steepest tangent line that can be drawn to the surface at the point. The angle α determining this steepest

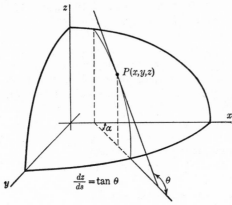

$$\frac{dz}{ds} = \tan \theta$$

FIG. 201.

tangent is given by

$$\tan \alpha = \frac{\dfrac{\partial z}{\partial y}}{\dfrac{\partial z}{\partial x}}.$$

PROBLEMS

1. The radius and height of a right circular cylinder are both increasing subject to the relation $h = 2\sqrt{r} + 3$. If v denotes its volume, find the value of dv/dr when $r = 4$ in. Explain the difference between this rate and $\partial v/\partial r$.

2. The radius of a right circular cone increases at $\frac{1}{2}$ in. per minute, and the height is always equal to $\frac{1}{4}r^2 + 4$. Evaluate dv/dr and dv/dt when $r = 6$ in. State in what units each rate is expressed.

3. The temperature at any point $P(x, y)$ of a plate is given by the equation $T = 0.4xy + 0.6\sqrt{y}$ where x and y are in inches and T is in degrees. If $y = 2x$, find the value of dT/dx at the point where $x = 2$ in. and explain the physical significance of the result.

HINT: As you move along the plate on the line $y = 2x$, x and y are both changing. The value of dT/dx is the rate of change of T relative to x—in degrees per inch of displacement in the x-direction.

4. If $z = xy^2 + 4x$ and if x and y vary subject to the relation $x^2 + y^2 = 25$, find the value of dz/dx at $(3, 4)$. Check your result by eliminating y between the two given equations and then differentiating.

5. If $z = xy + x^2$ and if x and y satisfy the relations $x = 4 \cos t$, $y = 3 \sin t$, find the value of dz/dt when $t = \frac{1}{4}\pi$. Check your result by expressing z directly in terms of t and then differentiating.

6. Two sides and the included angle of a triangle are x, y, and θ, respectively. At a certain instant $x = 15$ in., $y = 10$ in., and $\theta = \frac{1}{3}\pi$; x and y are increasing at 0.2 in. per minute and θ is decreasing at 0.015 radian per minute. At what time rate is the area changing?

7. The altitude of a right circular cone is 24 in. and is increasing at 0.3 in. per minute. The radius of the base is 9 in. and is decreasing at 0.06 in. per minute. At what time rate is its volume changing?

8. The pressure, volume, and absolute temperature of a gas are connected by the equation $pv = 50T$. At a certain instant $p = 1,800$ lb. per square foot and is decreasing at a rate of 24 lb. per square foot per minute; the temperature is 660° and is increasing at 0.8° per minute. At what time rate is the volume changing?

9. Sketch the first octant of the sphere $x^2 + y^2 + z^2 = 36$. Show the curve AB cut from the surface by the plane $y = 2x$. Draw the tangent to this curve at $P(2, 4, 4)$ and find its slope.

10. A line is drawn so as to intersect the z-axis and be tangent to the ellipsoid $x^2 + 2y^2 + z^2 = 25$, at $P(4, 2, 1)$. Find its slope.

11. The temperature at every point of a heated circular plate is given by the formula

$$T = \frac{72}{x^2 + y^2 + 4}$$

where T is in degrees and x and y are in inches, these being measured from an origin at the center of the plate. At the point $(2, 4)$ find the rate of change of T in the direction for which $\alpha = 30°$.

12. In Prob. 11 find the direction and magnitude of the greatest rate of change of T at the point $(2, 4)$.

13. If $v = \dfrac{50y}{x^2 + y^2}$, find the rate of change of v at the point $(4, 2)$ in the directions $\alpha = \arctan\left(-\frac{3}{4}\right)$ and $\alpha = \arctan \frac{4}{3}$.

14. If $v = \log \sqrt{x^2 + y^2}$, show that v is constant along any circle with center at the origin. Show also that at any point $P(x, y)$ the direction of the gradient of v is that of the radial line drawn through P and the origin.

15. If $T = f(x, y)$, show that at any point $P(x, y)$ the direction in which $dT/ds = 0$ is given by $\tan \alpha = \dfrac{-\partial T/\partial x}{\partial T/\partial y}$. Hence show that the direction in which dT/ds is largest is perpendicular to that in which it is zero.

16. The contour lines on a surface $z = f(x, y)$ are the curves cut from the surface by the planes $z = k$. Show that the direction of the contour line at any point P on the surface is given by

$$\tan \alpha = -\frac{\dfrac{\partial z}{\partial x}}{\dfrac{\partial z}{\partial y}}.$$

Hence show that the steepest curve at P is perpendicular to the contour line. HINT: The direction of the contour line is determined by putting $dz/ds = 0$. Why?

166. Differentiation of implicit functions.—We have already seen that an equation of the form

(1) $$\phi(x, y) = 0$$

may define y as a differentiable function of x. In such cases we have found $D_x y$ by a method that we called *implicit differentiation* (page 56). An equivalent method can be derived as follows: Consider the relation

$$U = \phi(x, y).$$

Then, whether x and y are independent variables or not,

(2) $$dU = \frac{\partial \phi}{\partial x}\, dx + \frac{\partial \phi}{\partial y}\, dy.$$

Now if x and y are restricted to values that satisfy (1), then $U \equiv 0$ and $dU \equiv 0$. If we replace dU in (2) by 0, and solve for dy/dx we have

(3) $$\frac{dy}{dx} = -\frac{\dfrac{\partial \phi}{\partial x}}{\dfrac{\partial \phi}{\partial y}} \qquad \left(\frac{\partial \phi}{\partial y} \neq 0\right).$$

Example

Assuming that the equation $x^3 + y^3 + 4x^2y - 25 = 0$ defines y as a function of x, find dy/dx.

Solution

Let
$$\phi(x, y) = x^3 + y^3 + 4x^2y - 25;$$
then
$$\frac{\partial \phi}{\partial x} = 3x^2 + 8xy; \qquad \frac{\partial \phi}{\partial y} = 3y^2 + 4x^2.$$

Using (3) we have

$$\frac{dy}{dx} = -\frac{3x^2 + 8xy}{3y^2 + 4x^2}.$$

We had seen previously that an equation of the form (1) may not define y as a function of x, and we now note that (3) is meaningless if $\partial\phi/\partial y = 0$. It can be shown that if (1) is satisfied by the coordinates (x_1, y_1) of a point P, and if the partial derivatives in (3) are continuous over an interval about this point, and if $\partial\phi/\partial y \neq 0$ at P, then (1) does define y as a function of x in the neighborhood of P and it has the derivative given by (3). Thus the given equation in the last example is satisfied by (2, 1). The partial derivatives are continuous and $\partial\phi/\partial y \neq 0$. Hence the equation certainly defines y as a function of x at least in the neighborhood of (2, 1). This function, which might be obtained by solving the given equation for y in terms of x, has a derivative whose value at (2, 1) is $-\frac{28}{19}$.

Consider now the relation

(4) $\phi(x, y, z) = 0.$

Assuming that (4) defines z as a function of x and y, we may find $\partial z/\partial x$ as follows: Let $U = \phi(x, y, z)$ so that

(5) $$dU = \frac{\partial\phi}{\partial x}\,dx + \frac{\partial\phi}{\partial y}\,dy + \frac{\partial\phi}{\partial z}\,dz.$$

Now if x, y, and z are restricted to values that satisfy (4), $U \equiv 0$ and $dU \equiv 0$. The symbol $(dz/dx)_y$, or $\partial z/\partial x$, denotes the rate of change of z relative to x when y is held constant $(dy = 0)$. Putting $dU = 0$ and $dy = 0$ in (5) and solving for dz/dx, we have

(6) $$\left(\frac{dz}{dx}\right)_y \text{ or } \frac{\partial z}{\partial x} = -\frac{\dfrac{\partial\phi}{\partial x}}{\dfrac{\partial\phi}{\partial z}} \qquad \left(\frac{\partial\phi}{\partial z} \neq 0\right).$$

In a similar way we find that

(7) $$\left(\frac{dz}{dy}\right)_x \text{ or } \frac{\partial z}{\partial y} = -\frac{\dfrac{\partial\phi}{\partial y}}{\dfrac{\partial\phi}{\partial z}} \qquad \left(\frac{\partial\phi}{\partial z} \neq 0\right).$$

The conditions under which an equation of the form (4) defines z as a differentiable function of x and y are similar to those just given for the case of an equation of the form (1). In general, an equation involving any number of variables defines any one of them as a function of the others. The partial derivative of this (dependent) variable with respect to any one of the other variables can be found by means of formulas like (6) and (7).

Example

Find $\partial U/\partial y$ from the equation $U^2 + xU + y^2 + z^2 + 4 = 0$.

Solution

Let
$$\phi(x,\, y,\, z,\, U) = U^2 + xU + y^2 + z^2 + 4.$$
Then
$$\frac{\partial \phi}{\partial y} = 2y, \qquad \frac{\partial \phi}{\partial U} = 2U + x,$$
and
$$\frac{\partial U}{\partial y} = -\frac{\dfrac{\partial \phi}{\partial y}}{\dfrac{\partial \phi}{\partial U}} = -\frac{2y}{2U + x}.$$

This derivative measures the rate of change of U relative to y when x and z are held constant.

167. Partial derivatives of higher order.—The partial derivatives $\partial z/\partial x$ and $\partial z/\partial y$ of a function $z = f(x,\, y)$ are themselves, in general, functions of x and y that in turn have partial derivatives with respect to x and y. The following notation is used to denote these *second partial derivatives:*

$$\frac{\partial}{\partial x}\left(\frac{\partial z}{\partial x}\right) = \frac{\partial^2 z}{\partial x^2} = f_{xx}(x,\, y).$$

$$\frac{\partial}{\partial y}\left(\frac{\partial z}{\partial y}\right) = \frac{\partial^2 z}{\partial y^2} = f_{yy}(x,\, y).$$

$$\begin{cases} \dfrac{\partial}{\partial y}\left(\dfrac{\partial z}{\partial x}\right) = \dfrac{\partial^2 z}{\partial y\,\partial x} = f_{xy}(x,\, y). \\[2ex] \dfrac{\partial}{\partial x}\left(\dfrac{\partial z}{\partial y}\right) = \dfrac{\partial^2 z}{\partial x\,\partial y} = f_{yx}(x,\, y). \end{cases}$$

It thus appears that there are four different second partial derivatives of a function of two variables. It can be shown, however, that the last two are identical for all values of x and y for which they are continuous; *i.e.*, if one differentiates $f(x, y)$ with respect to x and then differentiates the result with respect to y, he obtains the same result as if he had performed the differentiations in the reverse order.

The notation can easily be extended to derivatives of higher order. Thus, there are four partial derivatives of $f(x, y)$ of third order, *namely*,

$$\frac{\partial^3 f}{\partial x^3}, \quad \frac{\partial^3 f}{\partial x^2 \, \partial y}, \quad \frac{\partial^3 f}{\partial x \, \partial y^2}, \quad \frac{\partial^3 f}{\partial y^3}.$$

Here, the symbol $\dfrac{\partial^3 f}{\partial x \, \partial y^2}$ denotes the result of differentiating $f(x, y)$ successively three times—twice with respect to y and once with respect to x. The order in which these differentiations are performed is immaterial.

PROBLEMS

In each of the following cases find $D_x y$ by two methods, without first solving for y:

1. $x^3 + xy^2 - 4 = 0$.   2. $xy^2 + x - 16 = 0$.
3. $xy + 2y + 4x - 7 = 0$.   4. $x^3 + y^3 - 6xy = 0$.
5. $y^3 + 2xy = x^2 + 4$.   6. $x^4 - xy^3 = x + 2y + 4$.

In each of the following cases find $\partial z / \partial x$ and $\partial z / \partial y$:

7. $x^2 + y^2 + 4z^2 = 20$.   8. $x^2 + 4xy + y^2 - z^2 + 4 = 0$.
9. $xyz - z^3 + x^2 + y^2 = 4$.   10. $x^4 - 2xyz^2 + y^3z + 3 = 0$.

11. $x^3 + U^2z + 4xyz + U^3 + 2 = 0$; find $\dfrac{\partial U}{\partial z}$.

12. $\dfrac{y}{x} + \dfrac{3z}{x^2 y} = 4$; find $\dfrac{\partial z}{\partial x}$.

13. Find $\partial v / \partial t$ from the equation $x^2 + y^2 + v^2 - t^2 x + 2t = 0$.
14. Find $\partial z / \partial t$ from the equation $z^3 + x^3 + t^3x + xy^2 = 4$.
15. Show that the normal to the surface defined by the equation $\phi(x, y, z) = 0$, at a point P on the surface, has the direction numbers

$$\left(\frac{\partial \phi}{\partial x}\right)_P : \left(\frac{\partial \phi}{\partial y}\right)_P : \left(\frac{\partial \phi}{\partial z}\right)_P.$$

16. Show that the equation of the tangent plane to the surface defined by the equation $\phi(x, y, z) = 0$, at a point P on the surface, is

$$\left(\frac{\partial \phi}{\partial x}\right)_P (x - x_1) + \left(\frac{\partial \phi}{\partial y}\right)_P (y - y_1) + \left(\frac{\partial \phi}{\partial z}\right)_P (z - z_1) = 0.$$

What are the equations of the normal line?

17. Find the equations of the tangent plane and normal line to the ellipsoid $x^2 + 2y^2 + 2z^2 = 14$ at $(2, 1, 2)$.

In each of the following, find $\partial^2 z/\partial x^2$, $\partial^2 z/\partial y^2$, and $\partial^2 z/\partial x\,\partial y$:

18. $z = 4x^2 y^2 + y^3$.   **19.** $z = xy^2 + 2y^3 + 4$.

20. $z = \dfrac{x + y}{x - y}$.   **21.** $z = \dfrac{xy}{x + y}$.

22. $z = y \sin (x + y)$.   **23.** $z = e^x \sin y$.

24. Verify that $\dfrac{\partial^2 z}{\partial x\,\partial y} = \dfrac{\partial^2 z}{\partial y\,\partial x}$ for the function

$$z = 6y^3 + 5xy^2 - 4x^3 + 2.$$

25. Using three different orders of differentiation, find $\partial^3 z/\partial x\,\partial y^2$ for the function

$$z = x^3 y^2 - 4xy^4 + 4x^2 y^3.$$

26. Same as Prob. 25 for the function $z = \dfrac{x - y}{x + y}$.

27. Verify that $\dfrac{\partial^2 z}{\partial x^2} + \dfrac{\partial^2 z}{\partial y^2} = 0$ if $z = \log \sqrt{x^2 + y^2}$.

28. Verify that $\dfrac{\partial^2 z}{\partial x^2} + \dfrac{\partial^2 z}{\partial y^2} = 0$ if $z = Ae^x \cos y$.

29. Verify that $\dfrac{\partial^2 U}{\partial x^2} + \dfrac{\partial^2 U}{\partial y^2} + \dfrac{\partial^2 U}{\partial z^2} = 0$ if $U = (x^2 + y^2 + z^2)^{-\frac{1}{2}}$.

30. Verify that $\dfrac{\partial^2 z}{\partial x^2} - \dfrac{\partial^2 z}{\partial y^2} = 0$ if $z = \cos (x + y) + \cos (x - y)$.

31. Verify that $\dfrac{\partial^2 z}{\partial x^2} + \dfrac{\partial^2 z}{\partial y^2} = 0$ if $z = \log (x^2 + y^2) + \arctan \dfrac{y}{x}$.

32. Verify that $\dfrac{\partial^2 z}{\partial x^2} + \dfrac{\partial^2 z}{\partial y\,\partial x} - 6\dfrac{\partial^2 z}{\partial y^2} = 0$ if

$$z = 9x^2 - 6xy + y^2 + 2x + y.$$

33. Verify that $\dfrac{\partial^2 z}{\partial t^2} = a^2 \dfrac{\partial^2 z}{\partial x^2}$ if $z = A \cos (kat) \sin (kx)$ where A and k are arbitrary constants.

CHAPTER XXVI

MULTIPLE INTEGRALS

168. Definite double integral.—The symbol

$$\int_{x=a}^{x=b} \left[\int_{y=c}^{y=d} f(x, y)dy \right] dx, \quad \text{or simply} \quad \int_a^b \int_c^d f(x, y)dy \, dx$$

is called a *definite double integral*. Its value is defined in terms of two successive integrations as follows: First integrate $f(x, y)$ with respect to y between the limits $y = c$ and $y = d$; in this integration x is treated as a constant. Then, integrate the result with respect to x between the limits $x = a$ and $x = b$.

Example

Evaluate $\int_1^2 \int_0^3 (x^2 + y^2)dy \, dx$.

Solution

Integrating with respect to y between limits $y = 0$ and $y = 3$, we have

$$\int_1^2 \int_0^3 (x^2 + y^2)dy \, dx = \int_1^2 x^2 y + \frac{y^3}{3} \Big]_{y=0}^{y=3} dx$$
$$= \int_1^2 (3x^2 + 9)dx.$$

Integrating next with respect to x gives

$$= x^3 + 9x \Big]_1^2$$
$$= 16.$$

In applied problems the limits c and d are often functions of x instead of constants.

Example

Evaluate $\int_0^1 \int_x^{x^2} (x^2 + 3y + 2)dy \, dx$.

Solution

$$\int_0^1 \int_x^{x^2} (x^2 + 3y + 2)dy\, dx = \int_0^1 x^2y + \frac{3y^2}{2} + 2y \Big]_x^{x^2} dx$$

$$= \int_0^1 \left(\frac{5x^4}{2} - x^3 + \frac{x^2}{2} - 2x \right) dx$$

$$= \frac{x^5}{2} - \frac{x^4}{4} + \frac{x^3}{6} - x^2 \Big]_0^1$$

$$= -\frac{7}{12}.$$

169. Definite multiple integral.—The notation just used can easily be extended to functions of any number of variables. Thus, the symbol

$$\int_a^b \int_c^d \int_e^f f(x, y, z)dz\, dy\, dx$$

means that $f(x, y, z)$ is to be integrated with respect to z between the limits $z = e$ and $z = f$, x and y being treated as constants; the result is to be integrated with respect to y between the limits $y = c$ and $y = d$, x being treated as a constant; and finally this result is to be integrated with respect to x between the limits $x = a$ and $x = b$.

Example

Evaluate $\int_2^4 \int_1^2 \int_0^1 (xyz)\, dz\, dy\, dx$.

Solution

$$\int_2^4 \int_1^2 \int_0^1 (xyz)dz\, dy\, dx = \int_2^4 \int_1^2 \frac{xyz^2}{2} \Big]_0^1 dy\, dx$$

$$= \frac{1}{2} \int_2^4 \int_1^2 xy\, dy\, dx$$

$$= \frac{1}{2} \int_2^4 \frac{xy^2}{2} \Big]_1^2 dx$$

$$= \frac{3}{4} \int_2^4 x\, dx$$

$$= \frac{3}{4}\,(6) = \frac{9}{2}.$$

In later applications the limits on $z(e$ and $f)$ often are functions of x and y, and the limits on $y(c$ and $d)$ may be functions of x.

Example

Evaluate $\int_0^1 \int_0^x \int_0^{x+y} dz\, dy\, dx$.

Solution

In this case $f(x, y, z) \equiv 1$, and since $\int (1) dz = z$, we have

$$\int_0^1 \int_0^x \int_0^{x+y} dz\, dy\, dx = \int_0^1 \int_0^x z \Big]_0^{x+y} dy\, dx$$

$$= \int_0^1 \int_0^x (x + y) dy\, dx$$

$$= \int_0^1 xy + \frac{y^2}{2} \Big]_0^x dx$$

$$= \int_0^1 \tfrac{3}{2} x^2 dx = \tfrac{1}{2}.$$

The student should note carefully that, in this book, limits on the *inside* integral sign refer to the variable indicated by the *inside* differential. In some textbooks the opposite convention is used.

PROBLEMS

Evaluate the following integrals:

1. $\int_1^4 \int_3^5 x\, dy\, dx$.

2. $\int_0^2 \int_1^3 2xy\, dy\, dx$.

3. $\int_0^3 \int_0^1 (x^2 + 3y^2) dy\, dx$.

4. $\int_{-4}^4 \int_0^2 (4y - x) dy\, dx$.

5. $\int_0^3 \int_0^{2x-x^2} x\, dy\, dx$.

6. $\int_2^6 \int_{\sqrt{x}}^x y\, dy\, dx$.

7. $\int_0^{\frac{1}{2}\pi} \int_0^{4\sin\theta} \rho\, d\rho\, d\theta$.

8. $\int_0^\pi \int_0^{1+\cos\theta} \rho\, d\rho\, d\theta$.

9. $\int_0^{\frac{1}{4}\pi} \int_2^{4\cos\theta} r\, dr\, d\theta$.

10. $\int_0^{\frac{1}{2}\pi} \int_0^{2a\cos\theta} r\, dr\, d\theta$.

11. $\int_0^1 \int_{-t}^t (z + t) dz\, dt$.

12. $\int_0^2 \int_0^{\sqrt{4-t^2}} \sqrt{4 - t^2}\, du\, dt$.

13. $\int_0^1 \int_0^2 \int_1^4 xy\, dz\, dy\, dx$.

14. $\int_{-4}^4 \int_2^4 \int_0^1 (x + 3z^2) dz\, dy\, dx$.

15. $\int_2^4 \int_0^x \int_0^{\sqrt{x+y}} z\, dz\, dy\, dx$.

16. $\int_0^\pi \int_0^{2\pi} \int_0^a \rho^2 \sin\phi\, d\rho\, d\theta\, d\phi$.

17. $\int_0^{\frac{1}{2}\pi} \int_0^{a\cos\theta} \int_0^{\sqrt{a^2-r^2}} r\, dz\, dr\, d\theta$.

170. Area by double integration.—We may easily express as a double integral the (algebraic) area $PQRS$ bounded by the curves $y = f(x)$ and $y = \varphi(x)$ and the ordinates at $x = a$ and $x = b$. For, from previous considerations

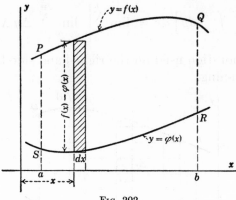

Fɪɢ. 202.

(Fig. 202),

$$PQRS = aPQb - aSRb$$
$$= \int_a^b f(x)dx - \int_a^b \varphi(x)dx$$
$$= \int_a^b [f(x) - \varphi(x)]dx.$$

But this last integral is exactly the same as $\int_a^b \int_{\varphi(x)}^{f(x)} dy\, dx$; hence,

$$\boldsymbol{PQRS = \int_a^b \int_{\varphi(x)}^{f(x)} dy\, dx.}$$

In order to interpret this double integration as a double summation process we may divide the area into small rectangular *elements* with bases Δx and altitudes Δy (plus some little irregular areas) by drawing lines parallel to the axes as shown in Fig. 203.   The first of the two integrations (with respect to y) amounts to summing up all the elements that lie in a vertical strip and taking the limit of the sum as $\Delta y \to 0$, x and Δx remaining fixed; *i.e.*,

$$\left[\int_{\varphi(x)}^{f(x)} dy \right] \cdot \Delta x = [f(x) - \varphi(x)] \cdot \Delta x$$
$$= \text{area } klmn$$
$$= \lim_{\Delta y \to 0} \sum_{\varphi(x)}^{f(x)} \Delta y \cdot \Delta x.$$

The second integration amounts to finding the limit of the sum of such strips from $x = a$ to $x = b$ as $\Delta x \to 0$. Hence,

$$\int_a^b \left[\int_{\varphi(x)}^{f(x)} dy \right] dx = \lim_{\Delta x \to 0} \sum_a^b \left[\lim_{\Delta y \to 0} \sum_{\varphi(x)}^{f(x)} \Delta y \, \Delta x \right]$$

where the notation used on the right-hand side has a fairly obvious meaning.

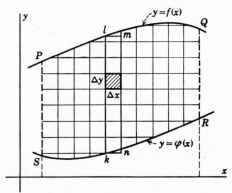

FIG. 203.

Whenever it is more convenient one may of course integrate first with respect to x and then with respect to y.

Example

Compute the area enclosed by the parabola $y^2 = 2x + 4$ and the line $y = x - 2$.

Solution

The area is shown in Fig. 204. It is convenient in this case to integrate first with respect to x, thus summing the little area elements into a horizontal strip extending from the parabola to the line. The limits for this integration are from $x = \frac{1}{2}(y^2 - 4)$ to $x = y + 2$. We then sum these strips by integrating with respect to y between the limits $y = -2$ and $y = 4$. Thus

$$A = \int_{-2}^4 \int_{\frac{1}{2}(y^2-4)}^{y+2} dx \, dy$$
$$= \int_{-2}^4 [(y + 2) - \frac{1}{2}(y^2 - 4)]dy$$
$$= \int_{-2}^4 (4 + y - \frac{1}{2}y^2)dy = 18.$$

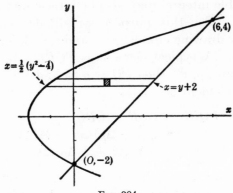

Fig. 204.

171. Area in polar coordinates.

—The area bounded by the polar curves $\rho = f(\theta)$ and $\rho = g(\theta)$ and the radial lines $\theta = \theta_1$ and $\theta = \theta_2$ may also be expressed as a double

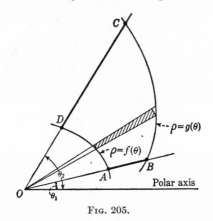

Fig. 205.

integral. Referring to Fig. 205, we have

$$ABCD = OBC - OAD$$

$$= \tfrac{1}{2} \int_{\theta_1}^{\theta_2} g^2(\theta)d\theta - \tfrac{1}{2} \int_{\theta_1}^{\theta_2} f^2(\theta)d\theta$$

$$= \tfrac{1}{2} \int_{\theta_1}^{\theta_2} [g^2(\theta) - f^2(\theta)]d\theta.$$

But this is exactly the same as $\int_{\theta_1}^{\theta_2} \int_{f(\theta)}^{g(\theta)} \rho \, d\rho \, d\theta$; hence,

$$ABCD = \int_{\theta_1}^{\theta_2} \int_{f(\theta)}^{g(\theta)} \rho \, d\rho \, d\theta.$$

This double integral may also be interpreted as a double summation. For this purpose we divide the area into elements by drawing circular arcs and radial lines as shown in Fig. 206. A typical element is $PQRS$. If the coordinates of P are (ρ, θ), then $PQ = \rho \, \Delta\theta$ and $PS = \Delta\rho$. The area of the element is

$$
\begin{aligned}
PQRS &= OSR - OPQ \\
&= \tfrac{1}{2}(\rho + \Delta\rho)^2 \Delta\theta - \tfrac{1}{2}\rho^2 \Delta\theta \\
&= \rho \, \Delta\rho \, \Delta\theta + \tfrac{1}{2}(\Delta\rho)^2 \Delta\theta.
\end{aligned}
$$

It can be shown that the double integral given above is equal to the limit of the sum of such elements. The first

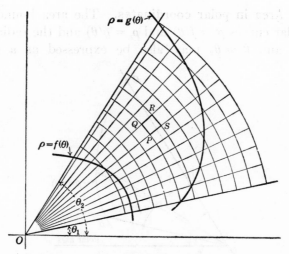

Fig. 206.

integration (with respect to ρ) sums them into a strip extending from $f(\theta)$ to $g(\theta)$ as shown in Fig. 205. The second integration sums these strips from $\theta = \theta_1$ to $\theta = \theta_2$.

172. Moments. Product of inertia.—Suppose that one multiplies the area of each little rectangular element in Fig. 203 by the square of the distance of the element from the x-axis and adds the quantities so obtained. The limit of this sum is the second moment of the area with respect to the x-axis; *i.e.*,

$$
I_x = \int\int y^2 dy \, dx
$$

where the limits are to be chosen so as to cover the area. Similarly,

$$I_y = \iint x^2 dy\, dx;$$
$$I_0 = \iint (x^2 + y^2) dy\, dx.$$

In polar coordinates we have

$$I_0 = \iint (\rho^2)\rho\, d\rho\, d\theta = \iint \rho^3 d\rho\, d\theta;$$
$$I_x = \iint (\rho \sin \theta)^2 \rho\, d\rho\, d\theta = \iint \rho^3 \sin^2 \theta\, d\rho\, d\theta; \text{ etc.}$$

The value of

$$\iint xy\, dy\, dx$$

taken over an area is called the *product of inertia* of the area with respect to the coordinate axes. Its value is, roughly speaking, the result of multiplying the area of each element by the *product* of its distances from the axes and adding the resulting quantities. It is important in connection with the theory of bending of beams and columns having unsymmetrical cross sections.

In general, the symbol

$$\iint_{(s)} f(x,\, y) dy\, dx \qquad \text{or} \qquad \iint_{(s)} f(\rho,\, \theta)\rho\, d\rho\, d\theta$$

is called the integral of the function $f(x, y)$ or $f(\rho, \theta)$ over the area or region S. As we have seen above, it may have various physical and geometrical interpretations, depending upon the nature of the function involved.

PROBLEMS

In each of the following problems compute the area bounded by the given curve or curves using a double integral:

1. $y = x^2$; $y = 5x$.
2. $y = 4x - x^2$; $x + y = 0$.
3. $y^2 = 4x$; $x^2 = 4y$.
4. $y^2 = 8 - 2x$; $y = x$.
5. $y = 2x - x^2$; $y = x^2 - 3x$.
6. $x^2 = 8y$; $y = \frac{1}{2}(x + 8)$.
7. $y = \dfrac{3x}{x^2 + 2}$; $4y = x^2$.
8. $y = \dfrac{x}{x^2 + 1}$; $5y = x$.
9. $\dfrac{x^2}{a^2} + \dfrac{y^2}{b^2} = 1$.
10. $x = 4y^2 - y^3$; $x = 4y - y^2$.
11. $\rho = 2 \sin 3\theta$.
12. $\rho = a(1 + \cos \theta)$.
13. $\rho = 2 + \sin \theta$.
14. $\rho^2 = a^2 \cos 2\theta$.

15. Find the area that is inside the lemniscate $\rho^2 = 8 \cos 2\theta$ and outside the circle $\rho = 2$.

16. Find the area that is common to the circle $\rho = 3 \cos \theta$ and the cardioid $\rho = \cos \theta + 1$.

17. Find the area that is inside the circle $\rho = a \cos \theta$ and outside the cardioid $\rho = a(1 - \cos \theta)$.

18. Show that for a given area $I_0 = I_x + I_y$.

19. Compute I_x for the area of the circle $x^2 + y^2 = r^2$ using a double integral.

20. Compute the product of inertia of the area of a rectangle $ABCD$ with respect to sides AB and BC. $AB = 6$ in. and $BC = 8$ in.

21. Compute the product of inertia of the area of one quadrant of the circle $x^2 + y^2 = r^2$.

22. Evaluate the double integral of the function $f(x, y) = x^2 + y^2$ over the area bounded by the coordinate axes and the line $x + 2y = 6$. Interpret the result.

23. Compute the value of I_0 for the area of the circle $\rho = 2r \cos \theta$.

24. Set up a double integral whose value is equal to I_x for the area inside the circle $\rho = 3 \cos \theta$ and outside the cardioid $\rho = 1 + \cos \theta$.

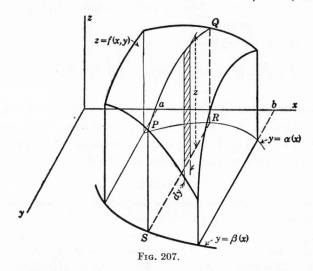

FIG. 207.

173. Volume by double integration.—We wish now to express as a double integral the volume between the xy-plane and the surface $z = f(x, y)$, bounded on the sides by two arbitrary cylindrical surfaces $y = \alpha(x)$ and $y = \beta(x)$, and the planes $x = a$ and $x = b$ (Fig. 207).

From previous considerations we know that

$$V = \int_a^b A(x)dx$$

where $A(x)$ is the area of the section $PQRS$ at a distance

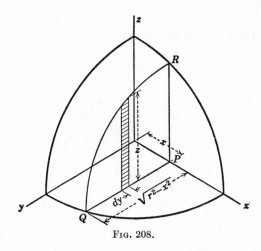

FIG. 208.

x from the yz-plane. Also

$$A(x) = \int_{\alpha(x)}^{\beta(x)} z\ dy = \int_{\alpha(x)}^{\beta(x)} f(x,\ y)dy$$

where x is held constant during the integration. Hence,

$$V = \int_a^b \int_{\alpha(x)}^{\beta(x)} f(x,\ y)dy\ dx.$$

Example

Express the volume of one octant of the sphere $x^2 + y^2 + z^2 = r^2$ as a double integral.

Solution (Fig. 208)

$$\text{Area } PQR = A(x) = \int_0^{\sqrt{r^2-x^2}} z\ dy.$$

$$V = \int_0^r A(x)dx = \int_0^r \int_0^{\sqrt{r^2-x^2}} z\ dy\ dx$$

$$= \int_0^r \int_0^{\sqrt{r^2-x^2}} \sqrt{r^2 - x^2 - y^2}\ dy\ dx.$$

It is important to interpret this integration also as a

double summation process. The quantity $z \, \Delta y \, \Delta x$ is the volume of a rectangular column with base Δy by Δx and height z, as indicated in Fig. 209. The student will easily see, using the figure, that the first integration (with respect to y) sums these columns into a slice extending from $y = 0$ to $y = \sqrt{r^2 - x^2}$. The second integration, then, sums all the slices from $x = 0$ to $x = r$.

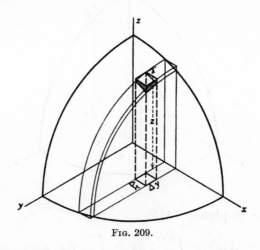

Fig. 209.

174. Volume by triple integration.—The student who has a clear mental picture of the process of computing area by means of a double integral will have no difficulty in extending his ideas to a third dimension. Just as an area is divided into rectangular elements by drawing lines parallel to the axes, a volume is divided into elements having the form of rectangular parallelepipeds (plus some little irregular pieces) by passing planes parallel to the coordinate planes. If the octant of a sphere shown in Fig. 210 be so divided, the little parallelepiped with edges Δz, Δy, and Δx is a typical volume element. The whole volume is the limit of the sum of such elements. The summation may conveniently be carried out as follows:

1. Sum the elements in a vertical column extending from the xy-plane to the surface. This requires integration

with respect to z from $z = 0$ to

$$z = f(x, y) = \sqrt{r^2 - x^2 - y^2}.$$

KM is a typical column.

2. Sum the columns in a slice parallel to the yz-plane extending from the x-axis to the bounding curve in the xy-plane. This requires integration with respect to y from $y = 0$ to $y = \varphi(x) = \sqrt{r^2 - x^2}$.

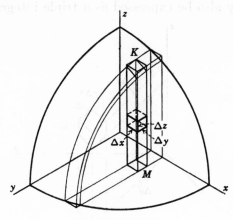

Fig. 210.

3. Sum the slices from $x = 0$ to $x = r$ by integrating with respect to x. We have, then,

$$V = \int_0^r \int_0^{\sqrt{r^2 - x^2}} \int_0^{\sqrt{r^2 - x^2 - y^2}} dz \, dy \, dx.$$

175. Moments by triple integration.—Suppose that one multiplies the volume of each element in Fig. 210 by the square of the distance $(y^2 + z^2)$ of the element from the x-axis and adds the resulting quantities. The limit of this sum is the value of I_x for the volume; *i.e.*,

$$I_x = \iiint (y^2 + z^2) dz \, dy \, dx$$

taken throughout the volume. Similarly,

$$I_{xz} = \iiint y^2 dz \, dy \, dx, \text{ etc.}$$

In general, the value of

$$\iiint f(x,\ y,\ z)dz\ dy\ dx$$

taken throughout a volume is called the integral of the function $f(x,\ y,\ z)$ over the volume. It may have various physical or geometrical interpretations depending upon the nature of the function $f(x,\ y,\ z)$ and on the physical meanings of the variables themselves.

176. Volume in cylindrical and spherical coordinates.—A volume may also be expressed as a triple integral in cylin-

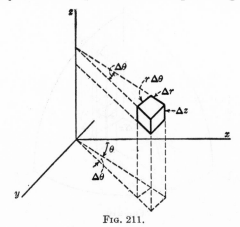

Fig. 211.

drical or spherical coordinates.* In the case of rectangular coordinates we divided the volume into elements by means of the three families of planes $x = k$, $y = k$, and $z = k$. These volume elements were rectangular parallelepipeds having dimensions Δx, Δy, and Δz.

The corresponding procedure in cylindrical coordinates is to divide the solid into elements by means of the concentric cylinders $r = k$, the planes $\theta = k$ that contain the z-axis, and the planes $z = k$. A typical element is shown in Fig. 211. It has the dimensions $r\ \Delta\theta$, Δr, and Δz, and the corresponding triple integral is

$$v = \iiint r\ dz\ dr\ d\theta.$$

* These coordinate systems are discussed on pp. 345–347.

Example

Using cylindrical coordinates find the volume cut from the sphere $x^2 + y^2 + z^2 = 25$ by the cylinder $x^2 + y^2 = 5x$.

Solution

In cylindrical coordinates the equations are

$$r^2 + z^2 = 25,$$
$$r = 5 \cos \theta.$$

The top half of the sphere and the corresponding part of the cylinder are shown in Fig. 212. The required volume, which is twice that shown in the figure, is given by

$$v = 2 \int_{-\frac{1}{2}\pi}^{\frac{1}{2}\pi} \int_0^{5 \cos \theta} \int_0^{\sqrt{25-r^2}} r \, dz \, dr \, d\theta.$$

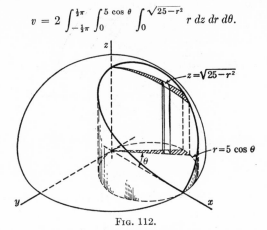

Fig. 112.

Here, the first integration (with respect to z) sums the volume elements into a column extending from the xy-plane up to the spherical surface ($z = 0$ to $z = \sqrt{25 - r^2}$). The second integration sums these columns into the wedge-shaped slice shown in the figure ($r = 0$ to $r = 5 \cos \theta$). The final integration sums these slices for the θ-interval from $-\frac{1}{2}\pi$ to $+\frac{1}{2}\pi$. For the purpose of evaluating the integral it is best to write it in the equivalent form

$$v = 4 \int_0^{\frac{1}{2}\pi} \int_0^{5 \cos \theta} \int_0^{\sqrt{25-r^2}} r \, dz \, dr \, d\theta.$$

We then have

$$v = 4 \int_0^{\frac{1}{2}\pi} \int_0^{5 \cos \theta} \sqrt{25 - r^2} \, r \, dr \, d\theta$$

$$= \tfrac{500}{3} \int_0^{\frac{1}{2}\pi} (1 - \sin^3 \theta) d\theta$$

$$= \tfrac{500}{3}(\tfrac{1}{2}\pi - \tfrac{2}{3}) = 150.7 \text{ cu. units.}$$

When spherical coordinates are used the volume is divided into elements by the spheres $\rho = k$, the cones $\phi = k$, and the planes $\theta = k$. A typical element is constructed as follows (Fig. 213):

Starting at any point $P(\rho,\ \theta,\ \phi)$, let ρ change by an amount $\Delta\rho$, keeping θ and ϕ fixed. We thus move to A and $PA = \Delta\rho$. Again, starting at P, let θ change by an amount $\Delta\theta$, keeping ρ and ϕ fixed. We thus move to B

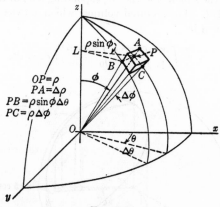

$$OP = \rho$$
$$PA = \Delta\rho$$
$$PB = \rho \sin \phi \Delta\theta$$
$$PC = \rho \Delta\phi$$

Fig. 213.

where PB is an arc of a circle with center at L and radius $LP = OP \sin \phi$; thus $PB = (\rho \sin \phi)\Delta\theta$. Finally, starting at P, let ϕ change by an amount $\Delta\phi$, keeping ρ and θ fixed. In this case we move to C where PC is an arc of a circle with center at O and radius $OP = \rho$; thus $PC = \rho \Delta\phi$. Completing the figure we have the volume element shown. Its dimensions are

$$PA = \Delta\rho; \qquad PB = (\rho \sin \phi)\Delta\theta; \qquad PC = \rho \Delta\phi.$$

It can be shown that the limit of the sum of the volumes of such elements is given by the triple integral

$$v = \iiint \varrho^2 \sin \phi\ d\varrho\ d\theta\ d\phi.$$

The limits must of course be chosen so as to cover the volume to be calculated.

Example

The volume of one octant of a sphere of radius a (Fig. 213) is given by

$$v = \int_0^{\frac{\pi}{2}} \int_0^{\frac{\pi}{2}} \int_0^a \rho^2 \sin \phi \, d\rho \, d\theta \, d\phi.$$

PROBLEMS

1. Using a double integral find the volume bounded by the coordinate planes and the plane $x + y + 2z = 6$.

2. Set up a double integral whose value is equal to the volume bounded by the coordinate planes, the plane $x + y = 4$, and the surface $z = x^2 + y^2$.

3. Set up a double integral whose value is equal to the volume in the first octant under the plane $4x + 6y + 3z = 24$ and inside the cylinder $x^2 + y^2 = 4$.

4. Set up a double integral whose value is equal to the volume of the wedge cut from the cylinder $x^2 + y^2 = 2x$ by the planes $z = 0$ and $z = x$.

In each of the following problems set up triple integrals for the required volume in both rectangular and cylindrical coordinates. In each case evaluate the simpler of the two integrals:

5. The volume lying above the xy-plane, inside the cylinder

$$x^2 + y^2 = 4,$$

and under the surface $2z = x^2 + y^2$.

6. The volume bounded by the paraboloid $x^2 + y^2 = 6 - z$ and the xy-plane.

7. The volume of the cap cut from a sphere of radius 5 in. by a plane whose distance from the center of the sphere is 4 in.

8. The volume lying above the xy-plane, inside the cylinder

$$x^2 + y^2 = 4,$$

and under the paraboloid $x^2 + y^2 + z = 8$.

9. The volume lying above the xy-plane, inside the cylinder

$$x^2 + y^2 = 4,$$

and under the cone $x^2 + y^2 = z^2$.

10. The volume cut from the paraboloid $z = r^2$ by the plane

$$z = r \cos \theta.$$

11. The volume lying above the xy-plane, under the paraboloid $z = x^2 + y^2$, and inside the cylinder $x^2 + y^2 = 2y$.

12. The volume common to the sphere $r^2 + z^2 = a^2$ and the cylinder $r = a \sin \theta$.

13. The volume lying above the xy-plane, inside the cylinder

$$x^2 + y^2 = 4,$$

and under the surface $x^2 + y^2 + 2 = z$.

14. The volume of the ellipsoid $2x^2 + 2y^2 + z^2 = 8$.

15. Using spherical coordinates find the volume of the cap cut from the sphere $x^2 + y^2 + z^2 = 25$ by the plane $z = 3$. Check your result by using the prismoid formula.

16. Using spherical coordinates, find the volume common to the sphere $x^2 + y^2 + z^2 = 8$ and the cone $x^2 + y^2 = z^2$.

17. Using cylindrical coordinates, find the volume common to the ellipsoid $4x^2 + 4y^2 + 9z^2 = 36$ and the cylinder $x^2 + y^2 = 3x$.

18. Using both cylindrical and spherical coordinates, find the volume cut from the sphere $x^2 + y^2 + z^2 = 25$ by the cylinder $x^2 + y^2 = 9$.

19. A solid cylinder with radius 6 in. and height 12 in. is cut by a plane that passes through a diameter of one base and is tangent to the other base. Find the volume of the smaller piece.

20. Find the volume bounded by the cone $x^2 + y^2 = z^2$ and the paraboloid $8z = x^2 + y^2 + 16$.

21. Set up integrals in both cylindrical and spherical coordinates for the volume that is inside the sphere $x^2 + y^2 + z^2 = 8$ and above the surface $z = \frac{1}{2}(x^2 + y^2)$. Compute the volume by one of these methods.

22. Compute the second moment of the mass of a solid homogeneous right circular cylinder with respect to an element of the cylinder using cylindrical coordinates. HINT: Take coordinate system so that equation of cylinder is $r = 2a \cos \theta$ where a is its radius. Find I_z by evaluating $\iiint r^2 \cdot \delta(r \, dz \, dr \, d\theta)$.

23. Find the second moment of the mass of a solid homogeneous sphere with respect to a diameter using cylindrical coordinates.

24. Find the second moment of the mass of a solid homogeneous right circular cone with respect to its axis using spherical coordinates.

CHAPTER XXVII

INFINITE SERIES

177. Introduction.—The student has encountered infinite series in using the binomial theorem for negative or fractional exponents and as a result of other elementary mathematical operations. Thus by ordinary division we obtain the "equation"

$$(1) \qquad \frac{1}{1 + x} = 1 - x + x^2 - x^3 + x^4 - x^5 + \cdots$$

where the dots indicate that the terms continue indefinitely in accordance with a known law. If we put $x = -\frac{1}{2}$, we have

$$2 = 1 + \tfrac{1}{2} + \tfrac{1}{4} + \tfrac{1}{8} + \tfrac{1}{16} + \cdots.$$

This result seems reasonable, since the sum on the right appears to approach 2 as a limit as we take more and more terms. On the other hand, if we put $x = 2$, we have

$$\tfrac{1}{3} = 1 - 2 + 4 - 8 + 16 - \cdots,$$

which appears to be an entirely unreasonable result.

If we multiply both sides of (1) by dx and integrate between the limits $x = 0$ and $x = x$, we have

$$(2) \quad \log (1 + x) = x - \tfrac{1}{2}x^2 + \tfrac{1}{3}x^3 - \tfrac{1}{4}x^4 + \tfrac{1}{5}x^5 - \cdots.$$

If the operations that we have performed are legitimate for some range of values of x, this last "equation" *may* furnish a means of calculating the natural logarithms of numbers. Thus putting $x = 1$ in (2), it may be true that

$$\log 2 = 1 - \tfrac{1}{2} + \tfrac{1}{3} - \tfrac{1}{4} + \tfrac{1}{5} - \cdots.$$

The purpose of this chapter is to study the conditions under which we can use infinite series in this manner.

391

178. Definitions.—A succession of numbers or terms formed according to a definite law is called a *sequence*. Thus the numbers 1, 4, 9, 16, 25 form a sequence, the general or *n*th term being n^2. The indicated sum of a sequence is called a *series*. It is a *finite* or an *infinite* series according as the number of terms is limited or unlimited. Thus the indicated sum

$$1 + \tfrac{1}{2} + \tfrac{1}{4} + \tfrac{1}{8} + \cdots + \frac{1}{2^{n-1}} + \cdots$$

is an infinite series. This same series is indicated by writing

$$\sum_{n=1}^{\infty} \frac{1}{2^{n-1}} \quad \text{or} \quad \sum_{n=0}^{\infty} \frac{1}{2^n}.$$

Thus either $1/2^{n-1}$ or $1/2^n$ may be regarded as the general term. Other examples of finite and infinite series are:

$$\sum_{n=1}^{5} (-1)^{n+1} \frac{1}{n} \equiv 1 - \tfrac{1}{2} + \tfrac{1}{3} - \tfrac{1}{4} + \tfrac{1}{5}.$$

$$\sum_{n=0}^{\infty} \frac{2^n}{n!} \equiv 1^* + \frac{2}{1!} + \frac{2^2}{2!} + \cdots + \frac{2^n}{n!} + \cdots$$

$$\sum_{n=1}^{\infty} \frac{1}{n^2} x^{2n} \equiv \frac{x^2}{1^2} + \frac{x^4}{2^2} + \frac{x^6}{3^2} + \cdots + \frac{x^{2n}}{n^2} + \cdots$$

We may sometimes write $\sum u_n$ to mean $\sum_{n=1}^{\infty} u_n$ or $\sum_{n=0}^{\infty} u_n$ in places where there can be no doubt as to what is meant. When we indicate an infinite series by writing

$$u_1 + u_2 + \cdots + u_n + \cdots$$

we may occasionally omit the formula for u_n. It should be clearly understood, however, that the series has not really

---

* In order that the relation $n! = n(n - 1)!$, which holds for $n \geqq 2$, may also hold for $n = 1$ we assign the value *one* to 0!

been determined unless u_n has been specified. Thus if one writes $1 + \frac{1}{2} + \frac{1}{3} + \cdots$, he *probably* means $\displaystyle\sum_{n=1}^{\infty} \frac{1}{n}$.

However, he *could* mean $\displaystyle\sum_{n=1}^{\infty}\left[(n-1)(n-2)(n-3) + \frac{1}{n}\right]$ or any one of an unlimited number of other things.

179. Sum of an infinite series.—An infinite series of numbers has no sum within the ordinary meaning of the word; for, no matter how many of the terms one might add, there would always be an unlimited number of them left over. We shall, however, *assign* a meaning to the word sum as applied to an infinite series by means of the following *definition:*

Consider a series

$$u_1 + u_2 + u_3 + \cdots + u_n + \cdots$$

and let S_n denote the sum of the first n terms; i.e., let

$$\begin{aligned}
S_1 &= u_1, \\
S_2 &= u_1 + u_2, \\
S_3 &= u_1 + u_2 + u_3, \\
&\cdots \cdots \cdots \cdots \\
S_n &= u_1 + u_2 + u_3 + \cdots + u_n.
\end{aligned}$$

If S_n, regarded as a function of n, approaches a limit S as $n \to \infty$, this limit is called the **sum** *of the infinite series and the series is said to be* **convergent**. *If S_n does not approach a limit as $n \to \infty$, the series is said to be* **divergent**.

Example 1

$$1 + \tfrac{1}{2} + \tfrac{1}{4} + \tfrac{1}{8} + \cdots .$$

In this case,

$$\begin{aligned}
S_1 &= 1, \\
S_2 &= 1 + \tfrac{1}{2} = 1\tfrac{1}{2}, \\
S_3 &= 1 + \tfrac{1}{2} + \tfrac{1}{4} = 1\tfrac{3}{4}, \\
S_4 &= 1 + \tfrac{1}{2} + \tfrac{1}{4} + \tfrac{1}{8} = 1\tfrac{7}{8}.
\end{aligned}$$

$$\cdots \cdots \cdots \cdots \cdots \cdots \cdots$$

It is *almost* obvious that $\lim_{n \to \infty} S_n = 2$. That this is actually true is easily shown in this case, because the terms of this particular series form a *geometric progression;* from the formula for the sum of n terms of such a progression, we have

$$S_n = 2[1 - (\tfrac{1}{2})^n].$$

From this expression we see easily that

$$\lim_{n \to \infty} S_n = 2;$$

i.e., the series is convergent with sum 2.

Example 2
$$1 + 2 + 3 + 4 + \cdots .$$

In this case, $S_1 = 1, S_2 = 3, S_3 = 6$, etc. Obviously $S_n \to \infty$ as $n \to \infty$; *i.e.*, the series is divergent.

Example 3
$$1 - 1 + 1 - 1 + \cdots .$$

In this case, $S_1 = 1, S_2 = 0, S_3 = 1, S_4 = 0$, etc. Certainly S_n does not approach a limit as $n \to \infty$. The series is therefore divergent. It is sometimes called *finitely oscillating* to distinguish its behavior from that of the series in Example 2.

In some cases we can establish the convergence or divergence of a given series by expressing S_n as a function of n and studying the behavior of this function when $n \to \infty$, as in Example 1 above. Usually, however, it will be impossible to do this and we shall have to develop other methods. First we shall consider two special series.

180. The geometric and harmonic series.—The series

(1) $$a + ar + ar^2 + ar^3 + \cdots + ar^n + \cdots$$

is a *geometric series* in which the first term is any number a and the ratio of any term to the preceding one is r. Thus if we take $a = 9$ and $r = \frac{2}{3}$, we have the series

$$9 + 6 + 4 + \tfrac{8}{3} + \cdots + 9(\tfrac{2}{3})^n + \cdots .$$

It is shown in algebra that the sum S_n of the first n terms of

(1) is given by the formula

$$S_n = a \frac{1 - r^n}{1 - r} = \frac{a}{1 - r} - \frac{ar^n}{1 - r} \quad (r \neq 1).$$

The term $\dfrac{ar^n}{1 - r}$ approaches zero as $n \to \infty$ if $|r| < 1$, but becomes infinite as $n \to \infty$ if $|r| > 1$. Hence:

The geometric series

$$a + ar + ar^2 + ar^3 + \cdots + ar^n + \cdots$$

is convergent with sum $\dfrac{a}{1 - r}$ *if* $|r| < 1$. *It is divergent if* $|r| \geqq 1$.

Example

The geometric series

$$9 + 6 + 4 + \tfrac{8}{3} + \tfrac{16}{9} + \cdots$$

in which $a = 9$ and $r = \tfrac{2}{3}$ is convergent with sum

$$S = \frac{9}{1 - \tfrac{2}{3}} = 27.$$

Consider now the *harmonic series*

$$1 + \tfrac{1}{2} + \tfrac{1}{3} + \tfrac{1}{4} + \cdots + \frac{1}{n} + \cdots.$$

Here, $S_1 = 1$, $S_2 = 1\tfrac{1}{2}$, $S_3 = 1\tfrac{5}{6}$, etc. Whether or not S_n approaches a limit as $n \to \infty$ is not immediately apparent; furthermore, we cannot see any way of expressing S_n as a simple function of n as we did in a preceding case. That the series is actually divergent can be established as follows:

$$\tfrac{1}{3} + \tfrac{1}{4} > \tfrac{1}{4} + \tfrac{1}{4} = \tfrac{1}{2}$$
$$\tfrac{1}{5} + \tfrac{1}{6} + \tfrac{1}{7} + \tfrac{1}{8} > \tfrac{1}{8} + \tfrac{1}{8} + \tfrac{1}{8} + \tfrac{1}{8} = \tfrac{1}{2}$$
$$\tfrac{1}{9} + \tfrac{1}{10} + \cdots + \tfrac{1}{15} + \tfrac{1}{16} > \tfrac{1}{16} + \tfrac{1}{16} + \cdots + \tfrac{1}{16}$$
$$+ \tfrac{1}{16} = \tfrac{1}{2}, \text{ etc.}$$

We thus see that S_n is arbitrarily large for sufficiently large values of n so that the series is *divergent*.

181. A necessary condition for convergence.—It is easy to prove that a series $\displaystyle\sum_{n=1}^{\infty} u_n$ cannot be convergent unless

$\lim\limits_{n \to \infty} u_n = 0$. For if the series is convergent with sum S, then

$$\lim_{n \to \infty} S_n = S \qquad \text{and also} \qquad \lim_{n \to \infty} S_{n-1} = S.$$

Then

$$\lim_{n \to \infty} (S_n - S_{n-1}) = S - S = 0.$$

But

$$S_n - S_{n-1} = u_n \qquad \text{so that} \qquad \lim_{n \to \infty} u_n = 0.$$

The above condition is *necessary* but not *sufficient* for convergence. This means that the series Σu_n is *certainly divergent* if $\lim\limits_{n \to \infty} u_n \neq 0$; if this limit *is* zero, the series *may be* convergent but it may be divergent. We have just seen that the harmonic series is divergent even though $u_n \to 0$ as $n \to \infty$.

The following two theorems are often useful in connection with the various tests for convergence and divergence:

Theorem I: *If the series* $\sum\limits_{n=1}^{\infty} u_n$ *is convergent with sum* S, *and if k is any nonzero constant, then the series* $\sum\limits_{n=1}^{\infty} ku_n$ *is also convergent and has the sum kS; if Σu_n is divergent then Σku_n is also divergent.*

The proof is as follows: If S_n is the sum of the first n terms of the series $\sum\limits_{n=1}^{\infty} u_n$, then kS_n is the corresponding sum for the series $\sum\limits_{n=1}^{\infty} ku_n$. If $\lim\limits_{n \to \infty} S_n = S$, then $\lim\limits_{n \to \infty} kS_n = kS$. If S_n does not have a limit, then neither does kS_n.

Example

The series

$$\tfrac{1}{2} + \tfrac{1}{4} + \tfrac{1}{6} + \cdots + \frac{1}{2n} + \cdots$$

can be written in the form

$$\tfrac{1}{2}\left(1 + \tfrac{1}{2} + \tfrac{1}{3} + \cdots + \frac{1}{n} + \cdots\right).$$

We have proved that the harmonic series is divergent so we can conclude immediately that this series is also divergent.

Theorem II : *The convergence or divergence of a series is not affected by adding or subtracting a finite number of terms either at the beginning or distributed through the series.*

The truth of this statement follows from the fact that the sum of such terms is a finite constant which can affect the sum (in case of convergence) but not the convergence or divergence of the series.

Example

The series

$$\tfrac{1}{10} + \tfrac{1}{11} + \tfrac{1}{12} + \cdots + \frac{1}{n+9} + \cdots$$

is simply the harmonic series with the first nine terms missing, and hence it is divergent. It could be indicated by the symbol $\displaystyle\sum_{n=10}^{\infty} \frac{1}{n}$, and we may thus regard its general term as being $\frac{1}{n}$ instead of $\frac{1}{n+9}$ if we wish.

PROBLEMS

In each of the following cases write down the first four terms of the given series:

1. $\displaystyle\sum_{n=1}^{\infty} \frac{2^n}{\sqrt{n+1}}.$

2. $\displaystyle\sum_{n=1}^{\infty} (-1)^{n+1} \frac{n}{n^2+1}.$

3. $\displaystyle\sum_{n=0}^{\infty} \frac{x^n}{(n+1)!}.$

4. $\displaystyle\sum_{n=1}^{\infty} (-1)^{n+1} \frac{n+1}{n \log n}.$

5. $\displaystyle\sum_{n=1}^{\infty} \frac{(2n)!}{2^{n-1}}.$

6. $\displaystyle\sum_{n=1}^{\infty} (-1)^n \frac{2^{2n+1}}{n!}.$

In each of the following cases find a formula for u_n that will fit the terms as given, assuming that the first term corresponds to $n = 1$:

7. $1 - 3 + 5 - 7 + \cdots.$

8. $\dfrac{2}{2^1} - \dfrac{3}{2^2} + \dfrac{4}{2^3} - \dfrac{5}{2^4} + \cdots.$

9. $\dfrac{1}{1 \cdot 2} + \dfrac{1}{3 \cdot 4} + \dfrac{1}{5 \cdot 6} + \cdots.$

10. $\dfrac{1}{1 \cdot 3} - \dfrac{1}{5 \cdot 7} + \dfrac{1}{9 \cdot 11} - \cdots$

11. $\dfrac{1}{\sqrt{5}} - \dfrac{3}{\sqrt{10}} + \dfrac{5}{\sqrt{17}} - \dfrac{7}{\sqrt{26}} + \cdots$

12. $\dfrac{1 \cdot 2}{3^2} + \dfrac{2 \cdot 3}{4^2} + \dfrac{3 \cdot 4}{5^2} + \cdots$

Show that each of the following series is convergent and in each case find the sum:

13. $4 + 3 + \frac{9}{4} + \cdots + 4(\frac{3}{4})^n + \cdots$

14. $\frac{1}{2} + \frac{1}{6} + \frac{1}{18} + \cdots + \dfrac{1}{2(3)^n} + \cdots$

15. $1 - \frac{1}{2} + \frac{1}{4} - \frac{1}{8} + \cdots + \dfrac{(-1)^{n+1}}{2^{n-1}} + \cdots$

16. $\displaystyle\sum_{n=1}^{\infty} \dfrac{12}{3^{n-1}}.$ **17.** $\displaystyle\sum_{n=1}^{\infty} 24 \left(\dfrac{1}{2^{2n}}\right).$

In each of the following cases show that the given series is divergent:

18. $\frac{1}{2} + \frac{2}{3} + \frac{3}{4} + \cdots + \dfrac{n}{n+1} + \cdots$

19. $\dfrac{2}{\log 2} + \dfrac{3}{\log 3} + \cdots + \dfrac{n}{\log n} + \cdots$

20. $\frac{3}{5} + \frac{3}{4} + \frac{9}{11} + \cdots + \dfrac{3n}{3n+2} + \cdots$

21. $\frac{1}{100} + \frac{1}{101} + \frac{1}{102} + \frac{1}{103} + \cdots + \dfrac{1}{100+n} + \cdots$

22. $\displaystyle\sum_{n=1}^{\infty} \dfrac{(-1)^n n}{4n-1}.$ **23.** $\displaystyle\sum_{n=1}^{\infty} \dfrac{2n}{3n+1}.$

24. $\displaystyle\sum_{n=0}^{\infty} \dfrac{n}{100+n}.$ **25.** $\displaystyle\sum_{n=4}^{\infty} \dfrac{(-1)^{n+1}n}{6n+2}.$

182. Tests for convergence.—There is no such thing as a single "universal" test that applies to all series and shows in every case whether or not the series is convergent. Instead, there are many tests, any one of which might serve in a particular case, and several pages will now be devoted to the most important of these tests. We shall first give several tests that apply to series in which all terms are *positive*, and afterward we shall consider series that contain both positive and negative terms.

In some of the proofs we may use the following:

Fundamental Principle : *If a function* $S_n = \varphi(n)$ *always increases as n increases but always remains less than a fixed number Q, then* $\lim_{n \to \infty} S_n$ *exists and is not greater than Q.*

183. The integral test.—The following test for convergence makes use of an improper integral: Let the general term of the series $\sum_{n=1}^{\infty} u_n$ be $f(n)$, and let $f(x)$ be the function obtained by replacing n by the continuous variable x. Now if for all values of $x > a$ (a a positive integer) this function $f(x)$ is positive and decreasing and if $f(x) \to 0$ as $x \to \infty$, then the series $\sum_{n=1}^{\infty} u_n$ is *convergent* if the integral $\int_a^{\infty} f(x)dx$ is convergent and *divergent* if this integral is divergent.

Example 1

Consider the series

$$\tfrac{1}{2} + \tfrac{1}{5} + \tfrac{1}{10} + \cdots + \frac{1}{n^2 + 1} + \cdots .$$

Here, $f(n) = \dfrac{1}{n^2 + 1}$ and $f(x) = \dfrac{1}{x^2 + 1}$. For all positive values of x this function is positive and decreasing, and as $x \to \infty$, $f(x) \to 0$. Also

$$\int_0^{\infty} f(x)dx = \int_0^{\infty} \frac{dx}{x^2 + 1} = \tfrac{1}{2}\pi.$$

Since this integral is *convergent*, the series is also *convergent*.

Example 2

Consider the harmonic series

$$1 + \tfrac{1}{2} + \tfrac{1}{3} + \tfrac{1}{4} + \cdots + \frac{1}{n} + \cdots .$$

Here, $f(n) = 1/n$ and $f(x) = 1/x$. For all $x > 1$ this function is positive and decreasing, and as $x \to \infty$, $f(x) \to 0$. In this case, however,

$$\int_1^{\infty} f(x)dx = \int_1^{\infty} \frac{dx}{x} = \infty .$$

Since this integral is *divergent*, the series is also *divergent*.

The proof for the case of convergence is as follows: Assume at first that the terms of the series $\sum\limits_{n=1}^{\infty} u_n$ are all positive, that each term after the first is smaller than the preceding one, and that $u_n \to 0$ as $n \to \infty$. By erecting

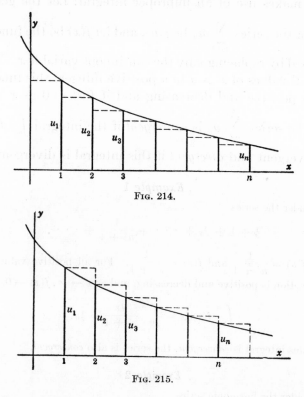

Fig. 214.

Fig. 215.

ordinates equal to u_1, u_2, u_3, $\cdots$ at the points $x = 1$, 2, 3, $\cdots$, the magnitudes of the terms can be represented by the areas of rectangles drawn as in Fig. 214. The curve whose equation is $y = f(x)$, where $u_n = f(n)$ and $f(x)$ satisfies the conditions of the theorem, has the general appearance shown. Suppose now that

$$\int_0^{\infty} f(x)dx$$

exists and has a value k.   It is evident that in this case S_n, which is represented by the sum of the areas of the n rectangles, is a quantity that increases as n increases but remains less than k.   It follows that $\lim\limits_{n \to \infty} S_n = S$ exists.

If the conditions imposed here on the terms u_n are not satisfied by the first few terms, but are satisfied from a certain place on, say for all $n \gtreqless n'$, then the above reasoning can be applied to the series starting with the term $u_{n'}$.

The proof for the case of divergence will be left to the student, Fig. 215 providing the necessary hint.

184. The comparison test.—One can often prove the convergence or divergence of a given series by comparing it with a series whose behavior is known.   In this connection we have the following two theorems:

1. *A series of positive terms is convergent if each of its terms is less than (or equal to) the corresponding term of a series that is known to be convergent.*

2. *A series of positive terms is divergent if each of its terms is greater than (or equal to) the corresponding term of a series that is known to be divergent.*

The student will probably regard these theorems as obvious and formal proofs will be left to the exercises. Naturally, in making the comparison, one may discard any finite number of initial terms in a series.

In order to use the comparison test one must of course have at hand a supply of series with known behavior. Thus we know that any geometric series is convergent if $|r| < 1$ and divergent if $|r| \geqq 1$.   By means of the integral test one can show that the "k-series"

$$\frac{1}{1^k} + \frac{1}{2^k} + \frac{1}{3^k} + \cdots + \frac{1}{n^k} + \cdots = \sum_{n=1}^{\infty} \frac{1}{n^k}$$

is convergent if $k > 1$ and divergent if $k \leqq 1$ (see Prob. 1 of the next set).   This series is often used in comparison tests.

Example 1

The series

$$(1) \qquad \frac{1}{1^2} + \frac{1}{2^2} + \frac{1}{3^2} + \cdots + \frac{1}{n^2} + \cdots = \sum_{n=1}^{\infty} \frac{1}{n^2}$$

is the k-series with $k = 2$, and it is convergent. The series

$$(2) \quad \frac{1}{1 \cdot 2} + \frac{1}{2 \cdot 3} + \frac{1}{3 \cdot 4} + \cdots + \frac{1}{n(n+1)} + \cdot \quad \cdot = \sum_{n=1}^{\infty} \frac{1}{n(n+1)}$$

can be shown to be convergent by comparison; for each term in (2) is smaller than the corresponding term in (1); *i.e.*, for every n,

$$\frac{1}{n(n+1)} < \frac{1}{n^2}.$$

Example 2

The series

$$(1) \qquad \tfrac{1}{2} + \tfrac{1}{3} + \tfrac{1}{4} + \cdots + \frac{1}{n+1} + \cdots$$

is known to be divergent. The series

$$(2) \quad \frac{1}{\sqrt{1 \cdot 2}} + \frac{1}{\sqrt{2 \cdot 3}} + \frac{1}{\sqrt{3 \cdot 4}} + \cdots + \frac{1}{\sqrt{n(n+1)}} + \cdots$$

can be proved to be divergent by comparison. For each term in (2) is larger than the corresponding term in (1); *i.e.*, for every n,

$$\frac{1}{\sqrt{n(n+1)}} > \frac{1}{n+1}.$$

185. The polynomial test.—One often encounters a series in which the general term is the quotient of two polynomials in n; *i.e.*, in which $u_n = g(n)/h(n)$ where $g(n)$ and $h(n)$ are polynomials in n. For this reason the following test is often useful:

Polynomial Test: *If $u_n = g(n)/h(n)$ where $g(n)$ and $h(n)$ are polynomials in n, then the series $\sum_{n=0}^{\infty} u_n$ is convergent if the degree of $h(n)$ exceeds that of $g(n)$ by more than 1; otherwise the series is divergent.*

Example 1

Consider the series

$$1 + \tfrac{3}{8} + \tfrac{5}{27} + \tfrac{7}{64} + \cdots + \frac{2n - 1}{n^3} + \cdots .$$

Here $u_n = \dfrac{2n - 1}{n^3}$; the degree of the denominator exceeds that of the numerator by 2 and therefore the series is *convergent* by the polynomial test. A method of proving the test immediately suggests itself. For we may factor out n^2 in the denominator, and write u_n in the form

$$u_n = \left(\frac{2n - 1}{n}\right)\left(\frac{1}{n^2}\right);$$

then, since the limit of the first factor is a constant, the terms are *smaller* than those of the convergent series $\displaystyle\sum_{n=1}^{\infty} k\left(\frac{1}{n^2}\right)$ where k is a suitable constant.

Example 2

Consider the series

$$\tfrac{3}{2} + \tfrac{4}{5} + \tfrac{5}{10} + \tfrac{6}{17} + \cdots + \frac{n + 2}{n^2 + 1} + \cdots .$$

Here, $u_n = \dfrac{n + 2}{n^2 + 1}$; the degree of the denominator exceeds that of the numerator by only 1, and the series is therefore *divergent* by the polynomial test. A method of proving this part of the test is also evident. For we may factor out n in the denominator, and write u_n in the form

$$u_n = \left(\frac{n + 2}{n + \dfrac{1}{n}}\right)\left(\frac{1}{n}\right);$$

then, since the limit of the first factor is a constant, the terms are *larger* than those of the divergent series $\displaystyle\sum_{n=1}^{\infty} k \cdot \frac{1}{n}$ where k is a suitable constant.

PROBLEMS

1. Using the integral test, show that the "k-series"

$$\frac{1}{1^k} + \frac{1}{2^k} + \frac{1}{3^k} + \cdots + \frac{1}{n^k} + \cdots = \sum_{n=1}^{\infty} \frac{1}{n^k}$$

is convergent if $k > 1$ and divergent if $k \leqq 1$.

Test each of the following series for convergence using the integral test:

2. $\dfrac{1}{3^2} + \dfrac{1}{5^2} + \dfrac{1}{7^2} + \cdots + \dfrac{1}{(2n-1)^2} + \cdots$.

3. $\dfrac{1}{2} + \dfrac{1}{5} + \dfrac{1}{10} + \cdots + \dfrac{1}{n^2+1} + \cdots$.

4. $\dfrac{1}{5} + \dfrac{2}{8} + \dfrac{3}{13} + \cdots + \dfrac{n}{n^2+4} + \cdots$.

5. $\displaystyle\sum_{n=1}^{\infty} \dfrac{n^2}{n^3+4}$.

6. $\displaystyle\sum_{n=1}^{\infty} \dfrac{n}{(n^2+1)^2}$.

7. $\displaystyle\sum_{n=1}^{\infty} \dfrac{1}{\sqrt{n^2+4}}$.

8. $\displaystyle\sum_{n=1}^{\infty} \dfrac{1}{(2n-1)^2}$.

9. $\displaystyle\sum_{n=0}^{\infty} \dfrac{n^2}{e^n}$.

10. $\displaystyle\sum_{n=1}^{\infty} \dfrac{\log n}{n}$.

11. Prove the integral test for the case of divergence.

12. If every term of a given series is smaller than the corresponding terms of a divergent series, can it be concluded that the series is convergent?

13. Show by using the integral test that the series

$$1 + \tfrac{1}{3} + \dfrac{1}{5} + \cdots + \dfrac{1}{2n-1} + \cdots$$

is divergent. Then, by comparison, show that the series

$$\sum_{n=1}^{\infty} \dfrac{1}{\sqrt{2n-1}}$$

is divergent.

Test each of the following series by using the comparison test:

14. $1 + \dfrac{1}{2^2} + \dfrac{1}{3^3} + \cdots + \dfrac{1}{n^n} + \cdots$

15. $\dfrac{1}{1\cdot 2} + \dfrac{1}{3\cdot 4} + \dfrac{1}{5\cdot 6} + \cdots + \dfrac{1}{(2n-1)(2n)} + \cdots$

16. $\dfrac{1}{\log 2} + \dfrac{1}{\log 3} + \dfrac{1}{\log 4} + \cdots + \dfrac{1}{\log (n+1)} + \cdots$

17. $\dfrac{\sqrt{1}}{2} + \dfrac{\sqrt{2}}{3} + \dfrac{\sqrt{3}}{4} + \cdots + \dfrac{\sqrt{n}}{n+1} + \cdots$

18. $\dfrac{1}{2\cdot 3\cdot 4} + \dfrac{2}{3\cdot 4\cdot 5} + \dfrac{3}{4\cdot 5\cdot 6} + \cdots$

$$+ \dfrac{n}{(n+1)(n+2)(n+3)} + \cdots$$

19. $\displaystyle\sum_{n=0}^{\infty} \frac{1}{2^n + 2}.$ **20.** $\displaystyle\sum_{n=0}^{\infty} \left(\frac{2}{3}\right)^n \frac{n}{n+1}.$

21. Prove the comparison test for the case of convergence. HINT: If every term of the series Σu_n is smaller than the corresponding term of the convergent series Σc_n, then the sum S_n of the first n terms of Σu_n must be less than the corresponding sum for the series Σc_n.

22. Prove the comparison test for the case of divergence.

23. Test the series given in Probs. 2 to 6 using the polynomial test.

24. Test the series given in Probs. 13, 15, and 18 using the polynomial test.

25. Explain why the polynomial test is not applicable to the series given in Probs. 14, 19, and 20.

26. To which ones of the series given in Probs. 5 to 10 is the polynomial test applicable?

186. The ratio test.—One of the most useful tests for convergence is the following:

Ratio test: *Given the series of positive terms*

$$u_1 + u_2 + u_3 + \cdots + u_n + \cdots = \sum_{n=1}^{\infty} u_n.$$

If $\displaystyle\lim_{n \to \infty} \frac{u_{n+1}}{u_n}$ *exists and has the value* ρ, *then the series is convergent if* $\rho < 1$. *It is divergent if* $\rho > 1$, *or if* $\displaystyle\lim_{n \to \infty} \frac{u_{n+1}}{u_n} = \infty$. *If* $\rho = 1$ *the test gives no information.*

In using this test one obtains the necessary expression for u_{n+1} by taking that for u_n and replacing n by $n + 1$.

Example

In the series

$$1 + \frac{2}{3} + \frac{3}{3^2} + \frac{4}{3^3} + \cdots + \frac{n}{3^{n-1}} + \cdots$$

we have

$$u_n = \frac{n}{3^{n-1}} \quad \text{and} \quad u_{n+1} = \frac{n+1}{3^n}.$$

We form the ratio

$$\frac{u_{n+1}}{u_n} = \frac{\dfrac{n+1}{3^n}}{\dfrac{n}{3^{n-1}}} = \frac{n+1}{3^n} \cdot \frac{3^{n-1}}{n} = \frac{n+1}{3n}.$$

Next, we find the limit of this ratio as $n \to \infty$:

$$\lim_{n \to \infty} \frac{u_{n+1}}{u_n} = \lim_{n \to \infty} \frac{n+1}{3n} = \tfrac{1}{3}.$$

Since this limit is *less than* 1, the series is convergent.

The proof of the test for the case of convergence is as follows: Suppose that

$$\lim_{n \to \infty} \frac{u_{n+1}}{u_n} = \rho < 1.$$

Then for all sufficiently large values of n, say for all $n > k$, the value of this ratio is arbitrarily near ρ and is therefore less than some number, say r, that lies between ρ and 1; *i.e.*,

$$\frac{u_{k+1}}{u_k} < r, \qquad \text{or} \qquad u_{k+1} < u_k r;$$

$$\frac{u_{k+2}}{u_{k+1}} < r, \qquad \text{or} \qquad u_{k+2} < u_k r^2;$$

$$\frac{u_{k+3}}{u_{k+2}} < r, \qquad \text{or} \qquad u_{k+3} < u_k r^3; \text{ etc.}$$

We see immediately that the terms, starting with u_{k+1}, are smaller than the corresponding terms of the convergent geometric series

$$u_k r + u_k r^2 + u_k r^3 + \cdots \quad (0 < r < 1).$$

Hence, the series is convergent by the comparison test.

The proof for the case of divergence is obtained by noting that if $\rho > 1$ the terms eventually increase and $\lim_{n \to \infty} u_n \neq 0$.

The fact that the test gives no information if $\rho = 1$ can be established by observing that there are both convergent and divergent series for which $\rho = 1$. Thus it can be shown that for the "k-series" previously discussed, the value of this limit is 1 for all finite values of k. The series, however, is convergent if $k > 1$ and divergent if $k \leq 1$.

187. Approximation of sum and estimation of error.— After proving that a given series is convergent, we may approximate its sum by adding up the first few terms. In this connection we need some way of estimating the error involved in using the sum of say the first k terms as an approximation to the sum of the series. We may denote this approximation by S_k, the sum of the series by S, and the difference between S_k and S, which is called the *remainder* after k terms, by R_k. Then

$$S_k = \sum_{n=1}^{k} u_n \quad \text{and} \quad R_k = \sum_{n=k+1}^{\infty} u_n.$$

Because of the fact that it applies in so many cases that are of practical importance, the following theorem concerning the remainder has a wide range of usefulness:

Theorem: *Let* $\sum_{n=1}^{\infty} u_n$ *be a series of positive terms such that*

$$\lim_{n \to \infty} \frac{u_{n+1}}{u_n} = \rho < 1.$$

Let $S_k = \sum_{n=1}^{k} u_n$ *be the sum of the first k terms, k satisfying the conditions that*

$$\frac{u_{k+1}}{u_k} = r < 1,$$

and for $n > k$ *the value of this ratio is less than r.　Then*

$$R_k < \left(\frac{r}{1-r}\right) \cdot u_k;$$

i.e., the error, or remainder after k terms, is less than $\dfrac{r}{1-r}$ *times the last term retained.**

The proof utilizes essentially the same argument that we used in proving the ratio test: Under the conditions

---

* The author is indebted to Prof. J. R. Britton of the University of Colorado for suggesting that a theorem of this kind should be given. The theorem is not stated here in its most general form, but rather in the form that appears to be most useful for our immediate needs.

specified,

$$R_k = u_{k+1} + u_{k+2} + u_{k+3} + \cdots$$
$$< u_k r + u_k r^2 + u_k r^3 + \cdots \quad (0 < r < 1).$$

The sum of this convergent geometric series is

$$u_k \left(\frac{r}{1 - r} \right)$$

from which the theorem follows.

Example 1

For the series

$$1 + \frac{2}{3} + \frac{3}{3^2} + \frac{4}{3^3} + \cdots + \frac{n}{3^{n-1}} + \cdots$$

we have

$$\lim_{n \to \infty} \frac{u_{n+1}}{u_n} = \lim_{n \to \infty} \frac{n+1}{3n} = \tfrac{1}{3}.$$

The series is therefore convergent. If we add up the first six terms, we find that

$$S_6 = 2.235.$$

The ratio of u_{n+1} to u_n at this point in the series is

$$\frac{u_{n+1}}{u_n} = \frac{n+1}{3n} \bigg]_{n=6} = \tfrac{7}{18},$$

and for $n > 6$ this ratio is *less* than $\tfrac{7}{18}$. Hence,

$$R_6 < \left(\frac{\tfrac{7}{18}}{1 - \tfrac{7}{18}} \right) \cdot u_6 = \frac{7}{11} \cdot \frac{6}{3^5} = 0.0157.$$

Thus in this case the remainder is less than $\tfrac{1}{11}$ of the last term retained, and we know that S is between 2.235 and 2.251.

Example 2

For the series

$$\frac{4}{1!} + \frac{4^2}{2!} + \frac{4^3}{3!} + \cdots + \frac{4^n}{n!} + \cdots$$

we have

$$\lim_{n \to \infty} \frac{u_{n+1}}{u_n} = \lim_{n \to \infty} \frac{4}{n+1} = 0.$$

The series is therefore convergent. If we add up the first seven terms, we find that

$$S_7 = 50.3.$$

The ratio of u_{n+1} to u_n at this point in the series is

$$\frac{u_{n+1}}{u_n} = \frac{4}{n+1}\bigg]_{n=7} = \tfrac{1}{2},$$

and for $n > 7$ this ratio is *less* than $\tfrac{1}{2}$. Hence,

$$R_7 < \left(\frac{\tfrac{1}{2}}{1 - \tfrac{1}{2}}\right) \cdot u_7 = u_7 = \frac{4^7}{7!} = 3.25.$$

The value of S then differs from 50.3 by less than 3.25. This example illustrates the useful fact that *if $r \leqq \tfrac{1}{2}$ then the remainder is less than the last term retained.*

PROBLEMS

Test the following series using the ratio test. If this test fails, use one of the tests previously given:

1. $1 + \dfrac{1}{2} + \dfrac{2}{2^2} + \dfrac{3}{2^3} + \cdots + \dfrac{n}{2^n} + \cdots$.

2. $1 + \dfrac{3}{2!} + \dfrac{3^2}{3!} + \dfrac{3^3}{4!} + \cdots + \dfrac{3^{n-1}}{n!} + \cdots$.

3. $1 + \dfrac{1}{6} + \dfrac{2!}{6^2} + \dfrac{3!}{6^3} + \cdots + \dfrac{n!}{6^n} + \cdots$.

4. $1 + \tfrac{1}{3} + \tfrac{1}{5} + \tfrac{1}{7} + \cdots + \dfrac{1}{2n-1} + \cdots$.

5. $1 + \dfrac{1}{4} + \dfrac{2}{4^2} + \dfrac{3}{4^3} + \cdots + \dfrac{n}{4^n} + \cdots$.

6. $\dfrac{100}{1!} + \dfrac{100^2}{2!} + \dfrac{100^3}{3!} + \cdots + \dfrac{100^n}{n!} + \cdots$.

7. $\dfrac{1 \cdot 2}{3^3} + \dfrac{2 \cdot 3}{4^3} + \dfrac{3 \cdot 4}{5^3} + \cdots + \dfrac{n(n+1)}{(n+2)^3} + \cdots$.

8. $\dfrac{\sqrt{1}}{4} + \dfrac{\sqrt{2}}{9} + \dfrac{\sqrt{3}}{16} + \cdots + \dfrac{\sqrt{n}}{(n+1)^2} + \cdots$.

9. $\displaystyle\sum_{n=1}^{\infty} \frac{3^n}{n \cdot 2^n}.$

10. $\displaystyle\sum_{n=1}^{\infty} \frac{2n-1}{2^{2n-1}}.$

11. $\displaystyle\sum_{n=1}^{\infty} \frac{1 + 2\sqrt{n}}{n}.$

12. $\displaystyle\sum_{n=1}^{\infty} \frac{2^n \cdot 4^{n-1}}{n!}.$

13. $\displaystyle\sum_{n=1}^{\infty} \frac{n^3}{(n+1)!}.$

14. $\displaystyle\sum_{n=1}^{\infty} \frac{(1,000)^n}{n!}.$

15. $1 + \dfrac{1 \cdot 2}{1 \cdot 3} + \dfrac{1}{1} \dfrac{2 \cdot 3}{3 \cdot 5} + \cdots + \dfrac{n!}{1 \cdot 3 \cdot 5 \cdots (2n-1)} + \cdots$.

16. Show that the series

$$1 + \frac{1}{1!} + \frac{1}{2!} + \frac{1}{3!} + \cdots + \frac{1}{(n-1)!} + \cdots$$

is convergent by the ratio test. Approximate its sum by adding the first five terms, and estimate the remainder.

17. Show that the series

$$1 + \frac{2}{2^1} + \frac{3}{2^2} + \frac{4}{2^3} + \cdots + \frac{n}{2^{n-1}} + \cdots$$

is convergent by the ratio test. Approximate its sum by adding the first six terms and estimate the remainder.

18. Show that the series

$$1 + 2 + \frac{2^2}{2!} + \frac{2^3}{3!} + \cdots + \frac{2^{n-1}}{(n-1)!} + \cdots$$

is convergent by the ratio test. Approximate its sum by adding the first eight terms, and estimate the remainder. Compare your result with the value of e^2 ($e = 2.718$).

19. It can be shown that the series

$$1 + \frac{1}{2} + \frac{1}{2^2 \cdot 2!} + \frac{1}{2^3 \cdot 3!} + \cdots + \frac{1}{2^{n-1} \cdot (n-1)!} + \cdots$$

converges and that its sum is $\sqrt{e}$. Estimate the error involved in using five terms to calculate $\sqrt{e}$.

20. How many terms must be used in approximating the sum of the series $\sum_{n=1}^{\infty} \frac{3^n}{n!}$ if the error must be less than 0.5?

188. Alternating series.—A series is called an *alternating series* if its terms are alternately positive and negative. Thus, if $u_1, u_2, \cdots$ are all positive numbers, then the series

$$(1) \quad u_1 - u_2 + u_3 - u_4 + \cdots + (-1)^{n+1}u_n + \cdots$$

is an alternating series. A *sufficient* condition for the convergence of such a series is given by the following:

Theorem I: *The alternating series (1) is convergent if each term is numerically less than the preceding one and* $\lim_{n \to \infty} u_n = 0$.

The proof is as follows: The sum S_{2n} of an *even* number of terms of (1) can be written in either of the two following ways:

$$(2) \quad S_{2n} = (u_1 - u_2) + (u_3 - u_4) + \cdots$$
$$+ (u_{2n-1} - u_{2n}).$$
$$(3) \quad S_{2n} = u_1 - (u_2 - u_3) - (u_4 - u_5) - \cdots$$
$$- (u_{2n-2} - u_{2n-1}) - u_{2n}.$$

Here, all the quantities in parentheses are positive because of the assumption that each term is numerically less than the preceding one. Equation (2) shows that S_{2n} is a positive increasing function of n while (3) shows that its value remains less than u_1. Hence S_{2n} must approach a limit as $n \to \infty$. The sum S_{2n+1} of an *odd* number of terms is

$$S_{2n+1} = S_{2n} + u_{2n+1}.$$

We have assumed that $\lim\limits_{n \to \infty} u_n = 0$ so that, of course, $u_{2n+1} \to 0$ as $n \to \infty$. It follows that S_{2n+1} approaches the same limit as S_{2n} when $n \to \infty$, and the series is therefore convergent.

Example

The series

$$1 - \tfrac{1}{2} + \tfrac{1}{3} - \tfrac{1}{4} + \cdots + (-1)^{n+1}\frac{1}{n} + \cdots$$

satisfies the conditions of the above theorem, and hence it is convergent.

The error involved when S_k is used as an approximation to S may be conveniently estimated by means of the following:

Theorem II: *If an alternating series satisfies the conditions of Theorem I, the remainder after k terms is numerically less than u_{k+1}; i.e., S_k differs from S by less than the first neglected term.* The proof of this theorem is left to the exercises.

189. Absolute and conditional convergence.—A series that contains an unlimited number of both positive and negative terms (not necessarily alternating) may be called a *mixed-term* series. *It can be shown that a given series of* *this type is certainly convergent if the series of positive terms obtained by replacing each term of the given series by its absolute value is convergent.*   In this case the original series is said to be *absolutely convergent.*

Example

The series

$$1 - \frac{1}{2^2} - \frac{1}{3^2} + \frac{1}{4^2} - \frac{1}{5^2} - \frac{1}{6^2} + \frac{1}{7^2} - \cdots,$$

in which each positive term is followed by two negative terms, is *absolutely convergent;* for the series

$$1 + \frac{1}{2^2} + \frac{1}{3^2} + \frac{1}{4^2} + \cdots + \frac{1}{n^2} + \cdots$$

is convergent.

A series of mixed terms *may* be convergent when the series obtained by replacing each term by its absolute value is divergent.   In this case the original series is said to be *conditionally convergent.*

Example

The series

$$1 - \tfrac{1}{2} + \tfrac{1}{3} - \tfrac{1}{4} + \cdots + (-1)^{n+1}\frac{1}{n} + \cdots,$$

which is convergent by the alternating series test, is only *conditionally convergent,* since the series

$$1 + \tfrac{1}{2} + \tfrac{1}{3} + \tfrac{1}{4} + \cdots + \frac{1}{n} + \cdots$$

is divergent.

Any of the tests for convergence that have been given for series of positive terms can be used to test a series of mixed terms for absolute convergence.   In particular, we may restate the **ratio test** as follows:

If $\lim\limits_{n \to \infty} \left| \dfrac{u_{n+1}}{u_n} \right| = \rho$ *then the series* $\sum\limits_{n=1}^{\infty} u_n$ *is absolutely convergent if* $\rho < 1$.   *If* $\rho > 1$, *or if* $\lim\limits_{n \to \infty} \left| \dfrac{u_{n+1}}{u_n} \right| = \infty$, *the series is divergent.   If* $\rho = 1$ *the test fails.*

The concepts of absolute and conditional convergence are necessary in studying the algebra of convergent series. It can be shown that if a given series of mixed terms is absolutely convergent then the positive terms alone form a convergent series and the negative terms form a convergent series. The sum of the given series is the difference between the sums of these separate series. If a given series is only *conditionally* convergent, then the positive terms alone form a *divergent* series and the negative terms form a *divergent* series. A consequence of this situation is the fact that an absolutely convergent series remains absolutely convergent, and with the same sum, when the terms are arranged in any other order; a conditionally convergent series may become divergent, or may converge to a different sum, if the terms are taken in a different order. Thus the series

$$1 - \tfrac{1}{2} - \tfrac{1}{4} + \tfrac{1}{3} - \tfrac{1}{6} - \tfrac{1}{8} + \tfrac{1}{5} - \cdots$$

is merely a rearrangement of the series

$$1 - \tfrac{1}{2} + \tfrac{1}{3} - \tfrac{1}{4} + \cdots + (-1)^{n+1}\frac{1}{n} + \cdots$$

It can be shown that the first series is convergent and its sum is half that of the second series.

If one multiplies together two convergent series having sums U and V, respectively, the resulting series will converge with sum UV if at least one of the series is absolutely convergent. If both series are only conditionally convergent the product series may be divergent.

PROBLEMS

Show that each of the following series is convergent. In each case determine whether the convergence is absolute or conditional:

1. $\tfrac{1}{2} - \tfrac{1}{4} + \tfrac{1}{6} - \tfrac{1}{8} + \cdots + (-1)^{n+1}\dfrac{1}{2n} + \cdots$.

2. $\dfrac{1}{\log 2} - \dfrac{1}{\log 3} + \dfrac{1}{\log 4} - \cdots + (-1)^{n+1}\dfrac{1}{\log (n + 1)} + \cdots$.

3. $\dfrac{1}{2 \log 2} - \dfrac{1}{3 \log 3} + \dfrac{1}{4 \log 4} - \cdots + (-1)^n \dfrac{1}{n \log n} + \cdots$.

4. $1 - \dfrac{1}{\sqrt{2}} + \dfrac{1}{\sqrt{3}} - \cdots + (-1)^{n+1} \dfrac{1}{\sqrt{n}} + \cdots$.

5. $\displaystyle\sum_{n=1}^{\infty} (-1)^{n+1} \dfrac{n}{(n+1)!}$.

6. $\displaystyle\sum_{n=1}^{\infty} (-1)^{n+1} \dfrac{1}{(2n)^2}$.

7. $\displaystyle\sum_{n=1}^{\infty} (-1)^n \dfrac{n}{2^n}$.

8. $\displaystyle\sum_{n=1}^{\infty} (-1)^n \dfrac{(2n)^2}{n^3}$.

9. $\displaystyle\sum_{n=1}^{\infty} (-1)^{n+1} \dfrac{(2n)^2}{4^{n-1}}$.

10. $\displaystyle\sum_{n=1}^{\infty} (-1)^{n+1} \dfrac{n}{n^2+2}$.

11. $\displaystyle\sum_{n=1}^{\infty} (-1)^{n+1} \dfrac{1}{n\sqrt{n}}$

12. $\displaystyle\sum_{n=1}^{\infty} (-1)^{n+1} \dfrac{n+1}{n\sqrt{n}}$.

13. $\displaystyle\sum_{n=1}^{\infty} (-1)^{n+1} \dfrac{2^{n-1}}{n!}$.

14. $\displaystyle\sum_{n=1}^{\infty} (-1)^{n+1} \dfrac{n^2}{2^{n-1}}$.

15. Estimate the error involved in approximating the sum of the series $\displaystyle\sum_{n=1}^{\infty} (-1)^{n+1} \dfrac{1}{n^2}$ by using the first six terms.

16. Estimate the error involved in approximating the sum of the series $\displaystyle\sum_{n=1}^{\infty} (-1)^{n+1} \dfrac{n}{(n+1)!}$ by using the first five terms.

17. Approximate the sum of the series

$$\dfrac{4}{1!} - \dfrac{4^2}{2!} + \dfrac{4^3}{3!} - \dfrac{4^4}{4!} + \cdots + (-1)^{n+1} \dfrac{4^n}{n!} + \cdots.$$

using the first 8 terms, and estimate the error. Is this approximation satisfactory?

18. Expand $(x+2)^{\frac{1}{3}}$ by the binomial theorem. From the series compute $\sqrt[3]{66}$ using two terms and estimate the error.

19. Write out a proof for Theorem 2, Art. 187.

190. Series of variable terms.—We have been considering series in which the individual terms are constants. We may now consider series in which the terms are functions of a variable x. Examples are:

(1) $x - \frac{1}{2}x^2 + \frac{1}{3}x^3 - \cdots + (-1)^{n+1}\dfrac{x^n}{n} + \cdots$.

(2) $(x - 2) + 2(x - 2)^2 + 3(x - 2)^3 + \cdots$
$$+ n(x - 2)^n + \cdots.$$

(3) $\sin x + \frac{1}{2}\sin 2x + \frac{1}{3}\sin 3x + \cdots$
$$+ \frac{1}{n}\sin nx + \cdots.$$

The first of these is called a *power series* in x; the second is a power series in $(x - 2)$. The third series is called a *trigonometric series*.

In general, series like the above are convergent for some values of x and divergent for others. In particular, a power series is convergent for all values of x in a certain interval, called the *interval of convergence*, and divergent for all values of x outside this interval. We shall now study the problem of determining this interval.

191. Interval of convergence of a power series.—A power series in x is any series of the form

$$a_0 + a_1x + a_2x^2 + \cdots + a_nx^n + \cdots = \sum_{n=0}^{\infty} a_nx^n$$

where the a's are constants. An interval such that the series converges for all values of x inside and diverges for all values of x outside can usually be found by means of the ratio test.

Example

Find the interval of convergence of the series

$$\frac{x}{1 \cdot 3} + \frac{x^2}{2 \cdot 3^2} + \frac{x^3}{3 \cdot 3^3} + \cdots + \frac{x^n}{n \cdot 3^n} + \cdots$$

Solution

The ratio of u_{n+1} to u_n is

$$\frac{u_{n+1}}{u_n} = \frac{x^{n+1}}{(n+1) \cdot 3^{n+1}} \cdot \frac{n \cdot 3^n}{x^n} = \frac{nx}{3(n+1)}.$$

The limit of this ratio when $n \to \infty$ (for any fixed value of x) is

$$\lim_{n \to \infty} \frac{nx}{3(n+1)} = \frac{x}{3}.$$

The series is *convergent* for all values of x for which the absolute value of this limit is *less* than one; *i.e.*, for all values of x such that

$$\left|\frac{x}{3}\right| < 1, \quad \text{or} \quad |x| < 3, \quad \text{or} \quad -3 < x < 3.$$

The series is *divergent* for all values of x for which this limit is *greater* than one in absolute value; *i.e.*, for $x > 3$ or < -3.

For $x = \pm 3$ the absolute value of the above limit is *equal* to one and the ratio test fails. We therefore substitute 3 and -3, respectively, for x in the given series and examine the resulting two series of constant terms: these series are:

$$1 + \tfrac{1}{2} + \tfrac{1}{3} + \cdots + \frac{1}{n} + \cdots \qquad \text{if } x = 3;$$

$$-1 + \tfrac{1}{2} - \tfrac{1}{3} + \cdots + (-1)^n \frac{1}{n} + \cdots \qquad \text{if } x = -3.$$

The first is the divergent harmonic series but the second is convergent by the alternating series test. The complete interval of convergence is then expressed by

$$-3 \leqq x < 3$$

and is represented graphically by the heavy line in Fig. 216. The small circle drawn about the point $x = 3$ indicates that this point is not included in the interval.

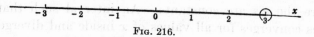

Fig. 216.

It is easy to show by using the comparison test that if a power series in x is convergent for $x = x_1$ then it is absolutely convergent for $|x| < |x_1|$; if it is divergent for $x = x_2$ then it is divergent for $|x| > |x_2|$. It follows that the interval of convergence of any power series in x is of the form $-k < x < k$ including neither or one or both of the end points. This interval may be so small as to consist only of the one point $x = 0$ $\left(\text{if } \lim_{n \to \infty} \frac{u_{n+1}}{u_n} = \infty \text{ for } x \neq 0\right)$, or it may be so large as to include all values of x

$$\left(\text{if } \lim_{n \to \infty} \frac{u_{n+1}}{u_n} = 0 \text{ for all values of } x\right).$$

Any series of the form

$$a_0 + a_1(x - b) + a_2(x - b)^2 + \cdots$$
$$+ a_n(x - b)^n + \cdots$$

is called a *power series* in $x - b$. The procedure for finding its interval of convergence is the same as that for a power series in x.

Example

Find the interval of convergence of the series

$$\frac{x - 3}{1 \cdot 2} + \frac{(x - 3)^2}{3 \cdot 2^2} + \frac{(x - 3)^3}{5 \cdot 2^3} + \cdots + \frac{(x - 3)^n}{(2n - 1) \cdot 2^n} + \cdots$$

Solution

Using the ratio test, we find that

$$\lim_{n \to \infty} \left| \frac{u_{n+1}}{u_n} \right| = \lim_{n \to \infty} \left| \frac{(x - 3)^{n+1}}{(2n + 1) \cdot 2^{n+1}} \cdot \frac{(2n - 1) \cdot 2^n}{(x - 3)^n} \right|$$
$$= \lim_{n \to \infty} \left| \frac{x - 3}{2} \cdot \frac{2n - 1}{2n + 1} \right| = \left| \frac{x - 3}{2} \right|.$$

The series is convergent, if

$$\left| \frac{x - 3}{2} \right| < 1, \quad \text{or} \quad |x - 3| < 2, \quad \text{or} \quad 1 < x < 5.$$

It is easy to show that the series converges if $x = 1$ and diverges if $x = 5$; the complete interval of convergence is then expressed by

$$1 \leqq x < 5$$

and is represented graphically in Fig. 217. It should be noticed that the interval of convergence of a power series in $x - b$ is bisected by the point $x = b$.

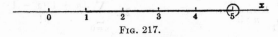

FIG. 217.

PROBLEMS

Find the interval of convergence of the following power series:

1. $1 + x + x^2 + \cdots + x^n + \cdots$.

2. $x + 2x^2 + 3x^3 + \cdots + nx^n + \cdots$.

3. $1 - x + \frac{1}{2}x^2 - \frac{1}{3}x^3 + \cdots + (-1)^n \frac{x^n}{n} + \cdots$.

4. $x + \dfrac{x^3}{\sqrt{3}} + \dfrac{x^5}{\sqrt{5}} + \cdots + \dfrac{x^{2n-1}}{\sqrt{2n-1}} + \cdots$.

5. $\dfrac{x}{1 \cdot 2} - \dfrac{x^2}{2 \cdot 2^2} + \dfrac{x^3}{3 \cdot 2^3} - \cdots + (-1)^{n+1} \dfrac{x^n}{n \cdot 2^n} + \cdots$.

6. $\displaystyle\sum_{n=1}^{\infty} \dfrac{x^n}{n(n+1)}$.

7. $\displaystyle\sum_{n=0}^{\infty} \dfrac{(n+1)x^n}{4^n}$.

8. $\displaystyle\sum_{n=0}^{\infty} \dfrac{(2x)^n}{n!}$.

9. $\displaystyle\sum_{n=1}^{\infty} \dfrac{x^n}{2^n \cdot n^2}$.

10. $\displaystyle\sum_{n=0}^{\infty} \dfrac{x^n}{(2n-1)^2 2^n}$.

11. $\displaystyle\sum_{n=0}^{\infty} \dfrac{x^n}{n!}$.

12. $\displaystyle\sum_{n=1}^{\infty} \dfrac{x^{2n-1}}{4^n}$.

13. $\displaystyle\sum_{n=1}^{\infty} \dfrac{nx^n}{(n+1)2^{n-1}}$.

14. $\displaystyle\sum_{n=1}^{\infty} \dfrac{n!\,x^n}{n^2}$.

15. $\displaystyle\sum_{n=1}^{\infty} (-1)^{n+1} \dfrac{x^{2n}}{2^n}$.

16. $(x-3) + 2(x-3)^2 + 3(x-3)^3 + \cdots + n(x-3)^n + \cdots$.

17. $(x-1) + \dfrac{(x-1)^2}{2 \cdot 2!} + \dfrac{(x-1)^3}{3 \cdot 3!} + \cdots + \dfrac{(x-1)^n}{n \cdot n!} + \cdots$.

18. $(x+1) - \tfrac{1}{2}(x+1)^2 + \tfrac{1}{3}(x+1)^3 - \cdots$
$$+ (-1)^{n+1} \dfrac{(x+1)^n}{n} + \cdots .$$

19. $(x+4) + \dfrac{(x+4)^2}{2} + \dfrac{(x+4)^3}{3} + \cdots + \dfrac{(x+4)^n}{n} + \cdots$.

20. $1 + \dfrac{x+2}{1^2 \cdot 2} + \dfrac{(x+2)^2}{2^2 \cdot 2^2} + \cdots + \dfrac{(x+2)^n}{n^2 \cdot 2^n} + \cdots$.

21. $\displaystyle\sum_{n=1}^{\infty} \dfrac{(x-2)^n}{(2n-1)(2n)}$.

22. $\displaystyle\sum_{n=1}^{\infty} \dfrac{n(x+2)^n}{4^n}$.

23. $\displaystyle\sum_{n=1}^{\infty} \dfrac{(x-3)^n}{n \cdot 3^n}$.

24. $\displaystyle\sum_{n=0}^{\infty} \dfrac{(n+1)(x-1)^n}{n!}$.

CHAPTER XXVIII

EXPANSION OF FUNCTIONS

192. Introduction.—By the simple process of long division and by the use of the binomial theorem, we have already obtained relations such as,

(1) $$\frac{1}{1-x} = 1 + x + x^2 + x^3 + \cdots .$$

(2) $$(1+x)^{\frac{1}{2}} = 1 + \frac{1}{2}x - \frac{1}{2^2\,2!}x^2 + \frac{3}{2^3\,3!}x^3$$
$$- \frac{3 \cdot 5}{2^4\,4!}x^4 + \cdots .$$

Both series are convergent in the interval $-1 < x < 1$. Furthermore, it can be shown that for any value of x in this interval *the sum of either series is the value of the function from which the series was obtained.* The series may, therefore, be said to *represent* the function for values of x in this interval; it may be used to compute the value of the function for any such value of x. Thus, putting $x = \frac{1}{9}$ in (2) we have

$$\frac{\sqrt{10}}{3} = 1 + \frac{1}{2(9)} - \frac{1}{2!\,2^2 9^2} + \frac{3}{3!\,2^3 9^3} - \frac{3 \cdot 5}{4!\,2^4 9^4} + \cdots$$

from which $\sqrt{10}$ can be computed with any desired degree of accuracy.

We now ask whether other functions such as $\sin x$, e^x, and $\log (1 + x)$ can be similarly represented by power series; specifically, "Is it possible, by getting the proper values for C_0, C_1, C_2, $\cdots$, to write

$$\sin x = C_0 + C_1 x + C_2 x^2 + C_3 x^3 + \cdots$$

in the same sense that (1) and (2) above are written?" If

it is possible, how does one determine the values for the C's?

Assuming that such an "expansion" of a given function in a power series is possible, we shall show in the next article how the values of the C's are found. For this purpose we shall need the following theorem, which will be stated without proof:

Theorem: *If the power series $C_0 + C_1x + C_2x^2 + \cdots$ converges in a certain interval and represents a function $f(x)$, then the series obtained by differentiating this power series term by term will converge in the same interval (with the possible exception of the end points), and will represent the derivative $f'(x)$ of this function.*

193. Maclaurin's series.—Assume that for all values of x in an interval of the form $-r < x < +r$ the power series $C_0 + C_1x + C_2x^2 + \cdots$ converges and represents the function $f(x)$; *i.e.*, assume that

(1) $f(x) = C_0 + C_1x + C_2x^2 + C_3x^3 + C_4x^4 + \cdots$.

We wish then to determine how the C's are related to the function $f(x)$. Putting $x = 0$ in (1), we have immediately

$$f(0) = C_0;$$

i.e., the first constant C_0 must be equal to the value of $f(x)$ when $x = 0$; next, differentiating (1) and then putting $x = 0$, we have

$$f'(x) = C_1 + 2C_2x + 3C_3x^2 + 4C_4x^3 + \cdots ,$$
$$f'(0) = C_1.$$

Differentiating again and putting $x = 0$, we get

$$f''(x) = 2C_2 + 2 \cdot 3C_3x + 3 \cdot 4C_4x^2 + \cdots ,$$
$$f''(0) = 2C_2, \quad \text{or} \quad C_2 = \frac{f''(0)}{2}.$$

Repeating the process, we find next

$$f'''(x) = 2 \cdot 3C_3 + 2 \cdot 3 \cdot 4C_4x + \cdots ,$$
$$f'''(0) = 2 \cdot 3C_3, \quad \text{or} \quad C_3 = \frac{f'''(0)}{3!}.$$

Proceeding in this way we see that in general

$$C_n = \frac{f^{(n)}(0)}{n!}.$$

Substituting these values for the C's in (1), we have

$$(2) \qquad f(x) = f(0) + f'(0)x + \frac{f''(0)}{2!} x^2 + \frac{f'''(0)}{3!} x^3 + \cdots$$

$$+ \frac{f^n(0)}{n!} x^n + \cdots.$$

This is called *Maclaurin's series*. It can obviously be formally written down for any function that is defined at $x = 0$ and has derivatives of all orders at this point. It must be emphasized, however, that we have not *proved* that the series represents the function. We have merely shown that if $f(x)$ can be represented by a series of the form (1), then the C's must have the values given in (2). Cases can be found in which the sum of the series is not equal to the value of the function but none will be encountered in our elementary work.

Example

Expand the function sin x in a Maclaurin series.

Solution

$$
\begin{array}{ll}
f(x) = \sin x & f(0) = 0 \\
f'(x) = \cos x & f'(0) = 1 \\
f''(x) = -\sin x & f''(0) = 0 \\
f'''(x) = -\cos x & f'''(0) = -1 \\
f^{(4)}(x) = \sin x & f^{(4)}(0) = 0 \\
f^{(5)}(x) = \cos x & f^{(5)}(0) = 1
\end{array}
$$

· · · · · · · · · · · · · · ·

Substituting in (2) the values found above in the right-hand column, we have

$$\sin x = 0 + 1 \cdot x + \frac{0}{2!} x^2 + \frac{-1}{3!} x^3 + \frac{0}{4!} x^4 + \frac{1}{5!} x^5 + \cdots$$

or

$$\sin x = x - \frac{x^3}{3!} + \frac{x^5}{5!} - \cdots.$$

The series can easily be shown to converge for all values of x. It may then be used to compute sin x for any value of x—and since it is an alternating series, the error made in stopping at any term is less than the first neglected term.

PROBLEMS

Verify the following expansions and show that the series are convergent for all values of x:

1. $e^x = 1 + x + \dfrac{x^2}{2!} + \dfrac{x^3}{3!} + \cdots + \dfrac{x^n}{n!} + \cdots.$

2. $\sin x = x - \dfrac{x^3}{3!} + \dfrac{x^5}{5!} - \cdots + (-1)^n \dfrac{x^{2n+1}}{(2n+1)!} + \cdots.$

3. $\cos x = 1 - \dfrac{x^2}{2!} + \dfrac{x^4}{4!} - \cdots + (-1)^n \dfrac{x^{2n}}{(2n)!} + \cdots.$

Verify each of the following expansions and show that in each case the series converges for values of x between -1 and $+1$:

4. $\log (1 + x) = x - \dfrac{x^2}{2} + \dfrac{x^3}{3} - \dfrac{x^4}{4} + \cdots + (-1)^{n+1} \dfrac{x^n}{n} + \cdots.$

5. $\log (1 - x) = -x - \dfrac{x^2}{2} - \dfrac{x^3}{3} - \dfrac{x^4}{4} - \cdots - \dfrac{x^n}{n} - \cdots.$

6. $\arctan x = x - \dfrac{x^3}{3} + \dfrac{x^5}{5} - \dfrac{x^7}{7} + \cdots$

$$+ (-1)^{n+1} \dfrac{x^{2n-1}}{2n-1} + \cdots.$$

7. From the results of Probs. 4 and 5 show that

$$\log \frac{1+x}{1-x} = 2 \left(x + \frac{x^3}{3} + \frac{x^5}{5} + \cdots + \frac{x^{2n-1}}{2n-1} + \cdots \right).$$

What is the interval of convergence?

8. From the result of Prob. 1, write down the Maclaurin series for the function e^{-x^2}. What is the interval of convergence?

9. Compute sin 9° from the series of Prob. 2 using two terms. Estimate the error.

10. Compute cos 20° from the series of Prob. 3 using four terms. Estimate the error.

11. Compute $\sqrt{e}$ from the series of Prob. 1 using five terms. Estimate the error.

12. Show by using the series of Prob. 2 that when $x \to 0$ the difference between sin x and x is an infinitesimal of third order relative to x.

13. Show by using the series of Prob. 3 that when $x \to 0$, cos x differs from $(1 - \frac{1}{2}x^2)$ by an infinitesimal of fourth order relative to x.

14. For what size angles may one replace $\sin \theta$ by θ (radians) if the error must be less than 0.0005'

15. From the series of Probs. 2 and 3 show that $\sin (-x) \equiv -\sin x$ and $\cos (-x) \equiv \cos x$.

16. Expand $\sqrt{1+x}$ by the binomial theorem and show that the series converges for values of x between -1 and $+1$.

In each of the following cases find the first three or four terms of the Maclaurin series for the given function:

17. $\tan x$.	**18.** $\sec x$.	**19.** $\log (\sec x + \tan x)$.
20. $\log \sec x$.	**21.** $\log \cos x$.	**22.** $x^2 e^{-x}$.
23. $e^x \sin x$.	**24.** $x \log (1+x)$.	

25. Explain why $\log x$ cannot be expanded in a Maclaurin series. What about $x^{\frac{1}{2}}$?

194. Taylor's series.—A function $f(x)$ cannot be expanded in a Maclaurin series unless it is defined and has derivatives of all orders *at the point where $x = 0$*; thus, such functions as $\log x$ and $\sqrt{x}$, cannot be so expanded.

It is fairly obvious also that the Maclaurin series, when it can be obtained, is useful in computing the value of $f(x)$ *primarily for values of x near* 0; for it is for such values of x that the terms involving x^3, x^4, x^5, etc., decrease rapidly.

We shall now derive a formula for the expansion of a function in powers of $(x - a)$ where a is a constant that may be selected arbitrarily; such a series is useful for computing the value of $f(x)$ for values of x near a. The procedure is the same as that used in deriving Maclaurin's series.

Assume that in some interval of the form

$$a - r < x < a + r$$

the series $C_0 + C_1(x - a) + C_2(x - a)^2 + \cdots$ converges and represents the function $f(x)$; we may then write, for all values of x in this interval, which includes the point $x = a$,

$$(3)\ f(x) = C_0 + C_1(x - a) + C_2(x - a)^2 + C_3(x - a)^3 + C_4(x - a)^4 + \cdots .$$

Differentiating successively, we obtain the equations:

$$f'(x) = C_1 + 2C_2(x - a) + 3C_3(x - a)^2 + 4C_4(x - a)^3 + \cdots ;$$

$$f''(x) = 2!C_2 + 3!C_3(x - a) + 4 \cdot 3C_4(x - a)^2 + \cdots ;$$

$$f'''(x) = 3!C_3 + 4!C_4(x - a) + \cdots ;$$

$$\cdots \cdots \cdots \cdots \cdots \cdots \cdots \cdots \cdots \cdots \cdots \cdots$$

Substituting $x = a$ in these equations and solving for the C's, we obtain

$$C_0 = f(a), \qquad C_1 = f'(a), \qquad C_2 = \frac{f''(a)}{2!}, \qquad C_3 = \frac{f'''(a)}{3!},$$

and we can easily see that

$$C_n = \frac{f^{(n)}(a)}{n!}.$$

Substituting these values for the C's in (3), we have

$$(4) \quad f(x) = f(a) + \frac{f'(a)}{1!}(x - a) + \frac{f''(a)}{2!}(x - a)^2$$

$$+ \frac{f'''(a)}{3!}(x - a)^3 + \cdots + \frac{f^{(n)}(a)}{n!}(x - a)^n + \cdots .$$

This is called *Taylor's series*. It is the expansion of $f(x)$ in powers of $(x - a)$ and is, in general, valid in an interval that is bisected by the point $x = a$. It converges most rapidly, of course, for values of x *near* a because for such values the terms involving $(x - a)^2$, $(x - a)^3$, etc., decrease rapidly. The Maclaurin series is obviously a special case of this more general expansion; it is obtained by taking $a = 0$.

Example

Expand the function $\log x$ in a Taylor's series taking $a = 1$.

Solution

$$f(x) = \log x \qquad f(1) = 0$$

$$f'(x) = \frac{1}{x} \qquad f'(1) = 1$$

$$f''(x) = -\frac{1}{x^2} \qquad f''(1) = -1$$

$$f'''(x) = +\frac{2}{x^3} \qquad f'''(1) = 2!$$

$$f^{(4)}(x) = -\frac{3 \cdot 2}{x^4} \qquad f^{(4)}(1) = -3!$$

. . . .

Substituting in (4) the values found above in the right-hand column, we have

$$\log x = 0 + 1(x-1) + \frac{-1}{2!}(x-1)^2 + \frac{2}{3!}(x-1)^3 + \frac{-3!}{4!}(x-1)^4$$
$$+ \cdots$$
$$= \frac{x-1}{1} - \frac{(x-1)^2}{2} + \frac{(x-1)^3}{3} - \frac{(x-1)^4}{4} + \cdots.$$

The interval of convergence is $0 < x \leqq 2$.

195. Operations with power series.—Operations that one can always perform in dealing with a *finite* number of terms are not necessarily permissible when *infinite* series are involved. Thus, we have already seen that changing the order of the terms in a conditionally convergent series may change its sum or cause it to become divergent.

The following remarks concerning operations with infinite series in general and power series in particular will be found useful. Proofs are omitted.

Addition.—If two convergent series of constant terms having sums U and V, respectively, are added term by term, the resulting series is convergent with sum $U + V$. Consequently, if two power series representing, respectively, $f(x)$ and $g(x)$ be so added, the resulting series will converge and represent $f(x) + g(x)$ for all values of x for which *both* series are convergent.

Multiplication.—If two convergent series of constant terms having sums U and V, respectively, are multiplied together by the usual rule for multiplying polynomials, the resulting series is convergent with sum $U \cdot V$ provided at least one of the two series is *absolutely* convergent. If both are only conditionally convergent, the product

series may diverge; if it does converge, however, its sum will
be $U \cdot V$.   Any power series is absolutely convergent for all
values of x in the *interior* of its interval of convergence.
Consequently, if two power series representing $f(x)$ and
$g(x)$, respectively, be so multiplied, the resulting series will
certainly converge and represent $f(x) \cdot g(x)$ for all values of
x in the interior of *both* intervals of convergence.

Differentiation and Integration.—For series of variable
terms, in general, the questions of differentiation and
integration involve the conception of "uniform" convergence, which cannot be treated here.   For the special case
of *power series*, however, the necessary theorem concerning
differentiation was stated in Art. 192 and was used in
deriving both Maclaurin's and Taylor's series.   The
corresponding statement concerning term by term integration is as follows:

*If the power series representing $f(x)$ be integrated term by
term between the limits a and b, the resulting series will converge and represent $\int_a^b f(x)dx$ provided both limits are in the
interior of the interval of convergence.*

A definite integral may sometimes be evaluated when the
indefinite integral cannot be found, by expanding the
integrand in a power series and integrating term by term.

Example

Evaluate $\int_0^{\frac{1}{2}} e^{-x^2}dx$.

Solution

We cannot find an indefinite integral; but

$$e^{-x^2} = 1 - x^2 + \frac{x^4}{2!} - \frac{x^6}{3!} + \cdots .*$$

The series converges for all values of x, hence the limits 0 and $\frac{1}{2}$ are inside
the convergence interval; we have, then,

---

* This series is easily obtained by writing down the well-known **series** for
e^x and then replacing x by $-x^2$.

$$\int_0^{\frac{1}{2}} e^{-x^2}dx = \int_0^{\frac{1}{2}} \left(1 - x^2 + \frac{x^4}{2!} - \frac{x^6}{3!} + \cdots \right) dx$$

$$= x - \frac{x^3}{3} + \frac{x^5}{5 \cdot 2!} - \frac{x^7}{7 \cdot 3!} + \cdots \Big]_0^{\frac{1}{2}}$$

$$= 0.4613.$$

Term by term differentiation or integration may also provide an easy method of obtaining the power series for many functions.

Example

Expand arctan x in a Maclaurin series.

Solution

The series for $\dfrac{1}{1 + x^2}$, obtained by long division, is

$$\frac{1}{1 + x^2} = 1 - x^2 + x^4 - x^6 + \cdots, \qquad |x| < 1.$$

Integrating both sides between limits $x = 0$ and $x = x$, we have

$$\int_0^x \frac{dx}{1 + x^2} = \int_0^x (1 - x^2 + x^4 - x^6 + \cdots)dx,$$

or,

$$\arctan x = x - \frac{x^3}{3} + \frac{x^5}{5} - \frac{x^7}{7} + \cdots, \qquad |x| < 1.$$

PROBLEMS

1. Expand $\sin x$ in a Taylor series taking $a = \frac{1}{6}\pi$.

2. Expand $\cos x$ in a Taylor series taking $a = \frac{1}{4}\pi$.

3. Expand $\log x$ in a Taylor series taking $a = 2$.

4. Expand $\sqrt{x}$ in a Taylor series taking $a = 1$. Find the interval of convergence. Compute $\sqrt{1.5}$ to three decimal places.

5. Expand e^x in powers of $(x - 1)$.

6. From the Maclaurin series for the functions e^x and e^{-x}, find the corresponding series for the function $\frac{1}{2}(e^x + e^{-x})$.

7. Differentiate the Maclaurin series for e^x and explain the result.

8. Differentiate the Maclaurin series for $\sin x$ and explain the result.

9. Obtain the first five terms of the Maclaurin series for the function $e^x \cos x$ by multiplying the corresponding series for e^x and $\cos x$. Check by expanding the function $e^x \cos x$ directly. What is the interval of convergence?

10. Same as Prob. 9 for the function $e^x \sin x$.

11. Expand $\dfrac{1}{\sqrt{1-x^2}}$ by the binomial theorem. By integration obtain the Maclaurin series for arcsin x.

12. By division obtain the expansion of the function $\dfrac{1}{1-x^2}$ in powers of x. From this result obtain by integration the series for the function $\log \dfrac{1+x}{1-x}$. Compute $\log 3$ by putting $x = \frac{1}{2}$ and using four terms. Estimate the error. $\left(\displaystyle\int \dfrac{dx}{1-x^2} = \frac{1}{2} \log \dfrac{1+x}{1-x} \text{ if } |x| < 1 \right)$

13. Evaluate $\displaystyle\int_0^1 e^{-\frac{1}{2}x^2} dx$ using the Maclaurin series.

14. Evaluate $\displaystyle\int_0^1 x^3 e^{-x^2} dx$ to three decimal places both with and without using the Maclaurin series.

15. Evaluate $\displaystyle\int_0^1 \sin(x^2) dx$ to four decimal places.

16. Sketch the curve whose equation is $y = \dfrac{e^x - e^{-x}}{x}$, and compute to three decimal places the area under it in the interval from $x = 0$ to $x = 1$.

17. Sketch the curve whose equation is $y = \dfrac{e^x - 1}{x}$, and compute to three decimal places the area under it in the interval from $x = 0$ to $x = 0.5$.

18. Sketch the curve whose equation is $x^4 + y^2 = 1$, and compute to three decimal places the area enclosed by it.

196. The remainder in Taylor's series.

—In deriving the coefficients for Taylor's series we assumed the existence of a power series in $(x - a)$ that converges in some interval about the point $x = a$ and represents the given function $f(x)$.

Let us now discard this assumption and assume only that $f(x)$ and its first n derivatives are defined over an interval that includes the point $x = a$. We can then write, for any point x in this interval,

$$(1) \quad f(x) = f(a) + f'(a)(x - a) + \frac{f''(a)}{2!}(x - a)^2 + \cdots$$
$$+ \frac{f^{(n-1)}(a)}{(n-1)!}(x - a)^{n-1} + R_n$$

where R_n denotes the remainder. This equation merely states that the value of $f(x)$, for any value of x in the interval under consideration, is equal to the sum of the n terms given on the right plus some positive or negative quantity R_n, which is defined by the equation itself to be whatever is required in order that the two sides may balance. If, for a certain value of x, it happens that

$$\lim_{n \to \infty} R_n = 0,$$

then Taylor's series not only converges but *converges to the value of $f(x)$* for this value of x.

It is possible to express R_n in several ways, one of the most useful being the following:

(2) $$R_n = \frac{f^{(n)}(x_1)}{n!} (x - a)^n, \qquad \text{where} \qquad a < x_1 < x.$$

The theorem stating that $f(x)$ is given exactly by (1) wherein R_n has the value given by (2) is called *Taylor's Theorem*. By using this theorem one can prove that the power series which we have obtained for elementary functions such as $\sin x$, $\cos x$, e^x, and $\log x$, do represent these functions within their respective intervals of convergence. The proof of Taylor's Theorem, and further discussion of these related matters, is best deferred to a course in advanced calculus.

197. Relations between the exponential and trigonometric functions.—We have already derived the following series:

(1) $$e^x = 1 + x + \frac{x^2}{2!} + \frac{x^3}{3!} + \cdots$$

(2) $$\sin x = x - \frac{x^3}{3!} + \frac{x^5}{5!} - \frac{x^7}{7!} + \cdots$$

(3) $$\cos x = 1 - \frac{x^2}{2!} + \frac{x^4}{4!} - \frac{x^6}{6!} + \cdots$$

We have seen that all these series are convergent for all real values of x.   It can be shown that in each case the remainder

R_n approaches zero as $n \to \infty$, no matter what value is assigned to x. Each series therefore represents the corresponding function for all real values of x.

No meaning has been given to the symbol e^x if x is an imaginary number. It can be shown, however, that the above series (1) is convergent for all *complex* as well as all real values of x. We may therefore agree arbitrarily to let the exponential function be defined for *all* values of x, complex as well as real, by the series; *i.e.*, if z is any number of the form $a + bi$, where a and b are real,

$$(4) \quad e^z = 1 + z + \frac{z^2}{2!} + \frac{z^3}{3!} + \cdots + \frac{z^n}{n!} + \cdots .$$

With the exponential function thus defined for complex values of z, we may derive certain relations between the trigonometric functions of the real number x and the exponential functions of the corresponding imaginary number ix as follows:

Substituting ix (where $i = \sqrt{-1}$) for z in (4) we have

$$e^{ix} = 1 + ix + \frac{i^2 x^2}{2!} + \frac{i^3 x^3}{3!} + \frac{i^4 x^4}{4!} + \cdots .$$

Using the relations $i^2 = -1$, $i^3 = -i$, $i^4 = 1$, etc., we can reduce this to the form

$$e^{ix} = \left(1 - \frac{x^2}{2!} + \frac{x^4}{4!} - \cdots \right) + i\left(x - \frac{x^3}{3!} + \frac{x^5}{5!} - \cdots \right).*$$

The series in parentheses represent $\cos x$ and $\sin x$, respectively; hence, we have the relation

$$(5) \qquad\qquad e^{ix} = \cos x + i \sin x.$$

Replacing x by $-x$ we have also

$$(6) \qquad\qquad e^{-ix} = \cos x - i \sin x.$$

---

* The rearrangement of terms is permissible because the series is *absolutely* convergent for all values of x.

Finally, by adding and subtracting (5) and (6), we deduce that

(7) $$\sin x = \frac{e^{ix} - e^{-ix}}{2i};$$

(8) $$\cos x = \frac{e^{ix} + e^{-ix}}{2}.$$

The relations (5), (6), (7), and (8) are of great importance in many of the applications of mathematics. They enable one to change exponential functions of the imaginary number ix over into trigonometric functions of the real number x, and vice versa. The student will have occasion to use them in the next chapter for the purpose of simplifying the solutions of certain differential equations.

Just as we define the exponential function for complex values of z by means of series (4), we may also define the trigonometric functions $\sin z$ and $\cos z$ for $z = a + bi$ by series (2) and (3), respectively; i.e.,

(9) $$\sin z = z - \frac{z^3}{3!} + \frac{z^5}{5!} - \frac{z^7}{7!} + \cdots ;$$

(10) $$\cos z = 1 - \frac{z^2}{2!} + \frac{z^4}{4!} - \frac{z^6}{6!} + \cdots .$$

If we let $z = ix$ in these series, we can deduce the relations

(11) $$\sin (ix) = i\frac{e^x - e^{-x}}{2};$$

(12) $$\cos (ix) = \frac{e^x + e^{-x}}{2}.$$

These equations express the trigonometric functions of the imaginary number ix in terms of the exponential functions of the real number x.

198. The hyperbolic functions.—The exponential functions

$$\frac{e^x - e^{-x}}{2} \qquad \text{and} \qquad \frac{e^x + e^{-x}}{2},$$

which appear in equations (11) and (12) of the preceding section, occur frequently in applied mathematics—so frequently, in fact, that it is useful to assign names to them and tabulate their values. From the way in which they occur in (11) and (12) it might be suspected that they have some properties that are similar to those of sin x and cos x. It can, in fact, be shown that they are related to the equilateral hyperbola in a manner somewhat analogous to that in which the trigonometric functions are related to the circle. The names chosen for them are accordingly the *hyperbolic sine* of x and the *hyperbolic cosine* of x, respectively. The abbreviations usually used are sinh x and cosh x. We have then, *by defintion,*

$$(1) \qquad \sinh x = \frac{e^x - e^{-x}}{2};$$

$$(2) \qquad \cosh x = \frac{e^x + e^{-x}}{2}.$$

The hyperbolic tangent of x is defined by the relation

$$(3) \qquad \tanh x = \frac{\sinh x}{\cosh x} = \frac{e^x - e^{-x}}{e^x + e^{-x}}.$$

The hyperbolic cotangent (coth), secant (sech), and cosecant (csch) are defined as the reciprocals of the hyperbolic tangent, cosine, and sine, respectively. The values of sinh x, cosh x, and tanh x, and their logarithms are given in tabular form in various books of tables. (See Table V in this book.)

The fundamental properties of the hyperbolic functions may be deduced directly from their definitions. As already remarked, many of these properties are analogous to those of the trigonometric functions.

Example 1

Show that $2 \sinh x \cosh x = \sinh 2x$.

Solution

$$2 \sinh x \cosh x = 2 \cdot \tfrac{1}{2}(e^x - e^{-x}) \cdot \tfrac{1}{2}(e^x + e^{-x})$$
$$= \tfrac{1}{2}(e^{2x} - e^{-2x})$$
$$= \sinh 2x.$$

Example 2

Show that $d/dx \sinh x = \cosh x$.

Solution

$$\sinh x = \tfrac{1}{2}(e^x - e^{-x});$$
$$\frac{d}{dx} \sinh x = \tfrac{1}{2}(e^x + e^{-x})$$
$$= \cosh x.$$

Example 3

Show that $d/dx \tanh x = \operatorname{sech}^2 x$.

Solution

$$\tanh x = \frac{e^x - e^{-x}}{e^x + e^{-x}};$$
$$\frac{d}{dx} \tanh x = \frac{(e^x + e^{-x})(e^x + e^{-x}) - (e^x - e^{-x})(e^x - e^{-x})}{(e^x + e^{-x})^2}$$
$$= \frac{4}{(e^x + e^{-x})^2}$$
$$= \operatorname{sech}^2 x.$$

The student should be careful to observe that, while some of the properties and formulas applying to the hyperbolic functions correspond exactly to those applying to the trigonometric functions, some of the relations contain important differences. Thus, for the circular functions we have the relation $\cos^2 x + \sin^2 x = 1$, while for the hyperbolic functions the corresponding relation is

$$\cosh^2 x - \sinh^2 x = 1.$$

Further important properties of these functions are brought out in the following problems.

PROBLEMS

1. From equations (5) and (6) of Art. 196, derive the relation $e^{\pm \pi i} = -1$; show also that $e^{2k\pi i} = 1$, if k is any integer.

2. Show that $e^{(a \mp bi)x} = e^{ax}(\cos bx \mp i \sin bx)$.

3. Prove the relations

$$\begin{cases} \sin (ix) = i \sinh x \\ \cos (ix) = \cosh x \end{cases} \qquad \begin{cases} \sinh (ix) = i \sin x \\ \cosh (ix) = \cos x. \end{cases}$$

4. Prove the identities

(a) $$\cosh^2 x - \sinh^2 x = 1$$
(b) $$\tanh^2 x + \operatorname{sech}^2 x = 1$$
(c) $$\coth^2 x - \operatorname{csch}^2 x = 1.$$

5. Prove the relations

(a) $$\cosh x + \sinh x = e^x$$
(b) $$\cosh x - \sinh x = e^{-x}.$$

6. Show that

$$\sinh (-x) = - \sinh x$$
$$\cosh (-x) = \cosh x$$
$$\tanh (-x) = - \tanh x.$$

7. Show that

(a) $$\sinh (2x) = 2 \sinh x \cosh x$$
(b) $$\cosh (2x) = \cosh^2 x + \sinh^2 x$$
(c) $$\tanh (2x) = \frac{2 \tanh x}{1 + \tanh^2 x}.$$

8. Show that

(a) $$\sinh (x \pm y) = \sinh x \cosh y \pm \cosh x \sinh y$$
(b) $$\cosh (x \pm y) = \cosh x \cosh y \pm \sinh x \sinh y$$
(c) $$\tanh (x \pm y) = \frac{\tanh x \pm \tanh y}{1 \pm \tanh x \tanh y}.$$

9. Show that

(a) $$\frac{d}{dx} (\sinh u) = \cosh u \frac{du}{dx}$$
(b) $$\frac{d}{dx} (\cosh u) = \sinh u \frac{du}{dx}$$
(c) $$\frac{d}{dx} (\tanh u) = \operatorname{sech}^2 u \frac{du}{dx}.$$

Differentiate the following functions using the formulas of Prob. 9:

10. $y = 4 \sinh \frac{1}{2}x.$ **11.** $y = \frac{1}{2} \tanh^2 x.$
12. $y = 2 \sqrt{\sinh 2x}.$ **13.** $y = \log \sinh x.$
14. $y = \frac{1}{2} \cosh^2 2x.$ **15.** $y = 2e^{-x} \sinh x.$

16. Sketch the graphs of the equations $y = \sinh x$ and $y = \cosh x$.

17. Show that the equation $y = (a/2)\,(e^{\frac{x}{a}} + e^{-\frac{x}{a}})$, which represents a catenary, can be written in the form $y = a \cosh (x/a)$. Sketch the curve. This is the curve in which a homogenous flexible cable hangs when suspended from two points and acted upon only by its own weight.

18. Show that for all (real) values of x

(a) $\qquad \sinh x = x + \dfrac{x^3}{3!} + \dfrac{x^5}{5!} + \cdots + \dfrac{x^{2n+1}}{(2n+1)!} + \cdots.$

(b) $\qquad \cosh x = 1 + \dfrac{x^2}{2!} + \dfrac{x^4}{4!} + \cdots + \dfrac{x^{2n}}{(2n)!} + \cdots.$

19. If $y = \sinh x$ then x is called the *inverse hyperbolic sine* of y $(x = \sinh^{-1} y)$. By solving the equation

$$y = \sinh x = \tfrac{1}{2}(e^x - e^{-x})$$

for x in terms of y, show that

$$x = \sinh^{-1} y = \log\,(y + \sqrt{y^2 + 1}).$$

Hence infer that $\sinh^{-1} x$ is simply another name for the function $\log (x + \sqrt{x^2 + 1})$.

20. Show that $\cosh^{-1} x = \log (x \pm \sqrt{x^2 - 1})$ for $x \geqq 1$. See Prob. 19.

21. Show that $\tanh^{-1} x = \tfrac{1}{2} \log \dfrac{1 + x}{1 - x}$ for $-1 < x < 1$. See Prob. 19.

22. Using the results of Probs. 19 to 21, show that

(a) $\qquad\qquad \dfrac{d}{dx} \sinh^{-1} u = \dfrac{\dfrac{du}{dx}}{\sqrt{u^2 + 1}}.$

(b) $\qquad\qquad \dfrac{d}{dx} \cosh^{-1} u = \dfrac{\pm\,\dfrac{du}{dx}}{\sqrt{u^2 - 1}} \qquad (u > 1).$

(c) $\qquad\qquad \dfrac{d}{dx} \tanh^{-1} u = \dfrac{\dfrac{du}{dx}}{1 - u^2} \qquad (-1 < u < 1).$

23. Evaluate $\displaystyle\int_0^1 \sinh (x^2)dx$, using three terms of the series of Prob. 18. Estimate the error.

24. Evaluate $\displaystyle\int_0^1 \cosh \sqrt{x}\, dx$, using four terms of the series of Prob. 18. Estimate the error. Evaluate also by letting $\sqrt{x} = z$ and using integration by parts.

CHAPTER XXIX

DIFFERENTIAL EQUATIONS

199. Definitions.—A differential equation is an equation containing differentials or derivatives. The following are typical examples:

$$(1) \qquad \frac{d^2y}{dx^2} - 6x = 0;$$

$$(2) \qquad x\frac{dy}{dx} + 3y = y^3;$$

$$(3) \qquad \left(\frac{d^2y}{dx^2}\right)^2 + 6\left(\frac{dy}{dx}\right)^3 = y.$$

These equations all contain derivatives. When only the first derivative is involved, the relation is frequently written in a form containing differentials instead. Thus, (2) may be written in the form

$$x\,dy = (y^3 - 3y)dx.$$

The **order** of a differential equation is that of the *highest ordered derivative* occurring in it. Thus, (1) and (3) above are of second order while (2) is of first order. The *exponent of the derivative of highest order* gives the **degree** of the differential equation. Thus, (1) and (2) are of first degree while (3) is of second degree.

200. Solutions of differential equations.—A solution of a differential equation is any relation between the variables involved that satisfies the equation. The student has already solved simple differential equations of the form

$$\frac{d^ny}{dx^n} = f(x)$$

by direct integration. He is familiar with the fact that such an equation has a solution which contains n arbitrary constants.   Example 1 in Art. 199 is of this type.   Writing it in the form

$$\frac{d^2y}{dx^2} = 6x$$

we have, after integrating twice,

$$y = x^3 + C_1 x + C_2.$$

This result is called the *general solution* of the given differential equation. Any solution that can be obtained from it by giving particular values to C_1 and C_2 is called a *particular solution.*

In general, any differential equation of order n has a solution called the *general solution*, which contains exactly n essential arbitrary constants. Usually it has no other solution except the *particular solutions* obtainable from this by giving particular values to the constants. There are important exceptional cases when equations of degree higher than the first are considered; such cases will not, however, be treated here.

There is no general procedure for solving a differential equation. Only a few types can be solved at all, and we shall treat in this chapter only the simplest of these—taking, in general, those which occur often in various elementary applications. When a solution, or what is supposed to be a solution, has been obtained by any method, its correctness can of course be determined by direct substitution.

Example

Show that $y = A \sin x + B \cos x$ is the general solution of the equation $\frac{d^2y}{dx^2} + y = 0$.

Solution

By differentiating twice we find that, if

$$y = A \sin x + B \cos x,$$
$$\frac{d^2y}{dx^2} = -A \sin x - B \cos x;$$

hence,

$$\frac{d^2y}{dx^2} + y = 0.$$

The given relation is then a solution of the differential equation, and since it contains two arbitrary constants, it is the general solution.

201. Separation of variables.—Any differential equation of first order and first degree can be written in the form

$$M\, dx + N\, dy = 0$$

where in general M and N are functions of both x and y. It is often possible to transform the equation so as to get all the terms containing x together with dx on one side, and all those containing y together with dy on the other. When this can be done, the general solution can be obtained by integrating the two sides separately and adding the arbitrary constant on either side. This case was discussed briefly in Chap. XV in connection with elementary applications of the indefinite integral.

Example

$$(1 + x^2)dy - xy\, dx = 0.$$

Solution

Dividing by $y(1 + x^2)$ and transposing, this becomes

$$\frac{dy}{y} = \frac{x\, dx}{1 + x^2}.$$

Integrating both sides, we have

$$\log y = \tfrac{1}{2} \log (1 + x^2) + \log C,$$

or

$$\log y = \log C \sqrt{1 + x^2},$$

from which

$$y = C \sqrt{1 + x^2}$$

The arbitrary constant was added in the form "log C" merely for convenience.

PROBLEMS

1. Give the order and degree of each of the following differential equations:

(a)
$$\frac{d^2y}{dx^2} + x\left(\frac{dy}{dx}\right)^2 = y.$$

(b)
$$\frac{d^2y}{dx^2} + 6\frac{dy}{dx} = 0.$$

(c)
$$\left(\frac{dy}{dx}\right)^3 + y = \left(\frac{d^2y}{dx^2}\right)^2.$$

2. Show that $y = e^x \sin x$ is a solution of the equation $\frac{d^2y}{dx^2} - 2\frac{dy}{dx} + 2y = 0$. Is it the general solution?

3. Using the illustrative example in Art. 200, find the equation of the curve which has at every point, $d^2y/dx^2 = -y$, and which goes through $P(0, 2)$ at $45°$. Sketch the curve.

4. Show that $y = Ae^{2x} + Be^{3x}$ is the general solution of the equation $\frac{d^2y}{dx^2} - 5\frac{dy}{dx} + 6y = 0$.

5. Show that $y^2 = 4x$ is a particular solution of the equation $dy/dx = 2/y$. Find the general solution by separating the variables and integrating. Interpret the result geometrically.

6. Show that $x^2 + y^2 = Cx$ is the general solution of the equation $y^2 - x^2 = 2xy \frac{dy}{dx}$. Interpret this geometrically.

Solve the following differential equations by separating the variables:

7. $y\, dx + x\, dy = 0.$ **8.** $x^2 \frac{dy}{dx} + y^2 = 0.$

9. $y^2 dx = (x + 1)dy.$ **10.** $\frac{dy}{dx} + y^2 = 1.$

11. $(1 - x)y\, dx + (1 + y)x\, dy = 0.$

12. $(1 + x^2)y\, dy = (1 + y^2)x\, dx.$

13. $L\frac{di}{dt} + Ri = E.$

14. $\sqrt{1 - y^2}\, dx = x^2 y\, dy.$ **15.** $x\, dy + 2y\, dx = xy\, dy.$

202. Homogeneous equations.—A polynomial in x and y is said to be *homogeneous* if all of its terms are of the same degree in x and y taken together; thus

$$x^2 - 3xy + 4y^2 \quad \text{is homogeneous of degree 2;}$$
$$x^3y + x^2y^2 - 2y^4 \text{ is homogeneous of degree 4;}$$
$$6x - 3y \qquad \text{is homogeneous of degree 1.}$$

More generally, any function of x and y is said to be *homogeneous of degree n* if the result of replacing x and y, respectively, by kx and ky is the same function multiplied by k^n; thus, the function

$$x^2 e^{\frac{y}{x}}$$

is homogeneous of degree 2.

A differential equation of the form

$$M\ dx + N\ dy = 0$$

is said to be homogeneous *if M and N are homogeneous functions of x and y of the same degree.* Such an equation can be transformed into an equation in which the variables are separable by the substitution

$$y = vx,$$

where v is a new variable. Differentiating $y = vx$ gives

$$dy = v\ dx + x\ dv;$$

this quantity must be substituted for dy when vx is substituted for y.

Example

$$(x^2 - y^2)dx + 2xy\ dy = 0.$$

We cannot separate the variables, but M and N are homogeneous functions, both of degree 2. Substituting

$$y = vx \qquad \text{and} \qquad dy = v\ dx + x\ dv$$

we get

$$(1 - v^2)dx + 2v(v\ dx + x\ dv) = 0.$$

Separating the variables and integrating, we have

$$\frac{2v\ dv}{v^2 + 1} = -\frac{dx}{x},$$
$$\log(v^2 + 1) = -\log x + \log C,$$
$$x(v^2 + 1) = C;$$

finally, since $v = y/x$, this reduces to

$$x^2 + y^2 = Cx.$$

The reason for this substitution is apparent when the given equation is written in the form

$$\frac{dy}{dx} = -\frac{M}{N};$$

for if M and N are homogeneous functions of the *same degree*, the right-hand side becomes a function of v alone when vx is substituted for y; *i.e.*, the x's all cancel out. The equation then takes the form

$$v + x\frac{dv}{dx} = \varphi(v)$$

and the variables are obviously separable.

PROBLEMS

Solve the following equations:

1. $x\,dy + (x+y)dx = 0.$ **2.** $2xy\,dy = (x^2 + 3y^2)dx.$

3. $(x^2 + y^2)dx + xy\,dy = 0.$ **4.** $\dfrac{dy}{dx} = \dfrac{y^2}{xy - x^2}.$

5. $y^2dx = (x^2 + 2xy)dy.$ **6.** $(x^3 - y^3)dx + xy^2dy = 0.$

7. $(2x - y)dy = (x - 2y)dx.$ **8.** $(x - \sqrt{xy})dy = y\,dx.$

9. Find the equation of the curve through $(1, 0)$, which has at every point $\dfrac{dy}{dx} = \dfrac{x+y}{x}.$ Sketch the curve.

10. What curve through $(1, 1)$ has at every point $\dfrac{dy}{dx} = \dfrac{x-y}{x+y}$?

11. Show that the equation $\dfrac{dy}{dx} = \dfrac{a_1x + b_1y + c_1}{a_2x + b_2y + c_2}$ is made homogeneous by letting $x = x' + h$ and $y = y' + k$, where (h, k) is the point of intersection of the lines represented by $a_1x + b_1y + c_1 = 0$ and $a_2x + b_2y + c_2 = 0.$

12. Using the method suggested in Prob. 11, solve the equation $\dfrac{dy}{dx} = \dfrac{x - y - 4}{x + y - 2}.$

203. Exact differential equations.—It may happen that the left-hand side of the equation

$$M\,dx + N\,dy = 0$$

is exactly the total differential of some function $f(x, y)$. In this case the solution is, of course,

$$f(x, y) = C.$$

Thus, the left-hand side of the equation

$$y^2dx + 2xy\ dy = 0$$

is exactly the differential of the function y^2x; the equation may be written in the form

$$d(y^2x) = 0,$$

and the solution is

$$y^2x = C.$$

An equation of this type is called an *exact differential equation*. Since ordinarily one cannot determine by inspection whether or not a given equation is exact, some test for exactness is necessary. Such a test can easily be obtained as follows: The total differential of any function $f(x, y)$ is

$$\frac{\partial f}{\partial x}\ dx + \frac{\partial f}{\partial y}\ dy.$$

If the expression

$$M\ dx + N\ dy$$

is the differential of $f(x, y)$, then

$$\frac{\partial f}{\partial x} = M \qquad \text{and} \qquad \frac{\partial f}{\partial y} = N.$$

Differentiating the first of these with respect to y and the second with respect to x, we have

$$\frac{\partial^2 f}{\partial y\ \partial x} = \frac{\partial M}{\partial y}, \qquad \frac{\partial^2 f}{\partial x\ \partial y} = \frac{\partial N}{\partial x}.$$

But these two second partial derivatives are identically equal for all values of x and y for which they are continuous. The condition that must be satisfied, then, in order that

$$M\ dx + N\ dy = 0$$

be an exact differential equation, is

$$\frac{\partial M}{\partial y} \equiv \frac{\partial N}{\partial x}.$$

Example

Test the equation $(3x^2y - y)dx + (x^3 - x + 2y)dy = 0$ for exactness. Solve the equation if it is exact.

Solution

$$M = 3x^2y - y, \qquad N = x^3 - x + 2y,$$
$$\frac{\partial M}{\partial y} = 3x^2 - 1. \qquad \frac{\partial N}{\partial y} = 3x^2 - 1.$$

Since $\partial M/\partial y = \partial N/\partial x$, the equation is exact; *i.e.*, there is a function $f(x, y)$ of which the left-hand side of the given equation is exactly the total differential. To find this function f we note that

$$\frac{\partial f}{\partial x} = M = 3x^2y - y.$$

Integrating with respect to x, holding y constant, we have

(I) $$f(x, y) = x^3y - yx + \varphi(y)$$

where $\varphi(y)$ consists of terms that are free from x. Similarly, since

$$\frac{\partial f}{\partial y} = N = x^3 - x + 2y,$$

we have upon integrating with respect to y, holding x constant,

(II) $$f(x, y) = x^3y - xy + y^2 + \Psi(x)$$

where $\Psi(x)$ consists of terms that are free from y.

Now, comparing (I) and (II), we see finally that

$$f(x, y) = x^3y - xy + y^2 + C.$$

The solution of the given equation is then

$$x^3y - xy + y^2 + C = 0.$$

From the way in which this solution was obtained, it is evident that *if a given equation is exact* its solution can usually be obtained as follows:

1. *Integrate $M\,dx$ with respect to x, holding y constant.*

2. *Integrate with respect to y only those terms in $N\,dy$ which are free from x.*

3. *Add the terms obtained in step 2 to the result of step 1 and equate the sum to a constant.*

Since in exceptional cases this procedure may give an incorrect result, the solution should always be checked by differentiation.

204. Integrating factors.—It can be shown that if the equation

$$M\, dx + N\, dy = 0$$

is not exact, it can always be made exact by multiplying through by some proper function of x and y. Such a function is called an *integrating factor*. There is no general method of finding an integrating factor, but in many simple cases one can be found by inspection. Consider, for example, the equation

$$y\, dx + 2x\, dy = 0,$$

which is not exact since $\partial M/\partial y \neq \partial N/\partial x$. Multiplying by y we get the exact equation

$$y^2 dx + 2xy\, dy = 0,$$

in which the left-hand side is exactly the differential of xy^2; y is then an integrating factor.

PROBLEMS

Show that each of the following equations is exact and find its general solution:

1. $(2x + y)dx + (x - 1)dy = 0$.

2. $(3x^2 + 2y)dx + (2y + 2x + 1)dy = 0$.

3. $(y \cos x + 1)dx + \sin x\, dy = 0$.

4. $\left(2xy + \dfrac{1}{x}\right) dx + x^2 dy = 0$.   **5.** $3x^2 y\, dx + \left(x^3 + \dfrac{1}{y}\right) dy = 0$.

6. $\dfrac{dy}{dx} = \dfrac{3x^2 y - y}{x - x^3}$.   **7.** $\dfrac{dy}{dx} = \dfrac{y + x - 1}{2y - x + 2}$.

8. $\dfrac{dy}{dx} = \dfrac{2x^2 + y^2 - 2xy}{x^2 - 2xy}$.

9. Show that the equation $(x^2 + y^2)dx + 2xy\, dy = 0$ is both exact and homogeneous. Solve it by both methods. Which method is easier?

10. Show that the equation $(x^2 - y^2)dx + 2xy\, dy = 0$ is not exact, and solve it by another method.

11. Solve the equation $\dfrac{dy}{dx} = \dfrac{y + x}{2y - x}$ by two methods.

12. Show that the equation $\dfrac{dy}{dx} = \dfrac{1}{2xy + 8y}$ can be solved either as an exact equation or by separating the variables. Are the methods equivalent?

13. Show that an equation in which the variables are separated is necessarily exact and that the method used in solving such equations is the same as that given for exact equations.

Show that the following equations are not exact, and try to solve them using an integrating factor.

14. $y\,dx - x\,dy = 0.$ **15.** $x\,dy - y\,dx = x\,dx.$

16. $y\,dx - x\,dy + xy^2dx = 0.$ **17.** $dy - \dfrac{2y}{x}\,dx = x^3dx.$

18. Solve the equation $y\,dx + (2x + 2)dy = 0$, both by separating the variables and by using an integrating factor.

205. Linear equations of first order.—A differential equation is said to be *linear* if it is of first degree in the dependent variable y and its derivatives. Such an equation of *first order* can always be written in the form

$$(1) \qquad\qquad \frac{dy}{dx} + Py = Q$$

where P and Q are functions of x alone. It can be solved by finding an integrating factor $R(x)$ such that when both sides are multiplied by R the left side becomes exactly the derivative of Ry.

To find such a factor, let us multiply both sides of (1) by R, where it is understood that R is a function of x yet to be determined; we get

$$(2) \qquad\qquad R\frac{dy}{dx} + RPy = RQ.$$

Now the derivative with respect to x of Ry is

$$R\frac{dy}{dx} + y\frac{dR}{dx}.$$

The left-hand side of (2) is then the derivative of Ry provided R is a function such that

$$y \frac{dR}{dx} = RPy;$$

separating the variables and solving for R, we have

$$\frac{dR}{R} = P\,dx,$$
$$\log R = \int P\,dx,$$
(3) $$R = e^{\int P\,dx}.$$

When both sides of (1) are multiplied by the function R given by (3), the left-hand side becomes exactly the derivative of Ry. The right-hand side is still a function of x alone. Integrating both sides, we obtain the solution

$$Ry = \int RQ\,dx.$$

Example

$$\frac{dy}{dx} + \frac{2y}{x} = 6x^3.$$

Solution

In this case $P = 2/x$;

$$\int P\,dx = \int \frac{2\,dx}{x} = 2\log x = \log x^2.$$
$$R = e^{\int P\,dx} = e^{\log x^2} = x^2.$$

Multiplying both sides of the given equation by this factor and integrating, we have

$$x^2 y = \int 6x^5 dx$$
$$= x^6 + C.$$

206. Bernoulli's equation.—The equation

$$\frac{dy}{dx} + Py = Qy^n$$

where P and Q are functions of x alone is known as *Bernoulli's equation*, after (James) Bernoulli (1654–1705). It can be transformed into a linear equation by letting

$$y = z^{\frac{1}{1-n}}$$

where z is a new variable.

Example

$$\frac{dy}{dx} - \frac{y}{x} = x^2 y^2.$$

Solution

Letting $y = z^{\frac{1}{1-2}} = z^{-1}$, the equation becomes

$$\frac{dz}{dx} + \frac{1}{x} \cdot z = -x^2$$

which is linear. An integrating factor is

$$e^{\int P \, dx} = e^{\int \frac{dx}{x}} = e^{\log x} = x.$$

Multiplying by this factor and integrating, we get

$$xz = \int -x^3 dx = -\frac{x^4}{4} + C.$$

Finally, since $z = y^{-1}$, the solution is

$$\frac{x}{y} + \frac{x^4}{4} = C.$$

PROBLEMS

Solve the following equations:

1. $\dfrac{dy}{dx} + 2y = x.$

2. $\dfrac{dy}{dx} + y = e^{-x}.$

3. $\dfrac{dy}{dx} = x + y.$

4. $x\dfrac{dy}{dx} + y = x^2.$

5. $\dfrac{dy}{dx} - \dfrac{2y}{x} = \dfrac{x+1}{x}.$

6. $\dfrac{dy}{dx} + \dfrac{y}{x} = \dfrac{\sin x}{x}.$

7. $\dfrac{dy}{dx} + \dfrac{y}{x} = \sin x.$

8. $\dfrac{dy}{dx} + y = \sin x.$

9. $\dfrac{dy}{dx} - \dfrac{xy}{x^2+1} = x.$

10. $x^2\dfrac{dy}{dx} - 2xy = 1.$

11. $\dfrac{dy}{dx} + \dfrac{y}{x \log x} = \dfrac{1}{x}.$

12. $\dfrac{dy}{dx} = \dfrac{e^x - 2xy}{x^2}.$

13. $\dfrac{dy}{dx} = \dfrac{3 - 2xy}{x^2}.$

14. $x\dfrac{dy}{dx} + y = e^x - xy.$

15. Show that Bernoulli's equation

$$\frac{dy}{dx} + Py = Qy^n$$

is transformed by letting $y = z^{\frac{1}{1-n}}$ ($n \neq 1$) into the linear equation

$$\frac{1}{1-n}\frac{dz}{dx} + Pz = Q.$$

Discuss the cases in which $n = 0$ and $n = 1$.

Solve the following equations:

16. $\dfrac{dy}{dx} + \dfrac{2y}{x} = xy^2.$

17. $3\dfrac{dy}{dx} + \dfrac{2y}{x} = \dfrac{2}{xy^2}.$

18. $\dfrac{dy}{dx} - \dfrac{y}{2} = y^3 e^{-x}.$

19. What curve through the origin has its slope at every point equal to the sum of the coordinates of the point?

20. The slope at any point of a curve that goes through $(0, 1)$ is equal to twice the product of the coordinates plus the abscissa. What is its equation?

207. Linear equations of higher order.—In the preceding articles we have given methods for solving certain commonly occurring types of differential equations of *first* order. We shall now consider the most important type of equation of higher order, namely, that which is of first degree in the dependent variable y and its derivatives. This so-called linear equation of order n may be written in the form

$$a_0\frac{d^n y}{dx^n} + a_1\frac{d^{n-1}y}{dx^{n-1}} + \cdots + a_{n-1}\frac{dy}{dx} + a_n y = f(x)$$

where the a's may, in general, be functions of x. We shall consider the equation, however, only for the special case in which the a's are all *constants*.

In studying this equation in the next two articles we shall confine our attention to the case of second order. The student will readily see, however, that the method applies to the general case. For reasons which will soon become obvious, we shall consider first the case in which the right-hand side of the equation is *zero*, and reserve for the following article the more general case in which it is a function of x.

208. Right-hand side zero.—Consider, as an example, the equation

$$\frac{d^2y}{dx^2} - 2\frac{dy}{dx} - 3y = 0.$$

Let us assume that for a proper value of m, the function

$$y = e^{mx}$$

might be a solution. Substituting this "trial solution" into the given equation and solving for m, we have

$$m^2e^{mx} - 2me^{mx} - 3e^{mx} = 0,$$
$$m^2 - 2m - 3 = 0,$$
$$m = -1, \text{ or } 3.$$

The function $y = e^{mx}$ then satisfies the given differential equation if $m = -1$ or $+3$; *i.e.*, $y = e^{-x}$ and $y = e^{3x}$ are two particular solutions. It may easily be shown that $y = Ae^{-x}$ and $y = Be^{3x}$, where A and B are arbitrary constants, are solutions, and finally that

$$y = Ae^{-x} + Be^{3x}$$

is a solution. Since this last solution contains the required number of arbitrary constants, it is the general solution.

This procedure may be used in solving any equation of the form

$$\frac{d^2y}{dx^2} + p\frac{dy}{dx} + qy = 0$$

where p and q are constants. The assumption that $y = e^{mx}$ is a solution leads to the *auxiliary equation*

$$m^2 + pm + q = 0.$$

If the two roots r_1 and r_2 of this equation are distinct, the general solution of the differential equation is

$$y = Ae^{r_1 x} + Be^{r_2 x}.$$

The case of equal roots.—If the roots r_1 and r_2 of the auxiliary equation are *equal*, the function

$$y = Ae^{r_1x} + Be^{r_2x} \text{ reduces to } y = Ce^{r_1x}$$

where $C = A + B$. Since it contains only one essential arbitrary constant, it cannot be the general solution. It can be shown that in this case the general solution is

$$\boldsymbol{y = Ae^{r_1x} + Bxe^{r_1x}.}$$

The proof is left as an exercise in the next set.

The case of complex roots.—If the roots of the auxiliary equation are the conjugate complex numbers $a \pm bi$, the general solution is

$$\begin{aligned} y &= Ae^{(a+bi)x} + Be^{(a-bi)x} \\ &= e^{ax}(Ae^{ibx} + Be^{-ibx}). \end{aligned}$$

This result may be put into a more convenient form by substituting for e^{ibx} and e^{-ibx} the equivalent trigonometric expressions, namely,

$$\begin{aligned} e^{ibx} &= \cos bx + i \sin bx \\ e^{-ibx} &= \cos bx - i \sin bx. \end{aligned}$$

This substitution gives, as an alternate form for the general solution,

$$y = e^{ax}[(A + B) \cos bx + i(A - B) \sin bx]$$

or,

$$\boldsymbol{y = e^{ax}(C \cos bx + D \sin bx),}$$

where C and D are arbitrary constants.

Example

$$\frac{d^2y}{dx^2} - 4\frac{dy}{dx} + 13y = 0.$$

Solution

Assuming a solution of the form $y = e^{mx}$, we obtain the auxiliary equation

$$m^2 - 4m + 13 = 0.$$

The roots of this are $m = 2 \pm 3i$. The general solution is then

$$y = e^{2x}(A \cos 3x + B \sin 3x).$$

PROBLEMS

Solve the following equations:

1. $\dfrac{d^2y}{dx^2} - 3\dfrac{dy}{dx} + 2y = 0.$ **2.** $\dfrac{d^2y}{dx^2} - \dfrac{dy}{dx} = 12y.$

3. $2\dfrac{d^2y}{dx^2} - 5\dfrac{dy}{dx} = 3y.$ **4.** $\dfrac{d^2y}{dx^2} = 4y.$

5. $\dfrac{d^2y}{dx^2} - 2\dfrac{dy}{dx} = 0.$ **6.** $\dfrac{d^3y}{dx^3} - 6\dfrac{d^2y}{dx^2} + 11\dfrac{dy}{dx} = 6y.$

7. $\dfrac{d^3y}{dx^3} - \dfrac{d^2y}{dx^2} = 4\left(\dfrac{dy}{dx} - y\right).$ **8.** $4\dfrac{d^3y}{dx^3} - 8\dfrac{d^2y}{dx^2} = \dfrac{dy}{dx} - 2y.$

9. $\dfrac{d^2y}{dx^2} - 4\dfrac{dy}{dx} + 4y = 0.$ **10.** $\dfrac{d^2y}{dx^2} + 2\dfrac{dy}{dx} + y = 0.$

11. $4\dfrac{d^2y}{dx^2} - 4\dfrac{dy}{dx} + y = 0.$ **12.** $\dfrac{d^2y}{dx^2} - 2\dfrac{dy}{dx} + 5y = 0.$

13. $\dfrac{d^2y}{dx^2} - 10\dfrac{dy}{dx} + 26y = 0.$ **14.** $\dfrac{d^2y}{dx^2} - 6\dfrac{dy}{dx} + 13y = 0.$

15. $\dfrac{d^3y}{dx^3} - 4\dfrac{d^2y}{dx^2} + 6\dfrac{dy}{dx} = 4y.$ **16.** $\dfrac{d^3y}{dx^3} - 5\dfrac{d^2y}{dx^2} + 8\dfrac{dy}{dx} = 4y.$

17. $\dfrac{d^4y}{dx^4} = 16y.$

18. At every point of a certain curve the sum of the first and second derivatives is equal to twice the ordinate. The curve goes through the origin with slope 3. What is its equation?

19. What curve passing through $(0, 2)$ and having a horizontal tangent line at that point has at every point $d^2y/dx^2 = y$?

20. What curve passing through the origin at 45° has at every point $\dfrac{d^2y}{dx^2} + y = 2\dfrac{dy}{dx}$? Sketch the curve.

21. What curve passing through $(0, 1)$ at 45° has at every point

$$\frac{d^2y}{dx^2} + 5y = 2\frac{dy}{dx}?$$

22. Find a particular solution of the equation $\dfrac{d^2Q}{dt^2} + 4\dfrac{dQ}{dt} + 5Q = 0$, satisfying the conditions that $Q = 5$ and $\dfrac{dQ}{dt} = 0$ when $t = 0$.

23. A point starts from rest at $(2, 0)$ and moves along the x-axis, its acceleration being always toward the origin and equal to four times the distance from the origin. Find its position and velocity at any time.

24. A chain 4 ft. long is stretched out on a smooth table with 1 ft. of its length hanging over the edge and then released. Using the relation $F = \dfrac{w}{g} a$ show that, when any length y (< 4 ft.) is hanging over, the acceleration is $\dfrac{d^2y}{dt^2} = \dfrac{g}{4} y$. Find the amount over the edge at the end of t sec.

25. The angular acceleration of a simple pendulum of length L ft. is $\dfrac{d^2\theta}{dt^2} = -\dfrac{g}{L}\sin\theta$ where θ is the angular displacement from the vertical. If θ is small, $\sin\theta$ may be replaced by θ with negligible error. With this assumption, and assuming that $\theta = \theta_1$ and $d\theta/dt = 0$ when $t = 0$, express θ in terms of t. Find the time of one complete oscillation.

26. The equation $\dfrac{d^2y}{dx^2} - 2r\dfrac{dy}{dx} + r^2y = 0$ has both roots of its auxiliary equation equal to r. Show by direct substitution that $y = Ae^{rx} + Bxe^{rx}$ is the general solution.

209. Right-hand side a function of x.—As an example, consider the equation

$$(1) \qquad \frac{d^2y}{dx^2} - 2\frac{dy}{dx} - 3y = 6x - 5,$$

which is the same as the first example in Art. 208 with the exception that the right side is now $6x - 5$ instead of 0.

Let us first try to find a particular solution. It is fairly obvious that a function, for which $\dfrac{d^2y}{dx^2} - 2\dfrac{dy}{dx} - 3y$ *might* equal $6x - 5$, would be a function of the form

$$y = ax + b.$$

Substituting this "trial solution" into the equation, we get

$$0 - 2a - 3(ax + b) = 6x - 5,$$

or

$$(-3a)x + (-2a - 3b) = 6x - 5.$$

Equating coefficients of like terms we see that the equation is satisfied if

$$-3a = 6 \qquad \text{and} \qquad -2a - 3b = -5.$$

Solving these equations we have $a = -2$, $b = 3$; *i.e.*, the function

(2) $$y = -2x + 3$$

is a particular solution. It can be shown that the general solution can now be obtained by simply adding to this particular solution *the general solution of the same equation with the right-hand side replaced by zero.* The general solution of the equation $\dfrac{d^2y}{dx^2} - 2\dfrac{dy}{dx} - 3y = 0$ is

$$y = Ae^{-x} + Be^{3x}.$$

The general solution of (1) is then

(3) $$y = -2x + 3 + Ae^{-x} + Be^{3x}.$$

The proof consists merely in showing that (3) is a solution of (1) and noting that it contains the required number of arbitrary constants. The student will readily see that (3) must be a solution if (2) is, because the two extra terms in (3) give *zero* when substituted in the left side of (1).

This procedure can be used in solving any linear equation with constant coefficients. The function that is added to the particular integral to get the general solution is called the *complementary function.* It is always obtained by replacing the right-hand side of the given equation by zero and solving the resulting equation by the methods of the preceding article. A particular solution is often most easily found by the method of *undetermined coefficients* as demonstrated in the example just given. In using this method one "guesses" at the general form of a solution and substitutes this "trial solution" with undetermined coefficients into the equation. Then, if the trial solution has been properly selected, it is usually easy to determine the coefficients so that the equation will be satisfied.

No general rule for selecting the form of a trial solution can be given. In a case such as

$$\frac{d^2y}{dx^2} + \frac{dy}{dx} = \cos x + 2\sin x,$$

one must think of a type of function that *could have* the sum of its first and second derivatives equal to

$$\cos x + 2 \sin x.$$

A proper guess would of course be a function of the form

$$y = a \cos x + b \sin x.$$

If the right-hand side were $4e^{2x}$ instead of $\cos x + 2 \sin x$, a proper trial solution would, of course, be $y = ae^{2x}$.

PROBLEMS

1. What is a proper trial solution for the equation

$$\frac{d^2y}{dx^2} - 2\frac{dy}{dx} - 3y = f(x),$$

if (a) $f(x) = 2x^2 + 3x + 4$, (b) $f(x) = 4 \sin x$, (c) $f(x) = e^{-x}$?

2. Why is $y = a \cos x$ not a proper trial solution for the equation $\frac{d^2y}{dx^2} - 3\frac{dy}{dx} + 2y = 2 \cos x$? Find a particular solution and the general solution.

3. Explain why we should take $y = ax^3 + bx^2 + cx + d$ as a trial solution for the equation $\frac{d^2y}{dx^2} - 3\frac{dy}{dx} + 2y = 4x^3$. Find a particular solution and the general solution.

4. Explain why $y = ax^3 + bx^2 + cx$ rather than $y = ax^2 + bx + c$ is a proper trial solution for the equation $\frac{d^2y}{dx^2} - 2\frac{dy}{dx} = 6x^2 + 2x + 3$. Find a particular solution and the general solution.

Solve the following equations:

5. $\frac{d^2y}{dx^2} - 6\frac{dy}{dx} + 8y = 2.$

6. $\frac{d^2y}{dx^2} - 2\frac{dy}{dx} + y = 3 \sin x.$

7. $\frac{d^2y}{dx^2} + \frac{dy}{dx} - 2y = 6 \sin x + 8 \cos x.$

8. $\frac{d^2y}{dx^2} + 2\frac{dy}{dx} = 8y + 4x + 7.$

9. $\frac{d^2y}{dx^2} - 5\frac{dy}{dx} + 6y = 4e^x.$

10. $\frac{d^2y}{dx^2} + 3\frac{dy}{dx} + 2y = 4x^2 + 8.$

11. $2\dfrac{d^2y}{dx^2} - \dfrac{dy}{dx} - 3y = 9x^2$.

12. $\dfrac{d^2y}{dx^2} - 2\dfrac{dy}{dx} + 2y = e^x$.

13. $\dfrac{d^2y}{dx^2} - 4\dfrac{dy}{dx} + 8y = 2x + 7$.

14. $\dfrac{d^2y}{dx^2} = 3e^x + 4y + 8$.

15. $\dfrac{d^2y}{dx^2} + \dfrac{dy}{dx} - 6y = 10e^{2x}$. HINT: If $y = ae^{2x}$ reduces the left side identically to zero, try $y = axe^{2x}$.

16. $\dfrac{d^2y}{dx^2} - 3\dfrac{dy}{dx} - 4y = 5e^{-x}$. See hint in Prob. 15.

17. $\dfrac{d^2y}{dx^2} + y = 2\sin x$.

18. $\dfrac{d^3y}{dx^3} - 3\dfrac{d^2y}{dx^2} + 2\dfrac{dy}{dx} = 12e^{3x}$.

19. $\dfrac{d^3y}{dx^3} + \dfrac{d^2y}{dx^2} = 2\sin x$.

20. $\dfrac{d^3y}{dx^3} + 4\dfrac{dy}{dx} = 4x$.

21. $\dfrac{d^2y}{dx^2} + \dfrac{dy}{dx} = x^2 + 2x + 4$.

22. $\dfrac{d^3y}{dx^3} + \dfrac{dy}{dx} = 6x^2$.

23. What is the equation of the curve that passes through (0, 2) at 45° and has at every point $d^2y/dx^2 = x + y$?

24. A chain 32 ft. long is hung over a smooth peg with 18 ft. of its length on one side. Using the relation $F = \dfrac{w}{g}a$ show that its acceleration is $\dfrac{d^2y}{dt^2} = g\left(\dfrac{y}{16} - 1\right)$ where y is the length of the longer side. Express y in terms of t.

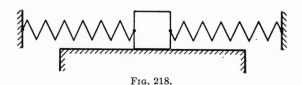

FIG. 218.

25. The block shown in Fig. 218 weighs 80 lb. and rests on a smooth table. The springs are unstressed when the block is in the position shown. A force of 10 lb. per foot is required to stretch or compress either spring.   Show that if the block is displaced a distance x to the right, the resultant force acting on it is $20x$ lb. to the left and its acceleration is

$$\frac{d^2x}{dt^2} = -\frac{gx}{4}.$$

Show that if the block is displaced 4 ft. to the right and released ($x = 4$ and $dx/dt = 0$ when $t = 0$), it will oscillate with respect to the position shown, the motion being described by the equation $x = 4 \cos \frac{\sqrt{g}}{2} t$.

It is assumed that the weights of the springs may be neglected.

26. Solve Prob. 25 for the case in which the coefficient of friction between block and table is $\mu = 0.5$.   Show in particular that in this case the block will not oscillate but will merely return to the original position and stop.   Discuss the cases in which $\mu < 0.5$ and $\mu > 0.5$.

27. Discuss Prob. 25 for the case in which the motion takes place in a resisting medium in which the resistance is proportional to the velocity. Show that the differential equation is

$$\frac{80}{g}\frac{d^2x}{dt^2} + k\frac{dx}{dt} + 20x = 0$$

where k is a positive constant.   Note that in this case the motion will be oscillatory only for values of k for which the auxiliary equation has complex roots.

Forms containing $a + bx$

1. $\displaystyle \int \frac{dx}{x(a+bx)} = -\frac{1}{a}\log\frac{a+bx}{x} + C.$

2. $\displaystyle \int \frac{dx}{x^2(a+bx)} = -\frac{1}{ax} + \frac{b}{a^2}\log\frac{a+bx}{x} + C.$

3. $\displaystyle \int \frac{dx}{x(a+bx)^2} = \frac{1}{a(a+bx)} - \frac{1}{a^2}\log\frac{a+bx}{x} + C.$

4. $\displaystyle \int \frac{x^2\,dx}{(a+bx)^2} = \frac{1}{b^3}\left[a+bx - \frac{a^2}{a+bx} - 2a\log(a+bx) \right] + C.$

5. $\displaystyle \int \frac{x\,dx}{(a+bx)^3} = \frac{1}{b^2}\left[-\frac{1}{a+bx} + \frac{a}{2(a+bx)^2} \right] + C.$

Forms containing $\sqrt{a + bx}$

6. $\displaystyle \int x\sqrt{a+bx}\,dx = -\frac{2(2a-3bx)\sqrt{(a+bx)^3}}{15b^2} + C.$

7. $\displaystyle \int x^2\sqrt{a+bx}\,dx = \frac{2(8a^2-12abx+15b^2x^2)\sqrt{(a+bx)^3}}{105b^3} + C.$

8. $\displaystyle \int \frac{x\,dx}{\sqrt{a+bx}} = -\frac{2(2a-bx)\sqrt{a+bx}}{3b^2} + C.$

9. $\displaystyle \int \frac{x^2\,dx}{\sqrt{a+bx}} = \frac{2(8a^2-4abx+3b^2x^2)\sqrt{a+bx}}{15b^3} + C.$

Forms containing $\sqrt{x^2 + a^2}$

10. $\displaystyle \int \sqrt{x^2+a^2}\,dx = \frac{x}{2}\sqrt{x^2+a^2} + \frac{a^2}{2}\log(x+\sqrt{x^2+a^2}) + C.$

11. $\displaystyle \int x^2\sqrt{x^2+a^2}\,dx = \frac{x}{8}(2x^2+a^2)\sqrt{x^2+a^2}$
$$-\frac{a^4}{8}\log(x+\sqrt{x^2+a^2}) + C.$$

12. $\displaystyle \int \sqrt{(x^2+a^2)^3}\,dx = \frac{x}{8}(2x^2+5a^2)\sqrt{x^2+a^2}$
$$+\frac{3a^4}{8}\log(x+\sqrt{x^2+a^2}) + C.$$

13. $\displaystyle \int \frac{\sqrt{x^2+a^2}}{x}\,dx = \sqrt{x^2+a^2} - a\log\frac{a+\sqrt{x^2+a^2}}{x} + C.$

14. $\displaystyle \int \frac{\sqrt{x^2+a^2}}{x^2}\,dx = -\frac{\sqrt{x^2+a^2}}{x} + \log(x+\sqrt{x^2+a^2}) + C.$

15. $\displaystyle \int \frac{dx}{\sqrt{x^2+a^2}} = \log(x+\sqrt{x^2+a^2}) + C.$

457

16. $\int \dfrac{x^2 dx}{\sqrt{x^2 + a^2}} = \dfrac{x}{2}\sqrt{x^2 + a^2} - \dfrac{a^2}{2}\log(x + \sqrt{x^2 + a^2}) + C.$

17. $\int \dfrac{dx}{\sqrt{(x^2 + a^2)^3}} = \dfrac{x}{a^2\sqrt{x^2 + a^2}} + C.$

18. $\int \dfrac{x^2 dx}{\sqrt{(x^2 + a^2)^3}} = - \dfrac{x}{\sqrt{x^2 + a^2}} + \log(x + \sqrt{x^2 + a^2}) + C.$

19. $\int \dfrac{dx}{x\sqrt{x^2 + a^2}} = \dfrac{1}{a}\log \dfrac{x}{a + \sqrt{x^2 + a^2}} + C.$

20. $\int \dfrac{dx}{x^2\sqrt{x^2 + a^2}} = - \dfrac{\sqrt{x^2 + a^2}}{a^2 x} + C.$

Forms containing $\sqrt{x^2 - a^2}$

21. $\int \sqrt{x^2 - a^2}\, dx = \dfrac{x}{2}\sqrt{x^2 - a^2} - \dfrac{a^2}{2}\log(x + \sqrt{x^2 - a^2}) + C.$

22. $\int x^2\sqrt{x^2 - a^2}\, dx = \dfrac{x}{8}(2x^2 - a^2)\sqrt{x^2 - a^2}$
$$- \dfrac{a^4}{8}\log(x + \sqrt{x^2 - a^2}) + C.$$

23. $\int \sqrt{(x^2 - a^2)^3}\, dx = \dfrac{x}{8}(2x^2 - 5a^2)\sqrt{x^2 - a^2}$
$$+ \dfrac{3a^4}{8}\log(x + \sqrt{x^2 - a^2}) + C.$$

24. $\int \dfrac{\sqrt{x^2 - a^2}}{x}\, dx = \sqrt{x^2 - a^2} - a\arccos\dfrac{a}{x} + C.$

25. $\int \dfrac{\sqrt{x^2 - a^2}}{x^2}\, dx = - \dfrac{\sqrt{x^2 - a^2}}{x} + \log(x + \sqrt{x^2 - a^2}) + C.$

26. $\int \dfrac{dx}{\sqrt{x^2 - a^2}} = \log(x + \sqrt{x^2 - a^2}) + C.$

27. $\int \dfrac{x^2 dx}{\sqrt{x^2 - a^2}} = \dfrac{x\sqrt{x^2 - a^2}}{2} + \dfrac{a^2}{2}\log(x + \sqrt{x^2 - a^2}) + C.$

28. $\int \dfrac{dx}{x^2\sqrt{x^2 - a^2}} = \dfrac{\sqrt{x^2 - a^2}}{a^2 x} + C.$

29. $\int \dfrac{dx}{\sqrt{(x^2 - a^2)^3}} = - \dfrac{x}{a^2\sqrt{x^2 - a^2}} + C.$

Forms containing $\sqrt{a^2 - x^2}$

30. $\int \sqrt{a^2 - x^2}\, dx = \dfrac{x}{2}\sqrt{a^2 - x^2} + \dfrac{a^2}{2}\arcsin\dfrac{x}{a} + C.$

31. $\int x^2\sqrt{a^2 - x^2}\, dx = \dfrac{x}{8}(2x^2 - a^2)\sqrt{a^2 - x^2} + \dfrac{a^4}{8}\arcsin\dfrac{x}{a} + C.$

32. $\int \dfrac{\sqrt{a^2 - x^2}\, dx}{x} = \sqrt{a^2 - x^2} - a\log\dfrac{a + \sqrt{a^2 - x^2}}{x} + C.$

33. $\int \dfrac{\sqrt{a^2 - x^2}}{x^2}\, dx = - \dfrac{\sqrt{a^2 - x^2}}{x} - \arcsin\dfrac{x}{a} + C.$

34. $\displaystyle\int \frac{dx}{\sqrt{(a^2-x^2)^3}} = \frac{x}{a^2\sqrt{a^2-x^2}} + C.$

35. $\displaystyle\int \frac{x^2 dx}{\sqrt{a^2-x^2}} = -\frac{x\sqrt{a^2-x^2}}{2} + \frac{a^2}{2}\arcsin\frac{x}{a} + C.$

36. $\displaystyle\int \frac{dx}{x\sqrt{a^2-x^2}} = \frac{1}{a}\log\frac{x}{a+\sqrt{a^2-x^2}} + C.$

37. $\displaystyle\int \frac{dx}{x^2\sqrt{a^2-x^2}} = -\frac{\sqrt{a^2-x^2}}{a^2 x} + C.$

38. $\displaystyle\int \frac{x^2 dx}{\sqrt{(a^2-x^2)^3}} = \frac{x}{\sqrt{a^2-x^2}} - \arcsin\frac{x}{a} + C.$

Forms containing $\sqrt{2ax-x^2}$

39. $\displaystyle\int \sqrt{2ax-x^2}\,dx = \frac{(x-a)\sqrt{2ax-x^2}}{2} + \frac{a^2}{2}\arcsin\frac{x-a}{a} + C.$

40. $\displaystyle\int \frac{dx}{\sqrt{2ax-x^2}} = \arccos\frac{a-x}{a} + C.$

41. $\displaystyle\int \frac{x\,dx}{\sqrt{2ax-x^2}} = -\sqrt{2ax-x^2} + a\arccos\frac{a-x}{a} + C.$

42. $\displaystyle\int \frac{x^2 dx}{\sqrt{2ax-x^2}} = -\frac{(x+3a)\sqrt{2ax-x^2}}{2} + \frac{3a^2}{2}\arccos\frac{a-x}{a} + C.$

43. $\displaystyle\int \frac{dx}{x\sqrt{2ax-x^2}} = -\frac{\sqrt{2ax-x^2}}{ax} + C.$

44. $\displaystyle\int \frac{\sqrt{2ax-x^2}\,dx}{x} = \sqrt{2ax-x^2} + a\arccos\frac{a-x}{a} + C.$

45. $\displaystyle\int \frac{\sqrt{2ax-x^2}\,dx}{x^2} = -\frac{2\sqrt{2ax-x^2}}{x} - \arccos\frac{a-x}{a} + C.$

46. $\displaystyle\int \frac{\sqrt{2ax-x^2}\,dx}{x^3} = -\frac{(2ax-x^2)^{\frac{3}{2}}}{3ax^3} + C.$

Trigonometric forms

47. $\displaystyle\int \sin^2 x\,dx = \tfrac{1}{2}(x - \sin x\cos x) + C.$

48. $\displaystyle\int \cos^2 x\,dx = \tfrac{1}{2}(x + \sin x\cos x) + C.$

49. $\displaystyle\int \sin^n x\,dx = -\frac{\sin^{n-1} x\cos x}{n} + \frac{n-1}{n}\int \sin^{n-2} x\,dx.$

50. $\displaystyle\int \cos^n x\,dx = \frac{\cos^{n-1} x\sin x}{n} + \frac{n-1}{n}\int \cos^{n-2} x\,dx.$

51. $\displaystyle\int \sin^m x\cos^n x\,dx = \frac{\sin^{m+1} x\cos^{n-1} x}{m+n} + \frac{n-1}{m+n}\int \sin^m x\cos^{n-2} x\,dx$

$$= -\frac{\sin^{m-1} x\cos^{n+1} x}{m+n} + \frac{m-1}{m+n}\int \sin^{m-2} x\cos^n x\,dx.$$

52. $\displaystyle\int \tan^2 x\,dx = \tan x - x + C.$

53. $\int \tan^n x \, dx = \dfrac{\tan^{n-1} x}{n-1} - \int \tan^{n-2} x \, dx.$

54. $\int \cot^n x \, dx = - \dfrac{\cot^{n-1} x}{n-1} - \int \cot^{n-2} x \, dx.$

55. $\int \sec^n x \, dx = \dfrac{\sec^{n-2} x \tan x}{n-1} + \dfrac{n-2}{n-1} \int \sec^{n-2} x \, dx.$

56. $\int \arcsin x \, dx = x \arcsin x + \sqrt{1-x^2} + C.$

57. $\int \arccos x \, dx = x \arccos x - \sqrt{1-x^2} + C.$

58. $\int \arctan x \, dx = x \arctan x - \frac{1}{2} \log (1+x^2) + C.$

Miscellaneous forms

59. $\int x \sin x \, dx = \sin x - x \cos x + C.$

60. $\int x \cos x \, dx = \cos x + x \sin x + C.$

61. $\int e^{ax} \sin nx \, dx = \dfrac{e^{ax}(a \sin nx - n \cos nx)}{a^2 + n^2} + C.$

62. $\int e^{ax} \cos nx \, dx = \dfrac{e^{ax}(n \sin nx + a \cos nx)}{a^2 + n^2} + C.$

63. $\int x e^{ax} dx = \dfrac{e^{ax}(ax-1)}{a^2} + C.$

64. $\int x^n e^{ax} dx = \dfrac{x^n e^{ax}}{a} - \dfrac{n}{a} \int x^{n-1} e^{ax} dx.$

65. $\int x^n \log x \, dx = x^{n+1} \left[\dfrac{\log x}{n+1} - \dfrac{1}{(n+1)^2} \right] + C.$

Wallis's formulas

66. $\displaystyle\int_0^{\frac{\pi}{2}} \sin^n x \, dx = \int_0^{\frac{\pi}{2}} \cos^n x \, dx$

$= \dfrac{(n-1)(n-3) \cdots 4 \cdot 2}{n(n-2) \cdots 5 \cdot 3 \cdot 1},$ if n is an odd integer $> 1.$

$= \dfrac{(n-1)(n-3) \cdots 3 \cdot 1}{n(n-2) \cdots 4 \cdot 2} \cdot \dfrac{\pi}{2},$ if n is a positive even integer.

67. $\displaystyle\int_0^{\frac{\pi}{2}} \sin^m x \cos^n x \, dx$

$= \dfrac{(n-1)(n-3) \cdots 4 \cdot 2}{(m+n)(m+n-2) \cdots (m+3)(m+1)},$ if n is an odd integer $> 1.$

$= \dfrac{(m-1)(m-3) \cdots 4 \cdot 2}{(n+m)(n+m-2) \cdots (n+3)(n+1)},$ if m is an odd integer $> 1.$

$= \dfrac{(m-1)(m-3) \cdots 3 \cdot 1 (n-1)(n-3) \cdots 3 \cdot 1}{(m+n)(m+n-2) \cdots 4 \cdot 2} \cdot \dfrac{\pi}{2},$ if m and n are

both positive even integers.

NUMERICAL TABLES

TABLE I.—COMMON LOGARITHMS

N	0	1	2	3	4	5	6	7	8	9
10	0000	0043	0086	0128	0170	0212	0253	0294	0334	0374
11	0414	0453	0492	0531	0569	0607	0645	0682	0719	0755
12	0792	0828	0864	0899	0934	0969	1004	1038	1072	1106
13	1139	1173	1206	1239	1271	1303	1335	1367	1399	1430
14	1461	1492	1523	1553	1584	1614	1644	1673	1703	1732
15	1761	1790	1818	1847	1875	1903	1931	1959	1987	2014
16	2041	2068	2095	2122	2148	2175	2201	2227	2253	2279
17	2304	2330	2355	2380	2405	2430	2455	2480	2504	2529
18	2553	2577	2601	2625	2648	2672	2695	2718	2742	2765
19	2788	2810	2833	2856	2878	2900	2923	2945	2967	2989
20	3010	3032	3054	3075	3096	3118	3139	3160	3181	3201
21	3222	3243	3263	3284	3304	3324	3345	3365	3385	3404
22	3424	3444	3464	3483	3502	3522	3541	3560	3579	3598
23	3617	3636	3655	3674	3692	3711	3729	3747	3766	3784
24	3802	3820	3838	3856	3874	3892	3909	3927	3945	3962
25	3979	3997	4014	4031	4048	4065	4082	4099	4116	4133
26	4150	4166	4183	4200	4216	4232	4249	4265	4281	4298
27	4314	4330	4346	4362	4378	4393	4409	4425	4440	4456
28	4472	4487	4502	4518	4533	4548	4564	4579	4594	4609
29	4624	4639	4654	4669	4683	4698	4713	4728	4742	4757
30	4771	4786	4800	4814	4829	4843	4857	4871	4886	4900
31	4914	4928	4942	4955	4969	4983	4997	5011	5024	5038
32	5051	5065	5079	5092	5105	5119	5132	5145	5159	5172
33	5185	5198	5211	5224	5237	5250	5263	5276	5289	5302
34	5315	5328	5340	5353	5366	5378	5391	5403	5416	5428
35	5441	5453	5465	5478	5490	5502	5514	5527	5539	5551
36	5563	5575	5587	5599	5611	5623	5635	5647	5658	5670
37	5682	5694	5705	5717	5729	5740	5752	5763	5775	5786
38	5798	5809	5821	5832	5843	5855	5866	5877	5888	5899
39	5911	5922	5933	5944	5955	5966	5977	5988	5999	6010
40	6021	6031	6042	6053	6064	6075	6085	6096	6107	6117
41	6128	6138	6149	6160	6170	6180	6191	6201	6212	6222
42	6232	6243	6253	6263	6274	6284	6294	6304	6314	6325
43	6335	6345	6355	6365	6375	6385	6395	6405	6415	6425
44	6435	6444	6454	6464	6474	6484	6493	6503	6513	6522
45	6532	6542	6551	6561	6571	6580	6590	6599	6609	6618
46	6628	6637	6646	6656	6665	6675	6684	6693	6702	6712
47	6721	6730	6739	6749	6758	6767	6776	6785	6794	6803
48	6812	6821	6830	6839	6848	6857	6866	6875	6884	6893
49	6902	6911	6920	6928	6937	6946	6955	6964	6972	6981
50	6990	6998	7007	7016	7024	7033	7042	7050	7059	7067
51	7076	7084	7093	7101	7110	7118	7126	7135	7143	7152
52	7160	7168	7177	7185	7193	7202	7210	7218	7226	7235
53	7243	7251	7259	7267	7275	7284	7292	7300	7308	7316
54	7324	7332	7340	7348	7356	7364	7372	7380	7388	7396
N	0	1	2	3	4	5	6	7	8	9

TABLE I.—Common Logarithms.—(*Continued*)

N	0	1	2	3	4	5	6	7	8	9
55	7404	7412	7419	7427	7435	7443	7451	7459	7466	7474
56	7482	7490	7497	7505	7513	7520	7528	7536	7543	7551
57	7559	7566	7574	7582	7589	7597	7604	7612	7619	7627
58	7634	7642	7649	7657	7664	7672	7679	7686	7694	7701
59	7709	7716	7723	7731	7738	7745	7752	7760	7767	7774
60	7782	7789	7796	7803	7810	7818	7825	7832	7839	7846
61	7853	7860	7868	7875	7882	7889	7896	7903	7910	7917
62	7924	7931	7938	7945	7952	7959	7966	7973	7980	7987
63	7993	8000	8007	8014	8021	8028	8035	8041	8048	8055
64	8062	8069	8075	8082	8089	8096	8102	8109	8116	8122
65	8129	8136	8142	8149	8156	8162	8169	8176	8182	8189
66	8195	8202	8209	8215	8222	8228	8235	8241	8248	8254
67	8261	8267	8274	8280	8287	8293	8299	8306	8312	8319
68	8325	8331	8338	8344	8351	8357	8363	8370	8376	8382
69	8388	8395	8401	8407	8414	8420	8426	8432	8439	8445
70	8451	8457	8463	8470	8476	8482	8488	8494	8500	8506
71	8513	8519	8525	8531	8537	8543	8549	8555	8561	8567
72	8573	8579	8585	8591	8597	8603	8609	8615	8621	8627
73	8633	8639	8645	8651	8657	8663	8669	8675	8681	8686
74	8692	8698	8704	8710	8716	8722	8727	8733	8739	8745
75	8751	8756	8762	8768	8774	8779	8785	8791	8797	8802
76	8808	8814	8820	8825	8831	8837	8842	8848	8854	8859
77	8865	8871	8876	8882	8887	8893	8899	8904	8910	8915
78	8921	8927	8932	8938	8943	8949	8954	8960	8965	8971
79	8976	8982	8987	8993	8998	9004	9009	9015	9020	9025
80	9031	9036	9042	9047	9053	9058	9063	9069	9074	9079
81	9085	9090	9096	9101	9106	9112	9117	9122	9128	9133
82	9138	9143	9149	9154	9159	9165	9170	9175	9180	9186
83	9191	9196	9201	9206	9212	9217	9222	9227	9232	9238
84	9243	9248	9253	9258	9263	9269	9274	9279	9284	9289
85	9294	9299	9304	9309	9315	9320	9325	9330	9335	9340
86	9345	9350	9355	9360	9365	9370	9375	9380	9385	9390
87	9395	9400	9405	9410	9415	9420	9425	9430	9435	9440
88	9445	9450	9455	9460	9465	9469	9474	9479	9484	9489
89	9494	9499	9504	9509	9513	9518	9523	9528	9533	9538
90	9542	9547	9552	9557	9562	9566	9571	9576	9581	9586
91	9590	9595	9600	9605	9609	9614	9619	9624	9628	9633
92	9638	9643	9647	9652	9657	9661	9666	9671	9675	9680
93	9685	9689	9694	9699	9703	9708	9713	9717	9722	9727
94	9731	9736	9741	9745	9750	9754	9759	9763	9768	9773
95	9777	9782	9786	9791	9795	9800	9805	9809	9814	9818
96	9823	9827	9832	9836	9841	9845	9850	9854	9859	9863
97	9868	9872	9877	9881	9886	9890	9894	9899	9903	9908
98	9912	9917	9921	9926	9930	9934	9939	9943	9948	9952
99	9956	9961	9965	9969	9974	9978	9983	9987	9991	9996
N	0	1	2	3	4	5	6	7	8	9

TABLE II.—TRIGONOMETRIC FUNCTIONS

Angles	Sines		Cosines		Tangents		Cotangents		Angles
	Nat.	Log.	Nat.	Log.	Nat.	Log.	Nat.	Log.	
0° 00′	.0000	∞	1.0000	0.0000	.0000	∞	∞	∞	90° 00′
10	.0029	**7.**4637	1.0000	0000	.0029	**7.**4637	343.77	**2.**5363	50
20	.0058	7648	1.0000	0000	.0058	7648	171.89	2352	40
30	.0087	9408	1.0000	0000	.0087	9409	114.59	0591	30
40	.0116	**8.**0658	.9999	0000	.0116	**8.**0658	85.940	**1.**9342	20
50	.0145	1627	.9999	0000	.0145	1627	68.750	8373	10
1° 00′	.0175	**8.**2419	.9998	**9.**9999	.0175	**8.**2419	57.290	**1.**7581	89° 00′
10	.0204	3088	.9998	9999	.0204	3089	49.104	6911	50
20	.0233	3668	.9997	9999	.0233	3669	42.964	6331	40
30	.0262	4179	.9997	9999	.0262	4181	38.188	5819	30
40	.0291	4637	.9996	9998	.0291	4638	34.368	5362	20
50	.0320	5050	.9995	9998	.0320	5053	31.242	4947	10
2° 00′	.0349	**8.**5428	.9994	**9.**9997	.0349	**8.**5431	28.636	**1.**4569	88° 00′
10	.0378	5776	.9993	9997	.0378	5779	26.432	4221	50
20	.0407	6097	.9992	9996	.0407	6101	24.542	3899	40
30	.0436	6397	.9990	9996	.0437	6401	22.904	3599	30
40	.0465	6677	.9989	9995	.0466	6682	21.470	3318	2C
50	.0494	6940	.9988	9995	.0495	6945	20.206	3055	10
3° 00′	.0523	**8.**7188	.9986	**9.**9994	.0524	**8.**7194	19.081	**1.**2806	87° 00′
10	.0552	7423	.9985	9993	.0553	7429	18.075	2571	50
20	.0581	7645	.9983	9993	.0582	7652	17.169	2348	40
30	.0610	7857	.9981	9992	.0612	7865	16.350	2135	30
40	.0640	8059	.9980	9991	.0641	8067	15.605	1933	20
50	.0669	8251	.9978	9990	.0670	8261	14.924	1739	10
4° 00′	.0698	**8.**8436	.9976	**9.**9989	.0699	**8.**8446	14.301	**1.**1554	86° 00′
10	.0727	8613	.9974	9989	.0729	8624	13.727	1376	50
20	.0756	8783	.9971	9988	.0758	8795	13.197	1205	40
30	.0785	8946	.9969	9987	.0787	8960	12.706	1040	30
40	.0814	9104	.9967	9986	.0816	9118	12.251	0882	20
50	.0843	9256	.9964	9985	.0846	9272	11.826	0728	10
5° 00′	.0872	**8.**9403	.9962	**9.**9983	.0875	**8.**9420	11.430	**1.**0580	85° 00′
10	.0901	9545	.9959	9982	.0904	9563	11.059	0437	50
20	.0929	9682	.9957	9981	.0934	9701	10.712	0299	40
30	.0958	9816	.9954	9980	.0963	9836	10.385	0164	30
40	.0987	9945	.9951	9979	.0992	9966	10.078	0034	20
50	.1016	**9.**0070	.9948	9977	.1022	**9.**0093	9.7882	**0.**9907	10
6° 00′	.1045	**9.**0192	.9945	**9.**9976	.1051	**9.**0216	9.5144	**0.**9784	84° 00′
10	.1074	0311	.9942	9975	.1080	0336	9.2553	9664	50
20	.1103	0426	.9939	9973	.1110	0453	9.0098	9547	40
30	.1132	0539	.9936	9972	.1139	0567	8.7769	9433	30
40	.1161	0648	.9932	9971	.1169	0678	8.5555	9322	20
50	.1190	0755	.9929	9969	.1198	0786	8.3450	9214	10
7° 00′	.1219	**9.**0859	.9925	**9.**9968	.1228	**9.**0891	8.1443	**0.**9109	83° 00′
10	.1248	0961	.9922	9966	.1257	0995	7.9530	9005	50
20	.1276	1060	.9918	9964	.1287	1096	7.7704	8904	40
30	.1305	1157	.9914	9963	.1317	1194	7.5958	8806	30
40	.1334	1252	.9911	9961	.1346	1291	7.4287	8709	20
50	.1363	1345	.9907	9959	.1376	1385	7.2687	8615	10
8° 00′	.1392	**9.**1436	.9903	**9.**9958	.1405	**9.**1478	7.1154	**0.**8522	82° 00′
10	.1421	1525	.9899	9956	.1435	1569	6.9682	8431	50
20	.1449	1612	.9894	9954	.1465	1658	6.8269	8342	40
30	.1478	1697	.9890	9952	.1495	1745	6.6912	8255	30
40	.1507	1781	.9886	9950	.1524	1831	6.5606	8169	20
50	.1536	1863	.9881	9948	.1554	1915	6.4348	8085	10
9° 00′	.1564	**9.**1943	.9877	**9.**9946	.1584	**9.**1997	6.3138	**0.**8003	81° 00′
	Nat.	Log.	Nat.	Log.	Nat.	Log.	Nat.	Log.	
Angles	Cosines		Sines		Cotangents		Tangents		Angles

TABLE II.—TRIGONOMETRIC FUNCTIONS.—(*Continued*)

Angles	Sines		Cosines		Tangents		Cotangents		Angles
	Nat.	Log.	Nat.	Log.	Nat.	Log.	Nat.	Log.	
9° 00′	.1564	9.1943	.9877	9.9946	.1584	9.1997	6.3138	0.8003	81° 00′
10	.1593	2022	.9872	9944	.1614	2078	6.1970	7922	50
20	.1622	2100	.9868	9942	.1644	2158	6.0844	7842	40
30	.1650	2176	.9863	9940	.1673	2236	5.9758	7764	30
40	.1679	2251	.9858	9938	.1703	2313	5.8708	7687	20
50	.1708	2324	.9853	9936	.1733	2389	5.7694	7611	10
10° 00′	.1736	9.2397	.9848	9.9934	.1763	9.2463	5.6713	0.7537	80° 00′
10	.1765	2468	.9843	9931	.1793	2536	5.5764	7464	50
20	.1794	2538	.9838	9929	.1823	2609	5.4845	7391	40
30	.1822	2606	.9833	9927	.1853	2680	5.3955	7320	30
40	.1851	2674	.9827	9924	.1883	2750	5.3093	7250	20
50	.1880	2740	.9822	9922	.1914	2819	5.2257	7181	10
11° 00′	.1908	9.2806	.9816	9.9919	.1944	9.2887	5.1446	0.7113	79° 00′
10	.1937	2870	.9811	9917	.1974	2953	5.0658	7047	50
20	.1965	2934	.9805	9914	.2004	3020	4.9894	6980	40
30	.1994	2997	.9799	9912	.2035	3085	4.9152	6915	30
40	.2022	3058	.9793	9909	.2065	3149	4.8430	6851	20
50	.2051	3119	.9787	9907	.2095	3212	4.7729	6788	10
12° 00′	.2079	9.3179	.9781	9.9904	.2126	9.3275	4.7046	0.6725	78° 00′
10	.2108	3238	.9775	9901	.2156	3336	4.6382	6664	50
20	.2136	3296	.9769	9899	.2186	3397	4.5736	6603	40
30	.2164	3353	.9763	9896	.2217	3458	4.5107	6542	30
40	.2193	3410	.9757	9893	.2247	3517	4.4494	6483	20
50	.2221	3466	.9750	9890	.2278	3576	4.3897	6424	10
13° 00′	.2250	9.3521	.9744	9.9887	.2309	9.3634	4.3315	0.6366	77° 00′
10	.2278	3575	.9737	9884	.2339	3691	4.2747	6309	50
20	.2306	3629	.9730	9881	.2370	3748	4.2193	6252	40
30	.2334	3682	.9724	9878	.2401	3804	4.1653	6196	30
40	.2363	3734	.9717	9875	.2432	3859	4.1126	6141	20
50	.2391	3786	.9710	9872	.2462	3914	4.0611	6086	10
14° 00′	.2419	9.3837	.9703	9.9869	.2493	9.3968	4.0108	0.6032	76° 00′
10	.2447	3887	.9696	9866	.2524	4021	3.9617	5979	50
20	.2476	3937	.9689	9863	.2555	4074	3.9136	5926	40
30	.2504	3986	.9681	9859	.2586	4127	3.8667	5873	30
40	.2532	4035	.9674	9856	.2617	4178	3.8208	5822	20
50	.2560	4083	.9667	9853	.2648	4230	3.7760	5770	10
15° 00′	.2588	9.4130	.9659	9.9849	.2679	9.4281	3.7321	0.5719	75° 00′
10	.2616	4177	.9652	9846	.2711	4331	3.6891	5669	50
20	.2644	4223	.9644	9843	.2742	4381	3.6470	5619	40
30	.2672	4269	.9636	9839	.2773	4430	3.6059	5570	30
40	.2700	4314	.9628	9836	.2805	4479	3.5656	5521	20
50	.2728	4359	.9621	9832	.2836	4527	3.5261	5473	10
16° 00′	.2756	9.4403	.9613	9.9828	.2867	9.4575	3.4874	0.5425	74° 00′
10	.2784	4447	.9605	9825	.2899	4622	3.4495	5378	50
20	.2812	4491	.9596	9821	.2931	4669	3.4124	5331	40
30	.2840	4533	.9588	9817	.2962	4716	3.3759	5284	30
40	.2868	4576	.9580	9814	.2994	4762	3.3402	5238	20
50	.2896	4618	.9572	9810	.3026	4808	3.3052	5192	10
17° 00′	.2924	9.4659	.9563	9.9806	.3057	9.4853	3.2709	0.5147	73° 00′
10	.2952	4700	.9555	9802	.3089	4898	3.2371	5102	50
20	.2979	4741	.9546	9798	.3121	4943	3.2041	5057	40
30	.3007	4781	.9537	9794	.3153	4987	3.1716	5013	30
40	.3035	4821	.9528	9790	.3185	5031	3.1397	4969	20
50	.3062	4861	.9520	9786	.3217	5075	3.1084	4925	10
18° 00′	.3090	9.4900	.9511	9.9782	.3249	9.5118	3.0777	0.4882	72° 00′
	Nat.	Log.	Nat.	Log.	Nat.	Log.	Nat.	Log.	
Angles	Cosines		Sines		Cotangents		Tangents		Angles

TABLE II.—TRIGONOMETRIC FUNCTIONS.—(*Continued*)

Angles	Sines		Cosines		Tangents		Cotangents		Angles
	Nat.	Log.	Nat.	Log.	Nat.	Log.	Nat.	Log.	
18° 00′	.3090	**9**.4900	.9511	**9**.9782	.3249	**9**.5118	3.0777	**0**.4882	72° 00′
10	.3118	4939	.9502	9778	.3281	5161	3.0475	4839	50
20	.3145	4977	.9492	9774	.3314	5203	3.0178	4797	40
30	.3173	5015	.9483	9770	.3346	5245	2.9887	4755	30
40	.3201	5052	.9474	9765	.3378	5287	2.9600	4713	20
50	.3228	5090	.9465	9761	.3411	5329	2.9319	4671	10
19° 00′	.3256	**9**.5126	.9455	**9**.9757	.3443	**9**.5370	2.9042	**0**.4630	71° 00′
10	.3283	5163	.9446	9752	.3476	5411	2.8770	4589	50
20	.3311	5199	.9436	9748	.3508	5451	2.8502	4549	40
30	.3338	5235	.9426	9743	.3541	5491	2.8239	4509	30
40	.3365	5270	.9417	9739	.3574	5531	2.7980	4469	20
50	.3393	5306	.9407	9734	.3607	5571	2.7725	4429	10
20° 00′	.3420	**9**.5341	.9397	**9**.9730	.3640	**9**.5611	2.7475	**0**.4389	70° 00′
10	.3448	5375	.9387	9725	.3673	5650	2.7228	4350	50
20	.3475	5409	.9377	9721	.3706	5689	2.6985	4311	40
30	.3502	5443	.9367	9716	.3739	5727	2.6746	4273	30
40	.3529	5477	.9356	9711	.3772	5766	2.6511	4234	20
50	.3557	5510	.9346	9706	.3805	5804	2.6279	4196	10
21° 00′	.3584	**9**.5543	.9336	**9**.9702	.3839	**9**.5842	2.6051	**0**.4158	69° 00′
10	.3611	5576	.9325	9697	.3872	5879	2.5826	4121	50
20	.3638	5609	.9315	9692	.3906	5917	2.5605	4083	40
30	.3665	5641	.9304	9687	.3939	5954	2.5386	4046	30
40	.3692	5673	.9293	9682	.3973	5991	2.5172	4009	20
50	.3719	5704	.9283	9677	.4006	6028	2.4960	3972	10
22° 00′	.3746	**9**.5736	.9272	**9**.9672	.4040	**9**.6064	2.4751	**0**.3936	68° 00′
10	.3773	5767	.9261	9667	.4074	6100	2.4545	3900	50
20	.3800	5798	.9250	9661	.4108	6136	2.4342	3864	40
30	.3827	5828	.9239	9656	.4142	6172	2.4142	3828	30
40	.3854	5859	.9228	9651	.4176	6208	2.3945	3792	20
50	.3881	5889	.9216	9646	.4210	6243	2.3750	3757	10
23° 00′	.3907	**9**.5919	.9205	**9**.9640	.4245	**9**.6279	2.3559	**0**.3721	67° 00′
10	.3934	5948	.9194	9635	.4279	6314	2.3369	3686	50
20	.3961	5978	.9182	9629	.4314	6348	2.3183	3652	40
30	.3987	6007	.9171	9624	.4348	6383	2.2998	3617	30
40	.4014	6036	.9159	9618	.4383	6417	2.2817	3583	20
50	.4041	6065	.9147	9613	.4417	6452	2.2637	3548	10
24° 00′	.4067	**9**.6093	.9135	**9**.9607	.4452	**9**.6486	2.2460	**0**.3514	66° 00′
10	.4094	6121	.9124	9602	.4487	6520	2.2286	3480	50
20	.4120	6149	.9112	9596	.4522	6553	2.2113	3447	40
30	.4147	6177	.9100	9590	.4557	6587	2.1943	3413	30
40	.4173	6205	.9088	9584	.4592	6620	2.1775	3380	20
50	.4200	6232	.9075	9579	.4628	6654	2.1609	3346	10
25° 00′	.4226	**9**.6259	.9063	**9**.9573	.4663	**9**.6687	2.1445	**0**.3313	65° 00′
10	.4253	6286	.9051	9567	.4699	6720	2.1283	3280	50
20	.4279	6313	.9038	9561	.4734	6752	2.1123	3248	40
30	.4305	6340	.9026	9555	.4770	6785	2.0965	3215	30
40	.4331	6366	.9013	9549	.4806	6817	2.0809	3183	20
50	.4358	6392	.9001	9543	.4841	6850	2.0655	3150	10
26° 00′	.4384	**9**.6418	.8988	**9**.9537	.4877	**9**.6882	2.0503	**0**.3118	64° 00′
10	.4410	6444	.8975	9530	.4913	6914	2.0353	3086	50
20	.4436	6470	.8962	9524	.4950	6946	2.0204	3054	40
30	.4462	6495	.8949	9518	.4986	6977	2.0057	3023	30
40	.4488	6521	.8936	9512	.5022	7009	1.9912	2991	20
50	.4514	6546	.8923	9505	.5059	7040	1.9768	2960	10
27° 00′	.4540	**9**.6570	.8910	**9**.9499	.5095	**9**.7072	1.9626	**0**.2928	63° 00′
	Nat.	Log.	Nat.	Log.	Nat.	Log.	Nat.	Log.	
Angles	Cosines		Sines		Cotangents		Tangents		Angles

TABLE II.—TRIGONOMETRIC FUNCTIONS.—*(Continued)*

Angles	Sines		Cosines		Tangents		Cotangents		Angles
	Nat.	Log.	Nat.	Log.	Nat.	Log.	Nat.	Log.	
27° 00'	.4540	9.6570	.8910	9.9499	.5095	9.7072	1.9626	0.2928	63° 00'
10	.4566	6595	.8897	9492	.5132	7103	1.9486	2897	50
20	.4592	6620	.8884	9486	.5169	7134	1.9347	2866	40
30	.4617	6644	.8870	9479	.5206	7165	1.9210	2835	30
40	.4643	6668	.8857	9473	.5243	7196	1.9074	2804	20
50	.4669	6692	.8843	9466	.5280	7226	1.8940	2774	10
28° 00'	.4695	9.6716	.8829	9.9459	.5317	9.7257	1.8807	0.2743	62° 00'
10	.4720	6740	.8816	9453	.5354	7287	1.8676	2713	50
20	.4746	6763	.8802	9446	.5392	7317	1.8546	2683	40
30	.4772	6787	.8788	9439	.5430	7348	1.8418	2652	30
40	.4797	6810	.8774	9432	.5467	7378	1.8291	2622	20
50	.4823	6833	.8760	9425	.5505	7408	1.8165	2592	10
29° 00'	.4848	9.6856	.8746	9.9418	.5543	9.7438	1.8040	0.2562	61° 00'
10	.4874	6878	.8732	9411	.5581	7467	1.7917	2533	50
20	.4899	6901	.8718	9404	.5619	7497	1.7796	2503	40
30	.4924	6923	.8704	9397	.5658	7526	1.7675	2474	30
40	.4950	6946	.8689	9390	.5696	7556	1.7556	2444	20
50	.4975	6968	.8675	9383	.5735	7585	1.7437	2415	10
30° 00'	.5000	9.6990	.8660	9.9375	.5774	9.7614	1.7321	0.2386	60° 00'
10	.5025	7012	.8646	9368	.5812	7644	1.7205	2356	50
20	.5050	7033	.8631	9361	.5851	7673	1.7090	2327	40
30	.5075	7055	.8616	9353	.5890	7701	1.6977	2299	30
40	.5100	7076	.8601	9346	.5930	7730	1.6864	2270	20
50	.5125	7097	.8587	9338	.5969	7759	1.6753	2241	10
31° 00'	.5150	9.7118	.8572	9.9331	.6009	9.7788	1.6643	0.2212	59° 00'
10	.5175	7139	.8557	9323	.6048	7816	1.6534	2184	50
20	.5200	7160	.8542	9315	.6088	7845	1.6426	2155	40
30	.5225	7181	.8526	9308	.6128	7873	1.6319	2127	30
40	.5250	7201	.8511	9300	.6168	7902	1.6212	2098	20
50	.5275	7222	.8496	9292	.6208	7930	1.6107	2070	10
32° 00'	.5299	9.7242	.8480	9.9284	.6249	9.7958	1.6003	0.2042	58° 00'
10	.5324	7262	.8465	9276	.6289	7986	1.5900	2014	50
20	.5348	7282	.8450	9268	.6330	8014	1.5798	1986	40
30	.5373	7302	.8434	9260	.6371	8042	1.5697	1958	30
40	.5398	7322	.8418	9252	.6412	8070	1.5597	1930	20
50	.5422	7342	.8403	9244	.6453	8097	1.5497	1903	10
33° 00'	.5446	9.7361	.8387	9.9236	.6494	9.8125	1.5399	0.1875	57° 00'
10	.5471	7380	.8371	9228	.6536	8153	1.5301	1847	50
20	.5495	7400	.8355	9219	.6577	8180	1.5204	1820	40
30	.5519	7419	.8339	9211	.6619	8208	1.5108	1792	30
40	.5544	7438	.8323	9203	.6661	8235	1.5013	1765	20
50	.5568	7457	.8307	9194	.6703	8263	1.4919	1737	10
34° 00'	.5592	9.7476	.8290	9.9186	.6745	9.8290	1.4826	0.1710	56° 00'
10	.5616	7494	.8274	9177	.6787	8317	1.4733	1683	50
20	.5640	7513	.8258	9169	.6830	8344	1.4641	1656	40
30	.5664	7531	.8241	9160	.6873	8371	1.4550	1629	30
40	.5688	7550	.8225	9151	.6916	8398	1.4460	1602	20
50	.5712	7568	.8208	9142	.6959	8425	1.4370	1575	10
35° 00'	.5736	9.7586	.8192	9.9134	.7002	9.8452	1.4281	0.1548	55° 00'
10	.5760	7604	.8175	9125	.7046	8479	1.4193	1521	50
20	.5783	7622	.8158	9116	.7089	8506	1.4106	1494	40
30	.5807	7640	.8141	9107	.7133	8533	1.4019	1467	30
40	.5831	7657	.8124	9098	.7177	8559	1.3934	1441	20
50	.5854	7675	.8107	9089	.7221	8586	1.3848	1414	10
36° 00'	.5878	9.7692	.8090	9.9080	.7265	9.8613	1.3764	0.1387	54° 00'
	Nat.	Log.	Nat.	Log.	Nat.	Log.	Nat.	Log.	
Angles	Cosines		Sines		Cotangents		Tangents		Angles

TABLE II.—TRIGONOMETRIC FUNCTIONS.—(Continued)

Angles	Sines		Cosines		Tangents		Cotangents		Angles
	Nat.	Log.	Nat.	Log.	Nat.	Log.	Nat.	Log.	
36° 00′	.5878	9.7692	.8090	9.9080	.7265	9.8613	1.3764	0.1387	54° 00′
10	.5901	7710	.8073	9070	.7310	8639	1.3680	1361	50
20	.5925	7727	.8056	9061	.7355	8666	1.3597	1334	40
30	.5948	7744	.8039	9052	.7400	8692	1.3514	1308	30
40	.5972	7761	.8021	9042	.7445	8718	1.3432	1282	20
50	.5995	7778	.8004	9033	.7490	8745	1.3351	1255	10
37° 00′	.6018	9.7795	.7986	9.9023	.7536	9.8771	1.3270	0.1229	53° 00′
10	.6041	7811	.7969	9014	.7581	8797	1.3190	1203	50
20	.6065	7828	.7951	9004	.7627	8824	1.3111	1176	40
30	.6088	7844	.7934	8995	.7673	8850	1.3032	1150	30
40	.6111	7861	.7916	8985	.7720	8876	1.2954	1124	20
50	.6134	7877	.7898	8975	.7766	8902	1.2876	1098	10
38° 00′	.6157	9.7893	.7880	9.8965	.7813	9.8928	1.2790	0.1072	52° 00′
10	.6180	7910	.7862	8955	.7860	8954	1.2723	1046	50
20	.6202	7926	.7844	8945	.7907	8980	1.2647	1020	40
30	.6225	7941	.7826	8935	.7954	9006	1.2572	0994	30
40	.6248	7957	.7808	8925	.8002	9032	1.2497	0968	20
50	.6271	7973	.7790	8915	.8050	9058	1.2423	0942	10
39° 00′	.6293	9.7989	.7771	9.8905	.8098	9.9084	1.2349	0.0916	51° 00′
10	.6316	8004	.7753	8895	.8146	9110	1.2276	0890	50
20	.6338	8020	.7735	8884	.8195	9135	1.2203	0865	40
30	.6361	8035	.7716	8874	.8243	9161	1.2131	0839	30
40	.6383	8050	.7698	8864	.8292	9187	1.2059	0813	20
50	.6406	8066	.7679	8853	.8342	9212	1.1988	0788	10
40° 00′	.6428	9.8081	.7660	9.8843	.8391	9.9238	1.1918	0.0762	50° 00′
10	.6450	8096	.7642	8832	.8441	9264	1.1847	0736	50
20	.6472	8111	.7623	8821	.8491	9289	1.1778	0711	40
30	.6494	3125	.7604	8810	.8541	9315	1.1708	0685	30
40	.6517	8140	.7585	8800	.8591	9341	1.1640	0659	20
50	.6539	8155	.7566	8789	.8642	9366	1.1571	0634	10
41° 00′	.6561	9.8169	.7547	9.8778	.8693	9.9392	1.1504	0.0608	49° 00′
10	.6583	8184	.7528	8767	.8744	9417	1.1436	0583	50
20	.6604	8198	.7509	8756	.8796	9443	1.1369	0557	40
30	.6626	8213	.7490	8745	.8847	9468	1.1303	0532	30
40	.6648	8227	.7470	8733	.8899	9494	1.1237	0506	20
50	.6670	8241	.7451	8722	.8952	9519	1.1171	0481	10
42° 00′	.6691	9.8255	.7431	9.8711	.9004	9.9544	1.1106	0.0456	48° 00′
10	.6713	8269	.7412	8699	.9057	9570	1.1041	0430	50
20	.6734	8283	.7392	8688	.9110	9595	1.0977	0405	40
30	.6756	8297	.7373	8676	.9163	9621	1.0913	0379	30
40	.6777	8311	.7353	8665	.9217	9646	1.0850	0354	20
50	.6799	8324	.7333	8653	.9271	9671	1.0786	0329	10
43° 00′	.6820	9.8338	.7314	9.8641	.9325	9.9697	1.0724	0.0303	47° 00′
10	.6841	8351	.7294	8629	.9380	9722	1.0661	0278	50
20	.6862	8365	.7274	8618	.9435	9747	1.0599	0253	40
30	.6884	8378	.7254	8606	.9490	9772	1.0538	0228	30
40	.6905	8391	.7234	8594	.9545	9798	1.0477	0202	20
50	.6926	8405	.7214	8582	.9601	9823	1.0416	0177	10
44° 00′	.6947	9.8418	.7193	9.8569	.9657	9.9848	1.0355	0.0152	46° 00′
10	.6967	8431	.7173	8557	.9713	9874	1.0295	0126	50
20	.6988	8444	.7153	8545	.9770	9899	1.0235	0101	40
30	.7009	8457	.7133	8532	.9827	9924	1.0176	0076	30
40	.7030	8469	.7112	8520	.9884	9949	1.0117	0051	20
50	.7050	8482	.7092	8507	.9942	9975	1.0058	0025	10
45° 00′	.7071	9.8495	.7071	9.8495	1.0000	0.0000	1.0000	0.0000	45° 00′
	Nat.	Log.	Nat.	Log.	Nat.	Log.	Nat.	Log.	
Angles	Cosines		Sines		Cotangents		Tangents		Angles

TABLE III.—POWERS AND ROOTS

No.	Sq.	Sq. Root	Cube	Cube Root	No.	Sq.	Sq. Root	Cube	Cube Root
1	1	1.000	1	1.000	51	2,601	7.141	132,651	3.708
2	4	1.414	8	1.260	52	2,704	7.211	140,608	3.733
3	9	1.732	27	1.442	53	2,809	7.280	148,877	3.756
4	16	2.000	64	1.587	54	2,916	7.348	157,464	3.780
5	25	2.236	125	1.710	55	3,025	7.416	166,375	3.803
6	36	2.449	216	1.817	56	3,136	7.483	175,616	3.826
7	49	2.646	343	1.913	57	3,249	7.550	185,193	3.849
8	64	2.828	512	2.000	58	3,364	7.616	195,112	3.871
9	81	3.000	729	2.080	59	3,481	7.681	205,379	3.893
10	100	3.162	1,000	2.154	60	3,600	7.746	216,000	3.915
11	121	3.317	1,331	2.224	61	3,721	7.810	226,981	3.936
12	144	3.464	1,728	2.289	62	3,844	7.874	238,328	3.958
13	169	3.606	2,197	2.351	63	3,969	7.937	250,047	3.979
14	196	3.742	2,744	2.410	64	4,096	8.000	262,144	4.000
15	225	3.873	3,375	2.466	65	4,225	8.062	274,625	4.021
16	256	4.000	4,096	2.520	66	4,356	8.124	287,496	4.041
17	289	4.123	4,913	2.571	67	4,489	8.185	300,763	4.062
18	324	4.243	5,832	2.621	68	4,624	8.246	314,432	4.082
19	361	4.359	6,859	2.668	69	4,761	8.307	328,509	4.102
20	400	4.472	8,000	2.714	70	4,900	8.367	343,000	4.121
21	441	4.583	9,261	2.759	71	5,041	8.426	357,911	4.141
22	484	4.690	10,648	2.802	72	5,184	8.485	373,248	4.160
23	529	4.796	12,167	2.844	73	5,329	8.544	389,017	4.179
24	576	4.899	13,824	2.884	74	5,476	8.602	405,224	4.198
25	625	5.000	15,625	2.924	75	5,625	8.660	421,875	4.217
26	676	5.099	17,576	2.962	76	5,776	8.718	438,976	4.236
27	729	5.196	19,683	3.000	77	5,929	8.775	456,533	4.254
28	784	5.291	21,952	3.037	78	6,084	8.832	474,552	4.273
29	841	5.385	24,389	3.072	79	6,241	8.888	493,039	4.291
30	900	5.477	27,000	3.107	80	6,400	8.944	512,000	4.309
31	961	5.568	29,791	3.141	81	6,561	9.000	531,441	4.327
32	1,024	5.657	32,768	3.175	82	6,724	9.055	551,368	4.344
33	1,089	5.745	35,937	3.208	83	6,889	9.110	571,787	4.362
34	1,156	5.831	39,304	3.240	84	7,056	9.165	592,704	4.380
35	1,225	5.916	42,875	3.271	85	7,225	9.220	614,125	4.397
36	1,296	6.000	46,656	3.302	86	7,396	9.274	636,056	4.414
37	1,369	6.083	50,653	3.332	87	7,569	9.327	658,503	4.431
38	1,444	6.164	54,872	3.362	88	7,744	9.381	681,472	4.448
39	1,521	6.245	59,319	3.391	89	7,921	9.434	704,969	4.465
40	1,600	6.325	64,000	3.420	90	8,100	9.487	729,000	4.481
41	1,681	6.403	68,921	3.448	91	8,281	9.539	753,571	4.498
42	1,764	6.481	74,088	3.476	92	8,464	9.592	778,688	4.514
43	1,849	6.557	79,507	3.503	93	8,649	9.644	804,357	4.531
44	1,936	6.633	85,184	3.530	94	8,836	9.695	830,584	4.547
45	2,025	6.708	91,125	3.557	95	9,025	9.747	857,375	4.563
46	2,116	6.782	97,336	3.583	96	9,216	9.798	884,736	4.579
47	2,209	6.856	103,823	3.609	97	9,409	9.849	912,673	4.595
48	2,304	6.928	110,592	3.634	98	9,604	9.899	941,192	4.610
49	2,401	7.000	117,649	3.659	99	9,801	9.950	970,299	4.626
50	2,500	7.071	125,000	3.684	100	10,000	10.000	1,000,000	4.642

TABLE IV.—NATURAL LOGARITHMS

N	0	1	2	3	4	5	6	7	8	9
1.0	0.0 000	100	198	296	392	488	583	677	770	862
1.1	953	*044	*133	*222	*310	*398	*484	*570	*655	*740
1.2	0.1 823	906	989	*070	*151	*231	*311	*390	*469	*546
1.3	0.2 624	700	776	852	927	*001	*075	*148	*221	*293
1.4	0.3 365	436	507	577	646	716	784	853	920	988
1.5	0.4 055	121	187	253	318	383	447	511	574	637
1.6	700	762	824	886	947	*008	*068	*128	*188	*247
1.7	0.5 306	365	423	481	539	596	653	710	766	822
1.8	878	933	988	*043	*098	*152	*206	*259	*313	*366
1.9	0.6 419	471	523	575	627	678	729	780	831	881
2.0	931	981	*031	*080	*129	*178	*227	*275	*324	*372
2.1	0.7 419	467	514	561	608	655	701	747	793	839
2.2	885	930	975	*020	*065	*109	*154	*198	*242	*286
2.3	0.8 329	372	416	459	502	544	587	629	671	713
2.4	755	796	838	879	920	961	*002	*042	*083	*123
2.5	0.9 163	203	243	282	322	361	400	439	478	517
2.6	555	594	632	670	708	746	783	821	858	895
2.7	933	969	*006	*043	*080	*116	*152	*188	*225	*260
2.8	1.0 296	332	367	403	438	473	508	543	578	613
2.9	647	682	716	750	784	818	852	886	919	953
3.0	986	*019	*053	*086	*119	*151	*184	*217	*249	*282
3.1	1.1 314	346	378	410	442	474	506	537	569	600
3.2	632	663	694	725	756	787	817	848	878	909
3.3	939	969	*000	*030	*060	*090	*119	*149	*179	*208
3.4	1.2 238	267	296	326	355	384	413	442	470	499
3.5	528	556	585	613	641	669	698	726	754	782
3.6	809	837	865	892	920	947	975	*002	*029	*056
3.7	1.3 083	110	137	164	191	218	244	271	297	324
3.8	350	376	402	429	455	481	507	533	558	584
3.9	610	635	661	686	712	737	762	788	813	838
4.0	863	888	913	938	962	987	*012	*036	*061	*085
4.1	1.4 110	134	159	183	207	231	255	279	303	327
4.2	351	375	398	422	446	469	493	516	540	563
4.3	586	609	633	656	679	702	725	748	770	793
4.4	816	839	861	884	907	929	951	974	996	*019
4.5	1.5 041	063	085	107	129	151	173	195	217	239
4.6	261	282	304	326	347	369	390	412	433	454
4.7	476	497	518	539	560	581	602	623	644	665
4.8	686	707	728	748	769	790	810	831	851	872
4.9	892	913	933	953	974	994	*014	*034	*054	*074
5.0	1.6 094	114	134	154	174	194	214	233	253	273

If given number $n = N \times 10^m$, then $\log_e n = \log_e N + m \log_e 10$. Find $m \log_e 10$ from the following table:

Multiples of $\log_e 10$

$$\log_e 10 = 2.3026$$
$$2 \log_e 10 = 4.6052$$
$$3 \log_e 10 = 6.9078$$
$$4 \log_e 10 = 9.2103$$
$$5 \log_e 10 = 11.5129$$

$$- \log_e 10 = 7.6974 - 10$$
$$-2 \log_e 10 = 5.3948 - 10$$
$$-3 \log_e 10 = 3.0922 - 10$$
$$-4 \log_e 10 = 0.7897 - 10$$
$$-5 \log_e 10 = 9.4871 - 20$$

TABLE IV.—NATURAL LOGARITHMS.—(Continued)

N	0	1	2	3	4	5	6	7	8	9
5.0	1.6 094	114	134	154	174	194	214	233	253	273
5.1	292	312	332	351	371	390	409	429	448	467
5.2	487	506	525	544	563	582	601	620	639	658
5.3	677	696	715	734	752	771	790	808	827	845
5.4	864	882	901	919	938	956	974	993	*011	*029
5.5	1.7 047	066	084	102	120	138	156	174	192	210
5.6	228	246	263	281	299	317	334	352	370	387
5.7	405	422	440	457	475	492	509	527	544	561
5.8	579	596	613	630	647	664	681	699	716	733
5.9	750	766	783	800	817	834	851	867	884	901
6.0	918	934	951	967	984	*001	*017	*034	*050	*066
6.1	1.8 083	099	116	132	148	165	181	197	213	229
6.2	245	262	278	294	310	326	342	358	374	390
6.3	405	421	437	453	469	485	500	516	532	547
6.4	563	579	594	610	625	641	656	672	687	703
6.5	718	733	749	764	779	795	810	825	840	856
6.6	871	886	901	916	931	946	961	976	991	*006
6.7	1.9 021	036	051	066	081	095	110	125	140	155
6.8	169	184	199	213	228	242	257	272	286	301
6.9	315	330	344	359	373	387	402	416	430	445
7.0	459	473	488	502	516	530	544	559	573	587
7.1	601	615	629	643	657	671	685	699	713	727
7.2	741	755	769	782	796	810	824	838	851	865
7.3	879	892	906	920	933	947	961	974	988	*001
7.4	2.0 015	028	042	055	069	082	096	109	122	136
7.5	149	162	176	189	202	215	229	242	255	268
7.6	281	295	308	321	334	347	360	373	386	399
7.7	412	425	438	451	464	477	490	503	516	528
7.8	541	554	567	580	592	605	618	631	643	656
7.9	669	681	694	707	719	732	744	757	769	782
8.0	794	807	819	832	844	857	869	882	894	906
8.1	919	931	943	956	968	980	992	*005	*017	*029
8.2	2.1 041	054	066	080	090	102	114	126	138	150
8.3	163	175	187	199	211	223	235	247	258	270
8.4	282	294	306	318	330	342	353	365	377	389
8.5	401	412	424	436	448	460	471	483	494	506
8.6	518	529	541	552	564	576	587	599	610	622
8.7	633	645	656	668	679	691	702	713	725	736
8.8	748	759	770	782	793	804	815	827	838	849
8.9	861	872	883	894	905	917	928	939	950	961
9.0	972	983	994	*006	*017	*028	*039	*050	*061	*072
9.1	2.2 083	094	105	116	127	137	148	159	170	181
9.2	192	203	214	225	235	246	257	268	279	289
9.3	300	311	322	332	343	354	364	375	386	396
9.4	407	418	428	439	450	460	471	481	492	502
9.5	513	523	534	544	555	565	576	586	597	607
9.6	618	628	638	649	659	670	680	690	701	711
9.7	721	732	742	752	762	773	783	793	803	814
9.8	824	834	844	854	865	875	885	895	905	915
9.9	925	935	946	956	966	976	986	996	*006	*016
10.	2.3 026	036	046	056	066	076	086	096	106	115

TABLE V.—EXPONENTIAL AND HYPERBOLIC FUNCTIONS

x	e^x	e^{-x}	$\sinh x$	$\cosh x$	$\tanh x$
.00	1.000	1.000	.000	1.000	.000
.01	1.010	.990	.010	1.000	.010
.02	1.020	.980	.020	1.000	.020
.03	1.030	.970	.030	1.000	.030
.04	1.041	.961	.040	1.001	.040
.05	1.051	.951	.050	1.001	.050
.06	1.062	.942	.060	1.002	.060
.07	1.073	.932	.070	1.002	.070
.08	1.083	.923	.080	1.003	.080
.09	1.094	.914	.090	1.004	.090
.1	1.105	.905	.100	1.005	.100
.2	1.221	.819	.201	1.020	.197
.3	1.350	.741	.305	1.045	.291
.4	1.492	.670	.411	1.081	.380
.5	1.649	.607	.521	1.128	.462
.6	1.822	.549	.637	1.185	.537
.7	2.014	.497	.759	1.255	.604
.8	2.226	.449	.888	1.337	.664
.9	2.460	.407	1.027	1.433	.716
1.0	2.718	.368	1.175	1.543	.762
1.1	3.004	.333	1.336	1.669	.800
1.2	3.320	.301	1.509	1.811	.834
1.3	3.669	.273	1.698	1.971	.862
1.4	4.055	.247	1.904	2.151	.885
1.5	4.482	.223	2.129	2.352	.905
1.6	4.953	.202	2.376	2.577	.922
1.7	5.474	.183	2.646	2.828	.935
1.8	6.050	.165	2.942	3.107	.947
1.9	6.686	.150	3.268	3.418	.956
2.0	7.389	.135	3.627	3.762	.964
2.1	8.166	.122	4.022	4.144	.970
2.2	9.025	.111	4.457	4.568	.976
2.3	9.974	.100	4.937	5.037	.980
2.4	11.023	.091	5.466	5.557	.984
2.5	12.182	.082	6.050	6.132	.987
2.6	13.464	.074	6.695	6.769	.989
2.7	14.880	.067	7.406	7.473	.991
2.8	16.445	.061	8.192	8.253	.993
2.9	18.174	.055	9.060	9.115	.994
3.0	20.086	.050	10.018	10.068	.995
3.1	22.20	.045	11.08	11.12	.996
3.2	24.53	.041	12.25	12.29	.997
3.3	27.11	.037	13.54	13.57	.997
3.4	29.96	.033	14.97	15.00	.998
3.5	33.12	.030	16.54	16.57	.998
3.6	36.60	.027	18.29	18.31	.999
3.7	40.45	.025	20.21	20.24	.999
3.8	44.70	.022	22.34	22.36	.999
3.9	49.40	.020	24.69	24.71	.999
4.0	54.60	.018	27.29	27.31	.999
4.1	60.34	.017	30.16	30.18	.999
4.2	66.69	.015	33.34	33.35	1.000
4.3	73.70	.014	36.84	36.86	1.000
4.4	81.45	.012	40.72	40.73	1.000
4.5	90.02	.011	45.00	45.01	1.000
4.6	99.48	.010	49.74	49.75	1.000
4.7	109.95	.0090	54.97	54.98	1.000
4.8	121.51	.0082	60.75	60.76	1.000
4.9	134.29	.0074	67.14	67.15	1.000
5.0	148.41	.0067	74.20	74.21	1.000
6.0	403.4	.0025	201.7		1.000
7.0	1096.6	.00091	548.3		1.000
8.0	2981.0	.00034	1490.5		1.000
9.0	8103.1	.00012	4051.5		1.000
10.0	22026.5	.000045	11013.2		1.000

ANSWERS TO ODD-NUMBERED PROBLEMS

CHAPTER I

Arts. 6–7, pp. 11–14

1. $(20 + 5x)$ per cent.   **3.** $x \sqrt{64 - x^2}$.

7. 5.7 ft. square.   **9.** $S = \frac{1}{2}x$.

11. $A = \frac{1}{4}(x + 4) \sqrt{64 - (x - 4)^2}$.   **13.** \$21.   **15.** $V = \frac{4}{3}\pi(6x^2 - x^3)$.

17. $V = \frac{1}{4}\pi(256h - h^3)$.

19. $C = 4 \left(\pi x^2 + \dfrac{300}{x} \right)$; about 3.6 in.

21. $V = \frac{1}{12}\pi y(12 - y)^2$.   **23.** $V = \dfrac{9\theta^2}{\pi^2} \sqrt{4\pi^2 - \theta^2}$.

CHAPTER II

Arts. 14–15, pp. 28–30

1. 6.   **3.** 12.   **5.** $\frac{2}{5}$.   **7.** $6\frac{1}{4}$.   **9.** 0.   **11.** 3.

15. -2.   **17.** 2.   **19.** $\frac{1}{2}$.   **21.** ∞.   **23.** 3.   **25.** $\frac{1}{4}$.

27. 0.   **29.** 0.   **33.** $A = nr^2 \sin \dfrac{\pi}{n} \cos \dfrac{\pi}{n}$.

35. 6.   **37.** $13\frac{1}{2}$.   **39.** $|r| < 1$; $\dfrac{a}{1 - r}$.

CHAPTER III

Arts. 16–20, pp. 39–41

1. $D_x A = 2x$ sq. in. per in.   **3.** 216 cu. ft. per ft.

5. $-\frac{3}{4}$ g. per min.   **7.** -0.6 lb. per sq. in. per cu. in.

9. $2x$.   **11.** $2x - 4$.   **13.** $2 - 16x$.   **15.** $8x - 3x^2$.

17. $4x^3$.   **19.** $10x^4$.   **21.** $\dfrac{1}{2 \sqrt{x}}$.   **23.** $-\frac{1}{2}x^{-\frac{3}{2}}$.

25. $\dfrac{-5}{(x - 1)^2}$.   **27.** $\dfrac{-6}{(x - 4)^2}$.   **29.** $-\dfrac{2}{x^3}$.   **31.** $\dfrac{-8x}{(x^2 + 1)^2}$.

33. $\dfrac{16x}{(x^2 + 4)^2}$.   **35.** $\dfrac{4x}{(x^2 + 1)^2}$.   **37.** $6x^2 - \dfrac{1}{x^2}$.   **39.** 6.

41. $-\frac{1}{9}$.   **43.** 0.   **45.** $\frac{1}{2}$.

47. (a) $x > -2\frac{1}{2}$; (b) $x < -2\frac{1}{2}$.

49. (a) $x < 0$ or $x > \frac{5}{3}$; (b) $0 < x < \frac{5}{3}$.

51. 6 units per min.   **53.** $y' = 4 - 2x$.

57. $D_x v = 3x^2$; $D_x s = 12x$.

473

CHAPTER IV

Arts. 21–23, pp. 49–51

7. $3x^2 + 4$.

9. $6t - 1$.

11. $2x^2 - 8x + 5$.

13. $3x^2 - 32x^{-2}$.

15. $6(x^5 + x^{-4})$.

17. $3x^{\frac{1}{2}} + 2x^{-\frac{1}{2}}$.

19. $-3x^{-\frac{7}{4}} - 3x^{-\frac{3}{2}}$.

21. $-\frac{9}{5}x^{-3} - 4x^{-5}$.

23. $12(3x + 1)^3$.

25. $-\dfrac{2x}{\sqrt{4 - x^2}}$.

27. $\frac{3}{2}x^2 \sqrt{x^3 - 8}$.

29. $x(x + 1)^2(5x + 2)$.

31. $4x^3$.

33. $2x(x^2 + 1)(x^2 + 4)^2(5x^2 + 11)$.

35. $\dfrac{4x(3x^2 - 2)}{\sqrt{x^2 - 1}}$.

37. $\dfrac{-12}{(3x - 1)^2}$.

39. $\dfrac{7}{(x + 5)^2}$.

41. $\dfrac{-6x}{(x^2 + 1)^2}$.

43. $\dfrac{6(4 - x^2)}{(x^2 + 4)^2}$.

45. $\dfrac{2t}{(t^2 + 1)^2}$.

47. $(1 - 4y^2)^{-\frac{1}{2}}$.

49. $\dfrac{32x(x^2 - 4)}{(x^2 + 4)^3}$.

51. $\dfrac{54x + 12x^2 - x^4}{(x^3 + 27)^2}$.

53. $\dfrac{-4(3x^2 + 4)}{(x^2 - 4)^2 \sqrt{x^2 + 4}}$.

55. 2.

57. $\pm \frac{1}{2}(4 + x)^{-\frac{1}{2}}$.

59. $\dfrac{\pm x}{\sqrt{x^2 - 6}}$.

61. $\pm \frac{1}{2}(9 + x)^{-\frac{1}{2}}$.

63. $\dfrac{\mp 3x}{4 \sqrt{16 - x^2}}$.

65. -2.

67. $-\frac{1}{8}$.

69. $-\frac{1}{4}$.

71. $-\frac{9}{5}$.

73. $-\frac{1}{4} \sqrt{3}$.

77. $8x^3 - 9x^2 + 12x - 9$.

81. $D_r v = 4\pi r^2; \; D_r s = 8\pi r$.

83. $\dfrac{-2k}{x^3}$.

85. $v = \dfrac{\sqrt{2}\, x^3}{12}; \; D_x v = \dfrac{\sqrt{2}\, x^2}{4}$.

87. $v = \frac{1}{12}\pi y^3; \; \dfrac{dy}{dt} = \dfrac{1}{6\pi} = 0.053$ in. per min.

Arts. 24–25, pp. 54–56

1. $4(8x - 11)$.

3. $\dfrac{-12x}{(1 + 2x^2)^2}$.

5. $\dfrac{8x}{(1 - 4x^2)^2}$.

7. $-\dfrac{1}{t^2}$.

9. $\dfrac{8t(1 - t^4)}{(1 + t^4)^2}$.

11. 6 units per unit of time.

13. $\dfrac{dy}{dt} = +3$.

17. $-\frac{1}{2}$.

19. -2

21. $-\frac{1}{4}$.

23. $-\frac{1}{6}; \; -\frac{3}{2}$.

Art. 26, p. 58–59

1. $-\frac{2}{5}$.

3. $-\dfrac{x}{y}$.

5. $-\dfrac{b^2 x}{a^2 y}$.

7. $\dfrac{p}{y}$.

9. $\dfrac{2 - x}{y}$.

11. $\dfrac{4}{y(4 - x)^2}$.

13. -2.

15. 2.

17. $-4; 1$.

19. $-\frac{5}{4}$.

21. $\frac{3}{4}$.

23. $\frac{1}{2}$.

25. -1.

27. $-\frac{3}{8}$.

29. $-\frac{4}{3}$.

31. $\frac{1}{7}$.

33. $\dfrac{y + 2x}{8y - x}$.

35. $\dfrac{3 - 2y}{5 + 2x}$.

37. $\dfrac{3y + 4x}{2y - 3x}$.

39. $-\dfrac{4y^2 + 3x^2}{12y^2 + 8xy}.$

41. $\dfrac{y^2 - 8xy}{4x^2 + 6y^2 - 2xy}.$

43. $\dfrac{4 - 6x - 8y}{8x - 6y - 1}.$

45. $\dfrac{10xy^2 - 4x^3 - y}{x - 10x^2y}.$

47. $\dfrac{3 + 4y - 2x - 3x^2}{3y^2 - 4x + 1}.$

49. $\dfrac{32(2 - x^2)}{x^3y(x^2 - 4)^2}.$

CHAPTER V

Arts. 27–28, pp. 62–63

1. 2.   **3.** 1.   **5.** $\frac{41}{12}$.   **7.** $\frac{8}{15}$.   **9.** $\frac{14}{13}$; $\frac{7}{4}$.

11. $\frac{6}{7}$.   **13.** $\frac{30}{97}$.   **15.** $\frac{18}{31}$.   **17.** $\frac{57}{26}$.

19. $y = \frac{1}{3}x + 2$; $y = -3x + 2$.   **21.** $3x + 8y = 25$; $8x - 3y = 18$.

23. $3x + 4y = 40$; $4x - 3y = 20$.   **25.** $20x + 9y = 8$; $27x - 60y = 107$.

27. $y = -\frac{2}{3}x$; $y = \frac{2}{3}x$.   **29.** $2x + y = 2$; $x - 2y = 6$.

31. $3x + y + 10 = 0$.   **35.** $\tan \phi = \pm \frac{9}{17}$.

Arts. 29–31, pp. 67–69

1. (a) 55.6 ft. per sec.; -8.8 ft. per sec.   (b) 223.6 ft.   (c) 7.4 sec.

3. 205 ft. per sec.   **5.** 8.9 ft. per sec.

7. $A = 12 + 4t - t^2$.   **9.** 32 sq. in. per min.

11. 9 sq. ft. per min.   **13.** $7\frac{1}{2}$ m.p.h.; $2\frac{1}{2}$ m.p.h.

15. $5\sqrt{2}$ units per min.   **17.** 3π cu. ft. per min.

19. $v = \frac{1}{3}\pi y^2(3r - y)$; $\dfrac{dv}{dt} = \pi(2ry - y^2)\dfrac{dy}{dt}.$

21. 0.025 ft. per min.; 0.01 ft. per min.

23. $\dfrac{8\sqrt{3}}{3}$ ft. per sec.   **25.** About 3 cu. ft. per min.

Art. 32, p. 73–74

1. max. (3, 9).   **5.** max. (0, 0); min. (4, -8).

7. max. (1, 2); min. (3, -2).   **9.** max. (0, 4); min. (2, 0).

11. max. $(-1, \frac{5}{3})$; min. (3, -9).   **13.** min. $(-1, -6)$.

15. max. (0, 3); min. (2, -1).   **17.** max. $(-2, -8)$; min. (2, 8).

19. max. $(4, \frac{1}{8})$.   **21.** max. $(-4, -8)$; min. (0, 0).

23. max. (0, 3).   **25.** max. (1, 4); min. $(-1, -4)$.

27. min. $(-3, -\frac{4}{5})$.   **29.** max. $(0, -\frac{5}{3})$.

31. max. $(-2, -2)$; min. (8, 18).   **33.** max. $(-6, -9)$; min. (6, 9).

35. max. $(\pm 4, 32\sqrt{2})$; min. (0, 0).

Art. 33, pp. 75–78

1. 15; 5.   **3.** 12.   **5.** 60 sq. in.

7. 40 ft. by 30 ft.   **9.** 50 ft. by 30 ft.   **11.** $r = 8$ in.

13. 8 in.   **17.** (1, 3).   **19.** Base 3 ft. by 6 ft.

23. $V = \dfrac{16\pi}{3}\left(\dfrac{y^2}{y - 8}\right)$; $y = 16$ in.

25. $\dfrac{P}{6 - \sqrt{3}}.$ **27.** 10 in.   **29.** 170.

31. $3.35.   **35.** 4 ft. from A.   **37.** $9x^2 + 16y^2 = 288$.

CHAPTER VI
Arts. 34–35, pp. 81–82

1. 6.

3. $x + 3x^{-\frac{1}{2}}$.

5. $\dfrac{8}{(2-x)^3}$.

7. $\dfrac{36}{(2x-3)^3}$.

9. $\dfrac{16(3x^2+4)}{(x^2-4)^3}$.

11. x^{-3}.

13. $-\dfrac{16}{y^3}$.

15. $\dfrac{a^{\frac{1}{2}}}{2x^{\frac{1}{2}}}$.

17. $\dfrac{-b^4}{a^2y^3}$.

19. $\dfrac{2y-2x-16}{(x-8)^2}$.

21. $\dfrac{-16}{(y+4)^3}$.

23. $\dfrac{8(3x^2+4)}{(x^2-4)^3}$.

25. $-\frac{3}{4}$; 0; $-\frac{25}{64}$; $\frac{1}{5}$.

27. 1; -1.

29. 0; $-\frac{1}{4}$.

31. $\dfrac{(-1)^n(n+1)!}{x^{n+2}}$.

33. $\dfrac{-3b^6x}{a^4y^5}$.

35. $\dfrac{12x}{(2-y)^5}$.

37. $u\dfrac{d^2v}{dx^2} + 2\dfrac{du}{dx}\dfrac{dv}{dx} + v\dfrac{d^2u}{dx^2}$.

Arts. 36–39, pp. 87–88

1. max. $(-1, 0)$; min. $(1, -4)$; inf. $(0, -2)$.

3. max. $(1, 3)$; min. $(2, 2)$; inf. $(\frac{3}{2}, \frac{5}{2})$.

5. max. $(2, 0)$; min. $(4, -4)$; inf. $(3, -2)$.

7. min. $(0, -16)$.

9. min. $(-1, -5)$; inf. $(0, -\frac{9}{4})$, $(2, \frac{7}{4})$.

11. min. $(-2, -\frac{1}{4})$; inf. $(-3, -\frac{2}{3})$.

13. max. $(-3, -6)$; min. $(3, 6)$.

15. max. $(0. 6)$; inf. $\left(\pm \dfrac{1}{\sqrt{3}}, \dfrac{9}{2}\right)$.

17. inf. $(0, 2)$; $(\sqrt[3]{4}, \frac{4}{3})$.

19. min. $(0, 0)$; inf. $\left(\pm \dfrac{2}{\sqrt{3}}, 1\right)$.

21. max. $(0, -\frac{9}{4})$.

23. max. $(0, 0)$.

27. If $b = 0$.

29. 28 ft.; 24 ft. per min.; 6 ft./min.²

31. 9 ft.; -12 ft. per min.; -4 ft./min.² $2 < t < 4$.

CHAPTER VII
Art. 40, pp. 95–96

1. $3\frac{1}{2}$.

3. 12.

5. -0.1045; 0.4877; -0.5878.

11. $2\sqrt{5}$.

13. $\frac{1}{2}\sqrt{2}$; 7.

21. $60°$; $300°$; $70° \; 32'$; $289° \; 28'$.

23. $0°$; $120°$; $240°$.

25. $36° \; 52'$.

27. $30°$; $150°$; $199° \; 28'$; $340° \; 32'$.

31. $2\sqrt{2(1 - \cos\theta)}$.

Arts. 41–42, pp. 99–102

5. $\dfrac{4\sec^2 2x}{\sqrt{\tan 2x}}$.

7. $-2\cot 2x\csc^2 2x$.

9. $4 - \sin 2t$.

11. $-2a\csc^2 \frac{1}{2}t \cot \frac{1}{2}t$.

13. $4\cos\pi x(\cos\pi x - 2\pi x\sin\pi x)$.

15. $-2\csc^3 x\cot x - \csc x\cot^3 x$.

17. $-2x^3\csc^2(x^2+5) + 2x\cot(x^2+5)$.

19. $\dfrac{-2\cos x}{(1+\sin x)^2}$.

21. $\dfrac{\sec^4 x}{(1-\tan^2 x)^2}$.

23. $\dfrac{6\sec^2 t}{(4\tan t+1)^2}$.

25. $\sec^2 \frac{1}{2}x \tan \frac{1}{2}x$.

27. $-2\sin x - 4\cos 2x$.

29. $4\sec^2 \frac{1}{2}x(\tan^2 \frac{1}{2}x + \frac{1}{2}\sec^2 \frac{1}{2}x)$.

31. $\dfrac{\sin x}{(1-\cos x)^2}$.

33. $1; \; -\frac{1}{2}\pi^2$.

35. $1; 0$.

37. $\dfrac{y\sin x - \cos y}{\cos x - x\sin y}$.

39. $\tan \phi = \pm 2\sqrt{2}$.

41. $60°$.

43. $\tan \phi = \frac{50}{121}$ or 2.

47. max. $(0, 1)$, $(\pi, 1)$; min. $(\frac{1}{2}\pi, 0)$, $(\frac{3}{2}\pi, 0)$; inf. $(\frac{1}{4}\pi, \frac{1}{2})$, etc.

49. max. $(0, 1)$; min. $(\pi, 0)$; inf. $\left(\dfrac{\pi}{3}, \dfrac{9}{16}\right)$, $\left(\dfrac{5\pi}{3}, \dfrac{9}{16}\right)$.

51. max. $(53° \, 8', 5)$; min. $(223° \, 8', -5)$; inf. $(143° \, 8', 0)$, $(323° \, 8', 0)$.

53. max. $(0, 3)$, $(\pi, 3)$; min. $(\frac{1}{2}\pi, 1)$, $(\frac{3}{2}\pi, 1)$; inf. $(\frac{1}{4}\pi, 2)$, etc.

55. max. $(67\frac{1}{2}°, 1 + \sqrt{2})$; min. $(157\frac{1}{2}°, 1 - \sqrt{2})$; inf. $(22\frac{1}{2}°, 1)$, $(112\frac{1}{2}°, 1)$.

57. max. $\left(\dfrac{\pi}{6}, \dfrac{3\sqrt{3}}{2}\right)$; min. $\left(\dfrac{5\pi}{6}, -\dfrac{3\sqrt{3}}{2}\right)$; inf. $\left(\dfrac{\pi}{2}, 0\right)$, $\left(\dfrac{3\pi}{2}, 0\right)$, $(194° \, 29', -1.45)$.

59. $\frac{24}{7}$.

61. 0.08 radian per sec.

63. No.

65. $\frac{4}{3}a$.

Arts. 43–44, pp. 107–109

1. $\frac{1}{3}$.

3. $-4\sqrt{5}$.

5. 0.

11. $x = \sqrt{\frac{3}{28}}$.

17. $\dfrac{-1}{\sqrt{4-x^2}}$.

19. $\dfrac{-1}{2\sqrt{x}\sqrt{1-x}}$.

21. $\dfrac{4}{4+x^2}$.

23. $\dfrac{1}{x\sqrt{x^2-1}}$.

25. $\dfrac{1}{16+x^2}$.

27. $\dfrac{x^2}{1+x^2} + 2x\arctan x$.

29. $\dfrac{-1}{x\sqrt{2x-1}}$.

31. $\dfrac{1}{\sqrt{1-x^2}}$.

33. $\dfrac{1}{x^2+1}$.

35. $\sqrt{\dfrac{a-x}{a+x}}$.

37. $\dfrac{\sqrt{x^2-4}}{x}$.

39. $\dfrac{-108x}{(1-9x^2)^{\frac{1}{2}}}$.

41. $\dfrac{4x}{(x^2+4)^2}$.

43. $\dfrac{-x}{(1-x^2)^{\frac{3}{2}}}$.

47. $-\frac{1}{20}$ radian per min.

49. $4y - 2x = \pi - 2$.

51. 12 ft.

CHAPTER VIII
Arts. 45–48, p. 115

5. 2.7114.

7. 653.6; 0.07038.

9. $y = 4e^{3.55x}$.

Arts. 49–50, pp. 119–120

1. $x + y = 1$.

5. $\dfrac{8}{x}$.

7. $\cot x$.

9. $x(1 + 2 \log x)$.   **11.** $-2 \cot x$.   **13.** $\dfrac{2x \log_2 e}{x^2 + 6}$.

15. $\dfrac{3x}{3x^2 - 5}$.   **17.** $\dfrac{8 \log 3x}{x}$.   **19.** $\dfrac{1}{x \log x}$.

21. $\dfrac{1}{\sqrt{x^2 + a^2}}$.   **23.** $\dfrac{2}{x(x^2 + 1)}$.   **25.** $\dfrac{2x^2 - 4}{x(x^2 - 4)}$.

27. $\sec x$.   **29.** $\dfrac{13x^2 + 12}{x(3x^2 + 4)}$.   **31.** $\left(\dfrac{1}{e}, -\dfrac{1}{e}\right)$.

33. $-4xe^{-\frac{1}{2}x^2}$.   **35.** $-3^{-x} \log 3 - 3x^{-4}$.   **37.** $2xe^{-x^2}(1 - x^2)$.

39. $-\dfrac{1}{x^2} e^{\frac{1}{x}} \left(1 + \dfrac{1}{x}\right)$.   **41.** $e^{-x} \left(\dfrac{1}{x} - \log x\right)$.

43. $2e^{\frac{1}{2}x}(\cos \tfrac{1}{2}x + \sin \tfrac{1}{2}x)$.   **45.** $\dfrac{2}{x} (1 + \log x)$.

47. $8xe^{-x^2}(2x^2 - 3)$.   **49.** $\dfrac{2 \log x - 3}{x^3}$.

53. $2; -3$.

55. min. $\left(-1, -\dfrac{2}{e}\right)$; inf. $\left(-2, \dfrac{-4}{e^2}\right)$.

57. max. at $x = \dfrac{1}{\sqrt{2}}$; min. at $x = -\dfrac{1}{\sqrt{2}}$; inf. at $x = 0, \pm \sqrt{\tfrac{3}{2}}$.

59. max. $(0, 2)$; inf. $\left(\pm 1, \dfrac{2}{\sqrt{e}}\right)$.

61. min. $\left(\dfrac{1}{\sqrt{e}}, -\dfrac{1}{2e}\right)$; inf. $\left(\dfrac{1}{e \sqrt{e}}, -\dfrac{3}{2e^3}\right)$.

63. min. $(0, 0)$.   **65.** min. $(1, 0)$.

67. max. at $x = \tfrac{1}{2}$; min. at $x = \tfrac{5}{2}$; inf. at $x = 1, 3$.

Arts. 51–53, p. 122

1. $\dfrac{x(3x^2 + 6)}{\sqrt{x^2 + 3}}$.   **3.** $\dfrac{y(5x + 2)}{2x(3x + 2)}$.

5. $\dfrac{y}{2} \left(\dfrac{1}{x + 1} + \dfrac{2}{2x + 3} - \dfrac{1}{x}\right)$.

7. $\dfrac{y}{2} \left(\dfrac{1}{x + 5} + \dfrac{4}{4x + 3} - \dfrac{2x}{x^2 + 1} - \dfrac{2}{2x + 1}\right)$.

9. $y \left(\dfrac{1}{x} + \dfrac{x}{x^2 - a^2} - \dfrac{x}{x^2 + a^2}\right)$.   **11.** $y(1 + \log x)$.

13. $\dfrac{2y \log x}{x}$.   **15.** $y(\log 2 - \log x - 1)$.

19. $y \left(\dfrac{1}{\log x} + \log \log x\right)$.

CHAPTER IX
Arts. 54–55, p. 125

5. $\tfrac{7}{2}$.   **7.** $\sqrt{2}$.   **9.** $\tfrac{5}{3}$.   **11.** $\tfrac{5}{4}$.   **13.** 1.

Arts. 56–59, pp. 131–132

3. $R = \dfrac{5^{\frac{3}{2}}}{2}$.   **5.** $K = 0$.   **7.** $R = \dfrac{10^{\frac{3}{2}}}{8}$.   **9.** $R = \tfrac{4}{3}$.

11. $R = 8\sqrt{10}$. **13.** $R = \frac{1}{2}$. **15.** $R = \dfrac{5^{\frac{3}{2}}}{4}$. **17.** $R = \frac{1}{2}$.

19. $K = 12$. **21.** $K = \frac{1}{2}$. **23.** $K = 2$. **25.** $K = \dfrac{3\sqrt{3}}{2}$.

29. $(3, -2)$.

CHAPTER X

Arts. 60–61, p. 135

1. $\dfrac{-8}{t^2}; \dfrac{32}{t^3}$.

3. $\dfrac{3(t^2+1)}{2t}; \dfrac{3(t^2-1)}{4t^3}$.

5. $-\frac{1}{2}\cot\theta; -\frac{1}{8}\csc^3\theta$.

7. $-\cos t; -\frac{1}{8}$.

9. $-\frac{1}{2}; 0$.

11. $\dfrac{-1}{2\sin^3\theta\cos\theta}; \dfrac{3\cos^2\theta - \sin^2\theta}{12\sin^5\theta\cos^3\theta}$.

13. $8x - y = 12; x + 8y = 99; y = x^2 + 2x - 3$.

17. $2p\sec^3\theta$.

19. max. $(0, 4)$; inf. $\left(\pm\dfrac{4}{\sqrt{3}}, 3\right)$.

21. $4a$.

Arts. 62–63, pp. 140–141

3. $v = 8; a = \sqrt{1{,}040}; 4y = x^2 - 8x - 48$.

5. $v = \sqrt{26}; a = 2; y = 4x^2 - x^3$.

7. $v = 4; a = 4; x^2 + y^2 = 16$.

9. $v = 3; a = 5; \dfrac{(x-5)^2}{25} + \dfrac{(y+3)^2}{9} = 1$.

11. $v = \sqrt{2}; a = \sqrt{10}; y = xe^{-x}$.

19. $v_x = v_0\cos\alpha; v_y = v_0\sin\alpha - gt; a_x = 0; a_y = -g;$

$$y = (\tan\alpha)x - \dfrac{gx^2}{2v_0^2\cos^2\alpha}.$$

21. $45°$.

CHAPTER XI

Art. 64, pp. 144–147

17. $\dfrac{2(2\sqrt{x}+5)}{\sqrt{x}}$.

19. $x^{-\frac{3}{2}}(x-1)$.

21. $\dfrac{48x}{(x^2+3)^2}$.

23. $\dfrac{2x}{y(x^2+1)^2}$.

25. $\frac{1}{2}x(1 + 2\log x)$.

27. $6e^{x^2}(2x^2 + 1)$.

29. $(3\log 4)4^{3x}$.

31. $\dfrac{3x^2}{x^3+3}\log_{10} e$.

33. $-6\cos^2\frac{1}{2}\pi x\sin\frac{1}{2}\pi x$.

35. $6\sin x(2\cos^2 x - \sin^2 x)$.

37. $\sec^3 x$.

39. $-\dfrac{1}{2\sqrt{x-x^2}}$.

41. $4\left(\dfrac{x}{\sqrt{1-x^2}} + \arcsin x\right)$.

43. $2x\arctan x$.

45. $\dfrac{-2xy^2}{2x^2y+1}$.

47. $\dfrac{\cos x - y}{x}$.

49. $\dfrac{3x^2 + y^2 + 8x}{2y(4-x)}$.

51. $\dfrac{2x - 6xy}{3y^2 + 3x^2 + 2y}$.

53. $\frac{1}{2}\cos x$.

55. $e^{-x}(x^2 - 4x + 2)$.

57. $\dfrac{-9}{16y^3}$. **59.** $-5\csc^3\theta$. **61.** $x + y + 6 = 0$.

63. $\tan\phi = \pm 3; \pm\frac{3}{11}$. **65.** $\dfrac{1}{4\sqrt{2}}$. **67.** $-1 < x < 1$.

69. $h = 2.5D$. **73.** length $= 33\frac{1}{3}$ in. **75.** 4.7 ft. per sec.

CHAPTER XII
Arts. 65–66, pp. 152–154

3. $2\frac{1}{2}$. **5.** $\frac{3}{2}$. **11.** -6. **13.** $3\frac{1}{2}$. **15.** 0. **17.** 0.

19. 4. **21.** 2. **23.** $\frac{1}{2}$. **25.** 2. **27.** $\frac{1}{2}$. **29.** 0.

31. $\log 4$. **33.** 0. **35.** 2. **37.** 2. **39.** Large. **43.** ∞.

45. 0. **47.** $-\dfrac{2}{\pi}$. **49.** -3.

CHAPTER XIII
Arts. 67–69, pp. 159–160

7. $\frac{1}{3}x^3$. **9.** Third.

Arts. 70–72, pp. 163–164

1. $\dfrac{x\,dx}{\sqrt{x^2 + 5}}$. **3.** $-\dfrac{dx}{(x^2 - 1)^{\frac{3}{2}}}$. **5.** $21\cos 3\theta\,d\theta$.

7. $-\dfrac{dx}{\sqrt{4 - x^2}}$. **9.** $\dfrac{dx}{a^2 + x^2}$. **11.** $-\cot\theta$.

13. $\dfrac{\sin\theta}{1 - \cos\theta}$. **15.** $\dfrac{x}{4}$. **17.** -0.95; -0.75.

19. 5,600 sq. ft **21.** $4\pi r^2 t$ (t = thickness of metal).

23. πDLt. **25.** 0.00015. **27.** 2.070.

29. 2.516. **31.** 1.775. **33.** 27.54.

35. 0.1008.

Art. 73, pp. 166–167

1 3 sq. ft. **3.** 15 cu. in. **5.** $D < 12.7$ in.

7. $\theta > 58° 51'$. **9.** $-\sin\theta\,\Delta\theta$. **11.** $\theta < 24° 32'$.

13. $\theta > 57° 25'$. **15.** $N = 86.3 \pm 0.4$.

CHAPTER XIV
Art. 78, pp. 174–175

1. $\dfrac{3x^5}{5} + \dfrac{4x^3}{3} + 2x + C$. **3.** $\frac{3}{16}(4x + 1)^{\frac{4}{3}} + C$.

5. $18t^{\frac{1}{3}} + C$. **7.** $\frac{4}{9}s^{\frac{9}{4}} + C$.

9. $\dfrac{x^5}{5} + \dfrac{x^4}{2} + 3x^3 + 4x^2 + 16x + C$.

11. $\frac{1}{9}\tan^3 3x + C$. **13.** $-\dfrac{2}{x - 3} + C$.

15. $2(e^x + 4)^{\frac{1}{2}} + C$. **17.** $\dfrac{x^5}{5} + 2x^3 + 12x - \dfrac{8}{x} + C$.

19. $12x - \frac{1}{2}x^2 - \frac{1}{3}x^3 + C$. **21.** $\frac{1}{2}\log(2x + 1) + C$.

23. $\frac{1}{3} \log (\tan \theta + 2) + C.$

25. $\log \sin x + C.$

27. $- \frac{1}{2} \log (4 \cos \frac{1}{2}x + 3) + C.$

29. $\frac{1}{3} \log (3e^x + 4) + C.$

31. $\dfrac{3}{4(4 - 2x^2)} + C.$

33. $-(a^2 - x^2)^{\frac{1}{2}} + C.$

35. $- \frac{1}{8} \log (3 + 4 \cot 2x) + C.$

37. $\frac{1}{2} \log^2 \sin \theta + C.$

39. $\log (\sec \theta + \tan \theta) + C.$

45. $\sin x - \frac{1}{3} \sin^3 x + C.$

Art. 79, pp. 176–177

1. $\frac{1}{2}e^{2x} + C.$

3. $3e^{\tan 2\theta} + C.$

5. $\dfrac{(ae)^x}{1 + \log a} + C.$

7. $2(e^{\frac{1}{2}x} - e^{-\frac{1}{2}x}) + C.$

9. $\dfrac{a^2}{4} (e^{\frac{2x}{a}} - e^{-\frac{2x}{a}}) + ax + C.$

11. $- \dfrac{10^{\frac{1}{x^2}}}{2 \log 10} + C.$

13. $\frac{1}{2}e^{1+\sin 2x} + C.$

15. $- \frac{1}{3}e^{-x^3} - e^{-x} + C.$

17. $\frac{1}{2} \sin 2x + C.$

19. $- \frac{1}{2} \cot (x^2 + 1) + C.$

21. $\frac{1}{3} \sec 3\theta + C.$

23. $2 \sin \frac{1}{2}x + C.$

25. $x + \sin^2 x + C.$

27. $\frac{1}{2} \log (\csc x^2 - \cot x^2) + C.$

29. $\dfrac{1}{\pi} \log (\sec \pi\theta + \tan \pi\theta) + C.$

31. $2 \sin x - \log (\sec x + \tan x) + C.$

33. $2 \log (\sec \theta + \tan \theta) + C.$

35. $-8 \cos x + C.$

37. $\dfrac{1}{2\pi} \sin^2 \pi x + C.$

39. $- \dfrac{2 \cos^3 \theta}{3} + \cos \theta + C.$

Art. 80, pp. 178–179

1. $\frac{1}{6} \arctan \dfrac{3x}{2} + C.$

3. $\frac{1}{2} \arcsin \dfrac{2x}{\sqrt{10}} + C.$

5. $- \log (\cos x + \sqrt{\cos^2 x + 16}) + C.$

7. $\dfrac{1}{b} \arcsin \dfrac{bx}{a} + C.$

9. $\frac{1}{12} \log \dfrac{t^2 + 1}{t^2 + 7} + C.$

11. $\frac{1}{2} \arctan \dfrac{x + 1}{2} + C.$

13. $- \arcsin (1 - x) + C.$

15. $\dfrac{1}{2 \sqrt{10}} \arctan \dfrac{x^2 + 2}{\sqrt{10}} + C.$

17. $\frac{1}{4} \arcsin \dfrac{2t^2 - 3}{4 \sqrt{2}} + C.$

19. $\dfrac{1}{\log 2} \arcsin \dfrac{2^x}{3} + C.$

21. $u + C.$

23. $\log (x^2 + 4x + 8) + \arctan \dfrac{x + 2}{2} + C.$

25. $2(9x^2 - 12x)^{\frac{1}{2}} + 3 \log (3x - 2 + \sqrt{9x^2 - 12x}) + C.$

27. $\frac{1}{2} \log (x^2 + 4x - 5) + \frac{1}{6} \log \dfrac{x - 1}{x + 5} + C.$

29. $- \frac{2}{3}(3 - 6x - 9x^2)^{\frac{1}{2}} - \frac{2}{9}\sqrt{3} \arcsin \dfrac{3x + 1}{2} + C.$

31. $4(x^2 - 3x + 2)^{\frac{1}{2}} + 13 \log (x - \frac{3}{2} + \sqrt{x^2 - 3x + 2}) + C.$

33. $\frac{1}{18} \left[-7 \log (9x^2 - 6x - 15) - \frac{13}{4} \log \dfrac{3x - 5}{3x + 3} \right] + C.$

Art. 81, pp. 179–180

1. $- \csc x + C.$

3. $\tan \theta - 2 \log \cos \theta + C.$

5. $\dfrac{x^2}{2} - \tfrac{4}{5}x^{\frac{5}{2}} + \dfrac{x^3}{3} + C.$

7. $\dfrac{\cos^3 x}{3} - \cos x + C.$

9. $\dfrac{(\tan x - 4)^3}{3} + C.$

11. $9x + 6 \log (\csc x - \cot x) - \cot x + C.$

13. $\tfrac{1}{2} \log (4 - \cos^2 2x) + C.$

15. $\log (\sin x - \cos x) + C.$

17. $\tfrac{1}{2}e^{x^2} + C.$

19. $2x^2 + C.$

21. $- \tfrac{1}{3}(7 - x^2)^{\frac{3}{2}} + C.$

23. $\tfrac{1}{9}(2x^3 + 5)^{\frac{3}{2}} + C.$

25. $\tfrac{1}{4}x^2 - \tfrac{3}{2}x + \log (x - 3) + C.$

27. $2x + \tfrac{3}{2} \log (2x + 5) + C.$

29. $\tfrac{1}{2}x^2 - x + 2 \log (x + 2) + C.$

31. $x^2 - 5x + 5 \log (x + 3) + C.$

33. $\dfrac{1}{4\sqrt{5}} \log \dfrac{\sqrt{5}\,x - 2}{\sqrt{5}\,x + 2} + C.$

35. $\tfrac{1}{4} \arcsin \dfrac{2x^2}{3} + C.$

37. $\tfrac{5}{2} \log (x^2 + 4x + 8) - 2 \arctan \dfrac{x + 2}{2} + C.$

39. $-2 \sqrt{8x - x^2} + \tfrac{31}{2} \arcsin \dfrac{x - 4}{4} + C.$

41. $\tfrac{1}{8} \log (4x^2 - 4x + 7) - \dfrac{5}{4\sqrt{6}} \arctan \dfrac{2x - 1}{\sqrt{6}} + C.$

43. $- \tfrac{1}{2} \cos^4 x + C.$

45. $\tfrac{3}{2}(\tan x - \sec x) + C.$

47. $\arctan e^x + C.$

49. $- \tfrac{1}{2} \log (1 + 2e^{-x}) + C.$

51. $\tfrac{1}{3} \log (3 \tan x + 5) + C.$

53. $- \tfrac{1}{9} \cot^3 3\theta + C.$

55. $\tfrac{1}{3} \tan^3 x + C.$

57. $\tfrac{1}{16} \tan^4 \theta + C.$

59. $\dfrac{1}{x + \cos x} + C.$

61. $\tfrac{1}{2}x^2 - \log (x^2 + 2) + C.$

63. $\tfrac{1}{2}x^4 + \tfrac{3}{4} \log (2x^2 + 5) + C.$

CHAPTER XV
Arts. 82–83, pp. 183–184

1. $y = \tfrac{1}{6}x^3 - \tfrac{3}{2}x^2 + 3.$

3. $y = 4x^{\frac{3}{2}} - 21.$

5. $4xy - 9y + 1 = 0.$

7. $y = \dfrac{2}{6 - x^2}.$

9. $y = \dfrac{4}{x^2 + 1}.$

11. $x^2 - y^2 = 12.$

13. $x^2 - y^2 = C.$

15. $y + \log (y - 1) = \tfrac{1}{2}x^2.$

17. $y = \dfrac{-wx^2}{24EI} (x^2 - 4lx + 6l^2); \; y = \dfrac{-wl^4}{8EI}.$

Art. 84, pp. 187–189

1. $17.4g.$ **3.** 23.1 yr.   **7.** 9.5 gal.; 7.9 gal.   **9.** $72.7.$

11. $141\tfrac{1}{4}.$ **13.** $8.$ **15.** 21.7 hr.

Art. 85, pp. 191–193

1. $v = 80 - gt; \; y = 50 + 80t - \tfrac{1}{2}gt^2; \; 149.4$ ft.

5. $6,010$ ft.

7. $\dfrac{v - 8}{v + 8} = \tfrac{2}{3}e^{-\frac{gt}{4}}.$

9. $v = \dfrac{w}{k}\left(1 - e^{-\frac{gkt}{w}}\right).$

13. $v = 5(1 - e^{-\frac{gt}{100}}); \ x = 5t + \dfrac{500}{g} (e^{-\frac{gt}{100}} - 1).$

15. $v = 22.5 + 57.5e^{-\frac{gt}{22.5}}; \ 2.2 \text{ sec.}$

CHAPTER XVI
Art. 87, p. 196

1. $\frac{1}{3} \cos^3 x - \cos x + C.$

3. $- \cos x + \frac{2}{3} \cos^3 x - \frac{1}{5} \cos^5 x + C.$

5. $- \cos x + \cos^3 x - \frac{3}{5} \cos^5 x + \frac{1}{7} \cos^7 x + C.$

7. $- \frac{1}{6} \cos^6 x + C.$
9. $\frac{1}{5} \cos^5 x - \frac{1}{3} \cos^3 x + C.$

11. $\frac{1}{6} \sin^6 x - \frac{1}{4} \sin^8 x + \frac{1}{10} \sin^{10} x + C.$

13. $\frac{1}{2} \sec^2 x + \log \cos x + C.$
15. $\sec x + C.$

17. $\frac{1}{3} \sec^3 x - \sec x + C.$
19. $\frac{1}{2}x - \frac{1}{4} \sin 2x + C.$

21. $\frac{3}{8}x - \frac{1}{4} \sin 2x + \frac{1}{32} \sin 4x + C.$

23. $\frac{5}{16}x - \frac{1}{4} \sin 2x + \frac{3}{64} \sin 4x + \frac{1}{48} \sin^3 2x + C.$

25. $\frac{1}{8}\theta - \frac{1}{16} \sin 2\theta + C.$
27. $\frac{1}{128}(3x - \sin 4x + \frac{1}{8} \sin 8x) + C.$

29. $x + \sin^2 x + C.$

31. $x + \frac{1}{8} \sin 4x + \frac{1}{4} \sin 2x + 2 \sin x - \frac{4}{3} \sin^3 x + C.$

33. $\frac{2}{3} \sin^3 x + C.$
35. $- \frac{1}{20} \cos^5 2x + C.$

37. $\frac{1}{8}\theta - \frac{1}{32} \sin 4\theta + C.$

Arts. 88–90, pp. 198–200

1. $\tan x - x + C.$
3. $-2 \cot \frac{1}{2}\theta - \theta + C.$

5. $\frac{1}{3} \tan^3 \theta - \tan \theta + \theta + C.$

7. $\frac{1}{8} \tan^4 2x - \frac{1}{4} \tan^2 2x - \frac{1}{2} \log \cos 2x + C.$

9. $\frac{2}{3} \tan^3 \frac{1}{2}x + 2 \tan \frac{1}{2}x + C.$
11. $- \cot x + C.$

13. $\frac{1}{4} \tan^4 x + C.$

15. $\frac{1}{6} \tan^6 x + \frac{1}{2} \tan^4 x + \frac{1}{2} \tan^2 x + C.$

17. $\frac{1}{5} \tan^5 x + C.$
19. $\frac{1}{3} \sec^3 x - \sec x + C.$

21. $\frac{1}{7} \sec^7 x - \frac{1}{5} \sec^5 x + C.$
23. $\frac{1}{7} \sec^7 x - \frac{2}{5} \sec^5 x + \frac{1}{3} \sec^3 x + C.$

25. $\frac{1}{4} \sec^4 x + C.$
27. $\frac{2}{3} \cos^3 x - 2 \cos x + C.$

29. $\tan x - \cot x + C.$
35. $- \frac{1}{2}(\frac{1}{7} \cos 7x + \cos x) + C.$

37. $\frac{1}{2}(-\frac{1}{11} \sin 11x + \frac{1}{5} \sin 5x) + C.$

CHAPTER XVII
Arts. 91–92, pp. 203–204

3. $\frac{1}{3}(x^2 - 18) \sqrt{9 + x^2} + C.$
5. $- \dfrac{\sqrt{9x^2 + 25}}{25x} + C.$

7. $\dfrac{-(x^2 + 16)^{\frac{3}{2}}}{48x^3} + C.$

9. $\frac{625}{8} \arcsin \dfrac{x}{5} - \frac{1}{8}x(25 - 2x^2) \sqrt{25 - x^2} + C.$

11. $- \frac{1}{30}(5 - 2x^2)^{\frac{3}{2}}(5 + 3x^2) + C.$
13. $- \dfrac{\sqrt{7 - 4x^2}}{7x} + C.$

15. $\dfrac{1}{\sqrt{5}} \log \dfrac{\sqrt{5} - \sqrt{5 - x^2}}{x} + C.$
17. $\sqrt{x^2 - 1} - \operatorname{arcsec} x + C.$

19. $\frac{1}{15}(3z^2 + 32)(z^2 - 16)^{\frac{3}{2}} + C.$ **21.** $\frac{(y^2 - 4)^{\frac{3}{2}}}{12y^3} + C.$

23. $\frac{1}{3}(x^2 + 18)\sqrt{x^2 - 9} + C.$ **25.** $\frac{1}{a}\operatorname{arcsec}\frac{u}{a} + C.$

27. $\frac{\sqrt{4x^2 - 9}}{9x} + C.$ **29.** $\frac{1}{2}\left(\operatorname{arcsec} x + \frac{\sqrt{x^2 - 1}}{x^2}\right) + C.$

31. $\frac{1}{5}(x^2 - 16)^{\frac{5}{2}} + C.$
33. $\log (x + 1 + \sqrt{x^2 + 4x + 5}) + C.$

35. $\frac{x}{\sqrt{a^2 - x^2}} - \arcsin\frac{x}{a} + C.$

Arts. 93–94, pp. 205–206

1. $\frac{2}{15}(6x - 1)(1 + 4x)^{\frac{3}{2}} + C.$ **3.** $\sqrt{2x - 3}\,(\frac{1}{3}x + 9) + C.$
5. $x + 4\sqrt{x} + 8 \log (\sqrt{x} - 2) + C.$

7. $2\sqrt{3 + x} + 3 \log \frac{\sqrt{3 + x} - 3}{\sqrt{3 + x} + 3} + C.$

9. $\frac{3}{28}(2x + 9)^{\frac{7}{3}} - \frac{27}{16}(2x + 9)^{\frac{4}{3}} + C.$
11. $\frac{2}{7}(x + 5)^{\frac{7}{2}} - 6(x + 5)^{\frac{5}{2}} + 45(x + 5)^{\frac{3}{2}} + C.$
13. $\frac{1}{15}(3x^2 - 10)(x^2 + 5)^{\frac{3}{2}} + C.$

15. $2 \log (\sqrt{x} + \sqrt{x - 4}) - \frac{2\sqrt{x - 4}}{\sqrt{x}} + C.$

17. $-\frac{1}{3}\sqrt{\frac{6 - x}{x}} + C.$

19. $-\frac{1}{a}\sqrt{\frac{2a - x}{x}} + C.$ **21.** $\frac{2}{3}(x - 8)\sqrt{x + 4} + C.$
23. $e^x + 6 \log (e^x - 2) + C.$ **25.** $\log (\tan \frac{1}{2}x - 2) + C.$
27. $\frac{1}{2} \log \tan \frac{1}{2}x - \frac{1}{4}\tan^2 \frac{1}{2}x + C.$

Art. 95, pp. 208–209

1. $-e^{-x}(x + 1) + C.$ **3.** $\frac{1}{4}e^{2x}(2x^2 - 2x + 1) + C.$
5. $x \log x - x + C.$ **7.** $x \log^2 x - 2x \log x + 2x + C.$
9. $\frac{1}{2}x \sin 2x + \frac{1}{4}\cos 2x + C.$ **11.** $x \arcsin x + \sqrt{1 - x^2} + C.$
13. $x \arctan x - \frac{1}{2} \log (1 + x^2) + C.$
15. $(\frac{1}{4}x^4 - 4) \arctan \frac{1}{2}x + 2x - \frac{1}{6}x^3 + C.$
17. $\frac{4}{5}e^x(\sin \frac{1}{2}x - \frac{1}{2}\cos \frac{1}{2}x) + C.$
19. $\frac{1}{10}e^{2x}(\sin 4x - 2 \cos 4x) + C.$
21. $x \tan x + \log \cos x + C.$
23. $\frac{1}{8}(\cos x \sin 3x - 3 \sin x \cos 3x) + C.$
25. $-\frac{1}{2}\csc x \cot x + \frac{1}{2}\log (\csc x - \cot x) + C.$
27. $2(\sin \sqrt{x} - \sqrt{x} \cos \sqrt{x}) + C.$
29. $(x - \frac{1}{2}) \arcsin \sqrt{x} + \frac{1}{2}\sqrt{x - x^2} + C.$
31. $-\frac{1}{2}[(\cos x)\sqrt{1 + \cos^2 x} + \log (\sqrt{1 + \cos^2 x} + \cos x)] + C.$
33. $\frac{1}{3}x^3 + \frac{1}{2}x + \frac{1}{4}\sin 2x + 4 \cos x + 4x \sin x + C.$
35. $\frac{1}{4}\sec^3 x \tan x + \frac{3}{8}[\sec x \tan x + \log (\sec x + \tan x)] + C.$

Art. 96, pp. 213–214

1. $x + 3 \log (x - 3) + C.$ **3.** $-\frac{2}{3}x + \frac{11}{9} \log (3x - 5) + C.$

5. $\frac{3}{2} \log (x - 2) - \frac{1}{2} \log (x + 4) + C.$

7. $x + \frac{31}{3} \log (x - 5) - \frac{7}{3} \log (x - 2) + C.$

9. $3 \log x + 4 \log (x - 1) - \log (x - 3) + C.$

11. $4 \log (x + 2) - 2 \log (x - 3) - \log (x - 1) + C.$

13. $x + \frac{1}{3} \log (x + 1) + \frac{2}{3} \log (x - 2) - 2 \log (x + 2) + C.$

19. $-\dfrac{1}{x - 1} + 2 \log (x - 1) - 4 \log (x - 3) + C.$

21. $\frac{1}{18} \left[\log (x - 2) - \log (x + 2) + \dfrac{4}{x} \right] + C.$

23. $\log (x - 4) - \log (x - 3) + \dfrac{1}{x - 3} + C.$

27. $3 \log (x - 4) - \log (x^2 + 2x + 3) - \dfrac{3}{\sqrt{2}} \arctan \dfrac{x + 1}{\sqrt{2}} + C.$

29. $\log (x - 1) + 2 \log (x - 4) + \frac{3}{2} \log (x^2 + x + 4)$
$$- \frac{\sqrt{15}}{3} \arctan \frac{2x + 1}{\sqrt{15}} + C.$$

CHAPTER XVIII

Art. 100, pp. 225–226

3. 18.   **5.** $-4\frac{1}{2}.$ **7.** $\frac{28}{3}.$ **9.** $-12.$

11. 36.   **13.** $\frac{4}{3}.$ **15.** $2\pi.$ **17.** 2.

19. 12.   **21.** $5 \arctan 3 = 6.25.$ **23.** 2.86.

25. 2.38.   **27.** 3.   **29.** 48.   **31.** 7.85.

33. 7.31.   **35.** $2\sqrt{2}.$ **37.** $-\frac{32}{3}.$ **39.** $\frac{32}{3}.$

Arts. 101–103, pp. 230–231

5. 4.   **7.** $\frac{3}{4}\pi = 2.36.$ **9.** 104.5.   **11.** $\frac{2}{15}.$

13. $\frac{1}{2} \log 3 = 0.549.$ **15.** $2(1 + \log 5 - \log 3) = 3.022.$

17. 32.4.   **19.** $\pi.$ **21.** $\frac{1}{2}\pi a^2.$ **23.** 0.195.

25. 1.   **27.** $\frac{256}{15} = 17.1.$

Arts. 104–105, pp. 237–238

1. Divergent.   **3.** Divergent.   **5.** 2.   **7.** 1.

9. $\frac{1}{2}\pi.$ **11.** Divergent.   **13.** $\sqrt{8}.$ **15.** 4.

17. Divergent.   **19.** 3.   **21.** 3.   **23.** $\dfrac{\pi a^2}{4}.$

27. $12\pi.$ **29.** $\frac{3}{8}\pi a^2.$

CHAPTER XIX

Art. 107, pp. 242–243

7. $4\pi.$ **9.** $\frac{1}{2}\pi a^2.$ **11.** $\frac{9}{4}\pi.$ **13.** 4.   **15.** $\dfrac{19\pi}{2}.$

17. $\pi - \frac{3}{2}\sqrt{3} = 0.544.$ **19.** $2a^2 \left(\dfrac{\pi}{3} - \dfrac{\sqrt{3}}{4} \right) = 1.23a^2.$

21. $4(\sqrt{3} - \frac{1}{3}\pi).$ **23.** $8\pi.$ **25.** $a^2.$

Arts. 108–109, pp. 247–250

1. $\dfrac{500\pi}{3}$.　　　　**3.** 162π.　　　　**5.** $\frac{1}{3}\pi r^2 h$.

7. $\pi^2 - 2\pi = 3.586$.　　**9.** $16\pi^2$.　　　**11.** $\frac{1}{4}\pi a^2 b$.

13. 3.65 in.　　　　**15.** $9\pi \log 3 = 31.06$.　　**17.** 2π.

19. $\dfrac{128\pi}{9} = 44.7$.　　　　　　　**21.** $\frac{32}{105}\pi a^3$.

23. $2\pi^2 - 3\sqrt{3}\,\pi = 3.42$; $\frac{2}{3}\pi^2 + \sqrt{3}\,\pi = 12.02$.

25. $48\pi \sqrt{3} - \dfrac{64\pi^2}{3} = 50.6$.　　　**27.** $5\pi^2 a^3$.

29. $4\pi^2$.　　　**31.** $\frac{1}{2}\pi a^3$.　　　**33.** $2\pi^2 r^3$.

Art. 110, pp. 253–254

1. $\frac{5}{27}(9 - z)^2$ sq. in.; 45 cu. in.　　**3.** 12.

5. $30 \sqrt{2}\,\pi$.　　　　　　**7.** $\dfrac{15\pi}{4}$.

9. 4π.　　　　　　　**11.** 160π.

13. 18 cu. ft.　　　　**15.** $\dfrac{176\pi}{3} = 184.3$ cu. ft.

Arts. 111–112, pp. 259–260

1. $4\frac{1}{3}$.　　　　**3.** 4.70.　　　　**5.** 4.78.

7. 4.007.　　　**9.** $8a$.　　　　**11.** $6a$.

13. $\displaystyle\int_0^\pi \sqrt{1 + \cos^2 x}\, dx$.　　**15.** 49π sq. in.

17. $\dfrac{12\pi a^2}{5}$.　　　　**19.** $\pi[\sqrt{2} + \log(\sqrt{2} + 1)]$.

21. $\dfrac{64\pi a^2}{3}$.　　**23.** $\dfrac{32\pi a^2}{5}$.　　**25.** $4\pi^2 rR$.

Art. 113, pp. 263–264

1. $\dfrac{8}{\pi} = 2.55$.　　**3.** $\frac{5}{4}\pi = 3.93$.　　**5.** $\dfrac{8}{3\pi} = 0.849$.

7. $1\frac{3}{8}$.　　　　**9.** 0.　　　　**11.** 7.17.

13. 4.5.　　　　**15.** 15.　　　**17.** 10.5 ft. per minute.

CHAPTER XX
Arts. 114–115, pp. 267–268

1. 115; 114.　　　**3.** 27.3; 27.15.　　**5.** 0.9975; 1.

7. 18.1.　　　　**9.** 8.95.　　　**11.** 1.18.

13. 0.882.　　　**15.** 1.91.　　　**17.** 11.2.

Arts. 116–117, pp. 272–274

1. $\frac{80}{3}$.　　　**3.** 12.　　　**7.** 48π cu. in.　　**9.** $\dfrac{128\pi}{3}$.

11. 32π.　　**13.** 18.4.　　**15.** 36.1.　　**17.** 1.19.

19. 0.421.　　**21.** 33.8.　　**23.** 137 cu. ft.

CHAPTER XXI

Arts. 118–119, pp. 282–283

1. $(\frac{1}{2}a, \frac{1}{2}b, \frac{1}{2}c)$.
3. $2\frac{1}{2}$ in. above center of base.
5. $(\frac{1}{4}a, \frac{1}{4}b, \frac{1}{4}c)$.
7. $4\frac{1}{2}$ in. above center of base.
9. $\frac{9}{13}$ in. from plane surface.
11. $(0, 0, 13\frac{1}{3})$.
13. $(6, 0, 0)$.
15. 3.57 in. above apex.
17. $1\frac{1}{2}$ in. from plane surface.
19. $\frac{3}{16}\pi r$, $\frac{3}{32}\pi h$.
21. $\frac{4}{5}h$ from vertex.

Arts. 120–122, pp. 288–290

1. $(3, 0)$.
3. $\bar{x} = \bar{y} = \dfrac{8}{\pi} = 2.55$.
5. $(\frac{8}{5}, 2)$.
7. $(\frac{8}{5}, 4)$.
9. $(\frac{8}{5}, 1)$.
11. $(\frac{1}{2}\pi, \frac{1}{8}\pi)$.
13. $(\frac{16}{15}, \frac{128}{105})$.
17. (6 in., 3 in.).
19. (4 in., $5\frac{4}{9}$ in.).
21. (3.68 in., 5.27 in.).
23. $2\pi^2 r^2 R$.
25. $\dfrac{3,040\pi}{3}$ cu. in.

CHAPTER XXII

Arts. 123–126, pp. 295–297

1. $\dfrac{500}{3}; \dfrac{2,500}{7}$.
3. $\dfrac{4,096}{105}; \dfrac{128}{15}$.
5. $\frac{1}{9}(e^3 - 1); e - 2$.
7. $16 - 4\pi$.
9. $\frac{5}{4}\pi r^4$.
13. $\dfrac{bh^3}{36}$.
15. 160 in.⁴.
17. 145.7 in.⁴.
19. 166 in.⁴; 36.5 in.⁴.
23. $\dfrac{h}{\sqrt{3}}$.
25. 111.3 in.⁴; 7 2 in.⁴.

Arts. 127–132, pp. 305–307

1. $\frac{3}{10}mr^2$.
3. $\frac{3}{2}mr^2$.
5. $\frac{2}{3}ma^2$.
7. $\dfrac{512\pi\delta}{3}$.
9. $\dfrac{32\pi\delta}{3}$.
11. $\frac{3}{20}mr^2 + \frac{1}{10}mh^2$.
13. $\dfrac{7mr^2}{5}$.
15. $\dfrac{m}{6}(b^2 + h^2) = \dfrac{5m}{6}$.
17. $\dfrac{87}{4g}$.
19. $4:5$.
21. $\dfrac{\pi ab}{4}(a^2 + b^2)$.
23. $\dfrac{bh}{12}(b^2 + h^2)$.

CHAPTER XXIII

Arts. 133–136, pp. 313–316

1. $32w$; $y' = 4\frac{1}{12}$ ft.
3. 6,740 lb.; 7,860 ft.-lb.
5. 6,750 lb.; 1 ft. above bottom.
7. 267 lb.
9. 542 lb.; 1,342 lb.
11. $\dfrac{33w}{2} = 1,040$ lb.; $y' = 1.9$ ft.
13. $24\sqrt{2}\,w$ lb.; $\dfrac{8w}{3}$ lb.
15. 3.14 ft. below surface; 1,685 lb.

Arts. 137–138, pp. 319–320

1. 108 in.-lb.
3. 4,500 in.-lb.
5. $69\frac{1}{3}$ ft.-lb.; $8\frac{2}{3}$ lb.
7. 0.
9. 105,000 ft.-lb.
11. 34,500 ft.-lb.
13. $14,400\pi$ ft.-lb.
15. $14,080\pi$ ft.-lb.
17. 25,800 ft.-lb.
19. $2400 \log 2 = 1,664$ in.-lb.
21. 1,681,000 ft.-lb.

CHAPTER XXIV

Arts. 139–143, pp. 326–327

1. (a) $7; \frac{6}{7}:\frac{3}{7}:\frac{2}{7}.$ (c) $9; \frac{2}{3}:\frac{2}{3}:-\frac{1}{3}.$
3. (a) $7; 6:-3:-2.$
5. $(0, 0, 1\frac{1}{2}).$
7. $x^2 + y^2 + z^2 = 12x.$
9. $(0, 2, 3); (2, 0, 4).$
11. $\dfrac{1}{\sqrt{2}}:\dfrac{1}{2}.\dfrac{1}{2}.$

Arts. 144–147, pp. 333–334

1. (a) 0.9643. (c) 0.70711.
5. $x + \sqrt{2}\,y + z = 8.$
7. $(0, 2.8, 0).$
9. $85° 36'.$

Arts. 148–150, pp. 338–339

3. $\frac{6}{7}:\frac{2}{7}:\frac{3}{7}.$
5. (a) $x - 8 = y - 10 = \frac{1}{2}(z - 8).$

Arts. 151–156, pp. 344–345

1. (a) $x^2 + y^2 + z^2 = 4x.$ (c) $(x - 4)^2 + (y - 2)^2 + (z - 5)^2 = 25.$

Arts. 157–158, pp. 347–348

1. (a) $(2\sqrt{2}, 2\sqrt{6}, 4\sqrt{2}).$ (c) $(0, \sqrt{6}, -\sqrt{6}).$
5. $r^2 = 8.$
7. $r^2 + z^2 = 14.$
9. $r^2 + z^2 = 6z.$
11. $\rho = 4.$
13. $\rho = 4 \cos \phi.$
15. $\tan^2 \phi = 4.$
17. $r^2 + z^2 = 16, r = 4 \cos \theta; \rho = 4, \rho \sin \phi = 4 \cos \theta.$

CHAPTER XXV

Arts. 159–161, pp. 353–355

1. 72 cu. in. per in.; 27 cu. in. per in.
3. 4, 6, and -6 deg. per in.
5. $-\frac{1}{2}; -\frac{2}{3}.$
7. $-\frac{1}{3}; -\frac{2}{3}.$
9. $3x^2 + 10xy; 5x^2 + 6y^2.$
11. $\dfrac{y^2 + 2xy - x^2}{(x^2 + y^2)^2}; \dfrac{y^2 - 2xy - x^2}{(x^2 + y^2)^2}.$
13. $\dfrac{-y}{x^2 + y^2}; \dfrac{x}{x^2 + y^2}.$
15. $\dfrac{y}{e^x}\left(1 - \dfrac{y}{x}\right); \dfrac{y}{e^x}.$
17. $e^{(x-y)} - 2xy; -e^{(x-y)} - x^2.$
19. $-\dfrac{y}{2z^2}; -\dfrac{x}{2z}.$
21. $-\dfrac{c^2x}{a^2z}; -\dfrac{c^2y}{b^2z}.$
23. $-\dfrac{x}{z}; -\dfrac{y}{z}.$
27. $x + 2z = 5; y = 2.$

Arts. 162–163, pp. 361–362

1. $x + y - z = 2; \begin{cases} x - y = 0 \\ x + z = 4. \end{cases}$
3. $4x + 4y + z = 14; \begin{cases} x - y = 1 \\ 4z - x = 6. \end{cases}$

5. $x + 2y + 2z = 12$; $\begin{cases} 2x - y = 6 \\ y - z = 0. \end{cases}$

9. 301.4. **11.** $(2x + 6y^2)dx + (12xy + 2)dy.$

13. $-\dfrac{z}{x^2 y} dx - \dfrac{z}{xy^2} dy + \dfrac{1}{xy} dz.$

15. $\frac{1}{2}y \sin \theta \, dx + \frac{1}{2}x \sin \theta \, dy + \frac{1}{2}xy \cos \theta \, d\theta.$

17. $(2x - 2y \cos \theta) \, dx + (2y - 2x \cos \theta) \, dy + 2xy \sin \theta \, d\theta.$

19. 5.4 cu. ft. **21.** 0.035. **23.** 29.5 sq. ft.

Arts. 164–165, pp. 367–369

1. $64\pi.$ **3.** 3.5 deg. per in. **5.** $-16.$

7. $\dfrac{dv}{dt} = -1.7$ cu. in. per min. **9.** $-\dfrac{\sqrt{5}}{2}.$

11. ± 0.933 deg. per in. **13.** ± 2.5; 0.

Arts. 166–167, pp. 372–373

1. $-\dfrac{3x^2 + y^2}{2xy}.$ **3.** $-\dfrac{y + 4}{x + 2}.$ **5.** $\dfrac{2x - 2y}{3y^2 + 2x}.$

7. $-\dfrac{x}{4z}$; $-\dfrac{y}{4z}.$ **9.** $\dfrac{yz + 2x}{3z^2 - xy}$; $\dfrac{xz + 2y}{3z^2 - xy}.$

11. $-\dfrac{U^2 + 4xy}{2Uz + 3U^2}.$ **13.** $\dfrac{tx - 1}{v}.$

17. $x + y + 2z = 7$; $\dfrac{x - 2}{1} = \dfrac{y - 1}{1} = \dfrac{z - 2}{2}.$

19. 0; $2x + 12y$; $2y.$ **21.** $\dfrac{-2y^2}{(x + y)^3}$; $\dfrac{-2x^2}{(x + y)^3}$; $\dfrac{2xy}{(x + y)^3}.$

23. $e^x \sin y$; $-e^x \sin y$; $e^x \cos y.$ **25.** $6x^2 + 48xy - 48y^2.$

CHAPTER XXVI
Arts. 168–169, p. 376

1. 15. **3.** 12. **5.** $-\frac{9}{4}.$

7. $2\pi.$ **9.** $\frac{2}{3}\pi + \sqrt{3} = 3.83.$ **11.** $\frac{2}{3}.$

13. 3. **15.** 14. **17.** $\dfrac{a^3}{3} \left(\frac{1}{2}\pi - \frac{2}{3}\right)$

Arts. 170–172, pp. 381–382

1. $\frac{125}{6}.$ **3.** $\frac{16}{3}.$ **5.** $\frac{125}{24} = 5.2.$

7. $3 \log 3 - \frac{4}{3} = 1.96.$ **9.** $\pi ab.$ **11.** $\pi.$

13. $\frac{3}{2}\pi.$ **15.** $4(\sqrt{3} - \frac{1}{3}\pi).$ **17.** $a^2(\sqrt{3} - \frac{1}{3}\pi).$

19. $\dfrac{\pi r^4}{4}.$ **21.** $\dfrac{r^4}{8}.$ **23.** $\frac{3}{2}\pi r^4.$

Arts. 173–176, pp. 389–390

1. 18. **3.** $\frac{2}{3} \displaystyle\int_0^2 \int_0^{\sqrt{4-x}} (12 - 2x - 3y) \, dy \, dx.$

5. $4\pi.$ **7.** $\frac{14}{3}\pi = 14.66$ cu. in. **9.** $\frac{16}{9}\pi.$

11. $\frac{3}{2}\pi.$ **13.** $16\pi.$ **15.** $\frac{52}{3}\pi.$

17. $12\pi - 16.$ **19.** 288 cu. in. **21.** $\frac{1}{3}\pi(8\sqrt{2} - 7).$

23. $\frac{2}{5}mr^2.$

CHAPTER XXVII
Arts. 177–181, pp. 397–398

1. $\dfrac{2}{\sqrt{2}} + \dfrac{4}{\sqrt{3}} + \dfrac{8}{\sqrt{4}} + \dfrac{16}{\sqrt{5}}$.

3. $1 + \dfrac{x}{2!} + \dfrac{x^2}{3!} + \dfrac{x^3}{4!}$.

5. $\dfrac{2!}{1} + \dfrac{4!}{2} + \dfrac{6!}{4} + \dfrac{8!}{8}$.

7. $(-1)^{n+1}(2n-1)$.

9. $\dfrac{1}{(2n-1)(2n)}$.

11. $(-1)^{n+1} \dfrac{2n-1}{\sqrt{(n+1)^2+1}}$.

13. 16.   **15.** $\tfrac{2}{3}$.   **17.** 8.

Arts. 182–185, pp. 403–405

3. Convergent.   **5.** Divergent.   **7.** Divergent.
9. Convergent.   **15.** Convergent.   **17.** Divergent.
19. Convergent.

Arts. 186–187, pp. 409–410

1. Convergent.   **3.** Divergent.   **5.** Convergent.
7. Divergent.   **9.** Divergent.   **11.** Divergent.
13. Convergent.   **15.** Convergent.   **17.** 3.7; 0.26.
19. 0.0003.

Arts. 188–189, pp. 413–414

1. Conditional.   **3.** Conditional.   **5.** Absolute.
7. Absolute.   **9.** Absolute.   **11.** Absolute.
13. Absolute.   **15.** 0.02.   **17.** 0.47; 0.72.

Arts. 190–191, pp. 417–418

1. $-1 < x < 1$.   **3.** $-1 < x \leqq 1$.   **5.** $-2 < x \leqq 2$.
7. $-4 < x < 4$.   **9.** $-2 \leqq x \leqq 2$.   **11.** All values.
13. $-2 < x < 2$.   **15.** $-\sqrt{2} < x < \sqrt{2}$.   **17.** All values.
19. $-5 \leqq x < -3$.   **21.** $1 \leqq x \leqq 3$.   **23.** $0 \leqq x < 6$.

CHAPTER XXVIII
Arts. 192–193, pp. 422–423

7. $-1 < x < 1$.

9. 0.15643; 0.0000008.

11. 1.6484; 0.0003.

17. $x + \dfrac{x^3}{3} + \dfrac{2x^5}{15} + \dfrac{17x^7}{315} + \cdots$

19. $x + \dfrac{x^3}{6} + \dfrac{x^5}{24} + \dfrac{61x^7}{5,040} + \cdots$

21. $-\left(\dfrac{x^2}{2} + \dfrac{x^4}{12} + \dfrac{x^6}{45} + \cdots\right)$

23. $x + x^2 + \dfrac{2x^3}{3!} - \dfrac{4x^5}{5!} - \cdots$

Arts. 194–195, pp. 427–428

1. $\tfrac{1}{2}\left[1 + \sqrt{3}(x - \tfrac{1}{6}\pi) - \dfrac{(x - \tfrac{1}{6}\pi)^2}{2!} - \dfrac{\sqrt{3}\,(x - \tfrac{1}{6}\pi)^3}{3!} + \cdots\right]$

3. $\log 2 + \tfrac{1}{2}(x-2) - \tfrac{1}{8}(x-2)^2 + \tfrac{1}{24}(x-2)^3 - \cdots$

5. $e\left[x + \dfrac{(x-1)^2}{2!} + \dfrac{(x-1)^3}{3!} + \cdots\right]$

9. $1 + x - \dfrac{x^3}{3} - \dfrac{x^4}{6} - \dfrac{x^5}{30} + \cdots$

11. $x + \dfrac{x^3}{2\cdot 3} + \dfrac{1\cdot 3x^5}{2\cdot 4\cdot 5} + \dfrac{1\cdot 3\cdot 5x^7}{2\cdot 4\cdot 6\cdot 7} + \cdots$

13. $0.856.$ **15.** $0.3103.$ **17.** $0.570.$

Arts. 197–198, pp. 433–435

11. $\tanh x \operatorname{sech}^2 x.$ **13.** $\coth x.$

15. $2e^{-x}(\cosh x - \sinh x).$ **23.** $0.3579; 0.00001.$

CHAPTER XXIX
Arts. 199–201, pp. 438–439

3. $y = \sin x + 2\cos x.$ **5.** $y^2 = 4x + C.$

7. $xy = C.$ **9.** $\log(x+1) = C - \dfrac{1}{y}.$

11. $\log(xy) = x - y + C.$ **13.** $\log(E - Ri) = -\dfrac{Rt}{L} + CR.$

15. $\log(x^2 y) = y + C.$

Art. 202, p. 441

1. $x^2 + 2xy = C.$ **3.** $x^2(x^2 + 2y^2) = C.$ **5.** $y^2 + xy = Cx.$

7. $x^2 + y^2 - 4xy = C.$ **9.** $y = x\log x.$

Arts. 203–204, pp. 444–445

1. $x^2 + xy - y = C.$ **3.** $y\sin x + x = C.$

5. $x^3 y + \log y = C.$ **7.** $2y^2 - x^2 - 2xy + 4y + 2x = C.$

9. $x^3 + 3xy^2 = C.$ **11.** $x^2 + 2xy - 2y^2 = C.$

15. $\dfrac{y}{x} - \log x = C.$ **17.** $\dfrac{y}{x^2} = \dfrac{x^2}{2} + C.$

Arts. 205–206, pp. 447–448

1. $4y - 2x + 1 = Ce^{-2x}.$ **3.** $x + y + 1 = Ce^x.$

5. $2x + 2y + 1 = Cx^2.$ **7.** $xy + x\cos x = \sin x + C.$

9. $(y - x^2 - 1)^2 = C(x^2 + 1).$ **11.** $2y\log x - \log^2 x = C.$

13. $x^2 y - 3x = C.$ **17.** $x^2(y^3 - 1) = C.$

19. $x + y + 1 = e^x.$

Art. 208, pp. 451–452

1. $y = Ae^{2x} + Be^x.$ **3.** $y = Ae^{-\frac{1}{2}x} + Be^{3x}.$

5. $y = A + Be^{2x}.$ **7.** $y = Ae^x + Be^{2x} + Ce^{-2x}.$

9. $y = Ae^{2x} + Bxe^{2x}.$ **11.** $y = Ae^{\frac{1}{2}x} + Bxe^{\frac{1}{2}x}.$

13. $y = e^{5x}(A\cos x + B\sin x).$ **15.** $y = Ae^{2x} + e^x(B\cos x + C\sin x).$

17. $y = Ae^{2x} + Be^{-2x} + C\cos 2x + D\sin 2x.$

19. $y = e^x + e^{-x}.$ **21.** $y = e^x\cos 2x.$

23. $x = 2\cos 2t; \dfrac{dx}{dt} = -4\sin 2t.$ **25.** $\theta = \theta_1 \cos\sqrt{\dfrac{g}{L}}\,t; \; T = 2\pi\sqrt{\dfrac{L}{g}}.$

Art. 209, pp. 454–456

1. $y = ax^2 + bx + c;$

$y = a \sin x + b \cos x;$

$y = ae^{-x}.$

3. $y = Ae^{2x} + Be^x + 2x^3 + 9x^2 + 21x + \frac{45}{2}.$

5. $y = Ae^{2x} + Be^{4x} + \frac{1}{4}.$

7. $y = Ae^x + Be^{-2x} - 3\cos x - \sin x.$

9. $y = Ae^{2x} + Be^{3x} + 2e^x.$

11. $y = Ae^{-x} + Be^{\frac{2}{3}x} - 3x^2 + 2x - \frac{14}{3}.$

13. $y = e^{2x}(A \cos 2x + B \sin 2x) + \frac{1}{4}x + 1.$

15. $y = Ae^{-3x} + Be^{2x} + 2xe^{2x}.$ **17.** $y = A \cos x + B \sin x - x \cos x.$

19. $y = A + Bx + Ce^{-x} + \cos x - \sin x.$

21. $y = A + Be^{-x} + \frac{1}{3}x^3 + 4x.$ **23.** $y = 2e^x - x.$

INDEX

A

Absolute convergence, 411
Acceleration, in curvilinear motion, 137
in rectilinear motion, 86
Addition of infinite series, 425
Algebraic substitution, integration by, 204
Alternating series, 410
Angle, between two curves, 60
between two lines, 327
between two planes, 332
Approximate integration, 265
Approximation, differential as an, 162, 358
Arc, centroid of, 283
derivative of, 123
differential of, 255
length of, 254
Area, centroid of, 283
computation of, 217, 219
by double integration, 376, 379
first moment of, 283
in polar coordinates, 239, 379
second moment of, 291, 303
of surface of revolution, 257
Average value of a function, 260

B

Bernoulli's equation, 446
Branch of a function, 2, 57

C

Center, of curvature, 130
of gravity, 277
of pressure, 310

C

Centroid, of area, 283
of composite areas, 286
of mass, 277
of volume, 279
Change of limits, 229
of variable, 201–205
Circle of curvature, 130
Comparison test, 401
Complementary function, 453
Components, of acceleration, 138
of velocity, 136
Compound interest law, 185
Computation of e, 112
Concavity, 82
Conditional convergence, 411
Cone, 342
Constant of integration, 170
Continuity, 17, 350
Convergence, 393
absolute, 411
conditional, 411
of improper integrals, 233, 234
tests for, 398–417
Coordinates, cylindrical, 345
spherical, 346
Critical values, 10
Curvature, 126
center of, 130
circle of, 130
radius of, 129
Curves in space, 343
Curvilinear motion, 137, 189
Cylindrical coordinates, 345, 386
Cylindrical surfaces, 340

D

Definite integral, 215
double, 374
multiple, 375